RICHARD D. PFEIFF
284 PROSPECT ST.
E. ORANGE, N.J. 07017

Maintenance and Repair of Aerospace Vehicles

Northrop Institute of Technology Series

Other Books in the Series
BASIC SCIENCE FOR AEROSPACE VEHICLES, 3d ed.
ELECTRICITY AND ELECTRONICS FOR AEROSPACE VEHICLES
POWERPLANTS FOR AEROSPACE VEHICLES, 3d ed.

Maintenance and Repair of Aerospace Vehicles

THIRD EDITION

Northrop Institute of Technology

James L. McKinley

Ralph D. Bent

McGRAW-HILL BOOK COMPANY

New York   St. Louis   San Francisco
Dallas   London   Toronto   Sydney

Library of Congress Catalog Card Number: 67-17203

ISBN 07-047482-6

789101112 HDBP 754321

Preface

Maintenance and Repair of Aerospace Vehicles, formerly titled *Aircraft Maintenance and Repair,* is one of the Northrop Institute of Technology series of textbooks describing the construction, inspection, operation, maintenance, and repair of structures, systems, and powerplants for aircraft and other aerospace vehicles. These textbooks are designed to be of particular value to those preparing for Federal Aviation Administration certification as Airframe and Powerplant Mechanics and to technical personnel such as inspectors, maintenance engineers, shop foremen, and instructors.

Maintenance and Repair of Aerospace Vehicles covers those subjects which are specifically related to the repair and construction of airframes, aerospace structures, and systems provided for the operation of such devices. The other texts in the series are *Basic Science for Aerospace Vehicles, Electricity and Electronics for Aerospace Vehicles,* and *Powerplants for Aerospace Vehicles.*

The third edition of *Maintenance and Repair of Aerospace Vehicles* incorporates many additions and changes designed to bring the book up to date. Extensive new material has been included in the areas of arc welding, metals and materials, covering methods, hydraulic systems and pneumatic systems for large aircraft, auxiliary systems, and repair-station operation. All chapters have been updated as required. As a result, the text provides a most comprehensive source of information for the aerospace student, technician, and instructor.

Each topic in the Northrop series of texts is explained in a logical sequence so that the student may advance step by step and build a solid foundation for increasing his knowledge. The student's understanding of the explanations and descriptions given in the texts is greatly enhanced by the use of numerous pictures, charts, and line drawings. Review questions at the end of each chapter enable the student to test his knowledge after having studied the related material.

The Northrop texts are so organized by subject matter that instructors in public and private technical schools, training departments of aerospace companies, vocational schools, high schools, junior colleges, and other similar organizations are provided with a wealth of material arranged conveniently for classroom use. In addition, the texts may be used by a student for self-advancement or by the man on the job as a ready reference for practical application.

RALPH D. BENT

Acknowledgments

The authors wish to express their appreciation to the following organizations for their generous assistance in providing illustrations and technical information for this text:

Aeroquip Corp., Aircraft Division, Burbank, Calif.
Aircraft Tools, Inc., Los Angeles, Calif.
Aluminum Company of America, Los Angeles, Calif.
Anderson Equipment Company, Los Angeles, Calif.
Beech Aircraft Corporation, Wichita, Kans.
B. F. Goodrich Company, Akron, Ohio
Boeing Company, Renton, Wash.
Cessna Aircraft Company, Wichita, Kans.
Cherry Rivet Division, Townsend Company, Santa Ana, Calif.
Cleveland Twist Drill Company, Cleveland, Ohio
Cooper Engineering Company, Van Nuys, Calif.
DoAll Company, Des Plaines, Ill.
DeVilbiss Company, Los Angeles, Calif.
Douglas Aircraft Company, Inc., Long Beach, Calif.
E. I. Du Pont de Nemours & Company, Wilmington, Del.
Elastic Stop Nut Corporation, Union, N.J.
Eonair, Inc., Shafter, Calif.
Fairchild Aircraft and Missiles Division, Fairchild Engine and Airplane Corp., Hagerstown, Md.
Federal Aviation Administration, Washington, D.C.
Goodyear Tire and Rubber Company, Los Angeles, Calif.

Haynes Stellite Company, Kokomo, Ind.
Hi-Shear Corporation, Torrance, Calif.
International Nickel Company, New York, N.Y.
Kaynar Manufacturing Company, Inc., Kaylock Division, Fullerton, Calif.
Linde Division, Union Carbide Corporation, New York, N.Y.
Magnaflux Corporation, Chicago, Ill.
Nagel Aircraft Company, Torrance, Calif.
National Telephone and Supply Company, Cleveland, Ohio
Parker-Hannifan Corporation, Cleveland, Ohio
Piper Aircraft Corp., Lock Haven, Pa.
Pratt & Whitney Aircraft Division, United Aircraft Company, East Hartford, Conn.
Razorback Fabrics, Inc., Manila, Ark.
Rockwell Manufacturing Company, Power Tool Division, Pittsburgh, Pa.
Rohm and Haas Company, Los Angeles, Calif.
Singer Company, Los Angeles, Calif.
Special Metals, Inc., New Hartford, N.Y.
Standard Pressed Steel Company, Santa Ana, Calif.
Stanley Tools, New Britain, Conn.
Stits Aircraft Corporation, Riverside, Calif.
United Air Lines, South San Francisco, Calif.
Vickers, Inc., Detroit, Mich.
Weatherhead Company, Cleveland, Ohio
Wedgelock Company, North Hollywood, Calif.
Wiss Manufacturing Company, Newark, N.J.

Contents

CHAPTER 1

Aircraft Woodworking Tools and Machines

INTRODUCTION

Even though modern aircraft are usually constructed of metal, there are still many aircraft in operation which have wood construction. Some of these aircraft are many years old but at least one aircraft is still being manufactured of wood and will need to be maintained in airworthy condition. All wood aircraft require maintenance and repair from time to time; hence the aircraft maintenance technician must have knowledge of approved repairs and the skills necessary to accomplish the repairs.

It is not only essential that the technician have a good knowledge of the repair of wood aircraft structures but it is also useful for him to know and have the skill for precision woodwork because he will from time to time find that he needs to make wood fixtures, jigs, and similar items for use in the fabrication of sheet-metal parts. It is also necessary at times for the aircraft maintenance technician to do cabinet work inside the cabin of an airplane, and his woodworking skill will be of great value to him at such a time.

HAND TOOLS AND THEIR USE

Many of the repairs for aircraft wood structures are still made with **hand tools.** The quality of the repair may depend upon the selection of the proper tools and the skill with which they are used. The following list of hand tools should be ample for accomplishing the repair of almost any part on the airframe or in the plywood skin. The items marked with an asterisk (*) are those considered essential for emergency repairs

and are the minimum required for permanent repairs to plywood skins. Additional incidental tools used for disassembly and assembly of the airplane, such as wrenches and special tools, are also needed, but they do not belong in this list.

Backsaw, (14 to 18 teeth per inch)*
Bar, bucking, small*
Bits, auger*
Brace*
Clamps, bar
Clamps, C-*
Clamps, parallel, wood (Jorgenson)*
Clamps, strap
Compass, scribe (10 in. with thumbscrew lock)*
Counterbore
Countersink
Drill, hand*
Drills, twist, straight-shank, ($\frac{1}{16}$ to $\frac{1}{4}$ in.)*
Flashlight, (swivel or gooseneck)*
Hammer, common nail*
Hammer, tack, magnetic*
Knife, plywood*
Knife, pocket*
Mirror, inspection (dental-type)*
Plane, block*
Plane, jack or smooth*
Pliers, diagonal-cutting*
Rasp, wood, coarse, (half-round)*
Rasp, wood, fine (half-round)*
Saw, dovetail*
Saw, hand, crosscut, (10 to 14 teeth per inch)*
Saw, keyhole*
Saw, rip (5 to 6 teeth per inch)
Saw, scroll, or coping
Scraper, wood, small
Screwdrivers, common and crosspoint*
Spokeshave (narrow flat-bottom and round-bottom)
Square, combination *
Straightedge (long, 36 to 48 in.)*

We have named a rather large number of hand tools with which the repairman should be familiar; however, a skillful craftsman can get along with a smaller number. On the other hand, better-quality work can be done when the proper and most efficient tools are available for each operation.

Saws

There are many varieties of manually operated **saws** designed for all kinds of cutting, but we are concerned with only a few types in the study of aircraft woodwork. The most useful saws are the backsaw, dovetail saw, handsaw (crosscut and rip), keyhole saw, and scroll, or coping, saw.

In simple terms, a saw is a piece of hard steel upon which teeth have been cut. The purpose of the teeth, of course, is to provide sharp points which will cut into a material when the teeth are drawn across it. It is not possible in this text to describe all types of saws, but we shall discuss those which pertain to aircraft woodwork.

Woodsaws are generally made with one of two types of teeth. These are teeth for **crosscut saws** and teeth for **ripsaws.** The teeth of a crosscut saw are shown in Fig. 1·1. These teeth are filed at an angle to produce a sharp, knifelike edge and are alternately bent outward, one tooth to the left and one to the right. The bending of the teeth is done to provide "set" for clearance. This set causes the saw to make a cut, called the **kurf,** a little wider than the saw blade so there will be adequate clearance for free movement. A crosscut saw is designed for cutting across the grain of the wood. The sharp points of the teeth sever the fibers of the wood on each side, thus producing a reasonably smooth cut.

The teeth of a ripsaw are filed to form small chisels as illustrated in Fig. 1·2. The teeth are set to provide clearance in the cut, but the ends of the teeth are almost straight across. The sharp, chisel edges of the teeth bite into the wood, and the chips are carried out of the cut by the teeth. A ripsaw is designed to cut parallel to the grain of the wood. If a ripsaw is used for crosscutting, a very rough cut will result; if a crosscut saw is used for ripping, the teeth will load up and cause the saw to cut very slowly. Furthermore, if used in these ways the teeth will become dulled more rapidly than under normal use.

Saws for precision woodwork are shown in Fig. 1·3. The saw at the top of the illustration is called a **dovetail saw.** The dovetail saw has fine teeth, and since it has a stiffening strip of metal along the back, it has no tendency to bend while in use. The **backsaw** is shown at the bottom of the illustration. It is somewhat larger than the dovetail saw, but it is also used for precision cutting. A longer backsaw with finer teeth is often used in a miter box (angle guide) for mitering or cutting strips of wood at precise angles. This type of backsaw is called a **miter saw.**

The common **handsaw** is used by carpenters and other woodworkers for rough cutting of lumber. The

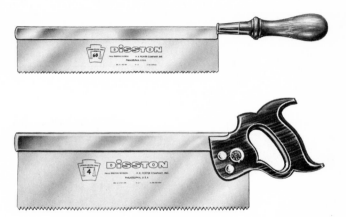

Figure 1·3 Dovetail saw and backsaw.

crosscut handsaw is used for cutting across the grain of a piece of wood to produce desired lengths for any required purpose. A handsaw is shown in Fig. 1·4. A handsaw with rip teeth is used for splitting boards lengthwise.

A **scroll,** or **coping, saw** is used for cutting comparatively thin wood within the limits of the throat (distance from the blade to the frame back). This saw is designed to make curved cuts and to cut out round or similar-shaped holes inside a piece of wood without cutting through the edges. This use is shown in Fig. 1·5.

The **keyhole saw** is designed to cut holes of various shapes in a piece of wood after a small hole is bored through the wood with a drill or an auger bit. The small tip of the keyhole saw is inserted through the drilled hole, and a cut is made to form a hole of the required size and shape. This saw is not limited to any distance from the edge of the material as is the coping saw. Care must be exercised in the use of the keyhole saw because it is easily overloaded and may bend. Pressure on the down or forward stroke should be comparatively light.

Figure 1·1 Teeth of a crosscut saw.

Figure 1·2 Teeth of a ripsaw.

Figure 1·4 Handsaw.

Figure 1·5   Scroll, or coping, saw.

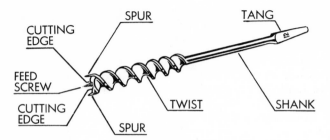

Figure 1·7   A wood, or auger, bit. Auger bits are sized by sixteenths of an inch, measuring the diameter. Bits vary in length from 7 to 10 in. Dowel bits are short auger bits about 5 in. long. (Stanley Tools)

The brace and auger bit

Every carpenter or other woodworker is familiar with the common **brace and bit.** The brace is the tool in which the auger bit is mounted to provide for hand driving of the bit. A typical brace is shown in Fig. 1·6. The **shell** of the brace is a threaded cylinder, or sleeve, placed over the **jaws** into which the bit is inserted. The shell and jaws together form the **chuck.** To place the bit in the chuck, the shell is turned counterclockwise until the jaws are spread sufficiently to insert the tang of the bit. After the bit tang is seated squarely in the jaws, the shell is turned clockwise until the tang is firmly gripped.

In the illustration of Fig. 1·6 it will be noted that this particular brace is equipped with a ratchet arrangement. The ratchet is controlled by means of a **cam ring** to provide for ratchet action either to the right or left. The ratchet is most important for boring holes in a restricted area where there is not sufficient room to turn the brace a full circle.

The **wood bit,** or **auger bit,** is illustrated in Fig. 1·7. The parts of the bit are clearly indicated in the drawing. The most critical parts of the auger bit are the **feed screw,** the **cutting edges,** and the **spurs.** When the cutting parts are kept sharp and even in dimension, the bit will cut most effectively. When the spurs become

dulled after prolonged use, they should be sharpened on the *inside* with a file or a small whetstone to preserve the outer diameter. If the spurs are sharpened by filing or stoning the outside, the diameter of the cut will be reduced and the bit will bind in the hole. The cutting edges should be sharpened on the top to maintain the clearance on the underside. Sharpening the cutting edge is shown in Fig. 1·8.

When drilling with an auger bit it is very common to chip the wood as the bit comes through the wood. The use of one of the following methods can be used to prevent this damage to the wood:

1. Clamp a flat piece of scrap wood tightly against the back side of the work.
2. Bore through from one side until the feed screw breaks through the other side as shown in Fig. 1·9. Then back the bit out and bore through from the other side.

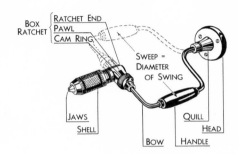

Figure 1·6   A typical bit brace. (Stanley Tools)

Figure 1·8   Sharpening the cutting edge of a bit.

3

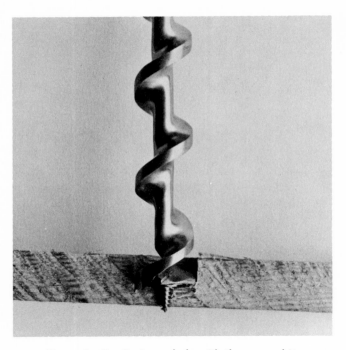

Figure 1·9   Boring a hole with the auger bit.

When boring holes in wood, the bit should normally be held at right angles to the work to prevent the bit from binding and to produce a straight hole.

Auger bits should be used only in wood or some other soft material, and care should be taken to avoid nails, screws, or other metal objects which may be in the wood.

Clamps

Clamps are manufactured in various sizes and designs and two types of clamps are of particular interest to the technician who makes repairs on aircraft wood structures. These are the **C-clamp** and the **parallel,** or **Jorgenson, clamp.**

The C-clamp is so named because of its general resemblance to the letter C. Several clamps of this type are illustrated in Fig. 1·10. C-clamps are gen-erally used to hold two or more pieces of material together temporarily while a permanent fastening is installed or, in the case of woodwork, while glue or another adhesive is setting. Figure 1·11 shows C-clamps holding the parts of a newly spliced rib.

When using C-clamps in wood repair work, the operator must remember that wood is easily crushed; it is therefore necessary that the pressure of the C-clamp be evenly distributed over an area consid-erably larger than the contact area of the C-clamp jaws. This is accomplished by placing blocks of hard-wood, called **caul blocks,** between the jaws and the work as shown in Fig. 1·11. On small work, the pres-sure obtained by twisting the screw of the C-clamp by hand is sufficient for gluing pressure.

Parallel clamps are shown in Fig. 1·12 where they are being used to hold a spliced spar in position and under pressure while the glue is drying. This type of clamp is also called a **hand screw,** or Jorgenson clamp. In using this clamp to hold glue joints it is usually necessary to protect the jaws of the clamp and the caul blocks from the glue by means of waxed paper. Other-wise the jaws and caul blocks may become bonded to the work.

To tighten parallel clamps correctly so the pressure will be evenly distributed, the following technique is effective:

1. Place the clamps on the work so the upper handle is to the right as you face the clamp.
2. Adjust the clamp so the jaws are parallel to the work on both sides but not too tight. The clamp should have considerable drag when it is moved from side to side.
3. Turn the top handle counterclockwise to loosen one-quarter turn.
4. Tighten the bottom handle by turning it clockwise as tight as possible by hand.
5. Tighten the top handle by turning clockwise as much as possible by hand.

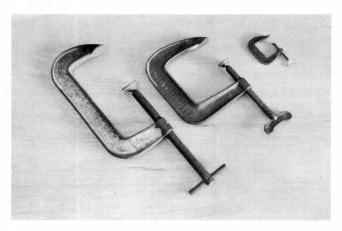

Figure 1·10   C-clamps.

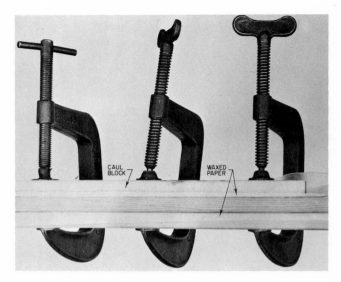

Figure 1·11   C-clamps used to hold a wood splice.

Figure 1 · 12   Parallel clamps holding a spar splice.

When the above operations are completed, the clamps should be exerting even pressure over the entire area under the jaws. This can be tested by attempting to move the clamps from side to side.

On glue joints, pressure should never be released once it has been applied. This is to prevent air from entering the joint and reducing the effectiveness of the bond. It is therefore recommended that the technique be practiced a few times before applying glue to the joint. The application of parallel clamps is shown in Fig. 1 · 13.

The hand drill

A **hand drill,** illustrated in Fig. 1 · 14, is a simple device designed to hold a drill bit and enable the operator to rotate the bit at a comparatively high speed. The hand drill provides a convenient means for drilling small holes in wood.

Figure 1 · 13   Installing parallel clamps.

Figure 1 · 14   A hand drill.

When using the hand drill to bore holes in wood, it is best to indent the wood with a sharp punch or awl to center the drill so it will start boring at the correct location.

The drill bit or twist drill may have a straight shank; a square, tapered tang, or a round, tapered shank. If the drill has a square tang, it is designed for use in a wood brace. If it has a round, tapered shank, as shown in Fig. 1 · 15, it must be used with a drill press which has a socket designed for this type of shank.

The standard dimensions for sharpening a drill bit are shown in Fig. 1 · 16.

Precision drilling

When boring holes which require great accuracy, such as for fittings in wing spars, the hand drill should not be used. In these cases a drill press is used to rotate the drill bit and a template or drill jig is employed to ensure accuracy of location and alignment.

The first requirement for precision drilling is the selection of a drill having the correct size and an accurately sharpened point. Drills are made in fraction, number, and letter sizes to provide for a wide variety of sizes. The drill should be used to make a sample hole in a wood scrap of the same type and thickness as the piece to be drilled. The hole size should be such that the bolt to go through the hole will have a snug push fit.

To construct the jig, a piece of medium- to high-carbon steel should be used so that it can be heat-treated after the guide hole or holes are drilled. Heat treating of the jig is recommended to make the jig wear-resistant and prevent enlarging of the hole by the drill.

The jig material should be steel stock ¼ in. thick

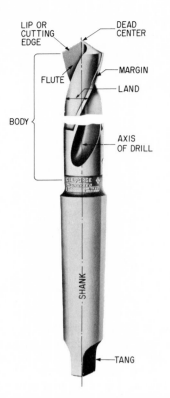

LIP OR
CUTTING
EDGE

DEAD
CENTER

MARGIN

FLUTE

LAND

BODY

AXIS
OF DRILL

SHANK

TANG

Figure **1·15**   *Principal parts of a drill. (Cleveland Twist Drill Co.)*

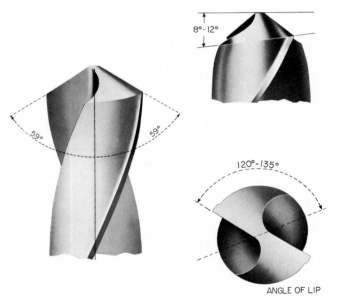

8°-12°

59°

59°

120°-135°

ANGLE OF LIP

Figure **1·16**   *A properly sharpened drill point. (Cleveland Twist Drill Co.)*

and 3 by 5 in. in size. Scale and rust should be removed, and all edges should be deburred (rough edges smoothed with a file or scraper).

Drill a hole in the steel stock the same size as that required in the spar. More than one hole of the same size or different sizes can be drilled to permit wider use of the jig for other jobs. After the holes are drilled and the edges of the holes smoothed with a countersink or other tool, layout dye (Dykem blue) should be applied to the surface of the jig. The dye is to provide a base for scribing guidelines on the jig.

Use a small drill, slightly less than one-half the diameter of the hole in the jig, together with a square to scribe a line across the hole but off-center. See Fig. 1·17*A*. Repeat this from the opposite edge of the jig to provide two parallel guidelines as shown in Fig. 1·17*B*. Repeat the operation from the other sides of the jig to produce lines at right angles to the first pair. These lines are guides for placing the jig in the correct position on the work to be drilled.

To lay out the exact location of the jig on the spar, single pencil lines must be drawn at right angles to each other in the exact location of the hole to be drilled in the spar. The pencil should be sanded to a chisel shape to make thinner lines. The end result will be no better than the original layout lines; hence great care should be employed to see that the location is marked accurately.

The next step in the operation is to set up the spar and jig for drilling. A piece of flat wood is placed on the back of the spar to prevent splitting when the drill is passed through. The jig is placed on the drilling side of the spar and is positioned using the pencil lines on the spar centered exactly between the pairs of lines scribed on the jig. See Fig. 1·18. The spar, jig, and backing block are clamped in place together with C-clamps as shown in Fig. 1·19. The entire assembly is now moved into position and secured on the bed of a drill press after locating it under the drill by moving the drill bit down into the jig hole while the drill press is not running. The hole is drilled by carefully lowering the point of the rotating drill bit through the jig hole and pressing it slowly through the spar and into the backing block.

With a heat-treated jig, the drill will break before it will drill a bad hole; however, a broken drill is much less expensive than a damaged spar.

Use of the counterbore

When it is necessary to drill large holes for bushings and fitting bolts, precision drilling is required; however, it is necessary to perform an operation in addition to that required for smaller holes. The procedure explained above is used to locate the position of the hole and to bore a pilot hole. The pilot hole must be

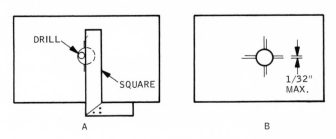

DRILL

SQUARE

1/32"
MAX.

A

B

Figure **1·17**   *Scribing guide lines on drill jig.*

6

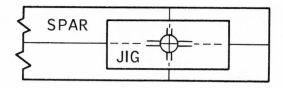

Figure 1 · 18   Centering the drill jig over the hole location.

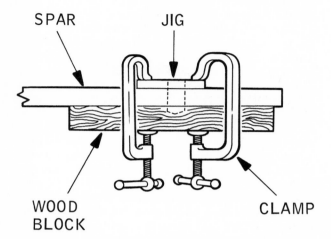

Figure 1 · 19   Jig, spar, and block clamped in position for drilling.

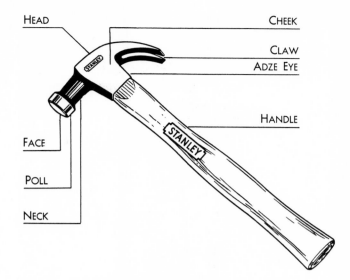

Figure 1 · 21   The nail hammer. (Stanley Tools)

the correct size to fit the pilot of a counterbore. The counterbore is illustrated in Fig. 1 · 20.

To bore the large hole, the counterbore pilot is inserted into the pilot hole, and the larger-diameter hole is bored approximately halfway through the spar. The spar is then turned over, and the hole is bored through from the opposite side.

Hammers

A common **nail hammer,** also called the **carpenter's hammer,** is illustrated in Fig. 1 · 21. The principal purpose of this hammer is to drive nails or to remove nails which have already been driven into wood. This hammer is also called a **claw hammer** because of the nail-pulling claw opposite the face of the hammer.

The head of a good-quality nail or claw hammer is made of forged steel with the face hardened to prevent wear. The face may be flat or slightly rounded. When the face is rounded, the hammer is called a **bellface hammer** and its purpose is to make possible the driving of a nail flush with the surface of the work without

marking the wood with the face of the hammer. The claw on the back of the hammer is designed for pulling nails and also may be used for prying apart boards which have been nailed together. Through the center of the hammer an eye is formed into which the handle is inserted. The eye is a hole which tapers from the center each way. After the handle is driven tightly into the eye, it is secured with steel or wooden wedges driven into the wood at the top of the head. This expands the handle into the tapered section of the hole at the top of the head and securely wedges the handle into the head. The hammer handle is made of hickory or some other high-quality, straight-grained hardwood.

In using the nail hammer the handle should be grasped firmly near the end as shown in Fig. 1 · 22. When the hammer is used to drive a nail, the force of the blow is applied through the wrist and forearm or through the entire arm depending upon the force required to drive the nail.

The nail hammer may be used effectively for pulling nails because the curved claws provide a fulcrum which makes it possible to apply considerable pulling force to the head of the nail. The proper method for pulling a nail is shown in Fig. 1 · 23. After the nail is partially withdrawn, it may be necessary to place a block of wood under the head of the hammer to extend its pulling range, as shown in the bottom part of Fig. 1 · 23. This is done to prevent the nail from bending and enlarging the hole as it is pulled from the wood.

Figure 1 · 20   A counterbore.

Figure 1 · 22   Gripping the hammer.

7

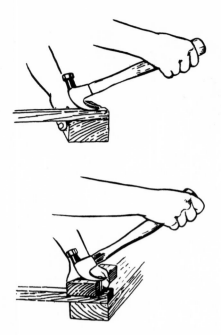

Figure 1·24 Using a magnetic tack hammer.

Figure 1·23 Pulling a nail with a nail hammer. To draw the nail, slip the claw of the hammer under the nail head; pull until the handle is nearly vertical and the nail partly drawn. Then, if necessary, place a block of wood under the head of the hammer to extend its pulling range.

The nail hammer should be used principally for the purposes suggested and should not be used as an all-around hammering or pounding tool. The face of the hammer can be caused to chip if it is used to hammer hard steel, rock, concrete, or any other very hard material. Care should be used in prying with the claws of the hammer because it is easy to apply excessive force and break the handle at the head.

The **magnetic tack hammer** is particularly useful to the aircraft maintenance technician because it is light and it will hold steel tacks or small nails on its magnetic face. Thus it is not necessary to hold the tacks or nails with the fingers. Fig. 1·24 shows how the magnetic tack hammer is employed in nailing a gusset to a wood rib. The nail is picked up with the nail head against the magnetic face of the hammer. The nail is then started into the wood with a light stroke of the hammer. The wood then holds the nail while the finishing strokes are applied with the nonmagnetic face of the hammer.

The Plane

One of the most essential tools for the woodworker is the **plane**. There are three common types of bench planes, namely, the **block plane,** the **smooth plane,** and the **jack plane.** The principal difference in these planes is their length. The smooth plane, illustrated in Fig. 1·25, has a length of from 7 to 9 in. The block plane is somewhat less than 7 in. long, and the jack plane is from 11 to 15 in. in length.

As shown in Fig. 1·25, the plane has two adjustments, one for the squareness of the cutting edge and the other for the extension of the cutting edge from the bottom of the plane. The squareness of the cutting edge is adjusted by the lateral adjusting lever as shown in the illustration. The depth of the cut is adjusted by the adjusting nut.

The double plane-iron assembly includes two parts: the iron, or blade, and the **chip breaker** as shown in Fig. 1·26. The chip breaker serves to strengthen the iron and breaks the shaving. The edge of the chip breaker must fit tightly against the plane iron so the wood chips cannot get under it and clog the plane and should be placed about $\frac{1}{32}$ to $\frac{1}{16}$ in. from the cutting edge of the iron.

There are three configurations for the shape of the cutting edge of a plane iron. These are for (1) the fore plane, (2) the jack plane, and (3) the jointer plane. The blade for the fore plane has a distinctly curved edge as shown in A of Fig. 1·27. This blade is too greatly curved for planing a perfectly flat, smooth surface; hence it should not be employed by the aircraft worker. The iron for the jack plane (B in Fig. 1·27) has a very slightly curved cutting edge, even though it appears almost square and straight. This shape of edge is most satisfactory for the aircraft woodworker because it provides good control of the cut and also makes a nearly flat cut. The edge of the plane iron for a jointer plane is perfectly square; however, this shape makes it somewhat difficult to use for the production of a perfectly smooth planed surface. With the square cutting edge, the corners of the blade extend below the surface of the plane; this results in a distinct edge or step on the surface of the wood where the corner of the blade has made its cut.

Since the jack-plane iron has a slightly rounded cutting edge, it can be adjusted so that the corners of the cutting edge do not extend below the bottom of the plane. Figure 1·28 illustrates how the cutting edge of the iron would appear below the bottom of the plane when it is adjusted properly. In this drawing the extended distance of the cutting edge is slightly exaggerated so the effect can be seen more clearly.

1.

TO PUT THE PLANE TOGETHER LAY THE PLANE IRON, BEVEL SIDE DOWN, ON THE FROG. BE SURE THE ROLLER ON THE LATERAL ADJUSTING LEVER, THE END OF THE "Y" ADJUSTING LEVER AND THE HEAD OF THE PLANE IRON CAP SCREW ARE CORRECTLY SEATED.

2.

SLIP THE LEVER CAP UNDER THE LEVER CAP SCREW AND PRESS DOWN THE CAM. IF THE PLANE IRON IS IN THE CORRECT POSITION THE CAM WILL EASILY SNAP IN PLACE. IF THE CAM WILL WILL NOT SNAP IN PLACE EASILY, SLIGHTLY LOOSEN THE LEVER CAP SCREW.

IF THE PLANE IRON, IS NOT FIRMLY HELD WHEN THE CAM IS IN PLACE SLIGHTLY TIGHTEN THE LEVER CAP SCREW.

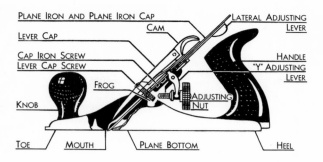

PLANE IRON AND PLANE IRON CAP
LEVER CAP
CAM
CAP IRON SCREW
LEVER CAP SCREW
FROG
KNOB
ADJUSTING NUT
TOE   MOUTH   PLANE BOTTOM

LATERAL ADJUSTING LEVER
HANDLE
"Y" ADJUSTING LEVER
HEEL

TO ADJUST FOR THE THICKNESS OF THE SHAVING SIGHT ALONG THE BOTTOM OF THE PLANE AND TURN THE ADJUSTING NUT UNTIL THE CUTTING EDGE PROJECTS ABOUT THE THICKNESS OF A HAIR.

4.

TO ADJUST FOR THE EVENNESS OF THE SHAVING SIGHT ALONG THE BOTTOM OF THE PLANE AND MOVE THE LATERAL ADJUSTING LEVER TOWARD THE RIGHT OR THE LEFT.

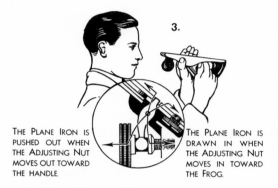

3.

THE PLANE IRON IS PUSHED OUT WHEN THE ADJUSTING NUT MOVES OUT TOWARD THE HANDLE.

THE PLANE IRON IS DRAWN IN WHEN THE ADJUSTING NUT MOVES IN TOWARD THE FROG.

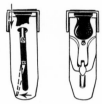

KNOB, LEVER CAP AND PLANE IRON CAP REMOVED TO SHOW THE ACTION OF THE LATERAL ADJUSTING LEVER.

Figure 1·25   A hand plane. (Stanley Tools)

It can be understood by examining the illustration that this blade shape and adjustment would produce a smooth cut without sharp edges or ridges at the sides of the cut. Furthermore, this adjustment provides good directional control of the plane because it is possible to use the edges of the plane bottom as runners or rails to give stability to the plane.

The plane iron should be sharpened so that the cutting edge is nearly square across the width of the blade with a very slight rise toward the center and should have a bevel of 25 to 30° for best results. The cutting edge should be ground with a coarse-grit grinding wheel to prevent overheating. The face, or grinding surface, of the wheel should be dressed so it is square and flat. The final cutting edge of the plane iron is attained by removing the wire burr with an India oilstone, taking care to keep the honed surface flat against the stone.

The plane iron is ground as shown in Fig. 1·29. Care must be taken to see that the iron is not overheated, since overheating will remove the temper and soften the cutting edge. After the plane iron is ground and a burr is noticed on the flat side, the edge should be honed on a fine India oilstone as mentioned previously. Honing of the iron is accomplished as shown in Fig. 1·30. The bevel of the iron is placed flat against the oiled stone, and the iron is then moved back and forth in a line parallel to the edge of the stone. Moderate pressure is applied at the cutting edge but not enough to gouge or scuff the stone. The cutting edge of the iron should be examined from time to time to see that the honing is removing the wire burr and is producing a smooth cutting edge. After the burr is removed from the flat side of the cutting edge, the iron should be turned over and laid gently on the stone so the toe and heel of the iron are against the stone at the same time. The iron is then moved in a figure-eight pattern on the stone to remove the small wire edge or burr along the cutting edge to the flat side. The foregoing honing procedure should be repeated at least once. The edge of the iron can be tested by cutting paper with it. When the edge of a piece of paper is drawn across the cutting edge of the iron, the paper should be cut smoothly and easily.

The plane should be used with great care if satisfactory results are to be obtained. The principal factors governing the quality of the work are (1) the sharpness of the plane iron, (2) the adjustment of the iron, (3) the extension of the cutting edge of the iron (about 0.005 in.), (4) the hardness and grain of the wood, (5) the direction in which the plane is moved, and (6) the proper application of pressure to the plane as it moves along the wood.

One may marvel at the ease with which a skilled craftsman appears to accomplish his work. The craftsman can grasp the plane lightly, place it on a board, and make a few deft strokes, and the surface of the wood becomes perfectly smooth and true. It may appear that he uses the plane in the same manner as the novice; however, the results are quite different.

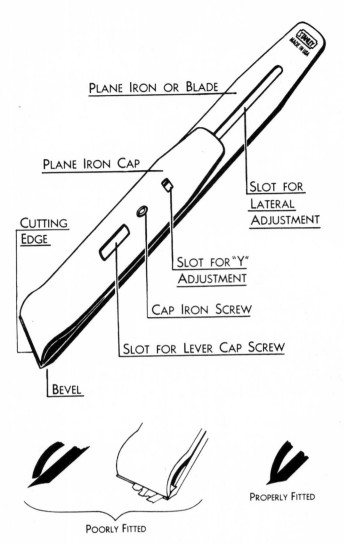

PLANE IRON OR BLADE

PLANE IRON CAP

CUTTING
EDGE

SLOT FOR
LATERAL
ADJUSTMENT

SLOT FOR "Y"
ADJUSTMENT

CAP IRON SCREW

SLOT FOR LEVER CAP SCREW

BEVEL

POORLY FITTED

PROPERLY FITTED

Figure 1·26   The plane iron. (Stanley Tools)

The craftsman has observed all the conditions necessary to perform good work, and he also has applied pressure expertly in the correct amount and at the proper points to obtain the best results. The application of pressure is the least noticed of all the techniques used, but it makes the greatest difference in planing control.

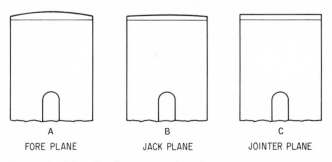

| A | B | C |
| FORE PLANE | JACK PLANE | JOINTER PLANE |

Figure 1·27   Configurations for plane-iron cutting edges.

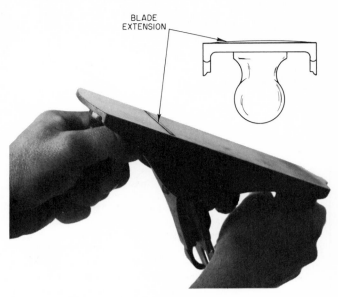

BLADE
EXTENSION

Figure 1·28   Extension of plane iron from plane bottom.

Figure 1·29   Grinding the plane iron.

There are three pressure points to be considered as a plane is moved over the wood surface. We shall call these point *A*, point *B*, and point *C*. Pressure is applied at one or the other of these points at various times, or it may be applied between the points such as *A* to *B*, *B* to *C*, etc. The application of pressure is illustrated in Fig. 1·31.

At the beginning of the plane stroke, as the cutting edge of the blade approaches the wood surface to be planed, the pressure is applied as shown by the arrow in the first photograph. As the blade moves along the surface the pressure is shifted to the center where it is applied at a 45° angle. This pressure is maintained until the blade approaches the end of the work or a point where the operator does not want to cut. Then

Figure 1·30 Honing the plane iron. Whet the plane iron on the oilstone to produce the real sharp cutting edge. Hold the plane iron in the right hand, with the left hand helping. Place the bevel on the stone with the back edge slightly raised and move the plane iron back and forth. To keep the bevel straight, be sure the hands move parallel to the stone so that the angle between the plane iron and the stone will stay the same throughout the stroke. Use enough oil to keep the surface of the stone moist. It keeps the stone sharp by preventing particles of steel from filling the pores of the stone. Try to wear the stone evenly.

Figure 1·31 Application of pressure at pressure points.

it is shifted to the rear as the plane moves to the end of the surface being planed, as shown in the bottom photograph.

When the technique described above is used, the plane will tend to remove high spots from the wood by cutting a thicker shaving at these points. As mentioned previously, the blade setting should be about 0.005 in., or less as the surface of the wood becomes flat, to produce the best results.

The technician who wishes to attain a high degree of skill with the plane should observe and practice all the techniques described here until he has developed the "touch" necessary to obtain the results he desires. The smaller the cut a novice practices with, the sooner he will get the all-important "feel" of the tool.

The wood chisel

The **wood chisel,** shown in Fig. 1·32, is a versatile and useful tool for the wood worker. Experience and careful observation will enable the technician to gain a high degree of skill with this tool, but caution must be exercised at all times.

One of the first requisites for skillful work with the wood chisel is a properly sharpened chisel. The chisel is ground and whetted in much the same way that the plane iron is sharpened. This operation was described in preceding paragraphs. The operator should watch the condition of the cutting edge of the chisel and resharpen it whenever the edge becomes rough or dulled.

The chisel is normally controlled with the left hand, which is pressed firmly on both the chisel and the wood. The force for cutting is applied with the right hand while the chisel is held slightly turned; thus the edge slides across the work while the chisel is pushed away from the operator. This gives a shaving action to the cutting edge and produces a smooth cut.

When the wood chisel is used for any wood-cutting operation, the direction of grain in the wood must be observed. If the chisel is forced between the layers of wood, it is quite likely that the wood will be split and the piece of wood damaged beyond repair.

Figure 1·32 Using a wood chisel.

To cut across the grain of a piece of wood, the chisel handle may be struck with a wood or rawhide mallet while holding the chisel vertically above the work.

POWER TOOLS FOR WOODWORKING

Most of the machine work required in making aircraft parts of wood or plywood can be carried out in an ordinary woodworking shop. Generally, standard woodworking machines can be used without change, but in some cases jigs and templates are provided for making parts such as spars, ribs, wing-tip bows, and similar framing parts. Woodworking tools suitable for making aircraft parts are described in the following paragraphs.

Circular saw

The **circular saw** is employed principally for ripping, beveling, crosscutting, and mitering; however, other operations, such as dadoing, grooving, rabbeting, and molding, can be performed on this machine using special setups and attachments.

The saw blade for a circular saw is a disk of steel with teeth cut on the rim. The teeth are shaped and ground to provide the best cutting performance for the type of work to be done. The teeth of a ripsaw have the appearance of sharply angled chisels; the teeth of a crosscut saw are ground with a bevel on opposite sides of the alternate teeth, similar to a hand crosscut saw. **Combination saws** have both crosscut and rip teeth. These are arranged so there are four or five crosscut teeth to one rip tooth. This saw will do a reasonably good job for both crosscut and ripsawing.

Crosscut teeth are arranged so one tooth will cut one side of the groove and the next will cut the other side of the groove. The teeth are given a "set" (bent outward slightly) to make a cut a little wider than the saw blade. The teeth of crosscut and rip power saws are shown in Fig. 1·33.

A **bench saw** is illustrated in Fig. 1·34. This is a typical power tool for a woodshop which handles comparatively light woodwork such as that encountered in aircraft repair. The saw is driven with a small a-c motor (¼ to ½ hp) designed for use with 110- or 220-volt single-phase power. The saw can also be operated with a motor designed for three-phase power of 220 or 440 volts. As seen in the illustration, the saw bench is provided with an adjustable fence and a protractor or miter gage to provide for a wide variety of sizes and angles. The fence, sometimes called a **rip fence,** is designed to guide the board being ripped. It assures that the cut will be uniform and the width of the cut board will be even throughout its length. The fence should never be used for crosscut work. During the ripping operation a slight pressure should be exerted against the fence. The miter gage makes it possible to cut a board at any desired angle.

While using the bench saw for crosscutting or angle cutting, a rip fence should be moved as far from the saw as possible, or it should be removed entirely. The

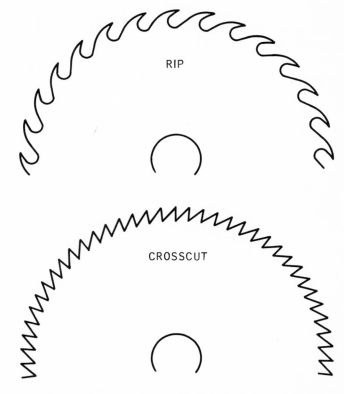

Figure 1·33 Teeth of crosscut and rip power saws.

use of the bench saw is illustrated in Fig. 1·35. Note that the operator is standing to one side so he will not be struck by a piece of flying wood. Also, the operator does not place his hands on the work in such a position that the work could slip and cause him to move his hand into the saw. Where it is necessary to cut small pieces, the operator uses a pusher to move the work against the saw. The work is moved in a direction opposite the direction of saw rotation; that is, the work moves against the rotation of the saw.

The height of the saw blade is adjustable to accommodate any thickness of wood up to the full capacity of the saw. The blade height should be adjusted so that

Figure 1·34 A bench saw.

12

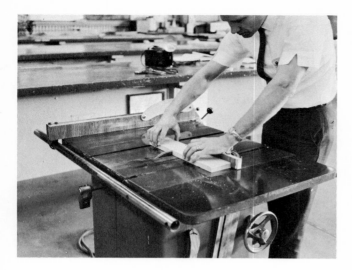

Figure 1 · 35   Use of a bench saw.

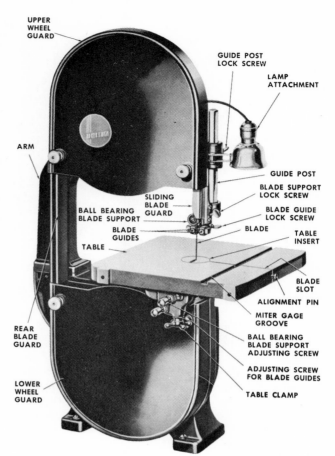

Figure 1 · 36   A band saw.

the saw teeth extend about ⅛ in. above the work; thus the operator can see the tips of the teeth clearly. In using any high-speed rotating tool for shaping or cutting, the operator should wear a face shield or safety glasses to protect his eyes. Safety in all such operations is of primary importance because serious injury can be caused almost instantaneously.

Band saw

A typical **band saw** is shown in Fig. 1 · 36. The band saw is used primarily for cutting curved outlines. Because of the narrow blade, it is easy to change the direction of a cut rapidly while the blade is cutting. The band saw is better suited for cutting very small pieces than is the bench saw, because the blade has much smaller teeth and it is both thinner and narrower.

In using the band saw, the **blade guide** should be adjusted so it is about ¼ in. above the work. This steadies the blade and reduces blade breakage as well as the possibility of injury to the operator. Figure 1 · 37 shows a technician cutting a circular hole in a piece of plywood.

Satisfactory operation of a band saw requires regular maintenance and lubrication, as well as proper adjustment of the wheels, blade tension, and alignment. The blade should be inspected periodically to make sure that it has no cracks or broken teeth and that the teeth are sharp.

The jigsaw

The **jigsaw** shown in Fig. 1 · 38 is used primarily for very fine and intricate work on comparatively small parts. It can be used for cutting very small curves and irregular outlines in sheets of wood without cutting through to the edge of the piece. This is accomplished by boring a small hole through the wood in the area to be cut, then inserting the jigsaw blade through the hole and installing the blade in the saw frame with the wood surrounding the blade. The wood is held steady in a position such that it will not bind the blade

before the saw is started. It is then moved carefully against the teeth of the blade to make a cut following the outline which has been marked on the surface of the wood. Some saws have two fingers used to press down on both sides of the blade to keep the work from jumping up and down. These fingers should be adjusted so that they contact the work.

Figure 1 · 37   Cutting a circular hole with the band saw.

13

Figure 1·38   A jigsaw.

Jointer

A **jointer,** illustrated in Fig. 1·39, is used to cut a smooth surface on wood which is to be joined by glue, or merely to smooth a rough surface. It is also used to provide a straight edge, to produce a plane surface, for squaring, tapering, rabbeting, and beveling. A rabbet is a cutout section along the end or edge of a board for making a lap-type joint between two pieces of wood. One type of rabbet joint is shown in Fig. 1·40.

The operator of a jointer must be very careful in the use of the machine and the material to avoid injury to himself or to the work. The cutting blades of a jointer are very sharp and move at an extremely high speed (about 3400 rpm).

In using the jointer, the operator must make certain that the tables are properly adjusted and that the cutters are set at the correct height. The fence must be at the proper position, and the angle of the tables

Figure 1·40   A rabbet joint.

must be checked. Because the use of a jointer may be somewhat awkward at first, it is good safe practice to pass the work through the machine while it is stopped to get the feel of the machine and to determine the best standing position.

When everything is in readiness, the jointer switch is turned on and the board is placed on the front table with the edge snugly against the fence. The operator stands at the side of the machine for proper balance. As the board is moved across the cutters, care must be taken to keep the hands clear. For working with comparatively small lengths of wood, a pusher should be used as a safety measure. The use of a jointer is shown in Fig. 1·41.

Disk sander

The **disk sander,** illustrated in Fig. 1·42, is a valuable power tool for producing fine woodwork. It is generally used to smooth rough-cut surfaces and to aid in shaping small parts where other tools would be less effective. Sanders are also made in configurations other than that shown in the photograph. A belt sander utilizes an endless belt of heavy fabric coated with emery or other cutting granules on the outer surface. The belt is supported between two drums, one of which is driven by an electric motor. A smooth steel table

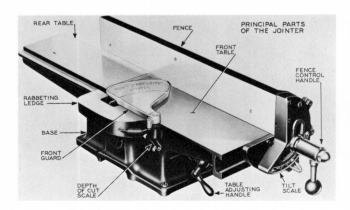

Figure 1·39   A jointer.

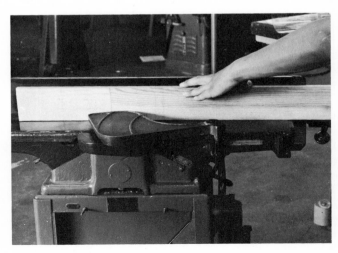

Figure 1·41   Use of a jointer.

Figure 1·42   The disk sander.

Figure 1·43   Using the disk sander.

supports the belt in the sanding area. Another type of sander is the **drum sander** which consists of a vertical drum around which is placed a cylinder of sanding cloth. The drum rotates at a high speed and also oscillates up and down.

Since the use of a sander is accompanied by hazards, the operator must exercise care as with other power tools. The space between the table and the disk must be kept at a minimum (⅛ in. or less), and very small or thin parts should not be sanded because of the danger that they may become wedged between the disk and the table. Such wedging can cause a very violent reaction from the rapidly spinning disk. Bits of material may be thrown violently from the disk at a speed which could inflict severe injury to the operator or other person in the vicinity. In using the disk sander, the operator should apply pressure on his work down against the steady rest (table) and at the same time protect his hands by keeping them in such a position that they cannot inadvertently be brought into contact with the disk. The use of a disk sander is shown in Fig. 1·43.

Soft wood joints to be glued should not be sanded because the pores of the wood become filled with fine sanding dust, thus reducing the glue penetration and weakening the glue joint.

Wood-turning lathe

A **wood-turning lathe,** such as the one shown in Fig. 1·44, is used to form various round and cylindrical shapes. The wood is mounted on center between the headstock and tailstock and rotated at a high speed. The cutting tool is generally held in the hand and rested against the tool rest which is mounted on the bed of the lathe.

The principal hazards in operating a wood lathe are (1) small chips and cuttings being thrown out from the wood, (2) the wood becoming cracked or broken and thrown from the lathe, (3) the operator's clothing becoming entangled in the rotating machinery or wood, and (4) the cutting tool gouging by cutting too deep and causing the wood to be thrown from the lathe.

Wood shaper

The **wood shaper,** like the wood lathe, is not likely to be used very often by the technician making aircraft wood repairs; however, it is a tool with which any woodworker should be familiar. The shaper consists of a high-speed spindle upon which can be mounted cutters of various shapes. The shaper is used for groov-

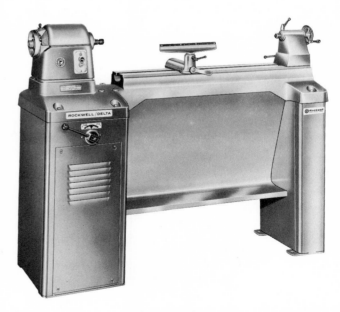

Figure 1·44   A wood-turning lathe. (Rockwell Manufacturing Co., Power Tool Div.)

15

ing, rabbeting, and forming different shapes for molding. It is also used with a special jig for **scarfing** (tapering) narrow stock or for scarfing wide sheets of plywood with a smooth-cutting saw.

Among power tools for woodworking, the shaper is considered the most dangerous. This is because the cutters are turning at a speed of around 6000 rpm and cannot be seen, and the work must usually be fed by hand. The operator must, therefore, be well trained in its use and must exercise extreme care to avoid injury to himself and any other person in the vicinity. Since the cutter rotates at a very high speed, any particles thrown from the cutter may have the force of a bullet.

REVIEW QUESTIONS

1. Why is it necessary that the certified aircraft repairman be familiar with wood repairs?
2. Name at least 20 woodworking tools required for the repair of wood aircraft structures.
3. Explain the difference between a crosscut saw and a ripsaw.
4. Describe a dovetail saw and explain its principal function.
5. What precaution must be taken in boring a hole through a piece of wood with the wood auger bit?
6. Explain how the spurs of an auger bit should be sharpened.
7. Name the two principal types of clamps used in aircraft woodwork.
8. What procedure is used to prevent damage to the wood when C-clamps are applied to the wood?
9. Describe the procedure for tightening parallel clamps.
10. What may happen if the clamp pressure on a glue joint is released after the clamp has been tightened and before the glue has set?
11. Describe the hand drill.
12. What device is used for precision boring?
13. Explain what means are used to assure that a precision hole is correctly located.
14. What is the principal advantage of a magnetic tack hammer?
15. What is the principal difference between the smooth plane and the jack plane?
16. Describe the two adjustments for the plane.
17. What are the functions of the chip breaker?
18. Describe the cutting edge of the plane iron for the jack plane.
19. Explain the advantage of a slightly curved cutting edge.
20. How much should the cutting edge of a plane iron extend below the bottom of the plane?
21. Describe the procedure for sharpening the plane iron.
22. Explain the application of pressure to various points on a plane as it is being used.
23. For what purposes is the wood chisel used?
24. What is the purpose of the rip fence on a bench saw?
25. At what height should the saw blade be adjusted when using the bench saw?
26. What safety precaution should be observed when cutting small pieces of wood on the bench saw?
27. In what direction should the work be moved relative to the rotation of a circular saw blade?
28. What is the principal advantage of a band saw?
29. How can a jig saw be used to cut a hole in a piece of wood without cutting through the edge of the work?
30. What is the purpose of a jointer?
31. Describe the precautions necessary in the operation of a jointer.
32. What adjustments should be made before using the jointer?
33. What precautions should be taken in the operation of a disk sander?
34. What are the principal hazards associated with the operation of a wood lathe?
35. For what purposes is a wood shaper used?

CHAPTER 2

Construction and Repair of Aircraft Wood Structures

Even though modern aircraft are usually constructed of metal, there are many older airplanes and some of recent construction that utilize partial or complete wood construction. It is for this reason that the certificated airframe and powerplant technician needs to know some facts about woods and the kinds suitable for aircraft structures. He must also know the details of approved wood construction and repair practices for aircraft.

The subject of woods in the construction of aircraft can be expanded to encompass all types of wood which have structural qualities suitable for this purpose.

To discuss all possibilities would require a complete volume; hence our purpose here will be to give the student or technician sufficient information to understand the construction of wood aircraft structures and to make any type of repair likely to be required.

There are two principal types of wood, and all woods may be classed as one or the other. There are **softwoods** and **hardwoods.** This classification is not entirely logical because there are some softwoods which are harder than some hardwoods. In general, however, the woods in the hardwood classification will be harder than those in the softwood classification.

Hardwoods

Hardwoods are those produced by broadleaf or deciduous trees such as birch, poplar, elm, hickory, oak, and maple. Softwoods come from the conifers (cone-bearing trees) and have needlelike or scaled leaves. Among such trees are the pines, spruces, firs, hemlocks, cedars, and redwoods. Hardwoods differ from softwoods in that the hardwood generally contains larger cells scattered among the small ones. Large pores serve to carry sap from the roots of the tree to the trunk and branches. To the technician familiar with woods, it is not difficult to distinguish a hardwood from a softwood. Open-grain hardwoods, such as oak and ash, are easily identified by the extra-large channels seen either at the end of a board or on the planed surface. Other hardwoods, such as maple or birch, contain pores which are much smaller and more uniform in size; hence it is more difficult to identify them. Two types of hardwood are illustrated in Fig. 2·1.

Softwoods

Softwoods, particularly aircraft spruce, are most often employed for aircraft wood structures. The greatest advantage of this type of wood is its high strength-to-weight ratio. Properly cured aircraft spruce is light in weight but has a high tensile strength for loads applied parallel to the grain. Aircraft-quality spruce is easy to work, is straight-grained, produces a good glue joint, and finishes well with spar varnish or a similar coating. If aircraft-quality spruce is not available, certain other woods may be substituted, provided they are of satisfactory quality. Among these are Douglas fir, noble fir, Western hemlock, and white or Port Orford cedar. Spruce and fir are shown in Fig. 2·2.

Terminology for woods

Even though the aircraft maintenance technician may not have occasion to use standard terminology for woods very often, it is considered desirable that

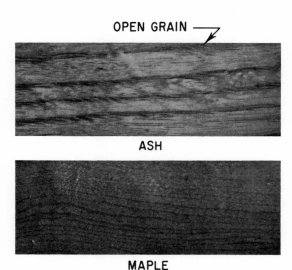

Figure 2·1 Two types of hardwood.

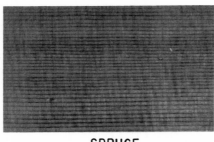

SPRUCE

FIR

Figure 2·2   Samples of spruce and fir.

the terms applied to woods be understood. The following definitions and the accompanying illustration, Fig. 2·3, should be studied and the meanings of the terms noted.

Annual rings are concentric layers of wood which can be seen at the end of a tree trunk which has been cut perpendicular to its length. The rings are caused by the different rates of growth during each year as the seasons change.

Springwood is the harder and denser part of each annual ring. This wood is formed after the rapid growth of the tree has decreased.

Sapwood is the part of a tree which is alive or partially alive and still carries sap. Sapwood begins immediately under the bark and continues inward to the heartwood.

Heartwood is the center part of a tree trunk which is dead and carries no sap. This part of the trunk serves only to support the tree.

Bark is the external covering of a tree trunk or branch.

Grain consists of lines in wood caused by the annual rings. It is also the direction of the wood fibers.

A **knot** is a deformation of grain and structure in a tree trunk caused by the growth of a limb.

A **check** is a radial crack which cuts across the annual ring.

A **shake** is a separation between the annual ring layers. Shakes are concentric with the annual rings.

Compression wood is wood in which the fibers have been damaged by a compression load.

A **spiral grain** is wood grain which grows in a spiral direction around a tree trunk.

Pin knots are small knots caused by the growth of twigs from the trunk of a tree.

Requirements for aircraft wood

The primary requirement for wood to be used in an aircraft structure is that it be sufficiently sound and of such quality that it will provide the strength required for the structure. To meet this standard, certain rules have been established with respect to aircraft woods.

Grain deviation or slope. In general, the wood should be straight-grained and the grain should not deviate more than 1 in. in 15; that is, in a piece of wood 15 in. in length, the grain direction should be generally parallel with the length of the piece and should not vary more than 1 in. This requirement applies to all woods used for structural support.

Type of cut. The way a board is cut has particular significance if it is to be used for a spar or other major structural part of an aircraft. The cut required for such parts is described as **quarter-sawed** or **edge-grained.** This means that the board is sawed so the annular rings are approximately perpendicular to the flat sides of the board. Quarter-sawed lumber is shown in Fig. 2·4. In actual practice, a board is considered to

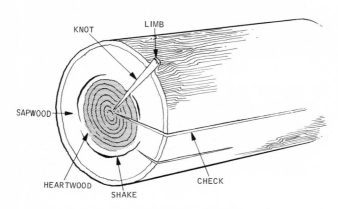

Figure 2·3   Nomenclature for woods.

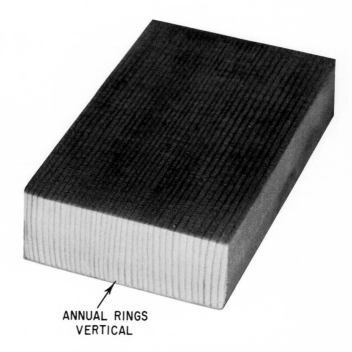

ANNUAL RINGS
VERTICAL

Figure 2·4   A quarter-sawed board.

be quarter-sawed if the annular rings form an angle of more than 45° with the wider flat surface of the board.

Rings per inch. The number of annular rings per inch in aircraft wood is also of considerable importance. A tree grown under conditions where the growth is extremely rapid will have fewer rings per inch than a tree grown more slowly. Furthermore, the wood with the fewer rings will not be so strong as the other. For aircraft structural parts, the minimum number of rings per inch (counted perpendicular to the rings) is six for most woods and eight for Port Orford cedar or Douglas fir.

Specific gravity. The specific gravity of aircraft woods should be from 0.34 to 0.40, depending upon the type of wood. Aircraft spruce should have a specific gravity of approximately 0.36.

Moisture content will have some effect on specific gravity and should be between 8 and 12 percent.

Decay and stain. Aircraft woods must be free from all types of decay. Some stains may be permitted if tests are made to be sure that the stain is not caused by decay or damage.

Shakes and checks. Aircraft wood containing shakes or checks must be discarded. This applies to any separation of wood fibers including cracks or splits of all types.

Compression failures. Wood damaged by compression loads must not be used for aircraft structures. It is often difficult to detect failures of this type; however, if the tip of an ink pen is touched to the wood near the suspected failure, the ink flow along the grain of the wood will be interrupted and will tend to spread across the grain where the failure exists.

Practical considerations. Specifications for aircraft woods as given in ANC-19 (government bulletin entitled *Wood Aircraft Inspection and Fabrication*) and in Federal Aviation Advisory Circular 43.13-1 provide that certain minor defects such as small solid knots and wavy grain may be permitted if such defects do not cause any appreciable weakening of the part in which they appear. As a practical rule, the aircraft maintenance technician should not use any wood about which he has doubts. The safe policy is to use wood which is straight-grained, free from cracks, knots, or any other possible defect, and is guaranteed as aircraft quality.

Drying and seasoning. Aircraft woods are **kiln-dried** to produce uniform strength and to reduce moisture content evenly. A **kiln** is a special oven in which the humidity and temperature are accurately controlled. The lumber to be dried is cut in sizes as small as possible considering the size of the finished parts to be manufactured. The temperature and humidity in the kiln are maintained at a level which will prevent too-rapid drying, thus avoiding the development of cracks or checks in the wood. Such defects are usually caused by uneven drying and the resultant variations in shrinkage in different parts of the wood.

Plywood

Plywood is composed of an uneven number of layers (plies) of wood veneer assembled with the grain of each layer at an angle of 90° to the adjacent layers.

The outside layers are called the **faces,** or the **face** and **back,** and the inner layers are called the **core** and **crossbands.** The core is the center ply and the layers between the core and outer layers are the crossbands.

The layers of plywood are bonded with special glues of the synthetic resin type. Flat aircraft plywood is usually assembled with a thermosetting (hardened by heat) glue in a large, heated hydraulic press. It must be emphasized that aircraft plywood is of much higher quality than commercial grades. Every layer of wood in a sheet of aircraft plywood must be of excellent quality to provide for uniform strength throughout.

Plywood has a number of advantages over solid wood in that it is not likely to warp, it is highly resistant to cracking, and its strength is almost equal in any direction when stresses are applied along the length or width of a panel. Its change in dimensions is negligible with changes in moisture content.

The most commonly used types of plywood for aircraft manufacture are mahogany and birch. The core and crossbands may be made of basswood or a similar wood which provides adequate strength. Mahogany has a lustrous reddish-brown appearance, while birch is of a light yellow or cream color. Mahogany offers a better gluing surface than birch because of its porosity.

When selecting or ordering plywood for aircraft use, the technician should make sure that the wood is of aircraft quality. Some commercial plywoods appear to be as good as aircraft plywood; however, it will be found that the quality is only on the surface and the strength does not compare with the aircraft quality product.

GLUES AND GLUING PROCEDURES

Glues are used almost exclusively for joining wood in aircraft construction and repair. A part is regarded as satisfactorily glued if the strength of the joint is about equal to the strength of the wood. A strong joint has complete contact of glue and wood surfaces over the entire area of the joint and a continuous film of glue between the wood layers unbroken by foreign particles or air bubbles.

To accomplish satisfactory glue work in aircraft wood structures, it is necessary that a number of exacting rules be observed and that all materials be of the high quality specified for aircraft woodwork. If either the glue or the wood is not of satisfactory quality, or if the techniques employed are not correct, the gluing job will be inferior and may result in failure.

Types of glues

A great variety of **glues** are manufactured; hence, the aircraft maintenance technician must exercise care to make sure that the glues he employs for aircraft woodwork are of a type approved for this purpose. Among the types of glues which may be purchased are animal glues, fish glues, casein glues, and synthetic resin glues. Animal and fish glues cannot be used for aircraft work because they are not waterproof and they are subject to fungus deterioration. Casein glue is satisfactory but it should be protected from fungus by means of chemical additives. The present practice is to employ synthetic resin glues because these are both waterproof and fungusproof, and they provide an excellent bond between properly prepared wood surfaces.

Resin glues

The synthetic resin glues most commonly used for aircraft repair are the resorcinol formaldehyde, phenol formaldehye, and urea formaldehyde types. These glues may come in powder form for mixing with water, or they may be in liquid form.

Powdered resin glues usually have a **catalyst** mixed with the powder, and after the glue is mixed with water, the catalyst acts to cause the glue to set. The working life of the glue must be considered to make sure that the glue does not become too thick while being applied.

Liquid resin glues will remain in a liquid state until the catalyst is added. The catalyst is usually in powder form mixed with walnut-shell flour or wood flour. In all cases the mixing and use of the glue should conform strictly to the manufacturer's instructions.

Since the working life of synthetic resin glues is affected by temperature, it may be necessary during hot weather for the glue to be placed in a water bath at a temperature of approximately 70°F in order to prolong the time during which the glue may be worked.

The best working and setting temperature for the application of resin glues is 70 to 75°F. If the glue is applied and allowed to set at a lower temperature, the strength of the joint may be adversely affected.

Since resorcinol formaldehyde glues have proved to be most satisfactory for aircraft woodwork, we shall limit further discussion to this type. The trade names of several such glues are Cascophen, Durez, Durite, Kaseno, Lauxite, and Penacolite. These glues are usually furnished in water-alcohol mixtures with a catalyst in powder form to be added a short time before the glue is to be applied. The catalyst must be added in a quantity indicated by the manufacturer and in the specified manner. The working life of these glues is from 2 to 4 hr, depending upon the make. This time must be carefully observed for the particular glue being used. The best working temperature is from 70 to 75°F and should be maintained as nearly as possible.

Mixing dry-resin glues

The glue manufacturer places instructions for mixing on the container. Some cold-setting resin glues require 1 part of glue powder to 0.4 part of water and some require 1 part of glue powder to 0.65 part of water; if the instructions are not available, however, a mixture of 2 parts of dry glue powder to 1 part of water by weight will generally be satisfactory. Notice that the proportions are by weight and not by volume. The water should be clean and within the temperature range of 16 to 21°C (60 to 70°F).

The glue powder is first dry-mixed and then weighed. From one-half to two-thirds of the required amount of water is placed in the mixing bowl or cup. The glue powder is stirred in slowly until the whole amount has been added. The first mixing is done slowly. When all lumps are dissolved and the glue is a thick, smooth paste, the remaining one-half or one-third of the water is added while continuing to stir the mixture. The mixing should continue for from 3 to 5 min after all the water is added. Finally, the glue is properly mixed if it has a light, creamy consistency and is free from lumps and air bubbles.

Moisture content of woods

The **moisture content** of wood when it is glued has a great effect on the warping of glued members, the development of checks in the wood, and the final strength of the joints. A moisture content at the time of gluing that is between 8 and 12 percent is generally regarded as satisfactory, but the higher the moisture content within this range the better will be the joint. If the moisture content is too low, the glue cannot wet the surface properly, and it sometimes produces what are called **starved joints,** that is, joints not adequately bonded. Gluing increases the moisture content of the wood; hence the moisture added in this manner must dry out or distribute itself in the wood before the part can be machined or finished. Other factors in establishing moisture content are the density and thickness of the wood, the number of plies, the glue mixture, and the quantity of glue used. If the moisture content of a joint is that which the glued member will have in use, the joint will be strong, and there is less possibility of warping.

If it is necessary to determine the moisture content of a sample of wood, the procedure is simple but it requires time. The equipment needed is a sensitive set of scales and an oven to provide a temperature slightly above the boiling point of water. The procedure is as follows:

1. Cut a small section (2 to 4 cu in.) of the wood to be tested from the sample at a point about 2 ft from the end. Wood cut too near the end of a board will not be likely to have the same moisture content as the portions 2 ft or more from the end.
2. Place the wood sample on a sensitive balance or pair of scales and record the exact weight in ounces or grams.
3. Put the test piece of wood in the drying oven and maintain the temperature at about 105°C (or 220°F) for several hours. When the sample has reached a condition of constant weight, record this weight and compare it with the weight before drying.

The percentage of moisture is obtained by subtracting the dry weight from the original weight and then determining what percentage of the original weight is represented by the difference between the dry weight and the original weight. For example, if the original weight were 8 oz and the dry weight is 7.5 oz, the difference is 0.5 oz. Then $0.5 \times 100/7.5 = 6.67$ percent. That is, the moisture content of the original sample was 6.67 percent.

Condition of surfaces to be glued

Wood surfaces to be glued should be smooth and true. Chapped or loosened grain, machine marks, and other surface irregularities are objectionable. Joints of about equal strength are made between two planed or smoothly sawed surfaces that are equally true.

In the past, some aircraft maintenance technicians believed they could obtain better surfaces for gluing by roughening the wood surfaces by tooth planing, scratching, or with coarse sandpaper; however, such practices usually produce a poor surface for gluing. The wood surface should not be sanded because this tends to fill the wood pores with wood dust and sand particles, thus making it impossible for the glue to penetrate the surface and produce a strong bond.

Proper gluing conditions

A strong joint in the wood is obtained from complete contact of glue and wood surfaces over the entire joint area and a continuous film of good glue between the wood layers that is unbroken by air bubbles or by foreign particles. Under these conditions, the glue penetrates the pores of the wood and forms a bond which is stronger than the bond between the original wood fibers. When broken, such a joint will not separate at the glue bond but will fracture in the wood outside the bond.

A proper correlation between gluing pressure and glue consistency at the moment that a pressure is applied is one of the principal factors in making strong glue joints. The consistency of the glue mixture after it is spread on the wood varies greatly. It depends upon such factors as the moisture content of the wood, the temperature of the glue room, the kind of glue used, and the extent to which the glue-coated surfaces are exposed to the air.

Good joints can be made by coating under favorable gluing conditions either one or both contact faces of the parts to be joined. Normally it is approved practice to spread glue on both surfaces. Excess glue that squeezes out after applying pressure should be wiped or scraped off. In any event, the instructions furnished by the manufacturer of the glue should be followed.

Gluing pressure

The functions of pressure on a glue joint are as follows: (1) to squeeze the glue out into a thin continuous film between the wood layers, (2) to force air from the joint, (3) to bring the wood surfaces into intimate contact with the glue, and (4) to hold them in intimate contact during the setting of the glue.

A light pressure is used with thin glue and a heavy pressure is used with thick glue. Corresponding variations in pressure are made with glues of intermediate consistencies. The pressure applied should be within the range approved for the types of wood being glued. For example, the gluing pressure should be between 125 and 150 psi for softwoods and between 150 and 200 psi for hardwoods.

Gluing pressure is applied by means of nails, screws, or clamps, depending upon the nature of the parts being glued. When possible to apply them, clamps should always be used. Otherwise, nails, screws, or other methods are necessary. When clamps are used, **caul blocks** are employed between the clamp jaws and the work to be glued. These blocks distribute the pressure and prevent the clamps from crushing the wood fibers immediately under the clamp jaws.

The first pressure applied to glue joints tends to decrease as the glue squeezes out from between the faces of the wood or distributes itself in the joint. To be sure that the proper amount of pressure is maintained, the clamps or other pressing devices should be kept in close adjustment for a short time after the first application of pressure.

Pressing time

The pressing time for typical glues used for aircraft wood repair vary, depending upon the surrounding temperature. At higher temperatures (80 to 100°F) the setting time for glues is considerably less than at 70°. Some glues may set in as little as 3 hr. To be sure that a glue joint is satisfactory, it is recommended that the glue be allowed to set for at least 7 hr under normal temperature before removing clamps. If time allows, it is best to let the joint remain under pressure overnight or longer. Additional strength is gained with the longer setting times.

Pressure must be applied and the contact made in the joint before the glue becomes too thick to flow properly. If glue is spread on dry wood, it becomes thicker more rapidly than it would in the container. If pieces of wood are coated with glue and exposed to a free circulation of air in the assembly process known as **open assembly,** the glue thickens faster than when the pieces are laid together as soon as the glue is spread. The latter process is called **closed assembly.** In other gluing operations the assembly time may be as little as 1 min or as long as 20 min, but the glue must remain at a satisfactory consistency throughout the period. Unless specifically stated to the contrary by the manufacturer of the glue, open assembly should not permit the glue to be exposed to the open air for more than 20 min.

How pressure is applied

For small joints, such as those found only in wood ribs, the pressure is usually applied by nailing the joint gussets in place after spreading the glue. Since small nails must be used to avoid splitting the wood, the gussets must be fairly large in area to compensate for the relatively small amount of pressure. The spacing of the nails should be at least four per square inch and never less than one nail for each linear inch.

The nails used for aircraft woodwork may be made of steel or brass wire. The diameter of the nails is usually 20 gage (AWG) and the length may be from ¼ in. to ¾ in. For nailing gussets the length is usually ¼ in. Steel nails should be coated with a special cement which serves two purposes: (1) The cement helps to hold the nail firmly in place after it is driven and (2) it contains an inhibiter which tends to prevent the nail from rusting due to dampness which may be encountered from time to time. Aircraft nails are used to hold plywood gussets in place until the glue has set, and they are also used with nailing strips to apply pressure to plywood skin when it is glued to ribs or other wooden structures.

Small brass screws may be used where the parts to be glued are comparatively small and do not allow application of pressure by means of clamps. Spar splices should be clamped by means of the clamps previously discussed. C-clamps must be applied with a pressure-distributing caul block at least twice as thick as the wood member to be pressed, because of the limited pressure area obtained with such clamps.

Cleanliness

As with all other aircraft repair operations, cleanliness and neatness are of the utmost importance in the repair of aircraft wood structures. The gluepot, brushes, and other gluing equipment should be cleaned with warm but not boiling water, because the latter will set the glue. All glue left over from a job should be discarded. Any glue spilled or dropped on tables or equipment should be removed before it sets.

CONSTRUCTION AND REPAIR

In this section we provide basic information regarding wood aircraft construction and describe repairs for various parts of wooden structures commonly found in aircraft. Before attempting to repair a damaged wooden aircraft structure, the technician must make certain that he understands the nature of the required repair and that he has the correct materials at hand to make the repair.

Nomenclature for wooden aircraft

The nomenclature for a wooden wing is shown in the illustration of Fig. 2·5. It will be observed that the parts are named according to standard practice for both metal and wooden wings. In the illustration, the **leading-edge strip,** the **plywood skin,** and the **corner block** are peculiar to wooden construction. Some of the nomenclature for a wooden fuselage is given in Fig. 2·6. Here again, the nomenclature is similar to that given for a metal fuselage of the semimonocoque type.

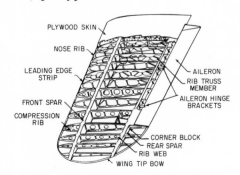

PLYWOOD SKIN
NOSE RIB
LEADING EDGE STRIP
FRONT SPAR
COMPRESSION RIB
AILERON
RIB TRUSS MEMBER
AILERON HINGE BRACKETS
CORNER BLOCK
REAR SPAR
RIB WEB
WING TIP BOW

Figure **2·5** *Nomenclature for a wooden wing.*

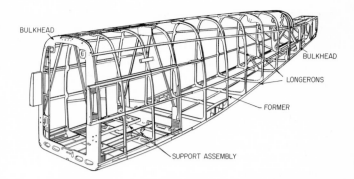

BULKHEAD
BULKHEAD
LONGERONS
FORMER
SUPPORT ASSEMBLY

Figure **2·6** *Nomenclature for a wooden fuselage.*

Bending wood

Curved wooden parts of an aircraft may be steamed and bent to shape, or they may be laminated and bent without steaming or other preparation. **Laminated wood** is a piece of wood built up of plies, or laminations, that have been joined (usually with glue) where the grain of all plies lies parallel. The plies are generally thicker than pieces of wood that could be called **veneer.** Laminated members, since they have a parallel grain construction, have about the same properties as solid wood, except that laminated members are usually more uniform in their strength properties and less prone to change shape with variations in moisture content. For producing curved members, laminated construction is widely used.

Whether the curved wooden parts are steamed and bent or laminated and bent without steaming, the grain follows the curvature of the aircraft part. This makes the part more serviceable and less subject to breaking or splitting than a part cut to shape. However, the wood must be straight-grained and free from defects if the curved member is to have the maximum strength.

In some cases it is more desirable to use solid wood instead of laminated wood. If it is necessary to bend the wood, only the best, clear, straight-grained material is selected. The replacement parts should be of the same wood as the part removed. Most bent parts are of ash, spruce, or oak.

Before bending, wood must be softened by the addition of moisture or heat, or both. Wood can be softened by soaking it in cold water, warm water, or boiling water, or by steaming. Steam bending is used in aircraft work where the bends are not severe. When the wood is bent, the fibers on the convex (belly out) side of the bend are in tension and will stretch only slightly before tension failure takes place. Wood on the concave (belly in) side is in compression; when softened properly it may be compressed considerably without failure, although this varies with the kind of wood used.

When the curvature is not too pronounced, parts of adequate strength may be formed from wood that has been air-dried to a moisture content of 12 to 15 percent. After the wood has been seasoned, and immediately before steaming, the wood should be surfaced, or it may be smoothly sawed to dimensions that are only enough greater than the final size to allow for finishing and shrinkage.

Subjecting the wood to boiling water or steam for about 1 hr per in. of bending thickness prepares the wood for bending, but it should not be boiled or steamed for more than 4 hr because such treatment weakens the wood. However, it is impossible to give any accurate general rule on this subject.

There are various forms of steam tanks, and it is fairly simple to make one by nailing together a rectangular wooden box large enough to hold the parts to be steamed. Steam is admitted through a pipe to the upper part at one end, and the other end is hinged for inserting and removing the part to be steamed. The corners of the box are reinforced with sheet metal held in place by screws. The box is fastened to supports in such a manner that it slopes slightly toward the end at which the steam enters. The steam should not be hotter than 212°F, which is the boiling point of water. In other words, the water is brought to a boiling temperature and held there as closely as possible.

Immediately after steaming, the wooden part must be bent. If the curvature is slight, the part may be bent by hand over a form of the desired shape. If the curvature is pronounced, most of the deformation (change of shape) is accomplished by compression or shortening. This is done by using a forming die and a holding strap, such as the one illustrated in Fig. 2·7. The wood to be bent is fitted snugly between the bulkheads shown in the picture and then bent over the forming die. In some cases, the type of clamp shown in the lower drawing of Fig. 2·7 does not hold. It is then necessary to use a vise-type clamp with outer and inner forming dies.

The wood, having been bent, should remain in the forms until it has cooled and dried enough to keep its shape. The forms are usually made with a slightly greater curvature than the curvature required for the finished part to provide for the tendency of the wood to straighten out somewhat after it is taken out of the forms. In addition, the forms should be designed so that they expose as much as possible of the bent piece to the drying effect of the air.

If the moisture content is to be determined, it can be found by means of electric moisture meters, but such instruments are not considered essential for the average aircraft wood repair shop. The usual method requires the use of an oven that can maintain a constant temperature of 100 to 105°C (212 to 221°F) and a balance scale accurate to within 0.1 percent. Specimens of solid wood are cut at least 1 ft from the end of the piece and 1 in. long, with the grain, as wide as the board from which they are cut. Plywood specimens can be used in any convenient size, but they should not be cut from an edge of the piece of wood.

The loose splinters are trimmed off and the specimen is carefully weighed. It is then dried for 24 hr

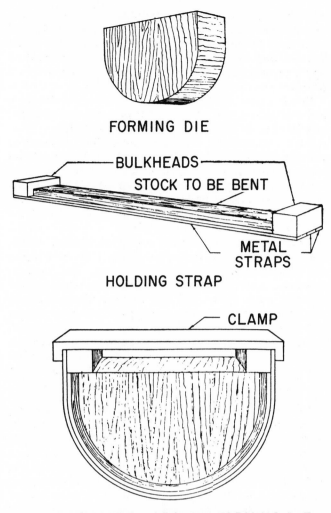

FORMING DIE

BULKHEADS
STOCK TO BE BENT

METAL STRAPS

HOLDING STRAP

CLAMP

BENDING STOCK AROUND FORMING DIE

Figure 2·7   Using a forming die and a holding strap.

in the oven at 100 to 105°C (212 to 221°F) and weighed immediately after it is taken out. The difference in weight of the specimen before and after being dried is divided by its weight when dry to obtain the moisture content of the piece before drying. This is expressed in percentage of the oven-dry weight when multiplied by 100. This method requires great care if the results are to be accurate. For example, the specimens must be piled in the oven in an open manner that permits the air to circulate freely while they are being dried.

Bending laminated wood members

Laminated wood members that do not require severe bending, such as wing-tip bows, may be formed without steaming or any other softening preparation. If the laminations are thin enough to take the necessary bend without splitting, they are cut to size and planed on both sides. Laminations sufficient in number to make up the required thickness are coated with glue and clamped in a form of the necessary shape. If desired, a steel strap may be used to hold the laminations over the forming die. Time is allowed for the glue to set and for the wood to dry thoroughly, after which the wooden part will retain the shape of the form; if there is any springback, it will be very slight. In certain cases, where it is not desirable to use very thin laminations, or where the bending curvature is severe, the laminations may be steamed and bent to shape before being glued together.

Figure 2·8 illustrates the **spline method** of bending a solid member. This method is used where a bend is required in the end of a solid member, such as a stabilizer leading edge or a spar flange. The wooden part is first slotted the length of the bend to be made, as shown in the upper drawing. A spline is inserted after applying glue to the surfaces, as shown in the middle drawing, and finally the part is bent to the necessary curvature, as shown in the bottom drawing of Fig. 2·8.

When curved plywood members are needed, several layers of veneer may be bent and glued in one operation, or the prepared plywood may simply be bent.

When built-up plywood members are desired, veneer strips or sheets are bent over a form after glue has been applied to their surfaces. The sheets or strips are held together, often with staples, while the glue sets; and then the member will retain its shape after it has been removed from the form. The grain of each successive layer of veneer should be perpendicular to that of the adjoining layer, but in some jobs the veneer is applied on the form with the grain running at an oblique angle of about 45° from the axis of the member. If the work is done carefully, a built-up plywood member should have about the same properties as a bent laminated member.

Parts such as the covering for the leading edge of a wing or a stabilizer may be formed of plywood which has been bonded with an adhesive which is subject to softening when heated. The plywood is soaked in hot water or steamed until it becomes soft. It is then bent over a form and clamped in place until dry. The curvature of the form must be a little sharper than the final curvature required to allow for

a small amount of springback that will take place after a member has been taken off the form. Figure 2·9 shows the forming block, the plywood, and the clamps used in this method.

In bending pieces of small radii or to hasten the bending of a great number of parts having the same curvature, it is sometimes necessary to use a heated bending form, such as that shown in Fig. 2·10. The surface temperature of this form may be as high as 149°C (300°F), if necessary, without damaging the plywood, but the plywood should be left on the form only long enough for it to dry to room conditions of temperature and humidity.

Splicing of spars

Wooden wing spars are often repaired by splicing sections either on the ends or between the ends of the spar. The sections of the spar are spliced by use of a glued scarf joint and reinforcing plates. The scarf joint has proved to be the most satisfactory splice for solid wood, laminated wood, and plywood.

The desired slope for the scarf in softwoods is 12:1, but a slope of not less than 10:1 will be acceptable. The scarf is cut to follow the grain of the wood and must be finished to a flat, smooth surface by use

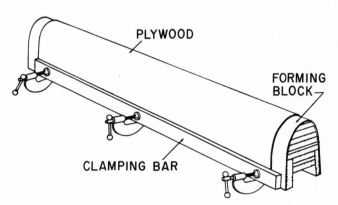

Figure 2·9   Forming a leading edge over a forming block.

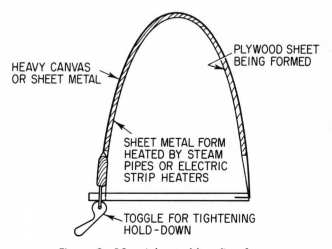

Figure 2·10   A heated bending form.

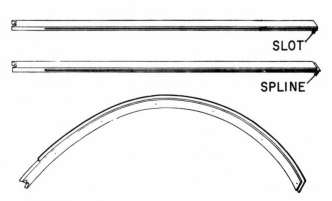

Figure 2·8   Spline method for bending a solid member.

of a plane. The scarfed surface must not be sanded, since this will fill the pores of the wood with wood dust and tiny sand particles.

Spar splices may be made at any part of a spar except under main structural fittings such as wing-attachment fittings, strut fittings, and landing-gear fittings. Splices may be made under minor fittings such as drag and antidrag wire fittings, provided certain conditions are observed. The reinforcement plates of the splice must not interfere with the location and alignment of the minor fittings. Re-inforcement plates may overlap the location of drag or antidrag wire fittings if the plates are on the front of the front spar or on the rear face of the rear spar, since this will not change the location of the fittings.

The techniques for gluing wood spar splices should follow those described earlier in this chapter. Great care must be taken to see that splices are properly clamped after gluing to make sure that even pressure is exerted throughout the glued area.

After a joint is glued and finished or smoothed to correct dimensions, reinforcement plates are attached by gluing. The plates are held in place by clamps and must not be nailed.

Acceptable methods for splicing various types of spars are shown in Figs. 2·11 through 2·14.

Figure 2·11 shows a typical solid or laminated spar splice. The dimensions shown must be closely followed to produce an acceptable splice. Laminated spars may be replaced with solid spars or vice versa provided the quality of the replacement is equal to or better than the original.

A splice for solid I spars is shown in Fig. 2·12. The reinforcement plates are contoured to fit the routing

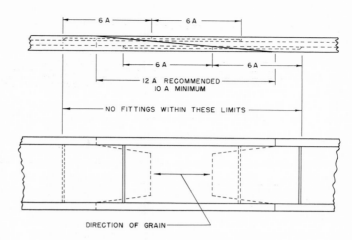

Figure 2·12   Splicing solid I spars.

of the spar in the web section. If the splice is made where the routing is feathered out to the full width of the spar, tapered plates conforming to the contour of the routing should be installed.

Figures 2·13 and 2·14 illustrate methods for splicing built-up I spars and box-spar flanges. The plywood webs and reinforcements replaced in these repairs must be of the same high-quality plywood as the original. Solid wood does not have the shear strength of plywood, since it does not have the variations of grain direction provided in plywood.

Box-spar webs are spliced as shown in Fig. 2·15. The face grain of the plywood replacement should be in the same direction as the original. The plywood replacement and reinforcements must be of the same

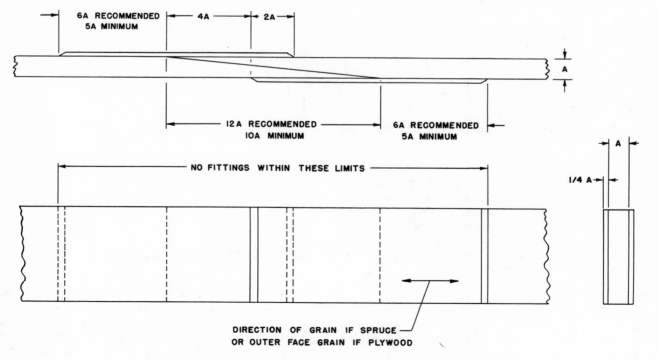

Figure 2·11   Splicing solid or rectangular spars.

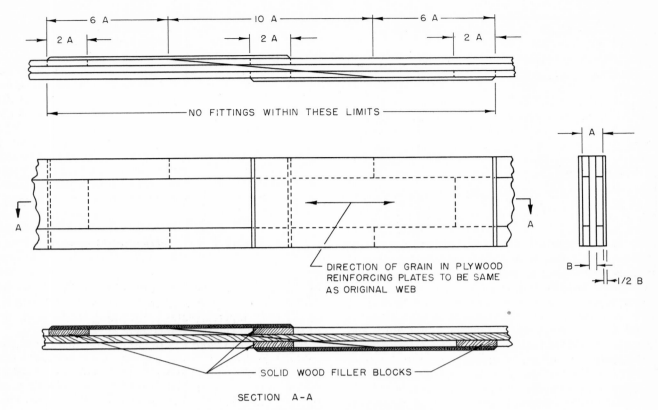

SECTION A-A

Figure **2·13** Splice for a built-up I spar.

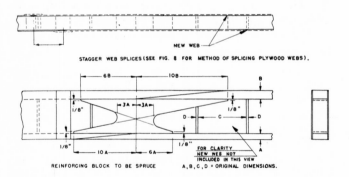

Figure **2·14** Splicing box-spar flanges by the plate method.

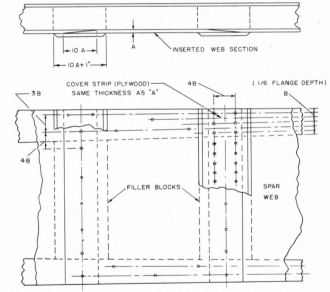

Figure **2·15** Method for splicing a box-spar web.

type as the original. This is important, since the strength of the spar is calculated on the basis of the type of plywood used in the construction.

Figure 2·16 illustrates repairs for a longitudinal crack in an internally routed spar and for local damage along one edge. A solid spar may also be repaired as shown in the figure.

Spar splicing techniques

In making a spar splice, the technician must observe certain conditions and practice his skills in a manner to produce a spliced joint as nearly perfect as possible. Among the conditions required are (1) a true and smooth surface on each member of the spliced joint, (2) a completed splice at least as strong as the original unspliced spar, (3) a thickness of the spar at the spliced joint which is the same as the original spar without regard to the splice plates, and (4) a glue joint which is almost invisible when observed from the side of the finished splice.

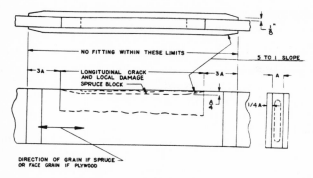

Figure 2·16 *Reinforcing a longitudinal crack in a solid or internally routed spar.*

To produce a satisfactory splice, the workman must employ a high degree of skill in planing the scarfed surfaces of the spar to be spliced. In doing this, the techniques described in the previous chapter must be employed. Note that the pressure applied to the plane as it moves over the surfaces of wood must be varied from *A* to *B* to *C,* as shown in Fig. 1·31. Periodically, the technician should check the trueness of the surface by means of a straightedge as shown in Fig. 2·17. This will enable him to observe high spots and then use his plane to remove such spots.

In starting to make a spar splice, the technician must plan his cut for both the original spar being spliced and for the new section to which it is to be joined. This requires careful measurement of the spar thickness and total length of the splice. Remember that the desired length of the splice should be 12 times the thickness of the spar. If the spar is ⅞ in. thick, the splice should be 10½ in. in length. In any case, the length of the splice could not be less than 8¾ in. in length.

After the damaged spar has been cut off to eliminate all cracked or otherwise damaged wood, the splice length is marked on the end of the cut spar and a diagonal line is drawn to indicate where the scarf cut is to be made. Since the spar will probably be in the wing, it will require a good measure of skill to cut the scarf with a dovetail or backsaw and then finish the scarfed surface to the required degree with a small hand plane. The new piece of spar stock to be installed can be scarfed and finished on the bench before it is joined to the section in the wing.

In cutting the scarf for a spar splice the slope of the scarf should, as nearly as possible, be in the same direction as the slope of the grain in the wood. If the grain of the wood is parallel with the edges of the lumber, the scarf can be cut from either side. It will be found, however, that there is often a small degree of slope to the grain when one observes the edge of board. The technician will observe the slope of the edge grain and cut the scarf so it will slope in the same direction.

One of the most critical operations in the splicing of a spar is to clamp the joint in the proper position after the glue has been applied. It must be remembered that the thickness of the glue will affect the thickness of the splice. For this reason, the two parts of the spar must be assembled to allow for the change as the joint is clamped and the glue squeezed out of the joint. The method for making this allowance is shown in Fig. 2·18. The completed splice will retain its full thickness if this operation is correctly performed.

The final operation in making the splice is to set the clamps with the correct pressure. The method for accomplishing this was explained in the previous chapter. The use of waxed paper to prevent adherence of the glue to the clamps and caul blocks of adequate thickness must not be overlooked.

Upon completion of the basic splice operation, excess glue is removed and the surface is smoothed. Reinforcing plates of the correct dimensions are then glued on the sides of the splice according to the specifications previously described and illustrated.

Wing-spar construction

In order to apply the foregoing instructions to the repair of wing spars, it will be helpful to note the various types of spar construction. A study of Fig. 2·19 will aid in understanding the construction of different types of wood spars.

Spars transmit air loads from the wing to the fuselage. Depending on the design, spars may extend from wing tip to wing tip or from wing tip to fuselage. The wing-fuselage fittings, ribs, and compression struts are attached to the spar.

The rectangular and laminated solid spars sometimes have reinforcing blocks glued on at the point of attachment of members and fittings. Weight is saved by the use of I spars, internally routed spars, and box spars. The box spar is made by connecting upper and lower flanges by plywood webs. At points of attachment of members and fittings to an I spar, reinforcing blocks are glued on, or, in the case of internally routed spars, the spar is left solid. Bulkheads are used for

Figure 2·17 *Checking the trueness of a planed surface.*

Figure 2·18 *Thickness allowance for a spar splice.*

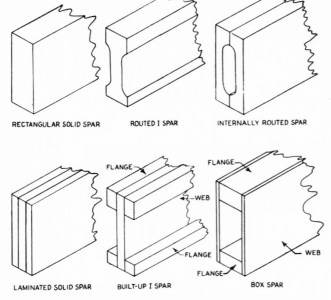

RECTANGULAR SOLID SPAR   ROUTED I SPAR   INTERNALLY ROUTED SPAR

LAMINATED SOLID SPAR   BUILT-UP I SPAR   BOX SPAR

FLANGE   FLANGE   WEB   FLANGE   FLANGE   WEB

Figure 2·19   Sections of different types of spars.

bracing the plywood against buckling, and they also serve as reinforcing blocks where fittings and members are attached.

When a wing-spar root fitting is assembled to the root end of a box spar, aluminum-alloy bushings, through which the fitting attachment bolts are inserted, provide more bearing surface and lessen the possibility of local crushing of the spar. When bushings are used, they are usually press-fitted into the member. The plywood web is nailed and glued to the reinforcing blocks. Small holes are drilled through the rear web at the lowest point of each compartment to permit ventilation and drainage of moisture condensed within the spar. Water will then drain from the compartment when the airplane is in a taxiing position. The holes and the inside of the spar are waterproofed with spar varnish.

Elongated holes

If elongated bolt holes exist in a spar or cracks are found in the vicinity of bolt holes, a new section of spar should be spliced into place or the spar replaced entirely, unless some other method of repair has been specifically approved by competent authority. If the spar roots are being replaced, it may be advantageous to laminate the new section of the spar, using aircraft plywood for the outer faces.

Rib construction and repair

Ribs give the wing and other airfoil sections the desired cross-sectional shape. In some wings, certain ribs take the compression load between the front and rear spars, in which case they replace the compression struts which would otherwise be separate members. A tapered wing may be tapered in width, tapered in thickness, or tapered in both thickness and width. Therefore the ribs of tapered wings vary in size from

wing tip to wing root, although the cross-sectional shape (airfoil section) of each rib is the same throughout in the normal design.

Some ribs are built with the nose section, the center section between the spars, and the trailing-edge section as separate units, all being butted against the spar and fastened with glue and nails. Other ribs are constructed in one unit and slipped over the spar to their proper stations.

The rib structure may consist of the truss type with plywood-gusseted joints, the lightened and reinforced plywood type, the full plywood-web type with stiffeners, or some other special design. It is very important that no change be made in the shape of an airfoil section during construction or repair.

Making and installing ribs

It is better if complete ribs are made from a drawing furnished by the manufacturer or from a drawing made by a repair agency and certified correct by the manufacturer; however, an original rib may be used as a pattern for making a new rib if it is not so badly damaged that comparison is inaccurate.

Wood ribs should not be attached to wood spars by nails driven through the rib cap strips because this method weakens the rib. The attachment should be made by means of glue, with cement-coated, barbed, or spiraled nails driven through the vertical rib members on each side of the spar. The drawing or pattern used for making the ribs is then retained on file for examination by any inspector who checks the work later.

Cap strips for wood ribs should be made of the high-quality aircraft spruce used for spars. Other types of wood may be used if they meet the requirements of the Federal Aviation Administration.

Rib cap strips are made by sawing the wood with the grain in strips slightly larger than required and then finishing with a jointer, a hand plane, or a power planer.

A wood rib is usually assembled in a **rib jig.** The rib jig is made by drawing a pattern of the rib on a smooth, flat plank and then nailing small blocks of wood to the plank so that they outline the rib pattern. During assembly, the cap strips are inserted between the blocks to hold them in the proper position for attachment of the vertical and diagonal members and the plywood gussets, which are attached with nails and glue. Figure 2·20 shows a rib assembled in the jig and a completed rib.

When a rib must be repaired or installed on a wing which is already assembled, it is usually necessary to build the rib on the wing. This requires great precision to make sure that the rib is the same shape and size as the original.

Repairs at a joint, between joints, at trailing edges, or at spars

Figures 2·21 to 2·25 show satisfactory methods of repairing damaged ribs. In Fig. 2·21, *A, B, C, D,* and *E* are the original dimensions. The reinforcement plates

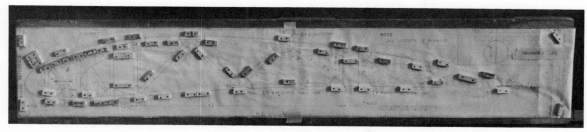

JIG

RIB

Figure 2·20　Rib jig and completed rib.

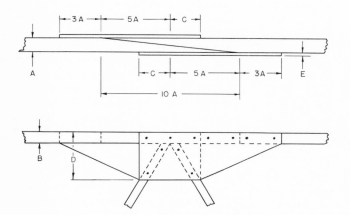

Figure 2·21　Repair of a rib at truss members.

are plywood-glued and nailed. The nail heads must not be embedded in the plywood. The damaged web members are entirely replaced. This illustrates repair at a joint or between joints.

Figure 2·22 illustrates an acceptable method for repairing the trailing edge of a wood rib where the ends of the cap strips have been damaged by crushing or rotting. The damaged wood is entirely removed, and a filler block is cut to fit the cap strips and re-form the end of the rib to the original dimensions. The filler block is so cut that the grain is in the same direction as that of the cap strips and is installed by gluing and nailing gussets to the sides. The joint between the filler block and the cut ends of the cap strip is also glued.

Figure 2·23 illustrates the proper method of making a splice in a cap strip between joints. The splice is made with at least a 10:1 scarf joint and glued. The reinforcement plates are plywood of the same thickness as the gussets used on the rib. They are glued and nailed, and the face grain is in the same direction as that of the gussets.

The illustration in Fig. 2·24 shows a rib cap strip splice at a spar. The original dimensions are shown

by *A, B, C, D, E, F,* and *G.* The recommended scarf for the splice is 12:1, as shown in the figure. The gusset, or reinforcing plate, used is sometimes called a **saddle gusset** since it straddles the spar and extends down both sides. The gusset is so cut that the face grain is in the direction shown and the thickness is the same as for other gussets in the rib. As in the attachment of all gussets where glue and nails are used, the nails must not be driven so far that the heads are embedded in the wood. It should be remembered that *the strength of a wood splice is provided by the glue and not by the nails.*

Repairing compression ribs

Methods for repairing various types of wood compression ribs are shown in Fig. 2·25.

The first rib shown is the I-section type with wide,

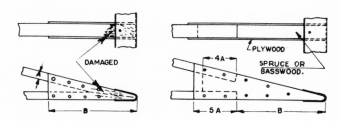

Figure 2·22　Methods for repairing damaged rib at trailing edge.

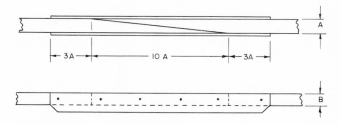

Figure 2·23　Splice of a cap strip between joints.

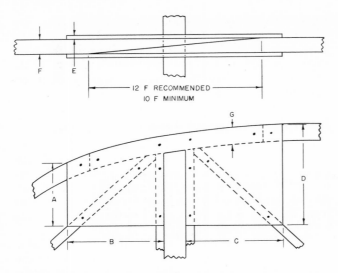

Figure 2·24   Repair of a cap strip at a spar.

shallow cap strips and a plywood-center web with rectangular compression members on each side. This rib is indicated by A in the figure. It is assumed that the rib is cracked through the cap strips, web, and the compression members. The cap strips of the rib are repaired according to methods shown in previous illustrations in this chapter. The compression members are cut and spliced as shown in D in the figure. It will be noted that this splice is similar to cap strip splices. To complete the repair, plywood reinforcing plates are glued to the sides of the rib. These plates restore the strength of the damaged web.

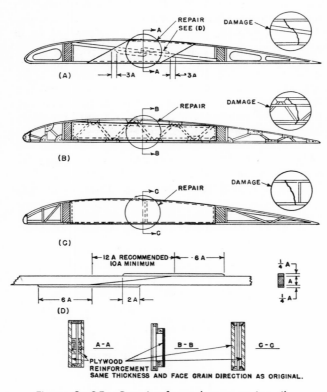

Figure 2·25   Repair of wood compression ribs.

The rib shown in B of Fig. 2·25 is constructed like a standard rib except that it has a plywood web attached to one side and rectangular compression members on the other side. This rib is repaired in the same way as the rib in A, but the plywood reinforcement is extended for the full distance between the spars. See section B-B.

The illustration in C shows an I-section rib with a vertical stiffening member on each side of the plywood web. The cap strips are repaired as in A and then plywood plates are installed on each side for the full distance between the spars. See section C-C.

Leading- and trailing-edge strips

The leading edge of the wing, of an aileron, or of other airfoil surfaces may be provided with special nose ribs, stiffeners, and a covering of sheet metal or plywood to maintain its shape, and also to provide for local stresses. A metal or wooden strip is used along the leading edge to secure the ribs against sidewise bending and to provide a surface for attaching the metal fabric, or plywood covering. In some airplanes, the metal or plywood covering acts as the stiffener for the ribs instead of the leading-edge strip.

Figure 2·26 shows the use of a template in shaping the leading edge. The curved portion of the leading-edge strip completes the contour along the nose of the wing; it is important in forming the leading edge of the strip to use a template, corresponding to the curvature, for checking the work. Figure 2·27 shows that the templates for a tapered leading-edge strip vary in shape to correspond to sections along the strip. A drawing of the leading edge is used to obtain the dimensions required for laying out the template.

The trailing-edge strip of any airfoil surface may be of wood or metal. The wooden strip is made similar to the leading-edge strip. Templates may be used to indicate the camber of the rib. If a metal channel is used, it is riveted to the cap strip.

The leading edges of wing and control surfaces are repaired by carefully made and reinforced splices, such as the one illustrated in Fig. 2·28, where a damaged leading-edge section of a horizontal or vertical stabilizer is repaired by splicing in a new section. To obtain additional gluing area, the skin is feathered into the strip. If this is done properly, only one reinforcing strip is required.

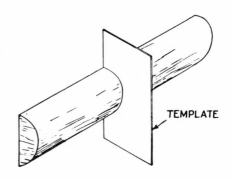

Figure 2·26   A template used to shape the leading edge.

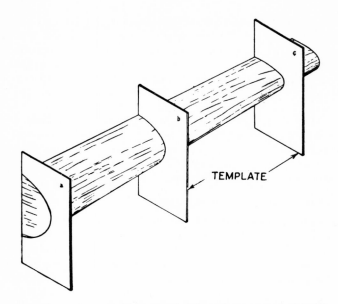

Figure 2·27 Templates for a tapered leading-edge strip.

Wing-tip bow construction and repair

A wing tip may have any of several shapes; for example, it may be square, elliptical, or circular in plan form. If the wing tip is elliptical or circular, a wooden or metal wing-tip bow is required for attaching the plywood or fabric covering. A wooden bow for this purpose consists of from 4 to 10 laminae, bent to the required shape. If the upper surface of the wing extends level to the wing tip, the wing-tip bow is curved upward from the leading edge, and the bow stock is made wide enough for the contour to be laid out on the curved stock, the bow being sawed to shape on a band saw.

After the bow is attached to the wing, it is worked to the required cross section by hand, either a spokeshave or a plane being used. Where both the lower and upper surfaces of the wing slope to form the tip, the bow is bent to shape and worked to the indicated cross section.

Figure 2·29 shows three types of wing-bow cross sections with the plywood surface and the tip bow indicated in each.

A wing-tip bow that has been badly damaged should be removed and replaced. A cracked or broken bow may be repaired by splicing in a new piece. The new piece may be spliced in at the spar. It should have the same contour as the original bow, and the splices should meet the requirements of a scarf joint, as explained elsewhere in this chapter.

The application of plywood skin

Plywood for the skin of the airplane is cut and shaped to fit the surface to be covered, enough material being allowed to provide for scarfing where needed. Depending upon the design, it may be necessary to cut the skin larger than is needed and to trim it to size after it has been glued to the frame, particularly in the case of wing tips.

The next step is temporarily to nail the plywood to the frame in one corner, make any required adjustments, and then nail in the opposite corner. These temporary nails are driven through small strips of wood so that they can be pulled out easily. The corners having been secured, the plywood is then pressed down against the framework with the hands to be sure that it is in the exact position and that all supporting members, such as ribs and spars, are properly contacted. Having been positioned correctly, the plywood is removed, and glue is applied to the supporting members to make them ready for attachment.

The nailing strips used to hold the plywood in place until the glue sets are strips of wood about ³⁄₁₆ to ¼ in. thick and ½ in. wide. The strips are first nailed near the center of the skin panel and then nailed outward in both directions. More nailing strips are applied, this time perpendicular to the first set, starting near the middle and working outward in whichever direction will avoid wrinkles and permit the plywood to lie smooth.

The nails are driven down tightly and enough nailing strips are used to cover the entire surface of the supporting members. The width of the supporting member determines the number of nailing strips required. One nailing strip is used on surfaces ½ in. wide. Several nailing strips, laid side by side, are used for covering wider surfaces.

The nails are driven so that those in one strip alternate with regard to those in an adjacent strip. If the plywood skin is from ¹⁄₁₆ to ³⁄₃₂ in. thick, ⅝-in. nails

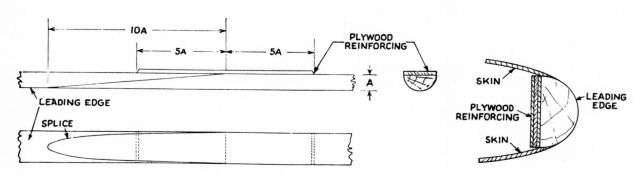

Figure 2·28 Repair of damaged leading-edge section.

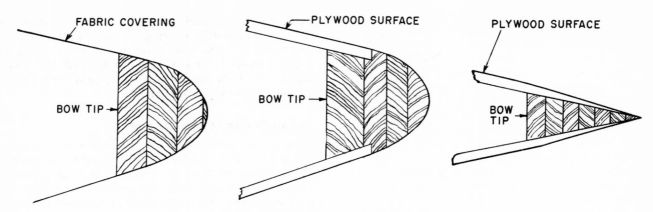

Figure 2·29 Wing-bow cross sections.

spaced at 1½-in. intervals are used for holding the skin to the ribs. The object is to space the nails as close together as possible without splitting one of the parts being glued. Wherever nailing strips come into contact with the glue, waxed paper is placed under the strips to prevent them from being glued to the member.

When a leading edge is to be covered, the plywood is first cut to the approximate size of the section to be covered. It is then softened by soaking it in warm water for about 20 min. Next, one edge is temporarily tacked along the top of the front spar. The plywood is then bent over the nose ribs, pulled down snugly, and held in place until it is dry. Shock cord can be used for holding it in place if it is wrapped tightly over the plywood. The advantage of shock cord, of course, is that it "gives" slightly.

When the plywood is thoroughly dry, the formed piece is fitted again and cut to the precise size. Glue is applied to the framework (nose ribs, spar, etc.), and the formed plywood is attached by means of nailing strips nailed down wherever the plywood touches the supporting members. These nailing strips may be started along one edge of the spar or along the leading-edge strip. More nailing strips are then laid over the nose ribs, starting with the center rib and working toward each end of the wing section. Soaking the nailing strips in warm water to make them bend easier is a good treatment for those nailing strips laid over the curved portion of the leading edge.

Although nailing strips usually provide a satisfactory method for applying pressure to glue joints when installing plywood skins, other methods are also used and some of these may be more effective than the nailing strips. One of these methods is to place a heavy piece of web strap around a wing immediately over a rib and the plywood after the glue has been applied. The strap is then tightened by small screw jacks, tapered blocks, or some other method, until the plywood skin is pressed firmly against the member to which it is being glued.

Another method which can be used is to apply pressure to the plywood over a glue joint by means of shot bags or sandbags. Great care must be exercised to make sure that the plywood is pressed against the

structure to which it is being attached and that there is a good glue film in all joints.

Repair of damaged plywood structures

When the stressed plywood skin on aircraft structures requires extensive repairs, it is essential that the manufacturer's instructions be followed carefully. When the repair is made according to manufacturer's specifications, the original strength of the structure is restored.

When a structure has been damaged extensively, it is best to replace a complete panel of plywood from one structural member to another. The structural members provide additional strength and backing for the plywood splices.

Before damaged plywood skin is replaced, the interior structure should be carefully inspected. All damage to interior members must be repaired before completing the skin repair.

Where sections of plywood are joined in a structure, aircraft glue is used to provide a strong, permanent joint. While a freshly glued joint is setting, pressure is applied by means of coated aircraft nails in a nailing strip, as described in a previous section of this chapter. After the nailing strips and nails are removed, the nail holes are filled with an approved wood filler, and the surface is finished by sanding and painting.

Surface patches

A **surface patch** is a type which is applied to the outer surface of a plywood skin. It is sometimes called a "scab" patch. Surface patches may be applied where damage has occurred to a skin between or along framing members. The damaged skin should be trimmed to a triangular- or rectangular-shaped opening, depending upon the exact location of the damage relative to the framing members. Where the framing members form a square corner and the damage does not extend to the next parallel member, a triangular opening should be made. The angles of the triangle should be rounded with a radius of at least five times the thickness of the skin. Doublers made of plywood at least as thick as the skin are applied on the undersurface of the patch seams to provide additional strength. These doublers are extended from one framing member to another and are strengthened at the ends by saddle gussets attached to the framing members. Figure 2·30 illustrates methods for making approved surface patches.

After a surface patch has been applied and the glue has set, the patch should be covered with fabric before completing the finishing. The fabric strengthens and protects the patch and reduces the drag a raised patch would cause. The fabric should overlap the original plywood skin by at least 2 in.

Surface patches are not permitted when the edges of the patch are forward of the 10 percent chord line. A patch which extends entirely around the leading edge so that the edges are aft of the 10 percent chord line is permissible. The leading edge of a surface patch should be beveled with an angle of at least 4:1. Surface patches may have a perimeter of as much as 50 in. and may extend from one rib to the next.

Splayed patches

A **splayed patch** is a patch fitted into the plywood to provide a flush surface; it must not, however, be confused with a scarf patch. The splayed patch has tapered edges joined with glue to tapered edges cut on the hole in the plywood skin. The slope of the edges is cut at a 5:1 angle.

Splayed patches may be used where the largest dimension of the hole to be repaired is not more than 15 times the skin thickness and the skin thickness is not more than $\frac{1}{10}$ in.

A splayed patch is applied as shown in Fig. 2·31. Two concentric circles are drawn around the damaged area with a pair of dividers. The difference between the radii of the circles is five times the skin thickness. The inner circle is cut out and a smooth bevel is made from the outer circle to the inner circle. A patch is cut and tapered to fit the hole and is beveled to match the bevel of the hole. Glue is applied to the beveled surfaces, and the patch is placed in the hole. The patch is the same type and thickness as the plywood being repaired. The patch is installed with the face grain in the same direction as that of the skin.

After the patch is in place, a pressure plate cut to the exact size of the patch is centered over the patch, with waxed paper between the two, and pressed firmly against the patch with a weight (sometimes a sandbag) or clamp. Since there is no reinforcing behind the splayed patch, care must be used to avoid excess pressure.

Flush patches

A scarfed **flush patch** is preferred for most plywood skin repairs. The **scarf patch** differs from the splayed patch in that the edges are beveled to a 12:1 slope instead of the 5:1 slope used in a splayed patch. The scarf patch also employs reinforcements under the patch where the glue joints occur.

In the application of any type of plywood patch, the curvature of the skin must be considered. Where the skin has a **compound** curve, that is, where the skin is curved in two directions, it is necessary to form the patch to the curvature of the skin before the patch can be installed. If the curvature is very slight, the patch material may be made from flat plywood.

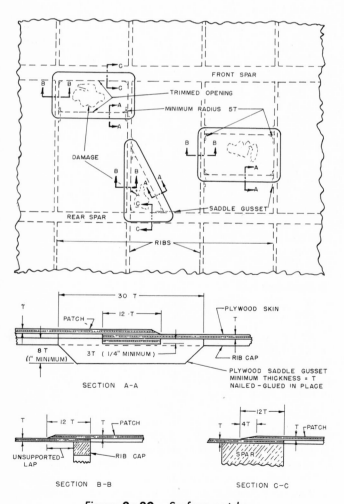

Figure 2·30 *Surface patches.*

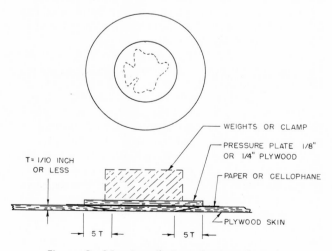

Figure 2·31 *Installation of splayed patch.*

Plywood can be curved to a limited extent by the application of heat and moisture and the use of forming blocks made to the correct curvature.

Where the curvature of the plywood skin is such that flat plywood cannot be formed to fit the double curve, it is necessary to obtain plywood *molded* to the correct curvature.

Scarf patches may be employed wherever the damaged plywood skin has a curvature with a radius of more than 100 times the thickness of the skin. In any event, the backing blocks or other reinforcements must be shaped to fit the curvature of the skin.

Figure 2·32 illustrates methods for making scarfed flush patches. A study of the illustration will aid in understanding the general principles involved in the installation of scarf patches.

When the back of the skin is accessible, temporary backing blocks are often used to give additional support until the glue joint has set. The backing blocks are shaped to fit the curvature of the skin and are used to hold the nails. After the patch is completed and the glue has set, the nails and backing blocks are removed.

When the damage to the skin is not greater in dimension than 25 times the skin thickness and the back side of the skin is accessible, a round scarf patch may be installed. A solid block of wood is shaped to fit the curvature of the skin and is cut to the same size as the outer dimension of the patch. After it has been trimmed to a circular shape, the center of the block is cut out to the same size as the hole in the skin. The block is installed on the back of the skin with waxed paper between the block and the skin. Nails are driven through nailing strips, through the scarf patch, and into the block. After the glue has set, the temporary backing block is removed along with the nailing strips and nails. This produces a patch which is flush on both sides. The patch is filled and finished to match the original skin.

In all types of large scarf patches, it is necessary to support the glued joints with backing. If the scarf is at a spar where the width of the spar exceeds the width of the scarf, it is not necessary to provide additional backing. When the scarf joint is along a rib, it is necessary to add plywood backing so that the width of the backing and the rib together is equal to the width of the scarf. The thickness of the backing is three times the thickness of the skin, with a minimum thickness of ¼ in. Where the ends of backing strips join the framing members such as ribs, the ends of the backing strips are supported by means of saddle gussets which are glued and nailed to the framing member. The saddle gussets are made of plywood and have a depth of at least 1 in. The length of the saddle gusset is 30 times the thickness of the skin, and the thickness is the same as that of the skin.

It is recommended that soft-textured plywood such as poplar or spruce be used for backing strips for scarfed flush patches in order to avoid warping of the patch and adjoining skin.

Plug patches

A **plug patch** has edges cut at right angles to the surface of the skin. The skin is cut out to a clean round or oval hole with square edges. The patch is cut to the exact size of the hole, and when installed, the edge of the patch forms a butt joint with the edge of the hole.

A circular plug patch, illustrated in Fig. 2·33, may be used where the cut-out hole is not more than 6 in. in diameter. Approved circular patches have been designed for holes of 6 and 4 in. in diameter. The patches are called "large" and "small," respectively.

The steps in the installation of a circular, or round, plug patch are as follows.

1. Cut a round patch of the correct dimension for the repair. The patch must be of the same material and thickness as the original skin.
2. Lay the patch over the damaged spot and mark a circle of the same size as the patch.

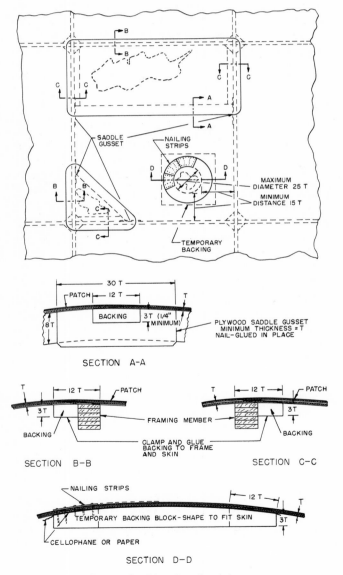

Figure 2·32 Scarf patches.

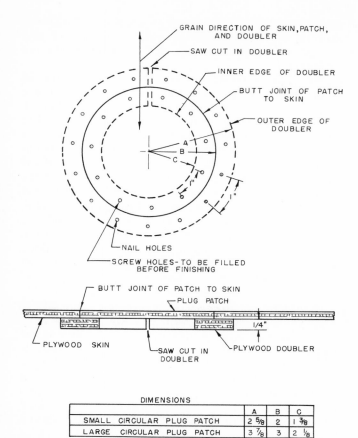

DIMENSIONS

	A	B	C
SMALL CIRCULAR PLUG PATCH	2 5/8	2	1 3/8
LARGE CIRCULAR PLUG PATCH	3 7/8	3	2 1/8

(TWO ROWS OF SCREWS AND NAILS REQUIRED
FOR LARGE PATCH)

Figure 2·33 A circular plug patch.

3. Cut the skin out so that the patch fits snugly into the hole around the entire perimeter.
4. Cut a doubler of ¼-in. plywood so that its outside radius is ⅝ in. greater than the hole to be patched and the inside radius is ⅝ in. less. For a large round patch, these dimensions would be ⅞ in. each. The doubler should be of a soft plywood such as poplar.
5. Cut the doubler through one side so that it can be inserted through to the back of the skin. Apply a coat of glue to the outer half of the doubler surface where it will bear against the inner surface of the skin.
6. Install the doubler by slipping it through the cut-out hole and centering it so that it is concentric with the hole. Nail it in place with nailing strips, using a bucking bar or similar object for backing. Waxed paper must be placed between the nailing strips and the skin.
7. After the glue has set in the installation of the doubler, apply glue to the surface of the doubler where the patch is to join and to the same area on the patch. Insert the patch in the hole.
8. Apply pressure to the patch by means of a pressure plate and No. 4 wood screws spaced approximately 1 in. apart. Waxed paper must be placed between the pressure plate and the skin. For a large patch, two rows of screws must be used in the patch and

two rows of nails must be used to join the skin to the doubler. After the glue has set, the nails and screws are removed.
9. Fill the nail and screw holes, sand, and finish to match the original surface.

Oval plug patches are installed in exactly the same way as round plug patches. The maximum dimensions for large oval patches are 7 in. in length and 5 in. in width. The dimensions for the doubler are the same as for a round patch. An oval patch is illustrated in Fig. 2·34.

Cutouts for access to the interior of wing panels

Where openings are not already provided in the cover for access to the interior of wing panels, it is often necessary to locate the cutouts, and they should be made adjacent to members of the wing frame. The cutaway section should be as small as possible and closed after the work is completed by the same method as that previously given for making repairs. A triangular cutaway section is easier to make than any other shape, and it presents a small area of opening.

Fiber insert nut plates

Fiber insert nut plates are installed at various locations in the wings and fuselage for the attachment of inspection doors, fuel-tank cap covers, and other parts. If one of these nuts is damaged, or if a machine screw breaks off in it, the portion of the wooden strip carrying the nut and extending about 1 in. on each side should be sawed out and replaced by a new section that is glued and nailed in place. These nut strips are ⅜-in. plywood strips with the nuts embedded at regular intervals. Finally, a 1/16-in.-thick plywood strip is glued and nailed over the nuts and drilled on correct centers to allow the passage of the machine screws. This is a better method of attaching nut plates than the use of wood screws.

Skis

Wooden ski runners which are fractured are usually replaced, but a split at the rear end of the runner having a length not more than 10 percent of the ski length may be repaired by attaching, with glue and bolts, one or more wooden crosspieces across the top of the runner.

Finishing repaired wood surfaces

Wood surfaces of an airplane structure which have been repaired must be finished to prevent the absorption of moisture, oil, or other contaminants and to prevent deterioration. In every case the proper finish must be selected and the surface prepared in accordance with approved practice.

The interior surfaces of wooden structures such as wings and control surfaces should be thoroughly coated with spar varnish or lionoil. Two coats of either finish brushed into the clean surface will usually be sufficient. Before the finish is applied, it is important to see that all excess glue, grease, oil, crayon marks, and similar contaminants are removed. Sawdust,

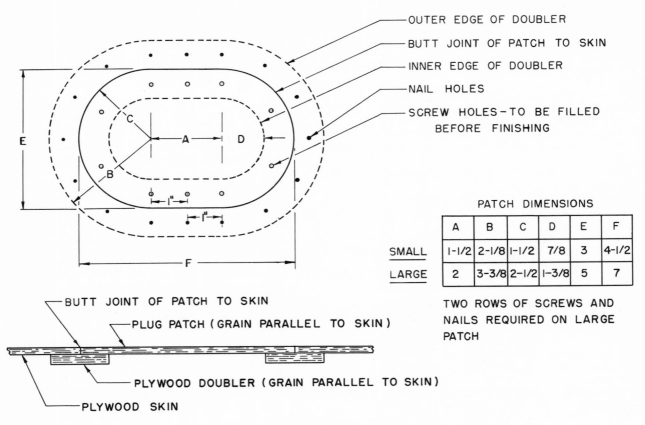

OUTER EDGE OF DOUBLER
BUTT JOINT OF PATCH TO SKIN
INNER EDGE OF DOUBLER
NAIL HOLES
SCREW HOLES—TO BE FILLED BEFORE FINISHING

BUTT JOINT OF PATCH TO SKIN
PLUG PATCH (GRAIN PARALLEL TO SKIN)
PLYWOOD DOUBLER (GRAIN PARALLEL TO SKIN)
PLYWOOD SKIN

PATCH DIMENSIONS

	A	B	C	D	E	F
SMALL	1-1/2	2-1/8	1-1/2	7/8	3	4-1/2
LARGE	2	3-3/8	2-1/2	1-3/8	5	7

TWO ROWS OF SCREWS AND NAILS REQUIRED ON LARGE PATCH

Figure 2·34   Oval plug patch.

shavings, loose wood particles, and similar material should also be removed from the inside of the structure.

When a structure is designed so that it is not possible to reach the interior after the outer skin is installed, it is necessary to finish the interior before the last pieces are fixed in place. In such cases, care must be taken to see that areas to be glued are not finished. After assembly, it is sometimes possible to reach through inspection holes with a small "touch-up" spray gun and apply finish to small areas.

Exterior surfaces, whether plywood or solid wood, are comparatively easy to finish. Such surfaces must be clean; that is, excess glue, grease, oil, etc., must be removed. Oil and grease spots can be removed with naphtha or a similar petroleum solvent. Small nail holes, scratches, or depressions in the wood surface should be filled with plastic wood or a similar compound, and the surface should be sanded smooth after the material has dried. Two coats of spar varnish, wood sealer, or MIL-V-6894 varnish should be applied as a base. MIL-V-6894 varnish is dopeproof and should be used when the final finish is to be lacquer or dope.

After the sealer or base varnish is applied to a wood surface and the varnish has dried, it may be necessary to sand the surface lightly to remove rough spots. The final finish can then be applied in as many coats as required. This is usually done with a spray gun. The operation of spray equipment is discussed in a following chapter.

End-grain wood surfaces require more finish than side grain surfaces because of the tendency of the grain to absorb the finish. It is good practice to use a wood filler before applying the varnish. The wood filler is applied after the end grain has been smoothed with sandpaper. After the wood filler has dried, a clear or pigmented sealer may be used in two or more coats. The surface can then be finished as previously described.

REVIEW QUESTIONS

1. What types of trees produce *softwoods? Hardwoods?*
2. What is an *open-grain* hardwood?
3. What is considered to be the best type of wood for aircraft structures?
4. What is the advantage of a good aircraft wood?
5. What are *annual rings* in wood?
6. What is the difference between checks and shakes?
7. What is meant by *compression* wood?
8. What is the maximum grain deviation or slope allowed for structural aircraft wood?
9. What is meant by the term *quarter-sawed?*
10. What is the minimum number of annual rings allowable per inch in aircraft structural woods?
11. Give the range of specific gravities for aircraft woods.
12. What should be the moisture content for aircraft woods?
13. Explain the term *kiln-dried.*

14. Describe aircraft plywood.
15. What are the advantages of plywood?
16. What are the most common types of plywood for aircraft use?
17. What types of glues are most satisfactory for aircraft wood assembly?
18. For what purpose is a *catalyst* used with aircraft glue?
19. From what source should information be obtained regarding the use of a particular glue?
20. Give a typical procedure for mixing a dry resin glue.
21. Describe a wood surface that is properly conditioned for gluing.
22. What is the effect of sanding on a wood surface to be glued?
23. What gluing pressures should be applied when making a glued joint in wood? Why?
24. How is gluing pressure applied?
25. What is the purpose of *caul blocks?*
26. What is a good average pressing time for a glue joint?
27. Explain *"open assembly"* of a glue joint.
28. In general, what is the maximum time that glue should be exposed to the air in the open-assembly process?
29. How are aircraft nails treated to prevent corrosion?
30. What is the purpose of a nailing strip?
31. Explain how wood can be formed to produce curved shapes.
32. What is the desired slope for the scarf in a spar splice?
33. Explain how reinforcement plates are applied to a spar splice.
34. How should the scarf cut be made in a piece of spar stock with respect to the slope of the grain in the wood?
35. Why is it necessary to make an allowance for thickness when gluing a spar splice?
36. What method is used to prevent glue from sticking to caul blocks and clamps?
37. Discuss the construction of I spars and box spars.
38. Describe an approved repair for elongated bolt holes in the end of a spar.
39. Explain how a duplicate rib can be constructed.
40. If the trailing edge of a wing rib is broken, how should the repair be made?
41. Describe a rib cap strip splice.
42. Discuss the use of nails in the installation and construction of ribs.
43. What precaution must be taken when driving aircraft nails into gussets on a wood rib?
44. How is a template used in the repair of leading edges?
45. Describe the construction of a wing-tip bow.
46. Explain how plywood is applied to a wing.
47. Why is a nailing strip used in the installation of plywood?
48. How is plywood held tightly in place while the glue is drying? Give three methods.
49. Describe the installation of a surface patch in a plywood repair.
50. What is the difference between a *splayed* patch and a *scarfed* patch?
51. Describe the installation of a *plug* patch in plywood.
52. What is the maximum diameter allowed for a circular plug patch?
53. Under what condition may a wooden ski be repaired with wooden crosspieces across the top of the runner?
54. Describe the finishing of a wooden surface.

CHAPTER 3

Approved Aircraft Covering Materials

Although the majority of modern aircraft are constructed of metal, there are still many requirements for aircraft fabrics of various types, and there are many fabric-covered aircraft certificated for operation. It is therefore essential that the aircraft maintenance technician be familiar with approved fabrics, tapes, sewing threads and, other materials required for aircraft covering.

Fabric covering for aircraft has been in use for many years because of its low cost, ease of installation, ease of repair, light weight, strength, and durability. In addition, the design and construction of a fabric covered airplane is such that it does not require the special manufacturing and repair equipment characteristic of the requirements for metal aircraft.

Nomenclature for fabrics

The words used in discussing textile materials such as aircraft fabric are not always familiar to the uninformed, hence it is necessary that we study and remember the special terms applicable to this particular class of materials.

Aircraft fabrics are manufactured of various high-grade materials woven together to make strong, durable cloth. The threads are woven at right angles, the **warp** being parallel to the length of the cloth and the **woof,** or **fill,** woven across the warp. This is illustrated in Fig. 3·1.

When a length of fabric comes from the mill, each edge of the material is bound by the fill and will not ravel. This naturally bound edge is called the **selvage,** or selvage edge. The selvage edge can be used as a reference to determine the direction of the warp and fill. It is usually desirable that the fabric be installed so the warp is nearly parallel with the longitudinal axis of the airplane.

Sometimes fabric is cut "on the bias." **Bias** is a cut, fold, or seam made diagonally across the warp and woof, as shown in Fig. 3·2. The principal advantage of a bias cut is that it permits the fabric to be stretched a small amount for fitting purposes.

Fabric specifications refer to the number of **threads per inch.** This term means the number of individual threads included in 1 in. of the material, either lengthwise or crosswise. It is an indication of the fineness of the material.

Bleaching is a chemical process used to whiten textile materials. Grade A airplane fabric is not bleached and is usually a light cream color. Bleaching, if not properly done, can weaken a material and make it unfit for use.

Calendering is a process of ironing fabric by threading it wet between a series of heated and cold rollers to produce a smooth finish. That is, it causes the **nap** to lay close to the surface. The nap is the "fuzzy" surface caused by the thousands of ends of individual fibers.

The weight of a fabric is designated in ounces per square yard. Specifications for a particular fabric usually indicate the weight required for approval of the material.

Mercerizing is a chemical process in which cotton is exposed to the action of a strong caustic solution which tends to shrink the material and give it a silky appearance.

Sizing is a textile glue used to stiffen and protect fabrics and threads. It gives "body" to a material.

Cotton fabrics

The standard approved aircraft covering has been, for many years, grade A mercerized cotton cloth. This material is identified by the SAE number AMS 3806,

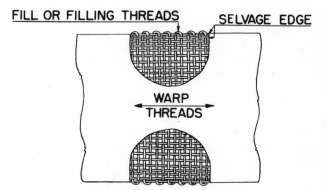

Figure 3·1   Warp and fill, or woof.

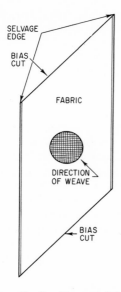

Figure 3·2   Bias-cut fabric.

and is described in FAA Technical Standard Order (TSO) C15. Approved fabric predoped with cellulose nitrate dope is numbered MIL-C-5643 and fabric predoped with cellulose acetate butyrate dope is numbered MIL-C-5642. The minimum tensile strength of approved grade A fabric in the new, undoped condition is 80 lb per in. This means that a strip of the fabric 1 in. in width must be able to support a weight of 80 lb in tension without breaking. The fabric can be tested with a pull-test machine or by securing a known width to the material in a suitably designed clamp and then suspending a weight from it. If the test strip is 2 in. wide, it should be able to support a weight of 160 lb. After fabric has been used on an airplane, its minimum permissible strength is 70 percent of new strength, or 56 lb per in., for grade A fabric undoped. This means that when the fabric on an airplane has deteriorated to the point where the strength is less than 56 lb per in., the fabric must be replaced. Fabric may be tested with approved testing machines while still on the airplane or a piece may be cut from the airplane and given a pull test after the dope has been removed. Testing of fabric will be discussed in the chapter describing covering and finishing processes.

The military specification for grade A fabric is MIL-C-5646. A fabric having this number or the number AMS 3806 (TSO C15) is suitable for aircraft having wing loadings greater than 9 lb per sq ft and a placarded never-exceed speed greater than 160 mph. Wing loading is determined by dividing the maximum gross weight of the airplane by the wing area.

Grade A fabric must have a thread count of 80 to 84 threads per inch in both length and width. The weight of the fabric must be not less than 4 oz per sq yd. The fabric is calendered after weaving to lay the nap and make the finished material smooth.

For aircraft having a wing loading of less than 9 psf and a placarded never-exceed speed less than 160 mph, a lighter-weight fabric may be used. This fabric is designated as **intermediate-weight aircraft fabric** and carries the number AMS 3804 (TSO C14). The minimum tensile strength of this fabric in the new, undoped condition is 65 lb per in. Remember that "pounds per inch" does not have the same meaning as "pounds per square inch." The thread count for intermediate fabric is 80 minimum to 94 maximum threads per inch for both warp and woof (fill).

Linen fabrics

For many years early in the history of aviation, linen was commonly used for the covering of aircraft. Linen, being woven from flax fiber, is strong, light, and durable. Aircraft linen is an especially fine grade of linen cloth, and if it complies with the requirements of TSO C15 it is suitable for use on certificated aircraft. The British specification 7F1 meets all the requirements of TSO C15.

Surface tape

Surface tape is usually cut from the same material that is being used to cover the airplane. The edges are **pinked** (cut with a saw-toothed edge) to provide better adhesion when doped to the surface and to reduce the tendency to ravel. It is used as a reinforcement at such places as the leading and trailing edges or airfoils, over rib lacings and seams, and around fittings and inspection openings on all doped fabric surfaces. In place of surface tape, fabric patches may be cut to fit around inspection holes and other openings. Surface tape helps to produce a streamlined surface, and it also waterproofs and protects rib lacings and stitchings over which it is applied, making the surface more durable.

A roll of surface tape is shown in Fig. 3·3. This tape should have the same fiber, yarn size, tensile strength, and number of threads per inch as the fabric upon which it is applied. The sizing must not exceed 2.5 percent; however, approved tape will usually fulfill this

Figure 3·3   A roll of surface tape.

requirement. The edges of the tape may be pinked, scalloped, or straight; however, the pinked edge is usually recommended.

All lacing and stitching should be covered with surface tape, but the tape should not be applied until after the first coat of dope has dried.

Reinforcing tape

Reinforcing tape is a special product that has a much larger warp thread than fill thread. It is used over ribs between the lacing cord and fabric covering to prevent the cord from cutting or wearing through the fabric and to help distribute the air loads. Reinforcing tape bearing the specification number MIL-T-5661, or equivalent, is approved for aircraft use. It is ordinarily obtainable in several widths that conform to the different widths of ribs or rib cap strips. This tape is of a material similar to the fabric covering used on the airplane, the yarn size, and the number of threads per inch are optional, and the tensile strength is at least 150 lb per ½ in. If a synthetic fabric or fiber glass covering is being installed, the reinforcing tape may be the standard cotton type or it may be a special tape designed and manufactured for use with the covering being applied. In all cases, it is wise to consult the specifications applicable to the job or process concerned. A roll of reinforcing tape is shown in Fig. 3 · 4.

Synthetic fabrics

The accomplishments of the modern plastic and textile industries have made it possible to develop fabric coverings for aircraft which are superior in strength and durability to grade A cotton fabric. One of the commonly used materials is a high-quality dacron cloth sold under several trade names. Among these are Ceconite and Eonnex. These fabrics comply with the requirements of TSO C-15 and provide an excellent long-life covering when properly applied and maintained. Specific directions for the installation of these fabrics are given in the section on covering and finishing.

Glass-fiber fabrics are also approved for use in covering aircraft; however, they are more difficult to apply than cotton or synthetic fabrics because the material shrinks very little and must be almost perfectly smooth and tight on the aircraft before it is doped. Furthermore, this material must be maintained with a flexible coating to avoid the possibility of surface cracking and a resultant breaking of the glass fibers due to vibration and abrasion. Among approved glass-fiber products are Air Fibre and Razorback.

In the application of any covering to a certificated aircraft, it is mandatory that the technician consult the approved specifications for the product he is using. Every product not covered by basic regulations must have a Special Type Certificate Number for the particular application. This number can be supplied by the manufacturer for his approved products and processes.

Sewing threads and lacing cords

The **twist** of a thread or cord may be either right or left. The term **S twist** designates a right-twist thread. The words **machine, machine twist, Z twist,** and **left twist** all refer to a left-twist thread. Figure 3 · 5 shows a left-twist cord. A thread or cord which has been sized to produce a hard, glazed surface to prevent the thread from fraying or weakening, is known as a **silk finish** thread or cord.

A **braided cord,** illustrated in Fig. 3 · 6, is made by weaving strands of thread together to form either a solidly woven cord or one with a hollow-channel center, such as that illustrated in Fig. 3 · 7. Some cords have a channel made with a hollow center which contains one or more straight, individual threads called a **core,** the purpose of which is to increase the strength of the cord and to hold the outer braided cover to a rounded contour. Figure 3 · 8 shows a braided cord with a core.

In the covering of aircraft, the braided cords are not commonly used; however, the technician should be aware of such materials because they are encountered occasionally. Braided cords meeting the specifications MIL-C-5649 and MIL-C-5648 are approved for use in lacing fabric to aircraft structures.

Machine thread, also called **machine-sewing thread,** is used in all machine sewing. It is made of cotton, carries a specification number V-T-276b, and is described as 20/4 ply to indicate the size. It has a tensile strength of 5 lb per single strand, and a nominal weight of 1 lb for 5000 yd. It is sometimes described as a white,

Figure 3 · 4   Reinforcing tape.

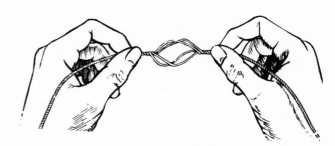

Figure 3 · 5   A left-twist cord.

Figure 3·6   A braided cord.

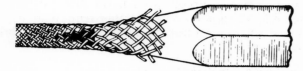

Figure 3·7   Braided cord with a hollow center.

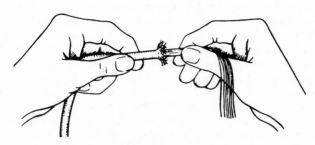

Figure 3·8   Braided cord with a core.

silk-finish, No. 16, four-cord cotton thread with a Z twist. This thread provides durable seams when used with a sewing machine.

Hand-sewing thread carries the specification number V-T-276b, Type III B, and is used for all hand sewing. It is an unbleached, cotton, silk-finish thread, No. 8, four-cord, with a tensile strength of 14 lb for a single strand, and a normal weight of 1 lb for 1650 yd.

Lacing cord, as mentioned previously is used for lacing fabric to the structure, and is often referred to as **rib-stitching cord** or **rib-lacing cord.** This is because it is commonly used for rib stitching or lacing the fabric to the wings of an airplane. Acceptable lacing cords carry the specification numbers MIL-T-6779 or MIL-C-2520A for a linen cord and MIL-T-5660 for a cotton cord. The cord must have a minimum tensile strength of 40 lb single or 80 lb double.

Lacing cord is often waxed when received; if it is not, it should be waxed lightly before use. Beeswax is suitable for this purpose. Waxing is accomplished by drawing the cord under tension across a piece of the wax.

Waxed cords are used for attaching chafing strips. These cotton cords may be either four-ply or five-ply, but they must be double-twist and waxed. The chafing strips are sometimes hand-sewn russet-leather reinforcing strips that are placed on movable brace wires or rods at their points of intersection and on places where chafing may occur on control cables and the tubing of the structure. In place of leather, it is common practice to use synthetic or plastic materials such as neoprene, Corprene, Teflon, and polyethylene

formed as sheet or tubing, to provide resistance to wear and abrasion.

Grommets

Grommets are installed where it is necessary to reinforce holes in textile materials used for drainage, lacing, or inspection. A grommet consists of one or two parts, depending upon the type. A **metal grommet,** used for lacing eyes, consists of two parts as shown in Fig. 3·9. These parts may be made of either brass or aluminum.

The smallest metal grommet generally used is No. 00 (5⁄32 in.). It is used for lacing holes in an opening made for inspection purposes. This particular type of inspection opening is not generally found on modern airplanes because different types of inspection openings have been designed.

Plastic grommets are used for drainage and ventilation purposes. These grommets are simply thin plastic washers which are doped directly on the fabric after the first coat of dope has dried. This installation is shown in Fig. 3·10. The grommets are placed on each side of a rib, as close to the rib as possible, on the underside of the trailing edges of wings and control surfaces, and under the lowest points of fabric-covered fuselages. Through the drain holes thus provided, any moisture which may collect inside the part will be drained.

Where exceptionally good drainage and ventilation is desired, as with seaplanes, **marine** or **seaplane grommets** are installed. A grommet of this type is shown in Fig. 3·11. This grommet is constructed with a streamlined aperture which creates a suction and causes in-

Figure 3·9   A metal grommet.

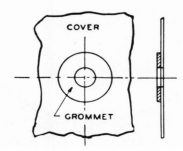

Figure 3·10   Installation of a plastic grommet.

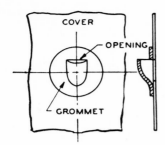

Figure 3·11   A seaplane grommet.

creased air circulation in the part to which it is applied.

Inspection grommets or "rings" are installed on the fabric of the fuselage or wings where it is necessary to examine fittings, internal bracing, cables, and similar items inside the covered structure. The plastic rings, about 4 in. in diameter, are often doped onto the fabric in the proper location; the center is not cut out until the first periodic or 100-hr inspection is made. At this time the fabric inside the ring is cut out; after the inspection is made, a metal inspection cover or plate is installed in the hole. The plastic ring provides support for the inspection plate, which is held in place by spring clips attached to the inside surface. An inspection ring is shown in Fig. 3·12.

Use of leather

Russet strap leather is sometimes used in the fabrication of reinforcing patches on doped fabric surfaces where heavy wear is caused by control cables and rods, and it can also be used for making chafing strips which are used anywhere on the structure where friction is encountered by the fabric covering. This leather has a hard, glazed surface that makes it reasonably impervious to the usual deteriorating influences.

Horsehide leather is thinner than russet strap leather and does not wear as well. The finish is soft, and the color is usually brown or black. It can be used for the same purposes as russet strap leather where the wear is less, and it can also be used to a certain extent for making reinforcing patches which are placed around flanges which protrude through the fabric covering. Figure 3·13 shows a sewed leather reinforcing patch applied where a control cable passes through a fabric cover.

Miscellaneous materials

Blued carpet tacks are sometimes used to hold the fabric covering in place on a wooden structure temporarily while the permanent hand sewing or tacking is being done. The finish protects the tacks from rust to some extent in the same manner that a blued finish protects a firearm. However, these tacks are solely used for *temporary* use. If driven in for permanent use they may split, crack, and otherwise weaken the wood in which they are placed, and they eventually work loose from the vibration of the airplane. Care must be taken that large tacks are not driven into small wood structures because of the danger of splitting the wood.

Brass, tinned iron, or **Monel metal tacks** are rustproof, and they do not cause the damage that results from the use of blued carpet tacks. These tacks are sometimes used for permanently tacking the covering on wooden structures.

Pins are used for holding the edges of the covering temporarily while the cover is being shaped to the structure before the hand sewing begins. A **T pin,** such as the one illustrated in Fig. 3·14, is desirable because it can be inserted and removed easily while the fabric is under tension.

Self-tapping screws are often used for the attachment of fabric to metal-rib structures; hence they take the place of rib lacing. When these screws are used, the holes should be redrilled where it is found necessary because of wear, distortion, etc., or a screw one size larger should be used as a replacement. The length of the screw should be sufficient to allow at least two

Figure 3·12   A plastic inspection ring.

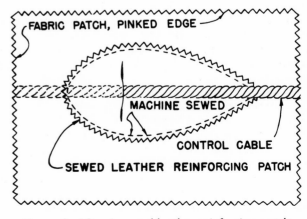

Figure 3·13   A sewed-leather reinforcing patch.

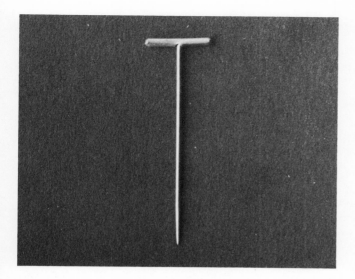

Figure 3·14   A T pin.

threads of the grip (threaded part) to extend beyond the metal on the inside. A thin washer, preferably made of plastic, should be used under the head of the screw, and pinked-edge surface tape should be doped over the heads of the screws.

Figure 3·15 shows the use of a self-tapping sheet-metal screw to hold fabric. Figure 3·16 shows the installation where the cap strip of the metal rib is dimpled. Note the use of reinforcing tape under the washer in both cases.

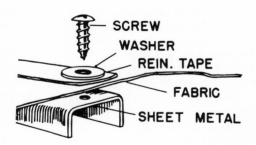

Figure 3·15   Use of a self-tapping screw to hold fabric.

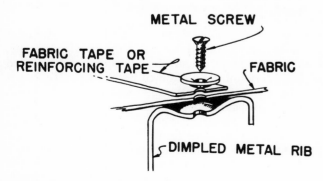

Figure 3·16   A self-tapping screw used in a dimpled metal rib.

Dope

Aircraft dope is technically defined as a colloidal solution of cellulose acetate butyrate or cellulose nitrate. A colloidal solution consists of very finely divided particles—particles so small they cannot be seen under an ordinary microscope. They do not settle out if suspended in water but rather pass through the pores of filter paper when any attempt is made to purify them in this manner. In spite of their small size, the particles in a colloidal solution are much larger than the *solute* molecules in a true suspension.

The cells of all plants are formed of **cellulose**, which has the same chemical composition as starch but is different in nature. Wood is principally cellulose with resins and other substances combined with or adhering to it. Cotton, linen, hemp, jute, and similar fibers are almost pure cellulose.

Aircraft dope is intended for use only on fabric-covered surfaces. If it is applied to metal surfaces, it lifts or peels off because it does not penetrate and adhere to metal. Although the dope is applied in a series of coats, each application dissolves all previously applied coats and forms a single film or layer when it dries.

The purpose of aircraft dope is to make fabric covers airtight and weatherproof with the addition of the minimum amount of weight and to increase the tautness and tensile strength.

Aircraft dope may be divided into two types, **clear** and **pigmented,** each of which is intended for its own purposes. There are a number of different nitrate dope compositions; however, a complete job of finishing can be done with only one basic type of dope. The best mixture for brushing, spraying, or hot-dope application may be obtained merely by the use of thinner. Usually dope can be brushed or hot-sprayed without any thinning provided the temperature is correct.

Aluminum-pigmented dope is made merely by adding aluminum powder or aluminum paste to the dope. For clear nitrate dope, 16 oz of aluminum paste or 8 oz of aluminum powder is added to 1 gal of the dope and mixed thoroughly to give the proper concentration of aluminum in the dope. To mix aluminum paste with dope, a small amount of the clear dope or dope thinner is mixed with the paste and the mixture is worked until all lumps are completely removed. Sufficient dope should be added so the mixture will flow easily, and after mixing completely the mixture is added to the clear dope and the entire amount is then stirred until the aluminum is evenly distributed. To obtain the best finish, a small amount of nitrate dope thinner should be added. This will help the minute flakes of aluminum to come to the surface and form a solid, light-tight layer.

Pigmented nitrate dope is available in a large number of colors and shades. It is used for the finishing coats applied to fabric-covered surfaces, for producing the desired color effect in any case where color is required, and for code markings and insignia applied to aircraft.

A **quick-building** (QB) **dope** is designed to make an extra-heavy layer for each coat, thus making fewer coats necessary than would be the case for ordinary nitrate dope. This type of dope contains an extra-large percentage of materials which form solids upon drying.

Another special type of dope is called **nontautening dope** and is designed to permit the application of extra coats of dope without the danger of over-tautening the fabric. Some operators specify two or three coats of nontautening dope after the initial coats of regular dope have tautened the fabric sufficiently to remove all wrinkles. The nontautening dope may be aluminum-pigmented or it may be followed by aluminum-pigmented dope.

Nitrocellulose dope

Some plasticizer, such as glycol sebacate, ethyl acetate, butyl acetate, or butyl alcohol, is added to a solution of nitrocellulose to make nitrocellulose or nitrate dope; then a thinner, such as benzol or ethyl alcohol, is sometimes added to reduce the thickness to the desired consistency. Although the principal purpose of the plasticizer is to produce a flexible film, it also helps the solvent in the tautening effect on the fabric-covered airplane part. When thinners are added, the operator must be careful to watch the consistency of the dope continuously, since thinners often evaporate with the volatile solvents. Approved specifications for nitrate dopes are MIL-D-5553 (clear) and MIL-D-5554A (pigmented).

A pigmented dope is always applied over the clear dopes to protect the fabric from sunlight. This kind of dope is simply clear dope with the addition of enough colored pigment, such as aluminum powder, to give the desired effect, but enough pigment must be used to obtain an opaque surface.

Cellulose acetate butyrate dope

Cellulose acetate butyrate dope, MIL-D-5549 or MIL-D-5551A, commonly called **butyrate dope,** or **CAB dope,** has certain features superior to **nitrate dope.** It is more resistant to fire, which is a great advantage, especially for military aircraft. Butyrate solvents are more penetrating than those in nitrate dope, and the dope can be successfully applied over nitrate dope. For this reason, butyrate dope is often used as a rejuvenator for finishes which have become badly weathered. Care must be taken to see that the fabric to be rejuvenated is in good condition; otherwise the tautening effect of the butyrate dope will cause it to tear or crack.

In doping a newly covered surface with butyrate, the technician must remember that butyrate dope has a greater tautening effect than nitrate. If the fabric is applied too tight, the structure may be damaged or pulled out of shape after the doping is completed.

Special fabric finishes

In this day of modern plastics and wonder materials, it is not uncommon that new aircraft finishes are discovered. A number of dope substitutes have been developed and some have been successful. It is not the purpose of this section to extol the merits of any particular product but it can be stated that certain plastic finishes can be used in place of dope. The technician is warned, however, that each product used must be approved by the Federal Aviation Administration and must be applied in accordance with the manufacturer's instructions. Approved materials and processes are covered by Technical Standard Orders or are given Special Type Certificate numbers.

Solvents and thinners

Acetone is a fast-evaporating dope solvent obtained in considerable amounts, along with wood alcohol and acetic acid, by the destructive distillation of wood. Large amounts are also made by fermenting molasses and corn, using a special organism to hasten the chemical action.

Acetone is a colorless liquid which boils at 56.5°C and freezes at −94.3°C. It is suitable for removing grease from fabric before doping and is very useful in cleaning dope and lacquer from suction-feed cups and spray guns. It is widely used as an ingredient in paint and varnish removers but should not be used as a thinner in dope because it dries so rapidly that the doped area cools quickly and collects moisture. The absorbed moisture in the fabric then prevents uniform drying and results in **blushing,** that is, a change in color.

Alcohols may be classified as butyl alcohol, denatured alcohol, ethyl alcohol, isopropyl alcohol, and methyl alcohol (wood alcohol). **Butyl alcohol** is a slow-drying solvent that is sometimes mixed with dope to retard drying when the humidity is excessive, thus preventing blushing. From 5 to 10 percent of butyl alcohol is generally enough for this purpose. Too much solvent will retard the drying and delay the finishing process.

Denatured alcohol is ethyl alcohol that has been rendered unfit for drinking by the addition of wood alcohol, benzine, or some other substance. It is used for thinning shellac to spray-gun consistency, and is also used as a constituent of many paint and varnish removers.

Benzene is obtained from coal tar and is sometimes called **benzol.** It should not be confused with **benzine,** which is a mixture of paraffin hydrocarbons obtained by the fractional distillation of petroleum. **Benzene** is used for cleaning aircraft equipment in which enamel, paint, or varnish has been used, and it is also used as a constituent of paint and varnish removers. An excessive amount of benzene fumes must not be inhaled, or they may cause a serious illness.

Thinners, also called **reducers,** are used to reduce the consistency of dopes, enamels, paints, etc.; for use in spray guns, to obtain a more efficient brushing consistency; and to reduce the thickness of the coats. One particular thinner is always best for each specific finishing material. Nitrate dope and lacquers are thinned by means of a thinner called **nitrate dope and laquer thinner.** Specifications TT-T-266a or MIL-T-6094A meet the requirements for this product. Butyrate dope must be thinned with **cellulose acetate butyrate dope thinner,** MIL-T-6096A or equivalent. The technician must always make certain he is using the correct thinner for the particular coating material he is mixing. The wrong type of thinner will usually make the coating unfit for use.

Retarder, or **retarder thinner,** is a special slow-drying thinner used to slow the drying time of dope. As explained previously, when humidity is comparatively high, rapid drying of dope will cause blushing. Retarder is mixed with the dope to reduce the tendency to blush. Blushing is caused by the condensation of moisture in the surface of the dope and results in a weak and useless finish. The condition is explained more fully in a later section. Retarder for nitrate dope carries the specification MIL-T-6095A. For butyrate dope, MIL-T-6097A is used.

Toluene or **toluol** is used as a thinner for certain types of paints and enamels but it is used most commonly for thinning zinc chromate primer. An approved specification for toluene is TT-T-548a. Toluene is a colorless hydrocarbon usually distilled from coal tar.

Ordinary paints, varnishes, and enamels are usually thinned with a petroleum thinner. Certain **naphthas** or **mineral spirits** are suitable. An approved thinner of this type is designated TT-N-97. A number of petroleum solvents are available under the common name of **paint thinner,** and the technician should be careful to select a high-grade type suitable for his purpose. Some of these thinners are slow-drying and others dry quite rapidly. Those that dry most rapidly are sometimes called **driers. Turpentine** can also be used for thinning common paints, varnishes, and enamels.

The technician must be particularly careful when he is using enamels and lacquers to prevent a mixing of the products. Lacquer is typified by the familiar "banana oil" smell, similar to that of nitrate dope, and should be thinned only with nitrate dope and lacquer thinner described previously. Acrylic nitrocellulose lacquer should be thinned with a thinner designed for the purpose under the specification MIL-T-19544 or equivalent. Lacquer must not be applied over enamel because it will cause the enamel to raise and blister. Enamel can be applied over lacquer or dope after the latter has dried.

Linseed oil, extracted from flaxseed, is often used with ordinary paints as a reducer or thinner. It is not commonly used with aircraft finishes, however, except perhaps for thinning lionoil or certain varnishes to be used on interior wood surfaces inside a wing or airfoil. Hot linseed oil is also used as a slushing compound for coating the inside of steel tubing to prevent rusting.

For some of the new plastic-type finishes such as vinyl, nylon, and acrylic enamels or lacquers, it is necessary to use solvents or thinners manufactured for the purpose. For example, nylon finish requires butyl alcohol as a thinner. Manufacturer's instructions on the container give specific directions regarding the thinners to be used. The technician should take care to read the directions for any finish with which he is not familiar.

Rejuvenators

A **fabric rejuvenator** is a thin, dopelike finish to which powerful solvents have been added. Its purpose is to soften and penetrate old dope finishes, thus replacing some of the solvents and plasticizers which have been lost by evaporation and oxidation over a period of years. If a dope finish is not badly cracked and if the fabric under the dope is still in good condition, rejuvenation can add considerable time to the life of the covering. On the other hand, if the fabric is weak, it is likely that the rejuvenation will further weaken it and hasten the need for a recover job. A material specifically manufactured as a rejuvenator, such as Fuller 3916, should be used generally for the rejuvenation of nitrate dope finishes. Thinned acetate butyrate dope can be used for rejuvenating either nitrate dope or butyrate dope finishes. This product will have more shrinking effect than nitrate rejuvenator; hence the fabric under the dope must be in very good condition.

An all-purpose rejuvenator of the acetate butyrate type suitable for both nitrate dope and butyrate dope finishes is marketed under the number TL-4188 by Fuller.

Primers

A **primer** is an undercoat applied to a metal to inhibit corrosion and to provide a good base for the application of paint, lacquer, or enamel. The primer is applied directly to the bare, clean metal.

There are a number of primers and surfacers available for aircraft use, three of which are most commonly employed. These are **zinc chromate primer, red iron oxide,** and **gray enamel undercoat.**

An approved zinc chromate primer is manufactured under specification MIL-P-6889A, Type I and Type II. Type I is used under normal atmospheric conditions; Type II is used under conditions of high humidity. This primer is best applied by spraying and is available in either a yellow or dark green color. The surface to which the primer is applied must be completely dry and clean.

Zinc chromate primer is commonly used on aluminum, aluminum-alloy, and magnesium surfaces and is also suitable for iron or steel. It is thinned with toluene to the proper consistency for spraying or brushing. Toluene has a characteristic odor and can be identified easily by any person who has had experience with it.

Red iron oxide primer is normally thinned with a petroleum thinner such as naphtha or mineral spirits. It can be sprayed or brushed on a surface; however, a better finish is obtained by spraying. After one coat of red iron oxide primer is applied to a surface, an additional coat which has been mixed with clear enamel or varnish can be applied as a final coating. This practice is employed where it is not necessary to use a special color coating over the primer for the sake of appearance. Red iron oxide primer is commonly used for iron or steel surfaces.

Gray enamel undercoat is a lacquer-type primer and surfacer used under colored lacquer, synthetic enamel, or acrylic lacquer. It is thinned with nitrate lacquer thinner. This type of undercoat is particularly suitable for fine sanding to provide a perfectly smooth base for the finish coats.

Lacquers

Lacquers were originally finishes developed in the Orient to produce a high gloss on wood products. They serve a purpose similar to varnishes; however, certain lacquers are more durable than typical varnishes. In general, a lacquer is a good finishing material for metal or wood. Lacquers may be pigmented to provide a desired color, and they may produce either a gloss finish or a dull finish.

A good standard gloss lacquer consists of nitrocellulose, cocoanut-modified alkyd, and plasticizer with fixed solvents of esters or ketones, alcohols, and hydrocarbons. It is designated by the specification number MIL-L-7178A and is thinned with nitrate dope and lacquer thinner MIL-T-6094. This lacquer can be obtained in the clear state or it may be pigmented in a variety of colors.

Lacquers are manufactured for special purposes such as fuel resistance and hydraulic-fluid resistance. The following specification numbers denote special-purpose lacquers:

MIL-L-6047	Fuel resistant
MIL-L-7146	Hydraulic-fluid resistant
MIL-L-6806	Clear coating for aluminum
MIL-L-006805	Dull black instrument lacquer
MIL-L-19537	Acrylic nitrocellulose lacquer

Nitrocellulose lacquers are usually thinned with nitrate dope and lacquer thinner mentioned previously. Acrylic lacquers must be thinned with a thinner designed for the purpose and numbered MIL-T-19544 or equivalent.

Enamels

Enamels are usually based on glyceryl phthalate resins or synthetic resins. A standard gloss enamel consists of pigments dispersed in synthetic resins combined with appropriate driers and thinners. MIL-E-7729 is an approved enamel of this type. These enamels can be applied by brush or spray to bare metal, primed metal, or wood. They are thinned with naphtha or mineral spirits. MIL-E-7729 can be obtained in three types: Type I for natural air drying; Type II for low bake, 175°F for 2 hr; and Type III for high bake, 320°F for 15 min.

Heat-resisting black enamel is a glyceryl phthalate type with the specification MIL-E-5557. This type of enamel is used for engine cylinders and other parts which are subjected to moderately high temperatures.

Varnishes

Standard varnishes, also called **spar varnish,** are based on phenol formaldehyde resin or glyceryl phthalate. The phenol formaldehyde type, MIL-V-6893 is superior for water resistance. This varnish is used for both wood and metal and is thinned with naphtha. The varnish can be aluminized by mixing 20 oz of aluminum paste to 1 gal of the varnish. The aluminum paste is first thoroughly mixed with 1 qt of naphtha to make a liquid for better mixing.

Glyceryl phthalate spar varnish is used in the same manner as the phenol formaldehyde type. Glyceryl phthalate varnish of an approved type carries the specification number MIL-V-6894. It may be aluminized as previously described.

New types of materials

It must be emphasized that the materials described in this chapter are not the only ones that may be approved for aircraft. We have given information on the products that are most commonly used; however, new types of materials may be approved at any time. Since industry has developed all types of new fabrics and finishes, the technician is likely to encounter new plastic materials, synthetic coatings, etc., that will be superior to those commonly used in the past. The word of caution we must offer is that the user of any product should make sure that anything he uses on an aircraft is tested and approved. Materials suitable for aircraft will usually be given a Special Type Certificate number by the Federal Aviation Administration.

REVIEW QUESTIONS

1. List some advantages of fabric covering.
2. What is the difference between *warp* and *fill* in fabric?
3. What is the *selvage* edge of fabric?
4. What is meant by cutting "on the bias?"
5. Define *mercerizing. Sizing.*
6. Give the SAE number, TSO number, and MIL specification number for grade A fabric.
7. What is the minimum tensile strength for grade A fabric?
8. To what extent may the tensile strength of fabric decrease while on the airplane before it is necessary to replace it?
9. Give the conditions which make mandatory the use of grade A fabric or the equivalent.
10. Under what conditions may *intermediate-weight*-aircraft fabric be installed on an airplane?
11. Describe *surface tape*. For what purposes is it used?
12. What is the purpose of *reinforcing tape?*
13. What precautions must be observed by the technician when applying synthetic or glass-fiber coverings to an aircraft?
14. What is the difference between S-twist and Z-twist threads?
15. Give the specifications for a typical, machine sewing thread.
16. What is the minimum tensile strength for rib-lacing cord?
17. For what purposes is a chafing strip used?
18. Under what conditions should seaplane grommets be installed?
19. Discuss the installation of a plastic inspection ring.

20. Describe the use of T pins.
21. Describe the attachment of fabric to metal-rib cap strips by means of self-tapping screws.
22. Name two common types of aircraft dope.
23. Describe the preparation of aluminum-pigmented dope.
24. What precautions must be observed when thinning dope?
25. At what point during a doping process is nontautening dope used?
26. Give the MIL specification number for approved clear nitrate dope.
27. Compare the tautening effects of nitrate and butyrate dopes.
28. What precaution must be taken if butyrate dope is used as a *rejuvenator?*
29. Why is acetone not recommended as a thinner?
30. What thinner should be used for nitrate dope?
31. What is the purpose of a *retarder?*
32. What is the cause of blushing?
33. Why cannot lacquer be applied over enamel?
34. What will occur if rejuvenator is applied to weak fabric?
35. Describe the purpose of a *primer.*
36. What thinner is used with zinc chromate primer?
37. Under what finishes may *gray enamel undercoat* be used?
38. For what purposes are *special* lacquers manufactured?
39. What thinners are used with enamels?
40. For what purposes are varnishes used?

CHAPTER 4

Covering and Finishing of Aircraft

Facilities and equipment

Although many aircraft manufactured currently are constructed of metal, there are still many in operation which are fully covered with fabric and dope and some which have fabric-covered surfaces. It is therefore necessary that the maintenance technician be fully informed regarding covering and finishing materials and processes. In recent years a number of new types of coverings have been developed and some of these have considerable advantage over the standard cotton-fabric and dope coverings. In all cases, the technician must make certain that he follow the methods of application specified for the covering being installed.

The fabric shop

The room or section of a building utilized for the preparation and installation of fabric covering is often called the **fabric shop.** This shop should be well-lighted, clean, well-ventilated, and of sufficient size to accommodate any size of aircraft upon which fabric is to be installed. It would be well to have the fabric shop air-conditioned or temperature-controlled, if possible, for two principal reasons: (1) the comfort of the workers and (2) the proper temperature and humidity for best results in covering.

Tools and equipment for covering

The degree of success the technician will have in producing a first-class covering job often depends upon the availability of suitable tools and equipment. The tools described here are generally considered necessary in addition to the standard hand tools usually available in an aircraft repair shop. A covering job can be accomplished without all of the tools and equipment mentioned; however, the need sometimes exists for every one of the items.

The small **harness awl** is useful for making small holes in fabric or other similar materials.

As explained in the chapter on wood repair, the **magnetic tack hammer** is most useful for picking up and holding tacks which are too small to be held in the fingers while driving.

The common **pocket knife** is always useful for cutting textile materials and wood.

A variety of **needles** is required for rib lacing and hand sewing. Straight upholsterer's needles up to 16 in. in length and 12-gage diameter are needed for rib lacing thick wings. Smaller needles of the same type are used for the thinner wings. For hand sewing, both straight needles and curved needles are needed. Typical upholsterer's needles are shown in Fig. 4 · 1.

Because temporary tacks are often used to hold fabric in place on wooden structures, it is often necessary to pull such tacks. The **claw tack puller** is the best tool for this purpose.

A pair of **bent-handle trimmer's shears,** 10 or 12 in. in length, is an absolute must for cutting fabric, tapes, etc. The shears must be handled carefully to avoid damaging the cutting edges and should be used only for cutting comparatively soft materials. Trimmer's shears are shown in Fig. 4 · 2.

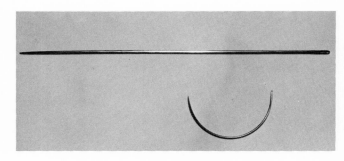

Figure 4 · 1 Upholsterer's needles.

Figure 4 · 2 Trimmer's shears.

Pinking shears are needed to produce the pinked edge that is required for tape, patches, and other fabric pieces which are to be cemented or doped to another surface. The cutting edges of pinking shears must be protected when not in use and must be kept sharp. The sharpening of pinking shears must be done by an expert who has the proper grinding equipment available. Pinking shears are shown in Fig. 4·3.

A metal or wooden **straight-edge** or **yardstick** is used for measuring and for marking straight lines.

A steel **measuring tape** at least 50 ft in length is necessary for measuring wings, fuselages, and lengths of fabric. The tape should be kept clean and dry.

A **sewing thimble** is useful for pushing a needle through thick seams where extra pressure is necessary.

A large **cutting table** is needed for laying out and cutting the aircraft fabric covering. The height should be convenient for the operators, but usually about 31 in. is approximately correct for the average person. The table should be 7 ft wide and 25 ft long. The top should be of hardwood in order to avoid splinters. Oak is preferred, but maple is acceptable. It should be sanded smooth, varnished with a varnish that will not chip easily, and then waxed. The edges of the table are usually marked off in feet and inches by means of brass tacks, or a rule may be fastened to the edge of the table. The table should be kept free from dust and polished frequently; care should be taken not to leave any wax or oil that will damage the fabric.

In many fabric shops, rolls of the covering material are mounted on rollers inside a storage cabinet placed near the cutting table so that, while the fabric can be unrolled as needed, only that which is about to be used is outside the cabinet. This installation makes it possible to avoid soiling or wrinkling the fabric.

Easels

An **easel,** such as the one illustrated in Fig. 4·4, may be used to support the airfoil in a nearly vertical position while the fabric covering is being rib-laced to the structure. An easel is usually made of metal tubing with welded joints and is supplied with two padded bracket rests, as shown in the illustration. In Fig. 4·5 two easels are being used to support a wing in a vertical position for rib lacing.

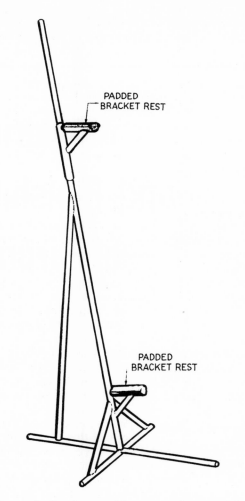

Figure **4·4** An easel for supporting an airfoil.

Trestles

Trestles, or "saw horses," are needed to support wing panels in the horizontal or flat position. The trestles must be adequately padded to prevent damage to the wing structure and fabric. Wing panels are placed on the trestles while measuring, fitting, and installing the fabric covering. Care must be taken to see

Figure **4·3** Pinking shears. (Wiss Manufacturing Co.)

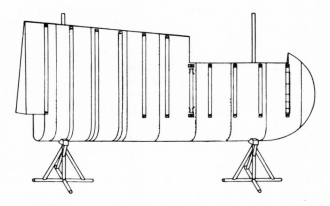

Figure **4·5** Two easels used to support a wing.

that the wing panel is supported at points where the structure is of sufficient strength to prevent damage.

Sewing machines

A **sewing machine** is basically a mechanism designed to join textiles or similar materials by means of a seam or seams consisting of a series of interlocked stitches. The sewing machine used for sewing aircraft fabric is a heavy-duty, industrial-type machine larger and more durable than the family sewing machine used by the average housewife.

The essential elements of a sewing machine are the **driving mechanism,** the **sewing-machine head,** the **feeding mechanism,** and the **controls.**

A sewing machine has various feeding mechanisms, such as the **needle-feed, drop-feed, compound-feed, puller-feed,** and **alternating-presser** mechanisms. A **needle feed** provides for the needle moving the material the regulated length of a stitch by itself while the presser foot holds the material in place on the throat plate. Thus a positive feed is ensured, because the needle pierces the fabric and prevents slippage while the stitch is being made.

In the **drop-feed** mechanism, a feed dog, consisting of rows of teeth, rises and moves the material under the presser foot. The feed dog by itself moves the material the regulated length of a stitch while the presser foot holds the fabric against the feed dog. Slippage can occur because this feed is not as positive as the needle feed, since the teeth of the feed dog do not pierce the fabric as the needle feed does. For this reason, when two or more plies of material are being sewed, the upper ply may slip and not come out evenly at the end of the seam. Since the ply length of the lower ply prevents the body of the fabric from coming into direct contact with the feed dog in some cases, there may be slippage in the lower ply.

A **compound feed** is merely a combination of a needle feed and a drop feed.

Some two-needle machines have a **puller feed** which consists of two rollers located back of the two needles. Where installed, the puller feed is used in conjunction with the compound feed. It is timed to operate slightly faster than the compound feed; hence it eliminates all puckering of the seam. It also pulls the fabric under the presser foot, thus lightening the burden of the operator and of the compound feed. The **alternating presser** is an extra foot that presses and holds the fabric alternately with the compound feed.

The type of machine used depends upon the quantity and quality of the fabric covering being manufactured. The operator of a fabric shop should consult the manufacturer's representative to determine the correct type of machine for various weights of fabric or duck. A good commercial machine is usually designed to sew materials from light to heavy weight. Figure 4·6 illustrates an industrial-type sewing machine suitable for aircraft-fabric work. This is a Singer, Model 212W140, designed for sewing aircraft fabric, various weights of duck, and similar materials. This is a high-speed, compound-feed, long-arm, two-needle, lock-

Figure 4·6 A commercial sewing machine. (Singer Co.)

stitch machine for stitching a variety of heavy fabrics. It has two belt-driven, automatically lubricated, rotary sewing hooks on vertical axles. The compound feeding mechanism consists of a needle feed and a drop feed which are simultaneously adjustable for stitches up to five to the inch.

The speed recommended for the Model 212W140 sewing machine is 4000 rpm, depending upon the material being stitched. It is advisable to run a new machine slower than the maximum speed for the first few minutes to allow time for the oil to reach the moving parts. The driving wheel turns toward the operator.

In setting up a sewing machine for operation the operator should follow the manufacturer's instructions carefully until he becomes thoroughly familiar with the machine. Instruction manuals are furnished with each machine.

In using a sewing machine, the tension of the thread for both the needle and the bobbin must be correct to produce a good seam. The tension on the needle thread is controlled by turning the thumb nut on the tension disk to the right to increase tension and to the left to decrease the tension. The tension for the bobbin does not often need adjustment; however, it is adjusted by turning the screw that holds a flat spring which presses against the emerging thread. When both the needle tension and the bobbin tension are correct, the seam produced will have the threads locked in the center of the fabric as shown in Fig. 4·7.

When the needle thread is under too much tension, or when the bobbin thread is not under enough tension, the needle thread appears on the top surface of the material as shown in Fig. 4·8. When the bobbin thread is too tight or the needle thread has insufficient tension, the bobbin thread will appear on the surface of the bottom layer of material as shown in Fig. 4·9.

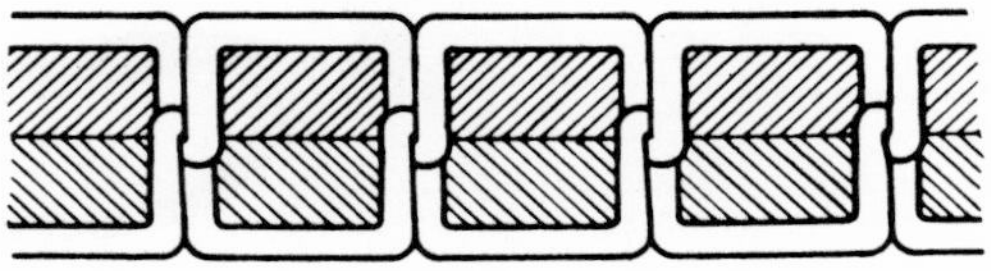

Figure 4·7 Diagram of a seam with correct tension for both the needle and the bobbin.

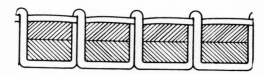

Figure 4·8   Seam with needle tension too great or bobbin tension too light.

Occasionally both tensions may be either too loose or too tight. Excessive puckering of the material and the frequent breaking of the thread indicate that the tension is too great. Loose stitches and a failure of the sewed pieces of material to be held together firmly are indications that the tension is too loose.

The number of stitches per inch of material can be checked with the number shown on the stitch indicator on the sewing machine by removing the thread from the machine, perforating a piece of paper with a row of needle holes made by the machine, and then counting the number of stitches for each inch along a ruler as illustrated in Fig. 4·10. This is important, since the indicator on the machine may be set for the necessary number of stitches per inch and yet the machine may be stitching a different number.

One of the important factors in determining the strength of a seam is the number of stitches per inch, but no arbitrary number can be given as a standard for all jobs. The exact number in each case depends upon the size of thread and the nature of the material being stitched. Where the strength of the seam is of primary importance, the number of stitches is specified.

The method of regulating the number of stitches to the inch sewed by a machine depends upon the design of the machine. Some machines have a knurled knob which is turned right or left, others have a thumbscrew which is loosened and moved up or down, and still others have a more complicated system of control.

Needles must be selected according to the type of machine in which they are to be used, the thread, and the materials to be sewed. If the wrong needle is used in the machine, there may be chafing, skipped stitches, and frequent thread breakages.

The **class of needle** refers to the length that is best suited to a particular type or model of sewing machine. The machine can be adjusted somewhat to accommodate different lengths, but this should not be accepted as a substitute for selecting the correct length and type of needle.

The **variety of needle** refers to the type of point, such as a round point or a cutting point. It also refers to whether the thread grooves are long or short. An even number indicates that the needle has a cutting point.

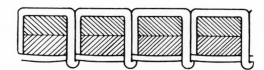

Figure 4·9   Seam with bobbin tension too great or needle tension too light.

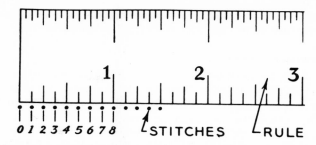

Figure 4·10   Measuring the number of stitches per inch.

An odd number indicates that the needle has a round point. Cutting-point needles are used for extra-heavy sewing, such as sewing very heavy leather materials. Round-point needles are used for sewing all types of cloth because they do not cut the strands when they are forced between the woven threads of the fabric.

If a round-point needle becomes dull, it functions as a cutting needle, pulling and cutting the threads and weakening the seams. The test is to slide a fingernail over the point of the needle. If the nail is scratched or caught by the needle, either a new needle should be installed or the old one should be sharpened. The usual method of sharpening a needle is to place it in the chuck of a drill press or drill motor, operate the drill at high speed, and hold a fine-grade sharpening stone lightly against the side of the needle, being careful to hold the stone at the proper angle. After being sharpened, the point of the needle is polished by rubbing it against a piece of russet leather. Crocus cloth or a piece of cloth with jeweler's rouge may also be used to polish the end of the needle.

The surface-tape cutter

A **surface-tape cutter** is used for cutting surface tape and also for making patches having pinked edges. This tool is also called a **pinking machine.** There are several types of these machines, one of which is illustrated in Fig. 4·11.

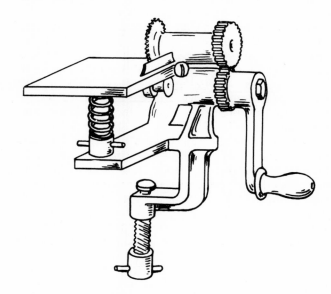

Figure 4·11   A surface tape cutter or pinking machine.

The smaller pinking machines can be operated either by a hand lever or by a motor. They may have one or two cutters for cutting various shapes of patches and various widths of tape.

The larger pinking machines have cutters that can be adjusted to various widths for cutting a roll of airplane fabric into different widths of surface tape simultaneously.

All surface-tape cutters should be provided with safety guards to protect the operator's hands, especially since the machine's appearance is deceptive and may cause the operator to become careless.

APPLICATION OF FABRIC COVERS FOR AIRCRAFT

Fabric covers are manufactured and applied to various aircraft structural units, such as control surfaces, fuselages, and wings. Even airplanes that are generally classified as "all metal" will sometimes have fabric-covered control surfaces. The instructions given here are general enough to meet the usual requirements and at the same time specific techniques are explained in enough detail so that the technician should not encounter any serious difficulty in applying his knowledge.

Nomenclature

The **nomenclature** of a typical fabric-covered wing is given in the drawing of Fig. 4 · 12. The names of parts given in the illustration are the same for wings having wooden spars and ribs and wings having metal spars and ribs. Some wings are constructed with wooden spars and metal ribs.

Control surfaces are generally constructed with spars and ribs, the spar being the principal spanwise structural member.

Fuselages incorporate **longerons** as the main longitudinal structural members. The longerons are joined with cross members and truss bracing with longitudinal strips called **stringers,** or formers, on the outside to give the proper shape to the structure.

General rules

It is good practice to use drawings or sketches when preparing to cover an airplane with fabric so that all details will be noted. The old cover can be used as a pattern if it is preserved at the time it is removed from the aircraft. Either a drawing or the old cover must be available to assure that the new cover is installed correctly and is provided with the needed reinforcements, inspection openings, and openings for fittings.

As mentioned previously, the fabric should be installed so the warp threads are parallel to the line of flight of the aircraft. Either the envelope method or the blanket method of covering is acceptable; however, the blanket method is more adaptable to some wings and surfaces. Detailed explanations for these methods are given later in this section.

When covering surfaces having sharp edges, either of wood or metal, the edges should be covered with fabric tape, masking tape, or some other type of tape which will prevent abrasion of the fabric or lacing cords.

All seams for large covers should be made parallel to the line of flight in order to reduce air resistance and to prolong the life of the fabric surface. Small fabric surfaces that do not require seams may have the warp threads of the fabric either parallel to or perpendicular to the line of flight. Seams should not be over a rib or be placed so that the rib lacing will pass through or be over any part of a seam.

When covering tapered wings or control surfaces, the seams should be placed so they will cross the fewest number of ribs possible, consistent with the efficient

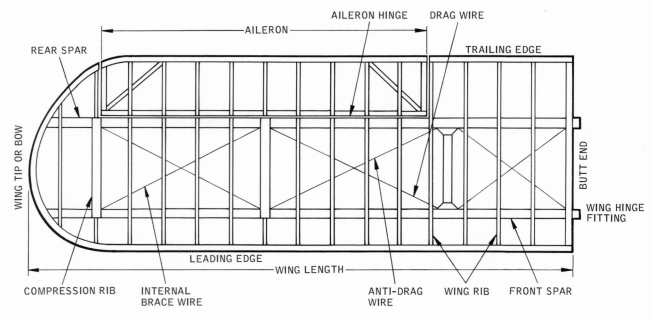

Figure 4·12   Nomenclature for a fabric-covered wing.

cutting of the pattern. Careful planning by the technician is necessary to accomplish this.

The only seam (whether hand-sewed or machine-sewed) extending spanwise to the wing or control surface should be at the trailing edge, except that in the case of tapered wings or control surfaces additional seams may be made at the tapered portion of the leading edge. Other spanwise seams can be accepted, but they are not desirable. The seam at the trailing edge or spanwise seams on the top or bottom of the surface should be covered by surface tape at least 3 in. in width, and the seam at the tapered leading edge should be covered by surface tape having a width of at least 4 in. The tape covering the trailing edge of wings or control surfaces of aircraft with never-exceed speeds in excess of 200 mph should have notches at least 1 in. wide and 1 in. deep cut in both edges, the notches spaced not to exceed 18 in. apart. This is to prevent the tape from tearing off in case a section comes loose.

To reduce the number of seams on a covered surface to a minimum, it is desirable to use wide strips of cloth. This saves time in making large covers and provides a neater and stronger surface.

To eliminate puckering and to form a smooth surface, wing covers should be hand-sewed or tacked along the top edge of flap and aileron recesses and wing butts as shown in Fig. 4·13. Hand sewing and tacking are not done at the bottom or center of recesses unless such recesses are extremely small.

Hand sewing or tacking should begin at a point where the machine sewing stops and should continue to a point where the machine sewing or uncut fabric is reached. Hand sewing should be locked at intervals of 6 in. and the seams should be finished with a lock stitch and a modified seine knot. A hand-sewed seam should have at least four stitches per inch, and can be made with either baseball stitches or plain overhand stitches. See Fig. 4·14.

When hand sewing or permanent tacking is done it is necessary to cut the fabric with sufficient width to allow the edge to be turned under before sewing or tacking. If temporary tacks are installed, they should be removed with a straight pull so the fabric will not be damaged.

Characteristics of seams

A **seam** is a series of stitches that join two or more pieces of cloth or other material. The characteristics of seams are appearance, strength, elasticity, and durability. The appearance of a seam is probably the least important of its characteristics, but a sloppy-looking seam does not inspire confidence, and it usually indicates that the other characteristics may be lacking. Neat workmanship is usually a sign of careful workmanship.

A seam should have enough strength to withstand the stresses to which it will be subjected. The principal factors affecting the strength are the type of stitch, the type of thread, the number of stitches to the inch, the construction of the seam, the size and type of needle point used in making the seam, and the tightness of the seam.

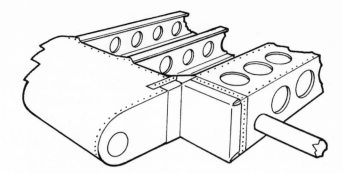

Figure 4·13 Securing of fabric at recesses and wing butts.

The elasticity required in a seam depends upon the elasticity of the material in which it is sewed. The type of seam, the length of the stitch, the tension of the thread, and the quality of the thread are the factors affecting the elasticity.

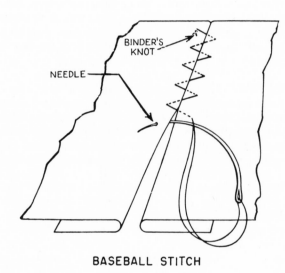

BASEBALL STITCH

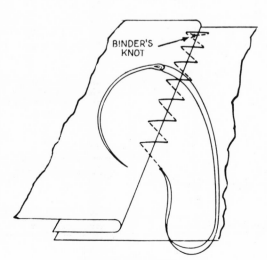

OVERHAND STITCH

Figure 4·14 Baseball stitch and plain overhand stitch.

The durability of the seam must be in proportion to the durability of the material in which it is sewed. When a seam is sewed in a tightly woven fabric, which is more durable than one which is loosely woven, the stitches of the seam must be tight, the thread must be well set into the material, and the seam must be made so that there will be as little wear as possible when the seam comes in contact with any other object.

Types of machine-sewed seams

The types of seams suitable for aircraft fabric covering are the **plain overlap seam,** the **folded-fell seam,** the **French-fell seam,** and the **modified French-fell seam.** The modified French-fell seam is most commonly used for machine sewing; however, the plain overlap seam may be used when selvage edges or pinked edges are sewed together. The several seams mentioned here are illustrated in Fig. 4·15.

Doped seams

Lapped and doped seams are permissible where there is sufficient support under the fabric to make a smooth and durable seam. This type of seam can be used at a wood-covered or metal-covered leading edge. When such a seam is made, the fabric should be overlapped at least 4 in. and covered with a pinked-edge tape at least 4 in. in width.

A lapped and doped seam can be made spanwise to the trailing edge of a wing or control surface, and in this case the lap should be at least 4 in. and should be covered with pinked-edge tape at least 3 in. in width. As explained previously, the surface tape at the trailing edge should be notched to a depth of 1 in. at both edges and the notches should be 1-in. wide and spaced not to exceed 18 in. apart.

Envelope cover for wings

An **envelope cover** for a wing is, as the name implies, a covering made in the form of an envelope before it is applied to the wing. The fabric is prepared by sewing together strips of the material with modified French-fell seams and then folding the material over to form an envelope which is sewed to fit the wing. The envelope is then slipped over the wing and the open end is hand-sewed, usually at the butt of the wing.

Before a wing can be covered, the necessary amount of fabric must be ordered. The length of the wing in feet is divided by the width of the fabric in feet to determine the number of strips required, and allowance is made for the overlapping seams and the material needed for sewing over the butt end of the wing. The length of the strips is found by measuring around a rib at the butt of the wing and then adding about 6 in. to allow for the trailing-edge seam. When the correct number of strips of material are ready, they are sewed together at the edges using a modified French-fell seam or a plain overlap seam. The former seam is preferred. The large sheet thus obtained is then folded so that the lower and upper seams coincide.

The folded sheet of fabric is placed on a cutting table, aligned, stretched taut, and tacked to the table at each corner. The wing is then placed in position on the fabric so it may be marked for size as shown in Fig. 4·16. If the envelope is to be prepared for a tapered wing, the marking would be done as shown in Fig. 4·17.

Before a wing is placed on the fabric for marking, the fabric must be stretched tight and tacked to the layout table at each corner. Additional tacks are placed where necessary to assure that the fabric is smooth and straight. The wing to be covered is then placed carefully on the fabric so the warp is parallel to the wing ribs. For a straight wing, the leading edge of the wing is placed parallel to the fold in the fabric so that the distance between the edge of the wing and the folded edge of the fabric is one-half the maximum profile thickness of the wing.

If the spacing described above is accurately determined, the cover-pattern dimensions will be correct, since they all depend upon this location. A mark is made along the trailing edge of the wing to indicate where the machine-sewed seam is to be located. The mark at the trailing edge is carried into the aileron recess when there is one, as shown in Fig. 4·16, but this mark is extended only about 4 or 5 in., and no other marks are made in that recess. The wing tip is marked, and the required allowances are made for the taper and the thickness of the wing at the tip. When the fabric cover has been marked with the wing structure in place, the wing is removed from the cutting table and pins are then inserted at a distance of about ½ in. inside the marks and at intervals of about 1 ft, thus holding both layers of the fabric together in a secure manner for cutting.

The fabric is cut about ½ in. outside the marks to allow for seams and then is sewed on a machine using a single needle. When the sewing is completed, the pins are removed and the cover is turned inside out. It is now ready to be placed on the wing.

In some cases the shape of the wing structure is such that the envelope cannot be sewed entirely around the edges before being placed on the wing structure. When this condition exists, a portion of the

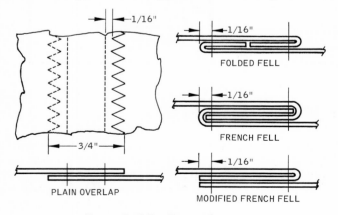

Figure 4·15 Types of seams.

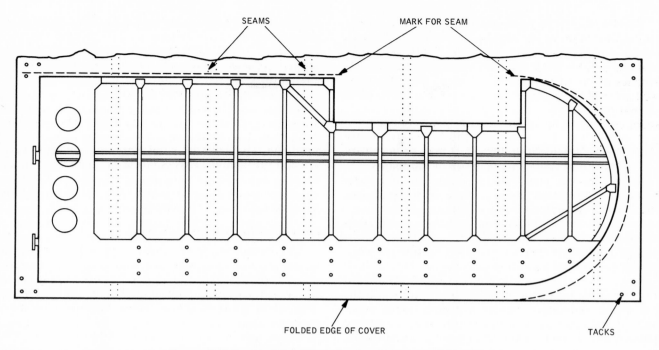

Figure **4·16** *Marking fabric for covering a straight wing.*

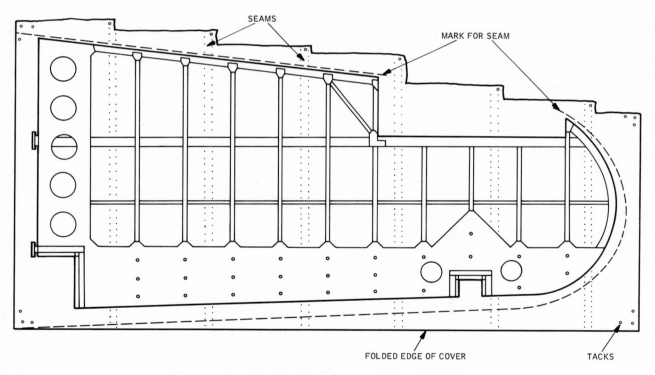

Figure **4·17** *Marking fabric for covering a tapered wing.*

edge sewing will have to be done by hand after the fabric is in place.

Slipping the cover over the wing structure may appear to be easy, but a few preliminary steps are necessary. The wing is placed on two or more trestles, the number depending upon the size of the wing. The upper camber side of the wing is up and the butt rests against some solid support so that the cover can be pulled into place without overturning the trestles. Talc may be dusted on the leading and trailing edges of the structure to make it easier to slip the cover into place.

55

The fabric envelope is pulled into place evenly, keeping the seam at the trailing edge where it belongs. The seams between the strips of fabric are then adjusted so they are parallel to the ribs and not extending on to any of the ribs. The entire cover must be under the same degree of tension and must be as smooth as possible.

The tightening and smoothing of the envelope must not be slighted. If the cover is too loose after every effort has been made to tighten it, it may be necessary to remove it and resew one or more of the seams.

To remove wrinkles from the fabric a light water spray is used over the entire surface. This shrinks the fabric and also smooths out the wrinkles. If this is not done the wrinkles will show even after several coats of dope are applied.

To prepare an envelope cover for a swept-back wing, the procedure is the same as that just described; however, it is necessary to cut and sew entirely around the wing because of the need to keep seams and the fabric warp parallel to the line of flight. Furthermore, in figuring the amount of fabric for the wing, a bit more will be needed than for the straight wing. The arrangement for cutting and sewing the fabric for a swept-back wing is shown in Fig. 4·18.

Blanket-type covering

Blanket-type covers are made by sewing together widths of fabric of sufficient length to form a blanket covering for the entire wing. The length of each strip is such that it will pass from the trailing edge of the wing around the leading edge and back to the trailing edge with sufficient extra length for sewing or over-lapping for a doped seam. For airplanes with a never-exceed speed of more than 150 mph, the trailing-edge seam must be sewed with a plain overhand stitch or a baseball stitch. Otherwise the seam may be over-lapped at least 1 in. and doped to the frame or the blanket.

When installing the blanket-type cover on a wing structure, the blanket is merely wrapped around the wing and pinned at the trailing edge, wing tip, and wing butt. It is pulled taut, and the pins are adjusted until the fabric fits the wing smoothly and with even tension throughout. Excess fabric can then be trimmed off and the seams sewed or doped as required. After the cover is completely installed, the fabric is lightly sprayed with water to remove wrinkles.

Procedures for re-covering a wing

The procedures described here apply to the removal of fabric and preparation of a wing for re-covering for all types of materials. It does not, however, apply to the actual installation and finishing of special fabric covers other than grade A fabric. These procedures will be described later.

When the wings of an airplane need to be re-covered, the wings are removed from the airplane and placed on padded trestles or vertical stands. After necessary records and notes are made regarding the condition of the wings and the locations of fittings and attachments, the old cover is removed. As explained previously, the cover should be removed carefully and kept in one piece unless a detailed drawing is made. Without a drawing, the old cover is needed as a pattern. During the removal of the old cover, the details of sewing, inspection holes, fittings, etc., should be noted so the new cover will be as well-installed as the original. If the

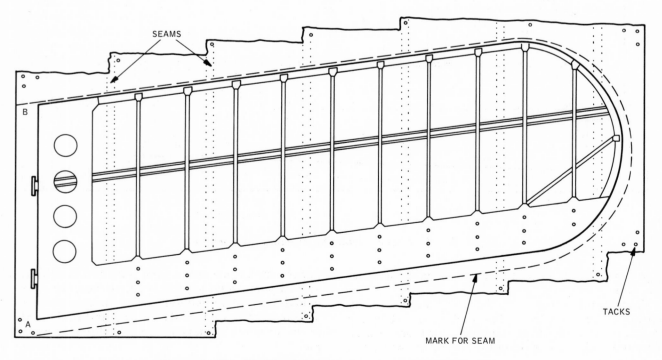

Figure 4·18 Marking fabric for covering a swept-back wing.

wing has metal ribs and the fabric is secured to the ribs by means of screws through the metal cap strips, the screws should be removed carefully one by one with a screwdriver. This can be done after the finishing tape has been stripped from the rib areas. To remove fabric which has been stitched around the ribs it is merely necessary to cut the stitching cord with a jackknife or similar tool.

After removal of the original covering from a wing or control surface, the structure must be inspected, repaired if necessary, and suitably prepared for re-covering. As mentioned previously, the old cover should be saved as a pattern unless a detailed drawing is made to assure correct installation of the new cover.

Wood wing and control-surface structures should be examined carefully to detect loose glue joints, cracked members, deterioration of wood due to dry-rot or fungus growth, excessive warping of members, and deterioration of interior finish. Cracked or otherwise damaged members should be repaired or replaced to restore the original strength of the structure. Loose glue joints should be disassembled, cleaned thoroughly so glue can bond to a bare wood surface, and reglued according to approved gluing practice.

If the interior finish has flaked, cracked, or otherwise become ineffective, the old loose finish should be removed by scraping or with sandpaper, and at least two coats of spar varnish should be applied after the surface has been sealed with an approved sealer.

Plywood surfaces, such as the area used for a walkway on a wing, which are to have fabric doped to them should be prepared by cleaning and smoothing them thoroughly with sandpaper and applying a fresh coat of dope. When covering a new wood surface, a brush coat of dopeproof sealer, equivalent to MIL-V-6894, should be applied and permitted to dry for about 4 hr. Before the fabric is installed, two coats of clear dope should be brushed on; at least 45 min should be allowed between coats for drying.

The ribs of wood wings should be stabilized by means of **interrib bracing** as shown in Fig. 4·19. The bracing consists of a cotton tape wrapped once around each rib and continued diagonally between the top and bottom cap strips of each successive rib. The tape should be placed approximately midway between the front and rear spars and should extend continuously from the butt rib to the tip rib. If the wings are designed with permanent rib bracing, it is not necessary to install the tape.

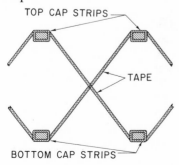

Figure 4·19 Application of interrib bracing.

All surfaces of the wing structure which will come into contact with the doped cover should be **dopeproofed** by means of aluminum foil, dopeproof paint, or cellulose tape to protect them against the action of the solvents in the dope. Metal surfaces such as clad-aluminum sheet and stainless-steel sheet do not require dopeproofing.

The wing or control-surface structure should be examined carefully for possible chafe points such as bolt heads, screw heads, sharp edges of metal, or protuberances of any kind which may rub against the fabric. All such points should be padded with fabric or tape to prevent wear of the fabric cover. After the cover has been installed, chafe points should be reinforced with doped-on patches of fabric, duck, or other suitable material. Where the fabric has an opening for the passage of control cables, control rods, or other moving devices, the opening should be reinforced with duck or leather to prevent wear. The protective material is usually sewed onto a fabric patch and the patch is doped to the fabric.

Installation of fabric

As mentioned previously, fabric may be applied to a wing by either the envelope method or the blanket method. Either method is satisfactory; however, there are some parts of the wing that require special attaching methods. Careful observation by the technician at the time that the original cover is removed will usually reveal the special techniques for the attachment of the fabric. In some cases, wood strips are attached to the wing structure so the fabric may be tacked at certain points, especially in the aileron cutout. Where there is a smooth metal or wooden surface of sufficient area, the fabric can be cemented with an approved lacquer cement, such as Airlac or an approved plastic cement. Wherever the fabric is cemented to the structure the technician must make certain he is using a cement which will provide a good bond between the fabric and the structure. Dope is not suitable for cementing fabric to metal or wood.

After the fabric is installed on the wing and all seams and cemented joints are finished, the fabric is attached to the ribs, either by **rib stitching** or by means of screws in the metal cap strips. Before the rib stitching is started, reinforcing tape must be placed on the fabric over each rib. The tape, as wide as the rib, should be used on both the top and bottom of the rib in order to protect the fabric from tearing and to distribute the flying loads over the fabric.

If the fabric is being installed on the wings of an airplane which is approved for a never-exceed speed in excess of 250 mph, **antitear strips** should be placed under the reinforcing tape on the top of the wing over all ribs. On the bottom of the wing, the antitear strips should be placed between the reinforcing tape and the fabric for all ribs in the area of the slipstream. The slipstream width is considered to be equal to the diameter of the propeller plus the space of one additional rib.

The antitear strips are made of the same grade of fabric as that used to cover the wing and are of sufficient width to engage the lacing cord on each side of the rib. Thus the strips would be at least ½ in. wider than the reinforcing tape. The antitear strips are installed by doping them onto the fabric before installing the reinforcing tape. This is done by brushing a wet coat of dope on the fabric where the strips are to be applied, placing the strips on the wet dope, and then brushing dope over the strips after they are in place.

In the slipstream area the antitear strips are started at the trailing edge of the wing, passed forward and around the leading edge, and then continued back to the trailing edge. On the portion of the wing outside the slipstream, the antitear strips start at the trailing edge, extend forward on the top of the wing, and continue around the leading edge back to the location of the front spar.

Rib lacing

Rib lacing, or **rib stitching,** must be accomplished in accordance with approved specifications. The proper type of waxed lacing cord must be used, and the stitches or loops must be spaced the same distance that was used on the original cover. If the spacing of the rib stitches is not easily determined, the chart of Fig. 4·20 can be used as a guide. Note that rib stitches outside the area of the slipstream on airplanes having a never-exceed speed below 170 mph can have a spacing of 3½ in. For the same never-exceed speed, the area within the slipstream area should have rib-stitch spacing of 2½ in. Airplanes having a never-exceed speed in excess of 250 mph should have the stitches spaced at 1 in.

Before rib stitching is started, the wing is placed in a stand to hold it in a vertical position so the technicians can work easily on both sides. The fabric on the top and bottom of the wing is then marked with a pencil to indicate where the stitches are to be made.

When the position for the start of the rib lacing is determined, a double loop-stitch is employed to lock the cord firmly. This is accomplished as shown in Fig. 4·21. First, one loop is passed around both cap strips from the bottom side of the wing to the top side so both ends of the cord are extending through the

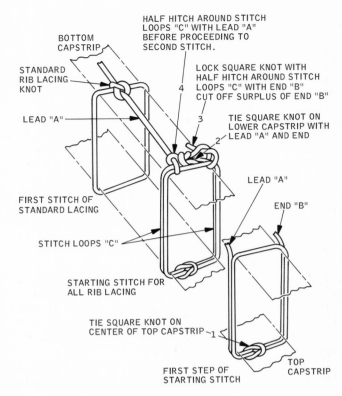

Figure **4·21** *How a double-loop stitch is made.*

fabric at the top of the wing, one on each side of the top cap strip. This is done by passing the rib-lacing needle and cord from the top to the bottom, around the bottom cap strip and back through the wing to the opposite side of the top cap strip. The two lengths of cord are then tied at the top cap strip with a square knot. The ends of the cord are then passed with the needle through the same holes in the fabric to each side of the bottom cap strip. At this point, they are again tied with a square knot. With the short end of the cord, a half hitch is made on one side of the square knot; with the long end (that which is to be used to continue the rib lacing), a half hitch is locked around both loops of cord on the other side of the square knot. The operators then can proceed with the stitching by inserting the needle through the wing at the point previously marked. The needle passes entirely through the wing on one side of the rib and then is passed back through the wing on the other side of the rib. The holes in the fabric should be made as close to the rib as possible so the cord will not tend to tear the fabric.

When the cord is brought back through the wing where the stitch is to be locked, it is passed around the preceding cord as shown in Fig. 4·22. This is the first step in making the **modified seine knot** which is standard for locking rib lacing. The modified seine knot is made according to the diagram in Fig. 4·22. To make the finished job as smooth as possible, the knot is pulled to one side of the cap strip. Care must be taken to see that the cord is pulled and held tight while the knot is being made in order to make sure that the finished lacing is sufficiently taut.

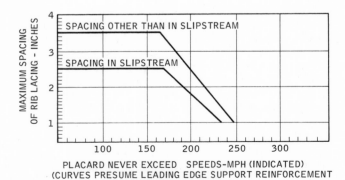

Figure **4·20** *Chart to show spacing of rib stitches. Note: (1) If original rib-stitch spacing cannot be determined, use spacing indicated in these curves. (2) Lacing should be carried to leading edge when velocity exceeds 275 mph.*

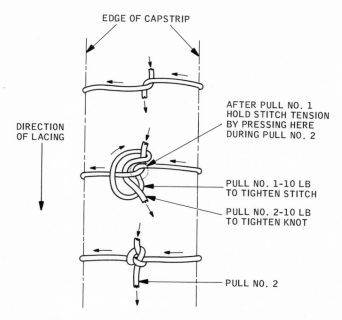

Figure 4·22 *Making a modified seine knot.*

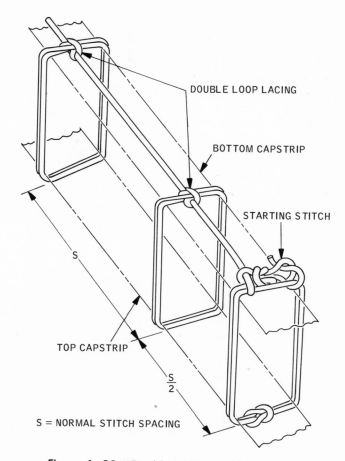

Figure 4·23 *Double-loop method of lacing.*

The spacing of the first and second loops of the rib stitching should be one-half the distance of the normal spacing. This is to provide extra strength. The last two loops of the stitching should also be spaced at one-half the normal distance. Because the modified seine knot has the possibility of slipping, the final knot at the end of the rib should be locked with an extra half hitch around the loop.

When it is desirable to obtain exceptional strength in the rib lacing, the double-loop method can be used. This is illustrated in Fig. 4·23. The modified seine knot is made in a manner similar to that for the single-loop method; however, the locking loop of the knot is passed around both loops of cord. This is shown in Fig. 4·24.

When it is necessary to join two pieces of cord, a **splice knot** such as that shown in Fig. 4·25 should be used. This type of knot insures that there will be no slippage after the knot is pulled tight.

Occasionally it may be necessary to lace fabric to portions of the fuselage in order to maintain the correct contour. In such cases the technician must carefully observe the original lacing at the time that the fabric is removed so he can duplicate the method when the new fabric is installed. The attachment of the fabric to the fuselage must be at least as strong as that employed by the manufacturer on the original installation of fabric.

Application of surface tape

Upon completion of rib lacing, the fabric cover should be ready for the **application of surface** (finishing) **tape.** This tape was described in the previous chapter along with other approved covering materials.

Surface tape should be applied over all rib lacing, seams, leading and trailing edges, and other points where reinforcement is necessary. However, this is done only after the first coat of dope has dried. The tape has pinked edges, as previously explained, and is

applied with dope of the type required for the job. A coat of dope is brushed on the areas where the tape is to be applied and then the tape is immediately placed on the wet dope. Another coat of dope is brushed over the tape and care is taken to see that all air bubbles are worked out from under the tape. An excess of dope will cause runs and sags and may drip through the fabric to the inside of the wing; hence the technician must use only the amount of dope required to fill the tape and bond it securely to the surface.

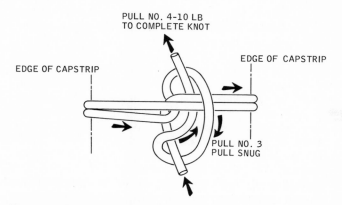

Figure 4·24 *Modified seine knot for double-loop lacing.*

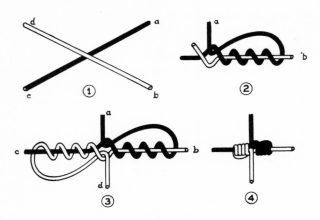

Figure 4·25   Making a splice knot.

Inspection rings, patches, and grommets

In addition to the installation of surface tape, it is also necessary to install other items with dope. If the wing requires plastic inspection rings, these are installed with the second coat of dope. As explained previously, plastic inspection rings are about 4 in. in diameter and are doped directly on the fabric in the proper locations. The fabric is usually not cut out of the inspection openings until it is time to make an inspection. At this time a metal inspection cover is clipped or snapped into place after the fabric is cut from inside the ring.

Plastic drain grommets are installed by doping in all low points of the wing and control surfaces where there is a possibility that moisture can collect. Seaplane or marine grommets should be installed with the second coat of dope on seaplanes or landplanes where there is a possibility that water may splash into the drain holes. These grommets are manufactured with a raised shield which deflects the water. The shield also tends to increase the flow of air from the drain hole.

Application of dope

There are no hard and fast rules for the application of dope to a new fabric cover; however, certain practices are almost universally acceptable and this section will describe these practices. Dope as it comes from the manufacturer is usually of a consistency satisfactory for brushing, provided that the temperature in the doping area is 70°F or more. When the dope is to be sprayed, it will normally require thinning to provide the best consistency for the spray gun unless a hot-dope technique is being employed. When it is necessary to thin the dope, the directions on the dope container should be followed unless the operator is thoroughly familiar with the type of dope being used and the characteristics of his spray equipment. The amount and type of thinner to be used will depend to a certain extent upon the temperature and humidity of the ambient air.

Blushing, as explained previously, will occur if the dope is applied in a cold, humid area. If the relative humidity is such that the **dew point** will be reached with a drop of a few degrees, blushing is very likely to occur. The **dew point** is that temperature when the moisture in the air will condense and form fog. If the temperature of the air is 68° and the dew point is 65°, a temperature drop of 3° will cause blushing. Because the evaporation of thinner from the dope as it is applied to a fabric surface will often cause a temperature drop of several degrees, depending upon the movement of air across the surface, blushing is likely to occur whenever the ambient temperature is within 5 to 10° of the dew point.

Blushing is a white, opaque condition that occurs as the result of moisture collecting in the surface layer of dope. It greatly reduces the strength and effectiveness of the dope and doping should stop immediately if the condition should be noticed. A mildly blushed surface can be corrected by placing the blushed part in a warm area and spraying on a light coat of retarder or thinner. The surface should then be allowed to dry, and if there is still a blushed condition the treatment can be repeated.

If blushing begins to occur while spraying or brushing dope, the best practice is to place the surface being doped in a warm room, suitably fireproofed, if such a room is available. Moderate blushing can be reduced with the use of retarder thinner. This thinner is slower-drying than normal thinner and the temperature of the freshly doped surface will not fall as low as it will with the use of normal thinner. The use of excessive amounts of retarder thinner is not recommended because it will produce unsatisfactory drying conditions. When blushing is severe and there is no warm area in which the work can be placed, it is advisable to wait until better conditions of temperature and humidity prevail.

General procedure for doping

The number of coats of dope applied to a surface and the method of application are variable; however, a satisfactory job can be attained with the following procedure:

1. Two coats of clear dope should be brushed on the new fabric surface. Surface tape and other doped-on attachments should be applied after the first coat of dope has dried. The purpose of brushing the first coats of dope is to assure good penetration of the dope through the fabric and to "lay" the nap of the fabric, that is, to cause the surface fibers of the fabric to lay flat against the surface. When the dope has dried, the surface is sanded, either wet or dry, to remove roughness. "Wet-or-dry" sandpaper should be used when wet sanding.

2. One more coat of clear dope is brushed or sprayed on the surface and sanded. During sanding, care must be taken not to sand heavily over slightly raised points, such as the rib stitching and surface tape because it is quite easy to sand through the fabric.

3. Two coats of aluminum-pigmented dope are sprayed on, and the surface is sanded between coats.

The dope must be completely dry before sanding. Drying usually takes 45 min or longer.

4. Three coats of pigmented dope of the desired color are next applied by spraying, and these are sanded and rubbed to produce a smooth, glossy finish. Where a very high gloss is desired, additional coats of dope are applied, sanded, and rubbed. Hand rubbing is done with an approved rubbing compound. After the rubbing is completed, the surface may be waxed to help preserve the finish.

Doping techniques

The first two coats of dope are applied to the fabric with a brush, using unthinned clear dope. A spray gun ordinarily should not be used for these coats because the air strikes against the new fabric, raises the nap, and dries the atomized dope so rapidly that it leaves a rough surface.

The first coat is expected to wet the fabric surface thoroughly, but it must not be applied too heavily or it will form a thick coat on the inner surface and cause a bad "spot" on the outer surface. The dope may also drip through to the opposite surface and form spots which cannot be removed.

If the shop is managed carefully, arrangements are made to apply the first coat of dope on the same day the fabric is attached to the structure. The reason is that the fabric is taut when it leaves the fabric shop, but after it stands for a few days the original tautness may disappear. Remember that tautness can be restored and wrinkles can be removed with a light spray of water applied to the undoped fabric.

In applying dope with a brush, the brushed strokes for the first coat should be parallel to any structural member, such as a rib, spar, etc., that is in contact with the fabric on the inside. The second coat can be brushed at 90° to the first coat; however, care must be taken to see that excess dope is not left along the ridges caused by the ribs and other raised structural members.

Sanding of the doped surface, after the dope has dried, is accomplished with either wet or dry sandpaper. "Wet-or-dry" sandpaper, grade 320 or 400, will produce a very smooth surface. After sanding, the surface should be wiped clean to remove all sand and loose dope particles before applying the next coat of dope.

Aluminum-pigmented dope

The purpose of **aluminum-pigmented dope** is to prevent the ultraviolet rays of the sun from penetrating to the fabric and causing deterioration. For this reason, at least two coats of this dope are sprayed on the surface. Sanding is done after each coat to provide a smooth surface, but the sanding must not be of such duration and intensity that it will remove the pigmented layer. The last of the successive coats of color-pigmented dope is applied in sufficient quantity to saturate all previous coats of dope and "flow out" the roughness of such coats in order to produce a smooth surface having a uniform color. Sanding and

rubbing are done to complete the job and provide a glossy surface.

The spray gun

In almost all paint and dope finishing work or aircraft, the finish is applied with a spray gun. The principal advantages of the spray gun are the speed with which paint or dope may be applied and the smooth finish of the sprayed surface.

Spray guns are manufactured in a number of different types and sizes. Sizes vary from the small airbrush guns to the heavy-duty production guns used with pressure tanks. Guns are made to spray all types of fluids including heavy, sticky compounds such as automobile undercoat. The operator must make certain that the gun he is using is the proper type for the liquid being sprayed.

One of the most popular spray guns for general use is the type MBC gun manufactured by the DeVilbiss Company. A gun of this type is shown in Fig. 4·26. The important parts are labeled in the drawing. Figure 4·27 shows the same spray gun used with a liquid container, also called a **cup**. The spray gun also can be used with a pressure tank, in which case the liquid is fed under pressure from the tank through a hose to the gun.

The best results in the use of a spray gun are obtained when the gun is properly maintained and serviced. Bearing surfaces and moving parts should be lubricated daily with a light oil. The lubrication of the gun should be accomplished according to the manufacturer's instructions.

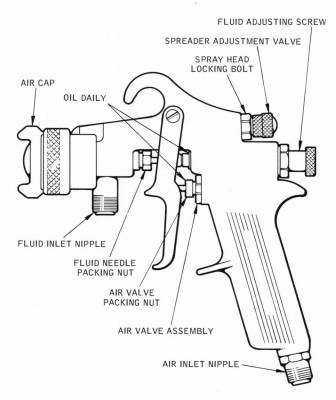

FLUID ADJUSTING SCREW
SPREADER ADJUSTMENT VALVE
SPRAY HEAD LOCKING BOLT
AIR CAP
OIL DAILY
FLUID INLET NIPPLE
FLUID NEEDLE PACKING NUT
AIR VALVE PACKING NUT
AIR VALVE ASSEMBLY
AIR INLET NIPPLE

Figure 4·26 Drawing of a typical spray gun.

Figure 4·27   Spray gun with paint cup. (DeVilbiss Co.)

After each use of the gun, it is necessary that it be cleaned thoroughly to prevent the accumulation of dried paint or dope in the nozzle and paint passages. It is not usually necessary to take the spray gun apart to clean it, because paint solvent or dope thinner sprayed through the gun will ordinarily clean out the paint or dope. The outside of the gun should be thoroughly washed with solvent or dope thinner.

It is desirable to disassemble the gun periodically and inspect it for wear and accumulation of dirt. Worn parts should be replaced.

The packing nuts around the fluid-needle and air-valve stem should be kept tight, but not so tight that parts cannot move freely.

It is not wise to allow the gun to become so dirty that soaking of the complete gun becomes necessary. Also, the gun should not be left immersed in solvent or thinner. It is especially important to avoid the use of caustic alkaline solutions for cleaning because alkalis destroy aluminum alloy.

An unbalanced or distorted spray indicates a dirty air cap. The air cap should be removed and washed thoroughly in clean thinner. If reaming of the air-cap holes is necessary, a matchstick, broom bristle, or some other soft material should be used. It is wrong to use a hard or sharp instrument because it may permanently damage the cap.

Spray-gun parts are not ordinarily removed, except

for the air cap. When replacing the air-valve assembly, the air-valve spring should be properly seated in the recess in the body of the gun. When removing any parts which seal on a gasket, the condition of the gasket should be examined. When the fluid tip is replaced, it must be tightened carefully.

Using the spray gun

The difference between a first-class finishing job and a poor job is often determined by the use of the spray gun. An experienced technician who has mastered the techniques in handling a spray gun will usually have no difficulty in producing a good finishing job.

The first requirement is to have the gun properly adjusted for the type of finish being applied. The operator may test the gun by trying it against a test surface. When the desired pattern is obtained, he may start applying the finish.

The air pressure for the gun must be correctly adjusted. This pressure is normally controlled by an air transformer. The device acts as a pressure regulator to provide the correct pressure as adjusted by the knob on the top. This unit has fittings for the incoming air from a standard air-pressure line and one or more outlet fittings for the attachment of the air hose to the gun.

Among the conditions which the operator of a spray gun must observe are the following:

Gun held at the correct distance from the surface being sprayed (6 to 8 in.)
Air pressure correctly adjusted
Release of the trigger at the end of each pass
Movement of the gun in a straight line
Paint strained before using
Correct type of air cap and nozzle for the finish being applied
Paint or dope thinned to the correct consistency
Cleanliness of the surface being sprayed
Temperature and humidity correct for spraying

The operator of paint spray equipment should obtain information from the manufacturer of the equipment to make sure he is following methods designed for the best results. He should also note the directions given by the manufacturer of the material used in the spray gun.

Problems with dope application

A poor dope job can be caused by a variety of conditions and improper techniques in application. If the spray gun is held too far from the surface being sprayed or if the dope is not thinned sufficiently, a condition called "orange peel" will result. If the gun is held too far from the work, the dope being sprayed will dry to some extent before hitting the surface and will be too thick to flow into a smooth continuous film. The result is a pebbly texture known as **orange peel**. This same condition will result from spraying a dope which is too thick when it is put in the gun.

Pin holes are usually caused by small bubbles on

the surface of the dope. These bubbles may develop as a result of not allowing sufficient time for drying between coats or after wet sanding. Sometimes such bubbles are trapped in dope which is too thick; when the bubble bursts, the dope does not level out but leaves a small crater.

Blisters on the surface of the dope may be caused by oil or water coming through the air line to the spray gun. It is necessary that a water trap be located in the air-pressure line and that the trap be drained regularly. The air compressors and pressure regulators should also be drained to make sure that water and oil are removed from the lines.

Runs, sags, streaks, and **overlapping lines** are usually the result of poor spraying techniques, incorrect nozzle for the material being used, and improper adjustment of the equipment. When the technician has become practiced with the spray gun and the material he is spraying, he will usually be able to gage his timing and handling of the gun so the proper amount of dope will be applied for each pass of the gun.

SPECIAL COVERING METHODS AND MATERIALS

As mentioned previously, a number of new covering methods, materials, and processes have been developed in recent years. The methods, in general, conform to the previous standards set forth in Federal Aviation Regulations; however, the materials and processes vary in several details. The new covering processes are covered by special approvals issued by the FAA under Supplementary Type Certificate numbers.

The Ceconite covering process

One of the most popular covering processes for fabric-covered aircraft is called the **Ceconite process,** developed by the Cooper Engineering Company. This process utilizes Ceconite 101, a fine-quality dacron fabric, which is applied, initially, according to the standard procedures approved by the FAA and described previously in this chapter. For the same weight, Ceconite 101 is much stronger and more durable than grade A cotton fabric specified in TSO C-15.

Ceconite 103 is a fine-weave, lightweight fabric for use as a finish over areas covered with plywood. This fabric may not be used as a primary structural material except for gliders.

FAA-approved Ceconite has CECONITE 101 or CECONITE 103 stamped on the selvage at 1-yd intervals. Ceconite-process STC numbers are specifically restricted to the users of Ceconite materials and processes and may not be used for other processes. These STC numbers are supplied free of charge to purchasers of Ceconite fabric.

Installation of Ceconite

The preparation of a wing, control surface, or fuselage for the installation of Ceconite is the same as that previously described for grade A fabric. The part

to be re-covered should be inspected, repaired, and refinished as necessary. All sharp or rough edges should be smoothed or taped to prevent chafing through the covering.

Covering methods include the envelope and blanket method and should, as nearly as possible, duplicate the original covering with particular attention to attachment method, rib lacing, and spacing of rib lacing, screws, or clips. Sewing, stitching, lacing, seam directions, etc., should be the same as those originally used by the manufacturer or should comply with pertinent Federal Aviation Regulations.

When Ceconite is applied with Super Seam, the special aviation cement developed for the purpose, the Ceconite fabric may be attached to the structure being recovered largely by cementing. The cemented method of re-covering is recommended for all aircraft where fabric width is sufficient to cover an entire side of a surface. If this is not possible, the fabric may be sewed in panels as described previously for the blanket method. When employing the cemented method for applying Ceconite to wings, the fabric may be run spanwise on one side and cemented to the leading and trailing edges as well as to the root ribs and the wing tips. The opposite side covering is then applied with at least a 4-in. overlap at the leading edge, a 3-in. overlap at the trailing edge, and at least a 1-in. overlap at the tip. Surface tape of 6-in. width should be cemented over the leading-edge overlap and at least a 3-in. tape should be cemented over the trailing-edge and wing-tip overlaps.

On the fuselage, Ceconite fabric should be applied with cement on opposite sides, making certain that the fabric cemented area is at least 1 in. in width. The top and bottom sections of fabric are then cemented to the fuselage with an overlap of at least 1 in. over the longerons and fabric previously cemented to the adjacent sides. Surface tape at least 2 in. wide is then cemented over the overlap seams. It is emphasized that for all cementing of Ceconite, the approved cement must be used.

For rib lacing, Ceconite D-693 or D-415 rib-lacing cord is used with Ceconite fabric. D-69 machine-sewing thread and D-207 hand-sewing thread are used for machine sewing and hand sewing, respectively. The surface tape to be used with Ceconite fabric may be either predoped grade A cotton (TSO C-15) or Air Fibre glass-fiber tape. Reinforcing tape may be either FAA-approved cotton tape or Special Ceconite Process tape.

After Ceconite fabric is installed by sewing or cementing on a wing, control surface, or fuselage, a preliminary shrinking of the fabric is done with heat to remove wrinkles and general slackness. Since Ceconite will shrink up to 10 percent, it is initially installed with a little more slack than when applying cotton fabric. After the preliminary shrinking is completed and the cover is found to be satisfactory in all respects, the final shrinking is accomplished, using an ordinary household iron set to approximately 240°F, the temperature normally used for ironing wool. The iron is passed over the fabric with a steady movement so that the iron is not in contact with any one area of fabric for more than 2 sec. The fabric shrinks immediately and should tauten sufficiently with a temperature of 240°F. A higher temperature will cause further shrinkage which could result in distortion of the structure on light airplanes.

For shrinking the Ceconite fabric on large surfaces, such as fuselages and wings, best results are obtained by using two or three applications of heat. The first application removes the slack and wrinkles, and the main tautening is accomplished with the second heating. For initial shrinking it is preferable to utilize a two-man team, each man being equipped with a steaming steam iron or an electric iron set at the correct temperature. The two operators should work on opposite sides of the area being covered.

In rare cases where satisfactory tautness is not obtained with the level of heat given above, the temperature may be raised in steps of 25° until the desired results are obtained. Under no circumstances should the temperature of the iron be above 400°F. Excessive temperature will cause the fabric to melt and assume the appearance of transparent plastic.

When using the iron to shrink Ceconite fabric, the best results are obtained by moving the iron at about 5 in. per sec. A motion similar to that used in ironing clothing is the most satisfactory. First the iron should be moved from side to side and then the same area should be ironed in a top to bottom motion. This assures uniform shrinking in all areas.

Small areas of doped Ceconite may be further tautened with heat by cautiously applying an electric iron in direct contact at a slightly increased temperature setting. However, prolonged application of heat (10 sec or more) at a temperature of 300°F or above may cause discoloration of the dope.

When doping a Ceconite cover, a nontautening dope should be used. This may be either nitrate or butyrate dope; however, the two different types should not be used together. If regular butyrate dope is used, tautening will continue for an extended time and this may distort the structure, especially on light aircraft. If regular butyrate dope is to be used for a Ceconite cover, a greater amount of slack must be allowed to compensate for the tautening of the dope.

Covering plywood with Ceconite

When it is necessary or desirable to cover a plywood surface with Ceconite fabric, the process is comparatively simple. First, the surface is cleaned, sanded, and sealed. Next, four coats of dope are applied and allowed to dry. The Ceconite fabric is then cemented to the surface around the edges, making the cemented seams at least 1 in. in width. The cemented seams are allowed to dry and then the fabric is shrunk with a hot electric iron in direct contact with the fabric until the fit is snug over the entire surface. Two coats of dope are brushed on the surface and allowed to dry. Final finishing is then applied to obtain the type of surface and color desired.

The Air Fibre covering process

The Cooper Engineering Company has developed a process, the **Air Fibre covering process,** for covering aircraft structures with glass cloth. The application of this process must follow the directions given in the Air Fibre manual, or in accordance with pertinent Federal Aviation Agency specifications.

In the Air Fibre process the preparation of the structure is the same as for other coverings; however, great care must be taken in the application of the glass cloth. Since glass cloth will shrink very little, the application at the start must assure that the cloth is applied in such a manner that all the wrinkles are removed. Butyrate dope is applied as a filler and for the finish.

The Poly-Fiber covering process

The **Poly-Fiber covering process** utilizes dacron fabric of the same type described for the Ceconite process. With the Poly-Fiber process, however, special coatings have been developed to take the place of the conventional nitrate and butyrate dopes. The Poly-Fiber process was developed and is controlled by the Stits Aircraft Corporation.

The coating (dope) developed for the Poly-Fiber process is a polyurethane marketed under the trade name Poly-Dope. This coating is supplied in two blends: Poly-Brush for brush application and Poly-Spray for use with a spray gun. Poly-Brush is applied for the first two coats and for attaching tapes and reinforcing patches.

The thinner for Poly-Dope, called Poly-Thinner, is used when it is necessary to reduce the consistency of the coating.

Poly-Fiber fabric may be attached to a wing or control surface by either the envelope or blanket method. When using the blanket method, the fabric can be attached to the edges of the surface by means of an approved cement called Poly-Tak. Wherever suitable surfaces are available to provide a cementing surface at least 1 in. in width, the cementing method is more efficient than sewing.

The lacing cord to be used with the Poly-Fiber process is a special cord having the name POLY-FIBER stamped on the spool. This is also true of the sewing thread used with this process.

Instead of the standard cotton reinforcing tape used with the conventional processes, a special pressure-sensitive tape reinforced with glass fiber is required. This tape is also identified with the word POLY-FIBER stamped on the spool or on the side of the roll. It is available in widths of ⅜ and ½ in.

The finishing tape required for this process is made of either glass fiber or dacron and is identified with the trade name.

When the Poly-Fiber fabric has been correctly attached to the airframe, wing, or other structure, heat is applied with an electric household iron to shrink the material, thus removing wrinkles and providing the desired tautness. Experience has shown that the best procedure is to tauten the fabric in several increments of heat increase, rather than applying a high temperature to obtain the final tautness on the first application. The first application of heat is applied with the iron set between 225 and 250°F. After the entire surface has been leveled or pulled snug with all wrinkles removed, the temperature is increased to about 350° and the operation is repeated. The iron is continually moved over the surface of the fabric at a rate of 4 to 7 in. per sec. A slower rate may be necessary over leading edges and other structural members where the structure acts as a heat sink. The fabric must not be heated to more than 400° because it will melt and deteriorate.

After the Poly-Fiber fabric has been shrunk in accordance with the prescribed procedure, one coat of Poly-Brush is brushed on the surface in a manner to provide good penetration. The brushing technique and drying time are approximately the same as for conventional nitrate and butyrate dopes. Poly-Brush is supplied in the correct consistency and drying characteristics for brushing. The material must be agitated frequently in order to disperse the white pigment, which is also a fire retardant. When the covering is applied over plywood, the wood should have one coat of the Poly-Brush dope applied before it is covered in order to assure good adhesion. After the fabric has been heat-shrunk over the structure, the first coat is brushed through to remove all bubbles.

When the first coat of Poly-Brush has dried, the surface tape, reinforcing patches, grommets, etc., are installed using Poly-Brush as an adhesive. Plastic grommets can also be attached with Poly-Tak cement. This cement is thinned with acetone when necessary.

If the temperature causes the Poly-Brush material to dry too rapidly, Poly-Thinner can be added to slow the drying time. The consistency of the coating must be such that all bubbles can be worked out before the coating dries.

The second coat of Poly-Brush is brushed on with brush strokes at 90° to the direction of brushing for the first coat. This aids in producing a more uniform coating. The second coat is applied after previous applications have dried.

To complete the finish, a minimum of two and a maximum of six coats of Poly-Spray are applied. At least 2 hr is allowed for drying between coats before lightly sanding each coat with 280- or 320-grit sandpaper. Before spraying, the coating material should be strained through a paint-strainer cone. Before and during the spray operation, the mixture should be agitated frequently.

The Poly-Spray is supplied in the correct consistency and drying time for spraying. When necessary, due to evaporation, the material may be thinned with Poly-Dope thinner. This thinner is a special blend which provides the proper reducing and drying time and no substitute should be used. Lacquer thinner can be used to clean the equipment after it has been used to spray Poly-Dope.

When the desired number of coatings have been applied, the surface is sanded and then wiped free of sanding particles. The final color is then applied with Du Pont Dulux Synthetic Enamel, pigmented butyrate dope, or lacquer as desired.

The Eonnex covering process

The **Eonnex covering process** for fabric-covered aircraft is similar to those previously described in that the fabric is a synthetic of the dacron type and is heat-shrinkable. The fabric is applied to a control surface, wing, or fuselage in the same manner as is employed for other fabrics. The fabric may be attached by cementing or sewing, depending upon the method appropriate for the particular application.

Eonnex coatings are plastics which utilize catalysts to harden or "set" the material. Eonnex No. 204 coating is a thermoplastic, which means that it can be softened by the application of heat. Numbers 200A, 201B, and 202A filler coatings contain thermoset plastics which react chemically in the presence of heat to form insoluable, infusible solids. The filler coatings are supplied in separate containers, because when they are mixed they begin to react and cure chemically. The rate of curing is dependent upon temperature; that is, a higher temperature will cause more rapid curing of the coating.

The Eonnex process is covered by Supplementary Type Certificates SA 4-1210 and SG 4-1240, issued by the Federal Aviation Administration Application of Eonnex materials must be accomplished in accordance with instructions given in Eonnex Manual 200.

Airframe preparation, before the application of Eonnex covering, must be complete and thorough. Since the life expectancy of the covering is considerably longer than that of cotton fabric, the interior structure must be prepared to withstand all deteriorating influences for many years. Eonite No. 22 sealer is recommended for all wood structure and No. 19 paint for use on metal. The surfaces to be preserved must be clean, dry, and free of any loose or brittle paint or varnish. Areas where it is not desired to have the fabric adhere may be taped with cellophane or masking tape to reduce adhesion. All sharp edges and protrusions must be padded with tape or other material to prevent abrasion of the fabric.

On some wings it may be desirable to run two or three lines of stabilizing tape between the ribs instead of the usual one. Part No. 3 tape can be used for this purpose. The reason for the extra taping is that the fabric pull is not even at all points during the application of the tautening heat, and the ribs may tend to distort due to unequal loads. After the coating is applied, this condition will not exist. The tapes should be run from rib to rib, parallel to the surface instead of diagonally from the top of one rib to the bottom of the next. The tape spans between ribs should be run, as explained in a previous section, so the tape is on the inside of the rib cap strip and does not contact the fabric except where the tape is wrapped around the cap strip.

In sewing Eonnex fabrics, either by hand or by machine, the stitch spacing must be in accordance with the specifications given in Eonnex Manual 200 or applicable Federal Aviation Administration specifications. The Eonnex manual permits the use of either single- or double-stitched seams. Single-stitched seams require more stitches per inch; however, if the machine is capable of the specified single stitch, an uncoated seam strength of over 100 lb will result, and the seam will be almost invisible after it is taped and coated.

The thread tension used with Eonnex thread No. 7 should be adjusted a bit looser than with cotton thread. The thread has a dry lubricant which comes off during the operation of the sewing machine; this condition is normal, however, and is no cause for concern.

Sewed seams are required wherever it is not possible to obtain at least a 1-in. overlap for cementing. If the sewing is done by hand, the No. 7 thread should be used double.

Eonnex fabric should be applied to the structure with slightly more slack than is used with cotton fabric. Excessive looseness will decrease porosity and coating adhesion after the fabric is heated and tautened and may cause slackness to develop in cold weather. Edges that are cemented to the structure must be installed using Eonnex No. 204 cement, fabric coating, or Pliobond manufactured by the Goodyear Tire and Rubber Company. Eonnex No. 204 cement will dry the most rapidly. Care should be exercised in cementing fabric to be sure that the areas are as free of wrinkles as possible. Small wrinkles may be removed by applying the heated Eonnex iron to the wrinkles after the cement is dry. This will improve the bond and also remove the wrinkles.

When using No. 204 cement as an adhesive to attach fabric to a structure, at least 1 hr should be allowed for solvent evaporation before the fabric is heat-tautened. Waiting time can be reduced by using the tautening iron, adjusted for medium heat, to "set" the joint under pressure after it is dry to the touch.

Eonnex is tautened with the use of heat applied by means of a radiant heater or an iron. A special iron has been designed for use with Eonnex fabrics and this would be the most suitable. The fabric is tautened in two steps, the first being to level the cover so that the seams are straight and the fabric is free from severe sags. For this purpose a temperature of 225 to 250°F is used. The iron is applied to the fabric as shown in Fig. 4·28. Caution must be used not to overheat the fabric or it will melt.

The Eonnex iron is set to a higher heat for final tautening than was used for the preliminary operation. The exact setting is determined by experience; however, most structures will withstand the tautening caused by the maximum heat of the Eonnex iron. If, after the final tautening, wrinkles still exist in corners or other areas due to the cover not being fitted properly, they may be removed by use of the special "close-quarter" iron designed for the purpose. This iron is designed for use in repair work and in small areas that cannot be reached with the standard iron.

The use of Eonnex irons are specified and required for final tautening because the thermostats are adjusted so that the fabric cannot be damaged no matter how

Figure 4·28 Applying the Eonnex iron to fabric for shrinking.

high the control is set. After the fabric is shrunk by means of the heated iron, the coatings will not cause any further shrinkage.

Ribs that are slightly bowed after the fabric has been tautened can usually be straightened by means of a rib-stitching needle. The eye end of the needle is inserted through the weave of the fabric and pressed against the bowed side of the rib until the rib is straight. While holding the rib in the straightened position, staples are driven through the fabric into the center of the cap strip with an office-type stapler. These staples are very fine wire and will not damage the cap strips. The staples need not be removed and are covered with the reinforcing tape.

When the fabric has been shrunk (tautened) to the proper degree and is properly fitted to the structure, the coatings are applied. The first of these coatings is the primer. One part of Eonnex No. 204 adhesive primer is mixed with one part of thinner according to the instructions on the container. This makes the primer almost water-thin. A special applicator pad is used to apply the primer as shown in Fig. 4·29. The pad is saturated with the primer and is then placed on the fabric and moved with straight strokes along the fabric. Since the primer is translucent-red, the areas that have been coated are plainly visible. The primer coating is usually dry in about 15 min; however, the areas where the fabric is over a solid structure will take longer.

As soon as the primer coat is dry, reinforcing tapes and covering attachments can be installed; or, if desired, these items can be installed after the first filler coat has dried.

The first filler coating is prepared by mixing No. 200A and No. 201B coatings and thinner in accordance with the instructions on the containers. The amount

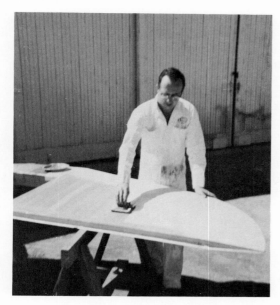

Figure 4 · 29   Applicator pad for Eonnex coatings.

mixed should be that which will be applied within 8 hr because the mixture will begin to set up shortly after this time. The coating, when prepared, is applied either with the special applicator pads or by means of a spray gun.

Instructions for using the applicator pads are as follows:

Pour the amount of coating that will be used within approximately 10 min into a container slightly larger than the applicator pad.

Dip the pad into the coating until the pad is completely saturated.

Holding the pad flat against the fabric, apply one full, wet, even coat. Do not attempt to completely fill the fabric weave. One side of a typical wing can be coated by this method in about 20 min. Less ventilation will be required for pad application than when using a spray gun.

The coating may be applied in one full, wet coat or two thin coats with a spray gun. If two thin coats are used, the second coat should be a cross coat, that is, the gun should be moved in a direction perpendicular to the direction used in applying the first coat. The two-coat system will result in faster drying. After the first filler coat is applied, no further coatings should be applied for at least 4 hr.

Reinforcing tape for use with the Eonnex process carries Eonnex Part No. 3. This tape has a pressure-sensitive adhesive coating and is installed without the use of cements. The tape can be removed and repositioned without destroying the effectiveness of the adhesive and should be approximately the same width as the rib cap strips over which it is installed.

The cover attachments should be the same as those employed on the original structure. Attaching methods for the fabric include rib stitching, sheet-metal screws, wire clips, etc. The spacing must be the same as the original or in accordance with pertinent FAA instruc-

tions. In rib stitching for Eonnex fabric covering, a modified knot has been approved. This knot is illustrated in Fig. 4 · 30. It will be observed that this knot is somewhat easier to make than the conventional modified seine knot used for other processes. Rib stitching is done with Eonnex No. 9 lacing cord.

The surface tape to be used with the Eonnex process is Eonnex No. 4. This tape is placed over rib-stitched areas and over seams. Reinforcement patches are made from No. 5A Fibreglas, Eonnex 205 or 206 fabric, or Celastic No. 4 tapes, and reinforcements are applied with fabric coating or No. 204 adhesive as a cement. Celastic is applied with methyl ethyl ketone (MEK) as a solvent.

Tapes are not required over seams that are cemented to the structure for at least 1 in. on each side. However, they may be desirable for appearance. Surface tape should be cut with a pointed end rather than straight across. This will prevent any tendency to unravel and presents a better finished appearance. Tapes over cap strips should extend 1 in. over the solid supporting structure of wing leading edges.

Conventional inspection rings are not recommended with the Eonnex process because they tend to embrittle. A double patch of Eonnex fabric or No. 5A glass cloth with a ring width of 1 in. is recommended. Celastic may also be used.

Celastic material is applied by immersing in Celastic solvent or MEK for approximately 10 sec and then immediately placing it in position on the area where it is to be used. It should not be disturbed until it is completely dry.

After the first filler coating has hardened sufficiently to sand, it is given a very light sanding. Dry sanding is

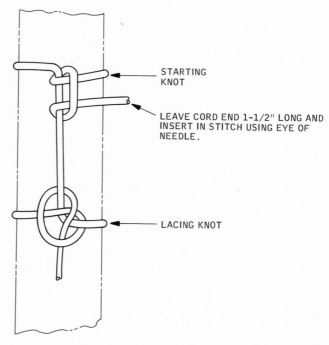

STARTING KNOT

LEAVE CORD END 1-1/2" LONG AND INSERT IN STITCH USING EYE OF NEEDLE.

LACING KNOT

Figure 4 · 30   Rib-lacing knot used when covering with Eonnex materials.

recommended. The best results are obtained using a 150C No-Fil Durite sandpaper or equivalent. If coatings tend to load the sandpaper, the use of 180 Durite Screen Bak sanding sheets is recommended.

The second filler coating employs Eonnex Nos. 202A and 201B with thinner mixed according to the instructions on the containers. Applicator pads or a spray gun are employed for the application.

After the second filler coating is applied, the coating is given a thorough sanding to produce a smooth surface. This sanding should also be done dry.

The finish paint for Eonnex coatings can be a good synthetic automobile enamel, acrylic enamel, or pigmented nitrate dope. These finishes should be applied according to standard practice.

Razorback glass-cloth covering method

An approved glass-cloth covering method has been developed by Razorback Fabrics, Inc. The application of this method must conform to installation instructions No. 39-6.

Before applying Razorback fabric, the structure to be covered should be prepared as for other types of covering. All wood surfaces to which the fabric will be bonded, such as catwalks and wood-covered panels, should be treated with two coats of cellulose acetate butyrate dope. The dope should be allowed to dry thoroughly before proceeding. On metal surfaces, particularly on agricultural aircraft, it is recommended that tubing, stringers, and all metal fittings be treated with an epoxy primer. Rust and corrosion can be reduced substantially by using a good grade of rust and corrosion inhibitor.

The blanket method of covering is used when installing Razorback fabric. For a typical wing, 72-in. glass cloth is installed lengthwise, inboard to outboard, starting on the bottom of the wing. The fabric is cemented to the leading edge of the wing with full-bodied butyrate dope. The cemented area must be 2 in. in width. The cloth is then spread over the bottom of the wing to the trailing edge where it is cemented for a minimum lap of 2 in. Tension applied to the cover should not be more than sufficient to remove all wrinkles. Surplus cloth is trimmed from the edges and from the wing bow and butt. The edges of the cloth are cemented down to provide a smooth surface. After the dope has dried, the wing is turned over and the top surface is covered. The edge of the cloth is attached to the leading edge while the wing is still bottom side up, in the same manner as explained for the bottom of the wing. The wing is then turned over again and the cloth is cemented to the trailing edge with just enough tension to remove wrinkles. The cloth is trimmed from the edges and cemented down as before. The finished application results in a single thickness of cloth on the leading edge except for the bottom side where there is a 2-in. lap. On the trailing edge there is a double thickness of cloth on the top and bottom sides.

Control surfaces are covered by wrapping a sheet of the cloth completely around the surface and cementing at the trailing edge with full-bodied butyrate dope.

The fuselage is normally covered in four sections. One sheet at the bottom is attached to the corner skin stiffeners or longerons with butyrate dope, one sheet on each side, and one sheet on the top.

The dope used with Razorback glass cloth must be cellulose acetate butyrate (CAB). A pressure pot should be used if possible with 18 lb pressure in the pot and 60 lb pressure on the line. The first coat of dope is thinned only enough so it will spray properly; it is sprayed in a manner which will avoid blowing the dope through the cloth. On metal surfaces such as the leading edge, air pockets and blisters will form. These can be eliminated before they occur by using a squeegee while spraying the first coat. As the dope is sprayed the squeegee is lightly stroked on the surface moving toward the open bays of the wing. This removes the air and allows the fabric to lie flat.

The second coat of dope can be sprayed a little heavier than the first, and each succeeding coat can be a little heavier than the preceding one. This practice will speed the process of filling the surface.

The first coats will cause Razorback glass to sag, but subsequent coats will draw it up. The tautening action in some cases is a little slower than normal, depending on humidity or drying conditions. Tautening action will occur between the second and fifth coats, or when the weave has been filled.

Razorback reinforcing tapes are attached to the ribs when the fabric has tautened as noted before. At this point, the required cloth-fastening process is accomplished. Finishing tapes should not be installed until the weave is completely filled.

Two additional coats of clear butyrate dope may be applied with a brush if desired. These should be allowed to cure before dry-sanding with No. 280 sandpaper. Care should be exercised to avoid sanding over rivets, ribs, and other protrusions which could easily be sanded through. After sanding the first time, additional coats of dope may be applied to build up the finish. One coat of aluminum-pigmented dope may be used for the purpose of a sand coat only. This coat should be completely wet-sanded off except for the fills, with wet-or-dry sandpaper. Aluminum-pigmented dope can be used as a base coat for light colors of pigmented dope.

Airplane structures covered with Razorback glass cloth must be marked with a RAZORBACK FABRICS, INC. decal before the part can be placed in service. When an entire airplane is covered, a decal must be installed on both sides of the vertical fin or rudder. The Razorback method is approved under appropriate Supplementary Type Certificate numbers issued by the Federal Aviation Agency.

Approved manuals for special covering processes

It must be emphasized that all special covering methods must be accomplished according to instructions given in the manual approved for the process by the Federal Aviation Agency. These manuals can be obtained from the manufacturers and dealers who supply the materials for the covering process.

REPAIR OF FABRIC COVERINGS

Tears in fabric

Small-to-medium tears in a fabric covering can usually be repaired by sewing and doping on a fabric patch. The objective is to restore the original strength and finish to the repaired area.

A single tear should be repaired by removing the surface dope around the area to be covered with the patch and then sewing the tear using a baseball stitch as shown in Fig. 4·31. The dope can be removed by softening and scraping or by sanding. The most satisfactory method is to apply a heavy coat of dope to the area and allow it to soften the old surface dope which can then be removed by scraping. Strong solvents such as acetone can be used to soften the old dope, but care must be taken to see that the solvent does not drip through the opening to the lower surface of the fabric where it will cause blisters. When the cleaned surface around the tear has been sewed and the stitches locked as required, a piece of pinked-edge surface tape or fabric is doped over the seam. The tape or fabric patch should extend at least 1½ in. beyond the tear in all directions. Additional coats of dope are applied to the patch, sanding between coats to produce a smooth finish. The final coats of pigmented dope are applied and finished according to procedures explained previously.

If a tear is of the V type, the procedure is the same as that described above; however, the sewing should start at the apex of the V in order to hold the fabric in place while the seams are completed.

The sewed-in patch

If the damage to a fabric surface is not longer than 16 in. in any direction and is such that the fabric cannot be sewed together, a sewed-in patch is used. The damaged area is cut out to make a smooth-edged opening, either oval or rectangular in shape. The dope is removed as explained previously. The patch is turned at the edges ½ in. and sewed to the edges of the opening. The patch should be fastened at several points before it is sewed in to make it easier to sew the seam. Surface tape is doped to the seams and the patch is finished in the usual manner. If the patch is nearer than

1 in. to a rib, the patch should be cut to extend at least 3 in. beyond the rib. After sewing the patch, it should be laced to the rib over a new section of reinforcing tape. The original lacing should not be removed.

The sewed-in repair panel

When the damaged area in a fabric is longer than 16 in. in any direction, it is necessary to repair the damage by means of a panel. The panel must extend from the trailing edge of the wing up to and around the leading edge and back to a point even with the front spar.

The damaged area is trimmed to within 1 in. of the ribs nearest the damage. After the old fabric has the dope removed, the panel of fabric is pinned in place and the edges are turned down ½ in. to provide a folded edge to be sewed to the old fabric. The patch is sewed into place using a baseball stitch and locking every 8 or 10 stitches. The ribs under the patch have reinforcing tape placed over them and the patch is laced to the ribs.

The patch is given a coat of clear dope and allowed to dry before installing surface tape over the seams. Surface tape is also doped over the edges of the panel at the leading and trailing edges. The repair is then finished with dope in the usual manner.

Doped repairs

Doped-on repair patches can be employed on all fabric-covered aircraft which have a never-exceed speed not greater than 150 mph. A doped-on patch can be used for a damaged area which does not exceed 16 in. in any direction. A repair of this type is made by trimming the damaged area and then removing the old dope in the area where the patch is to be applied. The patch is cut to a size which will overlap the old fabric at least 2 in. for any patch not over 8 in. For holes between 8 and 16 in. the patch should overlap one-quarter the distance of the major diameter of the repair.

Where doped-on patches extend over a rib, the patch should be laced to the rib after applying reinforcing tape. The old lacing and reinforcing tape should not be removed. Finishing of the patch is accomplished in the usual manner.

Doped-on panel repair

When the damage to an aircraft fabric surface is greater than 16 in. in length, a panel should be doped-on. In this type of repair, the old fabric is cut out along a line approximately 1 in. from the ribs nearest the repair. The fabric on the leading and trailing edges is not removed unless both the top and bottom of the wing is to be repaired. The surface tape is removed from the ribs adjacent to the repair but the lacing and reinforcing tape is left intact. The patch panel is cut to a size which will overlap the trailing edge by at least 1 in., extend around the leading edge and back to the forward spar, and extend at least 3 in. beyond the ribs on each side of the repair.

The area to be doped should have the old dope removed and the patch, having pinked edges, is doped

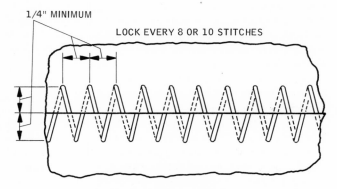

Figure 4·31   Sewing a tear with a baseball stitch.

into place along the edges. When the dope has dried, another coat of dope is applied to the doped seams. After this is dried, reinforcing tape is installed along the ribs and the patch is laced in. The panel is then given a coat of clear dope and allowed to dry. Surface tape is installed over the ribs and on all seams with the second coat of dope. The patch is then finished as described previously.

Repairs with glass cloth

Fabric covering can be reinforced or replaced with glass cloth, provided the FAA issues a Special Type Certificate for the process to be used. There are three classes of glass-cloth installation, namely, class A, class B, and class C.

In class A installations, the glass cloth is merely doped to the old fabric and acts as a reinforcement and protective layer. The old fabric must still be within the limits of strength approved by the FAA; that is, the fabric must not have deteriorated to less than 70 percent of the original strength. The outer layer of dope is removed from the old surface and the glass cloth is doped down using a dope or adhesive compatible with the glass cloth being installed.

Class B covering, which is the complete covering of the old fabric with glass cloth, can be approved if the old fabric has not deteriorated to below 50 percent of new strength. The glass cloth is laced to the ribs, and the lacing is covered with surface tape.

Class C covering involves the removal of the entire old covering and replacement with glass cloth. A typical process of this type has been described previously in this section.

FINISHING OF METAL AIRCRAFT AND PARTS

Although some of the materials used for the finishing of metal aircraft have been described previously, it is important that the technician be familiar with certain principles involved in metal finishing. In this section we shall not discuss the processes of plating or the special chemical finishes because they are not usually in the realm of general airframe maintenance. If such a process is required by the manufacturer, the work can be done by an organization which specializes in this type of work.

Corrosion protection

A metal fuselage is usually painted for two principal reasons: corrosion prevention and appearance. **Corrosion** is an electrochemical process in which oxygen or other elements combine with metals to form various compounds such as rust, aluminum oxide, metal chlorides, and other metal salts. The first requirement for corrosion is the presence of moisture; the other is a combination of dissimilar metals or metals and chemicals. If a metal is kept dry and clean it will not corrode; however, a little moisture in the presence of other elements can cause severe corrosion.

In the design and manufacture of aircraft structures, engineers are careful to avoid a design of any assembly of parts which requires the contact of dissimilar metals. If two dissimilar metals must be joined, the surfaces are insulated from each other by means of special coatings, treated tapes, or other means.

When preparing a metal structure for refinishing, the technician must be careful to avoid any condition which can cause corrosion and must remove any corrosion-causing condition which he may find. When in continuous contact with metals, hygroscopic materials (those which absorb and hold moisture), such as leather or canvas, are very likely to cause corrosion. Such materials should be waterproofed before installation.

Removal of paint

For the removal of coatings such as enamels and lacquers, a number of good paint removers are available. A wax-free dope and paint remover can be used; however, it contains highly volatile solvents and evaporates rather rapidly. Some removers are made with the consistency of thick cream, and these are applied with a brush and allowed to remain for a few minutes. The paint quickly softens and can be washed off with hot water. Directions for the use of paint removers are supplied with the material. The surfaces from which the paint has been removed should be washed thoroughly with water to remove any paint remover that remains on the surface or in crevices and seams. Finishes will not adhere to a surface which is not thoroughly clean.

Cleaning

The cleaning of metal structures is accomplished with approved cleaning agents recommended by a manufacturer of such materials. Some cleaners are used without dilution, and others are mixed with water. All such cleaners should be used according to the directions supplied by the manufacturer.

Where hard corrosion has formed on aluminum surfaces, it is permissible to use fine emery cloth, a fine wire brush, or fine sandpaper. These materials should be used only enough to remove the corrosion because they also remove some of the aluminum cladding. Steel wool should not be used because small particles of steel will become embedded in the aluminum and increase the tendency of the material to corrode.

Etching

Before clad-aluminum-alloy surfaces are painted, they should be treated with an approved etching compound in order to provide a good paint base. Among materials used for this purpose are phosphoric acid and certain patented etching compounds. Care must be taken to make sure that the material used is approved for the purpose and is used according to manufacturer's directions.

Priming

After a metal surface has been properly cleaned and etched, an approved primer is applied with a spray gun in order to reduce the possibility of corrosion and to provide a good base for the finishing coats. The primer may be zinc chromate, thinned to the correct consistency with toluene, or any one of several other types of primer suitable for application to an aluminum surface. It is well to apply two coats of primer unless the manufacturer specifies otherwise. Any runs or rough spots remaining on the primed surface after it has dried should be removed by light sanding with fine sandpaper. All traces of primer dust should be removed before finish coats of enamel or lacquer are applied.

Finishing

Several types of finishes are available for aircraft, the most common being acrylic lacquers, nitrate lacquers, and synthetic enamels. The lacquers are quick-drying, hence they are not as susceptible to the collection of dust particles as the enamels. Lacquers can be applied with a spray gun in the open air, provided there is little or no air movement and the working area is clean. The application of enamels should be done in a paint booth which is dustfree so the enamel will have time to dry and preserve the high-gloss finish which would otherwise collect dust particles.

A lacquered surface can be rubbed with a polishing compound and then waxed to produce a high-gloss surface. This should not be done until several days after the lacquer has dried.

REGISTRATION MARKS FOR AIRCRAFT

All aircraft registered in the United States must be marked with nationality and registration marks for easy identification. The marks must be painted on the aircraft or otherwise affixed so they are as permanent as the finish. The marks must contrast with the background and be easily legible. The letters and numbers must be made without ornamentation and must not have other markings or insignia adjacent to them which could cause confusion in identification.

Required markings

The registration and nationality markings for United States registered aircraft shall consist of the Roman capital letter N followed by the registration number of the aircraft. The registration number is issued by the Federal Aviation Agency when the aircraft is first registered.

When marks that include only the Roman capital letter N and the registration number are displayed on **limited, restricted,** or **experimental aircraft,** or on aircraft which have **provisional certification,** the words "limited," "restricted," "experimental," or "provisional airworthiness" must be displayed near each entrance to the cockpit or cabin. The letters must be not less than 2 in. or more than 6 in. in height.

Location of marks for fixed-wing aircraft

Registration marks for fixed-wing aircraft must be displayed on both sides of the vertical tail surface or on both sides of the fuselage between the trailing edge of the wing and the leading edge of the horizontal

stabilizer. If the marks are on the tail of a multi-vertical-tail aircraft, the marks must be on the outer surfaces of the vertical sections.

If the aircraft has engine pods or components which tend to obscure the sides of the fuselage, the marks can be placed on the pods or other components.

Location of marks for non-fixed-wing aircraft

Helicopters or other rotorcraft must have nationality and registration markings displayed on the bottom surface of the fuselage or cabin with the top of the marks toward the left side of the fuselage and on the side surfaces of the fuselage below the window lines as near the cockpit as possible.

Airships must have markings displayed on the upper surface of the right horizontal stabilizer and on the undersurface of the left horizontal stabilizer, with the top of the marks toward the leading edge, and on each side of the bottom half of the vertical stabilizer.

Spherical balloons must display markings in two places diametrically opposite each other and near the maximum horizontal circumference of the balloon.

Nonspherical balloons must have markings displayed on each side of the balloon near the maximum cross section and immediately above either the rigging band or the points of attachment of the basket or cabin suspension cables.

Sizes of nationality and registration marks

The height of letters and numbers for fixed-wing aircraft must be at least 12 in. Marks for airships and balloons must be at least 20 in. in height. The marks on the bottom of the fuselage or cabin of a rotorcraft must be four-fifths as high as the fuselage is wide or 20 in. in height, whichever is less. The marks on the sides of the rotorcraft cabin must be a minimum of 2 in. but need not be more than 6 in. in height.

The width of the characters in the markings must be two-thirds the height of the characters except for the number 1 and the letters M and W. The number 1 must have a width one-sixth the height and the letters M and W may be as wide as they are high. The thickness of the strokes or lines in the letters and numbers must be one-sixth the height of the characters. The spaces between the characters must not be less than one-fourth the width of the characters.

Laying out letters and numbers

Letters and numerals for the markings on aircraft are formed as shown in Fig. 4·32. The illustration is not intended to show the correct interval or spacing between the characters but merely to show the type and proportions of approved characters.

To lay out numerals or letters, a master template, such as the one shown in Fig. 4·33, can be constructed. With this device it is possible to lay out any letter or numeral. For some letters or numerals it is necessary to do a small amount of additional construction, but the template will provide the principal guidelines.

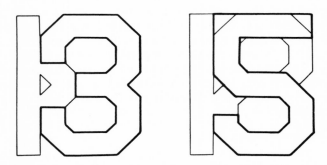

Figure 4·32 Letters and numerals for aircraft marking.

Figure 4·33 Template for laying out letters and numerals.

REVIEW QUESTIONS

1. What conditions should exist in a good fabric shop?
2. What types of needles are required for the installation of fabric covering?
3. What tool may be used to produce a pinked edge on fabric?
4. Explain the importance of proper thread tension when using a sewing machine.
5. What type of needle point is used for sewing cloth?
6. What is a pinking machine?
7. Why is it a good idea to save the old fabric in large sections when re-covering an airplane?
8. In what direction should fabric seams be placed on a fabric-covered surface?
9. What width of surface tape is required for trailing-edge seams?
10. Why is it necessary to notch the edges of surface tape at the trailing edge of a wing?
11. What types of hand stitching are used for hand-sewed seams? Which is the most desirable?
12. Name the types of machine seams used with aircraft fabric.
13. Describe a *modified French-fell* seam.
14. What width of lap is required for a lapped and doped seam at the trailing edge of a wing or control surface?
15. Describe the envelope and blanket methods for covering a wing.
16. After a fabric cover is installed on a wing and before it is doped, how are small wrinkles removed?
17. List items to be inspected and/or repaired in a wood wing before the covering is installed.
18. Describe the purpose and installation of interrib bracing.
19. What materials are used for dopeproofing?
20. How is damage to the fabric prevented at chafe points?
21. What is the purpose of reinforcing tape used over ribs?
22. Describe the function and installation of antitear strips.
23. What determines the spacing between rib stitches?
24. How is the first loop of rib lacing, or stitching, secured?
25. What type of knot is used to lock each stitch?
26. At what places must surface tape be installed?
27. At what point in the sequence of covering operations are inspection rings and drain grommets installed?
28. What is the advantage of seaplane grommets?
29. Why should the first one or two coats of dope be brushed on the fabric?
30. Explain why blushing occurs and what can be done to prevent it.
31. Why is aluminum-pigmented dope used with fabric covering?
32. List the conditions to be observed in using a spray gun.
33. What is the cause of orange-peel surface on spraying dope?
34. Give a brief discussion of the Ceconite covering process.
35. Explain the principal differences between the Ceconite process and the Poly-Fiber process.
36. What type of coatings are used with Eonnex covering?
37. What shrinking method is used for Eonnex fabric?
38. What special device is supplied for the application of Eonnex coatings?
39. Describe the Razorback covering method and name the materials used.
40. Under what conditions is a sewed-in patch required for damage fabric?
41. Explain the requirement for a sewed-in panel repair.
42. Under what conditions is a doped-on patch allowed?
43. When a repair patch or panel extends over a rib, what must be done with respect to the rib?
44. What are the three classes of glass-cloth installation or repair?
45. What are the principal reasons for applying a finishing coat to metal surfaces?
46. Why is it necessary to avoid contact between dissimilar metals?
47. Why is an aluminum surface etched before priming?
48. Why is a metal surface primed before applying the finishing coats?
49. What precautions must be taken to obtain the best results in applying an enamel finish?
50. What markings are required on aircraft of any type registered and operated in the United States?
51. Describe the size and form of the characters used for official aircraft markings.
52. What size markings are required on an airplane, and where are they located?

CHAPTER 5

Heat Treating and Inspection of Metals

TYPES OF MATERIALS EMPLOYED IN AEROSPACE VEHICLE STRUCTURES

In the design and construction of aircraft and other aerospace vehicles, many different types of materials are employed. For many years the most common types of materials used in the construction of aircraft were steel, wood, fabric, aluminum, and aluminum alloys. Copper and brass were employed for tubing and small fittings. More recently, aluminum alloys provided the major structural material for aircraft components because of their strength and light weight.

With the advent of the supersonic era, it has become necessary to develop metals that will be able to withstand both high stresses and high temperatures. To meet these needs, stainless steels and titanium alloys have come into being and are now serving as structural materials wherever conditions require their use.

In addition to the materials noted above, various plastics and synthetic material have been developed for aircraft use. Transparent plastics are used for windshields and windows, while others are employed for bushings, bearings, fairleads, tubing, ducting, and many other uses.

ALUMINUM AND ITS ALLOYS

The source of aluminum

Aluminum is obtained from bauxite ore, which is found in various parts of the world, and principally in Arkansas in the United States. Bauxite is a hydrated oxide of aluminum having the chemical formula $Al_2O_3 \cdot 2H_2O$.

The bauxite ore is given a caustic treatment, known as the **Bayer process,** which reduces the ore to a powder called **alumina,** or **aluminum oxide.** The alumina is mixed with a catalyst called **cryolite** and the mixture is placed in carbon-lined tanks which are equipped with large carbon anodes. A high level of electric current is applied, and this causes the carbon of the electrode to combine with the oxygen in the alumina to form carbon dioxide (CO_2) gas. The metallic aluminum which is left settles to the bottom of the tank and is drained off in the form of ingots. The electric current flowing through the mixture generates a high temperature, about 1900°F, which makes the process possible. The pure aluminum obtained from the refining process has various other metals mixed with it to form the many alloys which are available.

Aluminum alloys

There are nine series of aluminum alloys identified with four-digit code numbers. The first digit of these numbers indicates the major alloying element, as shown in Table 5·1.

Table 5·1

Code number	Major alloying element
1xxx	None
2xxx	Copper
3xxx	Manganese
4xxx	Silicon
5xxx	Magnesium
6xxx	Magnesium and silicon
7xxx	Zinc
8xxx	Other elements
9xxx	Unused series

The second digit of the code number indicates any modifications to the original alloy. In the 2xxx through the 8xxx numbers, the last two digits have little significance other than to identify the alloys and the sequence of development. In the 1100 series the last two digits indicate the amount of pure aluminum above 99 percent in hundredths of 1 percent. For example,

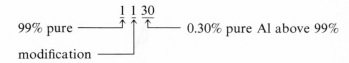

Aluminum identified by the number 1240 would be aluminum which is 99.40 percent pure with two modifications. In the 1xxx series, a modification is for the purpose of controlling one or more of the impurities.

An example of an alloy in the 2xxx series is as follows:

copper ──────────→ 2 1 17 ──── 17th alloy developed

1st modification ──────┘

Two forms of aluminum alloy are **cast** and **wrought.** Cast aluminum alloy is formed into a particular shape by melting and pouring it into a mold of the required shape. Wrought aluminum alloy is made by mechanically working the metal into the form desired by rolling, drawing, extruding, etc.

Aluminum-alloy designations

For many years aluminum and its alloys were designated by two-digit numbers with letters to indicate temper or hardness. In 1954, the four-digit system was adopted along with letters and numbers to indicate temper or hardness. Table 5·2 gives both the old and the new numbering system.

Table 5·2 Aluminum-alloy numbering system

Former numbering	Present numbering
2S	1100
3S	3003
14S	2014
17S	2017
A17S	2117
24S	2024
52S	5052
56S	5056
61S	6061
75S	7075

For pure aluminum such as 1100 or aluminum alloys which cannot be heat-treated, the condition of the metal is indicated by letters and numbers following the alloy number. The meaning of the letters is as follows:

O   Annealed (soft)
F   As fabricated
H   Strain-hardened

For heat-treatable alloys the letter T follows the number. The number following the T indicates the type of heat-treatment and tempering process, as indicated below:

T3   Solution heat-treated and cold-worked
T4   Solution heat-treated only (naturally aged)
T6   Solution heat-treated and artificially aged

T8   Solution heat-treated, cold-worked, and artificially aged
T9   Solution heat-treated, artificially aged, and cold-worked

The degree of hardness for non-heat-treatable alloys is indicated by a number following the H. These numbers vary from 12 to 38, depending upon the degree of hardness obtained. The maximum hardness obtainable for 1100 pure aluminum is indicated by H18, whereas the maximum hardness produced in 5052 alloy is H38.

Aluminum-clad alloys

Pure aluminum is highly resistant to corrosion because of a thin film of aluminum oxide which always forms immediately when the metal is exposed to the air. This layer forms an almost impervious coating which is quite hard and is not subject to ordinary corrosion. Because of the alloying metals contained in the aluminum alloys, a pure coating of aluminum oxide cannot form on the surface; hence the alloy will corrode easily.

To protect aluminum alloys from corrosion, a **cladding** process was developed. In this process a thin layer of pure aluminum is bonded to the surface of the alloy as the sheet is rolled. This layer gives the alloy sheet the same corrosion-resistance characteristics of pure-aluminum sheet.

TITANIUM AND ITS ALLOYS

History of titanium

The use of **titanium** as a structural material has become prevalent only during the past two decades. Prior to this time, the methods for refining and working titanium had not been developed to an extent which would make the use of the metal economically feasible.

Titanium was discovered in 1790 at Cornwall, England, by William Gregor, a priest who was also an amateur minerologist. Gregor isolated the oxide of titanium from black magnetic beach sand. A few years later, Gregor's findings were confirmed by Martin Klaproth, a German chemist, who gave the name "Titan metal" to the new element. Later the name was expanded to titanium.

The first isolation of pure metallic titanium in sufficient quantity for practical study was accomplished by Dr. M. D. A. Hunter in 1906. Dr. Hunter was searching for a suitable material for electric-lamp filaments and because of the reported high melting point of titanium, he believed it would be an ideal metal for the purpose.

The Kroll process, which has been widely used for extracting titanium metal, was developed by Wilhelm Kroll, a Luxembourg scientist, in 1932. This process was improved and employed by the United States Bureau of Mines, which began in 1946 to produce titanium sponge in 100-lb batches. Since that time, continued improvement has taken place; titanium is produced today in relatively large quantities as rod, bar, sheet, and other forms for use in the manufacture of a wide variety of metal products.

Use of titanium

Titanium and its alloys are used widely in the aerospace industry because of its high strength, light weight, temperature resistance, and corrosion resistance. The weight of titanium is approximately 56 percent of the weight of steel, but its strength is equal to that of steel.

The strength of titanium is maintained to temperatures of more than 800°F; hence it is useful in the cooler sections of gas-turbine engines, for cowling and baffling around engines, and for the skin parts of aircraft which may be subjected to elevated temperatures that would be damaging to aluminum alloys. The supersonic transport airplane being developed in the United States utilizes titanium extensively for the skin because of the atmospheric heating which occurs at high supersonic speeds. Titanium is also used for the manufacture of supersonic military aircraft.

Titanium may be worked by many of the methods employed for steel and stainless (corrosion-resistant) steel. It can be sheared, drawn, pressed, machined, routed, sawed, and nibbled. The operator handling titanium must be familiar with its peculiarities and special characteristics if he is to obtain good results. The cutting dies and shear blades used in cutting titanium must be of good-quality steel and must be kept very sharp.

When titanium is exposed to high temperatures, 1000°F and above, it must be protected from the atmosphere because at these temperatures it combines rapidly with oxygen. The usual method of protection is to heat the metal in an atmosphere of argon or helium gas. One of the most satisfactory methods for welding titanium is, therefore, heliarc, which is described in more detail in Chap. 8.

Titanium alloys

Titanium has excellent properties in the pure form and also with the addition of various alloying elements. The pure form may have small amounts of carbon and nitrogen with maximums of 0.10 and 0.05 percent, respectively. These maximums are also a requirement for alloyed types.

The addition of 8 percent manganese to the Republic Steel RS-110A titanium alloy brings about an increase of tensile strength. The pure material may have a tensile strength of 50,000 to 90,000 psi, and the addition of manganese brings this up to as high as 139,000 psi. Aluminum in amounts of 3 to 7 percent is commonly used as an alloying element. Other alloying elements include molybdenum, tin, iron, chromium, and vanadium. Alloying and heat treating have made it possible to develop titanium products with more than 180,000 psi tensile strength.

Two of the newer titanium alloys are Ti-6A1-4V and Ti-8A1-1Mo-1V. The latter of these, also called 8-1-1, is employed to a large extent on the supersonic transport. This alloy was chosen because of its high creep

resistance at high temperatures and its stiffness. Because of these qualities, it is more difficult to work than many of the other titanium alloys; however, its strength qualities outweigh the disadvantages of its workability. Extensive research has been carried out to discover the best methods for cutting, forming, and drilling the material, and it is now reasonably economical for the manufacturing of aerospace vehicle parts.

Corrosion resistance of titanium

Titanium is more resistant to corrosion than the majority of other metals. It can be exposed to strong acids and bases which rapidly attack many metals and will not be affected. For this reason it is used to make containers for various corrosive materials which cannot be stored in other metal containers. It is completely impervious to salt-water corrosion; hence it is ideal for use in marine engines, boats, and aircraft which may be exposed to salt spray.

Precautions

Two precautions must be observed while working with titanium. Both of these are necessary because of the strong affinity which titanium has for oxygen and other elements at high temperatures. At about 1950°F, titanium will ignite in the presence of oxygen and burn with an incandescent flame. Its affinity for nitrogen is even more pronounced because it will ignite at about 1500°F with nitrogen.

When cutting or grinding titanium in any appreciable quantity it is necessary to have fire-extinguishing equipment immediately available. The hot sparks from a grinding wheel can ignite an accumulation of titanium dust and chips to produce an extremely hot fire. It is recommended that liquid coolants of the proper type be used when grinding to avoid the possibility of such a fire.

As explained previously, if titanium is heated to temperatures above 1000°F, the metal should be protected by a surrounding atmosphere of inert gas. Otherwise it will combine with the oxygen and nitrogen in the air at rates depending upon the temperature.

STAINLESS STEELS

Stainless steels, also called **corrosion-resistant steels,** contain comparatively large quantities of chromium; the type commonly referred to as 18-8 contains both nickel and chromium. The proportions of these two elements is approximately 18 percent chromium and 8 percent nickel, hence the term 18-8. Some of the types vary considerably from these proportions; however, they may still be referred to as 18-8.

These chromium-nickel steels are called **austenitic steels** because of their crystalline structure, in which the ingredients are said to be in solid solution so that each crystal is composed of an intimate mixture of the constituents.

These steels have been given standard type numbers as follows: Types 301, 302, 304, 321, and 347. They are widely used for high-temperature applications because of their good characteristics of oxidation and corrosion resistance and high strength at elevated temperatures.

These steels are not hardenable by heat treating, but tensile strength and hardness can be increased by cold working. Their strength is such that they can be used in the manufacture of all types of structural parts including the skin of aircraft and rockets, medium-temperature parts of gas-turbine engines, hot parts of aircraft, bolts, nuts, cable, screws, tubing, and numerous other items.

The maintenance technician will often encounter stainless steels of various types, especially in all-metal aircraft and aircraft designed for supersonic speed. Cowlings, fairings, and baffles around jet engines are often constructed of stainless steel and the technician should watch for it in these areas. The skin of the RB-70 supersonic research bomber is almost entirely constructed of stainless-steel honeycomb material.

Identification of stainless-steel parts is important when it becomes necessary to make repairs. In any case of doubt, the technician should consult the manufacturer's manual to determine what material is used in a part which requires repair.

Stainless steels, because of their high coefficient of expansion, do not lend themselves well to gas welding, although it can be done if necessary. The welds are usually rough and distorted; hence the use of the heliarc process is much preferred.

HIGH-TEMPERATURE ALLOYS

Because of the need for metals which can withstand the extremely high temperatures found in gas-turbine engines, afterburners, thrust reversers, etc., and because of the high temperatures generated by air friction at high supersonic speeds, it has become necessary to develop metal alloys which retain their strength even though white hot. The products of high-temperature metal research have led to the development of **superalloys,** which utilize a wide variety of metal elements in combinations to produce the desired results.

Nickel-base alloys

Among common nickel-base alloys are **Inconel, Nimonic, Hastelloy, R-41, Waspaloy,** and **Udimet.** Some of these alloys contain as much as 80 percent nickel.

Inconel is a name given many of the high-temperature nickel-base alloys developed by the International Nickel Company. It has been used extensively for the hot parts of gas-turbine engines because of its strength and durability under high-temperature conditions.

Nimonic alloys are of British manufacture and contain approximately 75 percent nickel, 20 percent chromium, and smaller amounts of other elements. These alloys are also suitable for high-temperature applications.

The Hastelloys are developed and manufactured by the Haynes Stellite Company. They contain less nickel but more chromium, molybdenum, and iron than the alloys previously described.

Haynes Alloy No. R-41, also called Rene 41, includes a substantial amount of cobalt (about 14 percent) in addition to chromium and other elements. This alloy is particularly well suited for high-temperature applications because it retains high strength up to 1800°F.

Waspaloy was originally developed by the Pratt & Whitney Aircraft Division of the United Aircraft Company for use in the manufacture of turbine buckets. Its composition is similar to Rene 41; however, it contains more cobalt and less molybdenum.

The Udimet alloys, manufactured by Special Metals, Inc., withstand higher temperatures than most of the other superalloys. The Udimets are particularly useful in advanced jet engines for construction of the hot parts.

Cobalt-base alloys

The superalloys of the cobalt-base type are designed for use where high-temperature resistance and corrosion resistance are of primary importance. These alloys contain substantial amounts of tungsten, nickel, chromium, and molybdenum, in addition to cobalt.

Among the cobalt-base alloys in common use are Haynes Stellite No. 21 and No. 25. These alloys are particularly well adapted to use in temperatures from 1800 to 2100°F.

PRINCIPLES OF HEAT TREATING

Heat treating is any method employed for the controlled heating and cooling of metals in order to develop the desired hardness or softness, ductility, tensile strength, and grain structure. Annealing, normalizing, tempering, and hardening are all heat-treating processes. Quenching (rapid cooling) in oil, water, brine, or air is a part of the various heat-treating processes.

Ferrous metals, such as iron and steel, and some nonferrous metals, such as copper and aluminum, may be successfully heat-treated. The method used for any metal depends upon the kind of metal and the results desired.

Events in heat treating

The general cycle of events in heat treating includes the following processes and events:

1. **Heating** a metal to a temperature within or above its critical temperature under conditions that are carefully controlled.
2. **Soaking,** or **holding,** is the process of keeping a metal at an elevated temperature for a definite period of time so that it can become thoroughly saturated with heat and the necessary changes in grain structure can take place.
3. **Cooling** (quenching) is returning the metal to room temperature by means of air, water, oil, brine, etc.

Heat treatment for ferrous metals

Annealing is a form of heat treatment, used for metal or glass, which consists of heating and cooling operations for the purpose of removing gases and stresses; of inducing softness; of altering ductility, toughness, electrical resistance, or magnetic properties; or of refining the grain structure. Annealing is done by gradually heating the material to a point above the critical temperature, soaking (holding) it at this temperature for a definite length of time, then cooling it slowly according to the method prescribed for the specific material being annealed. Annealing differs from other forms of heat treating in the slow cooling of the metal.

Normalizing is a process of heating iron-base metals above their critical temperature to obtain better solubility of the carbon in the iron, followed by cooling in still air.

Hardening is done by heating the metal slightly above its critical temperature and then rapidly cooling it by quenching in oil, water, or brine. This produces a fine-grain structure, great hardness, maximum tensile strength, and minimum ductility. Material in this condition is usually too brittle for most uses, but this treatment is the first step in the production of high-strength steel. This method has been used for many years by blacksmiths for hardening certain tools. The tool is heated to a cherry red and then plunged into cold water. This produces a maximum of hardness. If more toughness is desired, the heated tool is plunged into the water for a moment and then removed. The color of the filed edge changes from gray to straw to blue. If the tool is placed back in the water when the filed surface turns to the straw color, the edge will be reasonably hard but will not be brittle.

Work hardening is simply any mechanical process that sets up a condition of hardness. It consists of repeatedly applying a mechanical force, such as rolling, hammering, bending, and twisting. This sets up stresses that resist outside forces.

Tempering (drawing) is a process generally applied to steel to relieve the strains induced during the hardening process. It consists of heating the hardened steel to a temperature below the critical range, holding this temperature for a sufficient period, then cooling in water, oil, air, or brine. The degree of strength, hardness, and ductility obtained depend directly upon the temperature to which the steel is raised. When high temperatures are reached in tempering, the ductility is improved at the expense of hardness, tensile strength, and yield strength.

Case-hardening treatments

Case-hardening treatments are given to iron-base alloys to produce a hard, wear-resisting surface and, at the same time, to leave the core of the metal tough and resilient. Three common methods are **carburizing, nitriding,** and **cyaniding.**

Carburizing consists of holding the metal at an elevated temperature while in contact with a solid, liquid, or gaseous material that is rich in carbon. Time must be allowed for the surface metal to absorb enough carbon to become high-carbon steel.

Nitriding is accomplished by holding special alloy steels at temperatures below the critical point in anhydrous ammonia. Nitrogen from the ammonia is absorbed into the surface of the steel as iron nitride and produces a greater hardness than carburizing, but the hardened area does not reach as great a depth as it does in carburizing.

Cyaniding is a fast method of producing surface hardness on an iron-base alloy of low carbon content. The steel may be immersed in a molten bath of cyanide salt, or powdered cyanide may be applied to the surface of the heated steel. During this process, the temperature of the steel must range from 1300 to 1600°F, the exact temperature depending upon the type of steel, the depth of the case hardening desired, the type of cyanide compound used, and the time that the steel is exposed to the cyanide. In using sodium cyanide or potassium cyanide, great care must be taken to avoid getting any of the cyanide into the mouth, eyes, or any other part of the body. These materials are deadly poisons.

Heat-treating techniques

As mentioned previously, heat treating is accomplished by heating metal to a certain prescribed temperature and then cooling it according to given directions depending upon the type of metal and the desired result. The heating is done in a furnace which may be gas-heated, oil-heated, or electrically heated. The metal is placed in the oven in suitable racks or containers, the heat of the oven is regulated to the required temperature, and the time which the metal is exposed to the heat is carefully controlled. After the heat has been applied, it is necessary to cool the metal according to the specified process. The cooling process must start the moment that the metal is removed from the heat. If the metal is to be quenched in a liquid, the methods shown in Figs. 5·1 and 5·2 may be used. Figure 5·1 shows a part being immersed with the part perpendicular to the bath. In Fig. 5·2 the part is im-

Figure 5·1 Quenching material in vertical position.

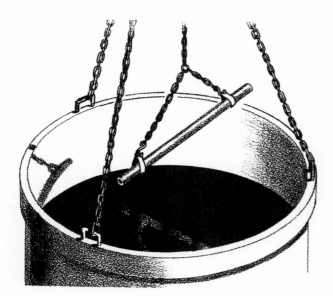

Figure 5·2 Quenching material at an angle.

mersed at an angle to the bath. The method of quenching, in any case, should follow the specified process.

When metal parts to be heat-treated are placed in a furnace it is necessary that they be properly supported. Because the metal may be required to soak for as long as 1 hr, there is a tendency for the material to sag. This causes warping and distortion of the parts. Figure 5·3 shows a method for supporting small parts.

The size and shape of parts to be heat-treated will often determine the methods of handling and supporting. Large sheet-metal parts require more careful support than small parts which have a thicker cross section. In any event, the operator must use care in the arrangement of parts in the furnace and the supporting structures used to hold the parts.

HEAT TREATING OF ALUMINUM ALLOYS

Basic purposes

The basic purposes of heat treating aluminum alloys are to increase their strength, improve their corrosion resistance, and to improve their workability. The latter effect is accomplished by annealing.

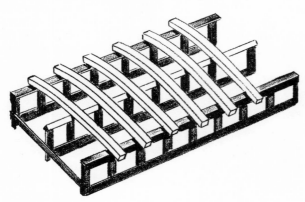

Figure 5·3 Support of small parts in the furnace.

Steps in heat treating

As mentioned previously, there are two principal steps in a heat-treating process: (1) heating the material to a required temperature for a specified time and (2) cooling the metal in a prescribed manner. An additional conditioning process takes place automatically for certain alloys. This is **age hardening,** which occurs over a period of hours or days after the material is quenched.

Methods for heating metal

There are two principal methods for heating the metal during a heat-treating process: (1) a furnace illustrated in Fig. 5·4 and (2) a molten salt bath. The liquid salt bath has the advantage of rapid heating and uniformity of temperature, but the hot-air furnace is more flexible in operation and is not as hazardous as the salt bath. The salt bath usually consists of molten sodium nitrate, potassium nitrate, or a combination of the two. The use of the salt-bath method requires additional washing of the parts after quenching.

Since close control of the temperature is necessary during heat treatment, an automatic control should be used with a recording device that produces a permanent record of the time and temperature relations.

The furnace must be arranged so that the parts can be immediately transferred to the quench. This is important because the parts must remain above the required temperature until they are quenched. If the

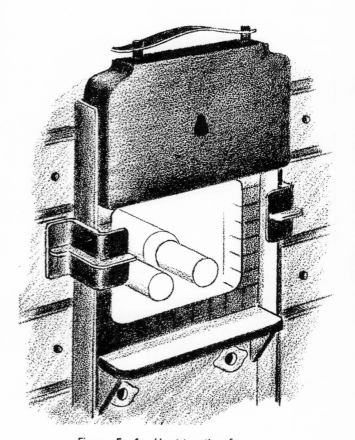

Figure 5·4 Heat-treating furnace.

metal cools below the required temperature before quenching, its corrosion resistance will be substantially reduced.

Conditions for heat treatment of aluminum alloys

Table 5·3 gives the temperatures required for **solution heat treating** common aluminum alloys together with quenching and aging data:

Table 5·3 Aluminum-alloy heat-treating data

Alloy	Temperature, °F	Quench	Aging Temperature	Time of aging
2014T	930–950	Hot water	335–345°F	10 hr
2017T	930–950	Cold water	Room	4 days
2117T	930–950	Cold water	Room	4 days
2024T	910–930	Cold water	Room	4 days
5053T	960–980	Water	312–325°F	18 hr
6061T	960–980	Water	315–325°F	18 hr
7075T	860–930	Cold water	345–355°F	6–10 hr

The time required for soaking a particular type of alloy depends upon the alloy and the thickness of the parts. Those parts clad with pure aluminum should not be soaked longer than necessary because diffusion of the alloying elements into the pure-aluminum coating takes place and can lead to a reduction in corrosion resistance. Table 5·4 gives suggested times for soaking of heat-treatable aluminum alloys:

Table 5·4 Aluminum-alloy soaking times

Alloy	Soaking time, (min)			
	Less than 0.032 in. thick	0.032– 0.125 in. thick	0.125– 0.250 in. thick	More than 0.250 in. thick
2014T	20	20	30	60
2017T	20	30	30	60
2117T	20	20	30	60
2024T	30	30	40	60
2024T (clad)	20	30	40	60
5053T	20	30	40	60
6061T	20	30	40	60
7075T	25	30	40	60
7075T (clad)	20	30	40	60

It will be noted in the table that the thinner sheets of clad material have slightly reduced soaking periods. This is to reduce the diffusion of alloying elements into the pure-aluminum coating.

Precipitation heat treatment

The process of heating and quenching metal for heat treating is called **solution heat treating.** This simply means that alloying elements are in **solid solution** with the base metal. Solid solution means that the alloying elements are evenly dispersed throughout the material.

The process of **artificially aging** an alloy after heat-treating to increase its strength is called **precipitation heat treatment.** When the temperature of the alloy is raised to an intermediate level as given in Table 5·3, certain alloying elements tend to precipitate out of the solid solution and form particles throughout the material. These microscopic particles give additional strength to the material. The time involved in the precipitation heat treatment is given in the table.

Intergranular corrosion

One of the effects of improper heat treating is **intergranular corrosion.** This is a condition wherein corrosion takes place between the grains of the metal. If an alloy is not quenched quickly enough during the heat-treating process, precipitation of alloying elements takes place and this causes formation of tiny electrolytic cells within the metal. Electrolytic action then takes place and brings about destruction of the aluminum.

Annealing

The **annealing process** for softening aluminum and aluminum alloys is a form of heat treatment requiring the heating and cooling of the material in accordance with specific instructions. The temperature range for a full anneal is 750 to 800°F. The full-annealing process is sometimes called **recrystallization.** After annealing, the metal is in the "0" temper condition, which is dead soft. The soaking time and cooling rates for annealing depend upon the type of alloy. In general, the metal should be soaked at the annealing temperature for at least 1 hr, but it may require more than this for some materials. The cooling rate should be not more than 50°F per hr until the material has reached a temperature of less than 500°F. For non-heat-treatable alloys or pure aluminum, the cooling rate is not important.

Stress relief

When aluminum or aluminum alloy is formed into various shapes from the flat-sheet condition, the formed product will usually contain areas where internal stresses exist. These stresses may cause distortion, cracking, or corrosion during the life of the part. It is therefore necessary that these stressed areas be eliminated and this is one function of heat treatment. The stresses in aluminum and its alloys can be reduced by solution heat treatment or by partial annealing at temperatures between 700 and 800°F. If the finished part is to attain full strength, a full heat treatment should be applied.

HEAT TREATMENT OF TITANIUM

Requirements for heat treatment

Heat treatment for titanium is required for some alloys but not for others. If a part is to be made, the technician must be certain he is using the specified material, and then he should determine whether the material should be heat-treated. Alloys which can be strengthened by heat treating are RS-120A, RS-135, RS-140, Ti-6A1-V, and Ti-8A1-1Mo-1V.

Temperatures for heat-treating titanium

The temperatures employed for the heat treatment of titanium range from 1450 to 1850°F. At these temperatures the atmosphere in the furnace must be inert, that is, argon gas should displace all air in the furnace to protect the material from combining with oxygen and nitrogen. The soaking time is specified according to the material. For 8-1-1, the soaking time is 8 hr at 1450°F. The material is then air-cooled. For RS-120A, 135, and 140, a water quench is used and this is followed by artificial aging at 1000 to 1100°F.

HEAT TREATMENT OF STAINLESS STEELS

The chrome-nickel stainless steels, commonly referred to as 18-8 steels, cannot be hardened by heat treating. These are types 302 through 347. They can be annealed at temperatures of from 1850 to 2050 and they can be work-hardened.

The chromium stainless steels, types 410, 416, 420, and 431 can be heat-treated to increase their hardness and strength. Hardening is accomplished by heating to a range of 1750 to 1900°F and quenching in oil.

HARDNESS INSPECTION

Importance of hardness testing

All materials required for the various structural parts of an airplane must be examined to determine their hardness as an indication of strength as specified either by the appropriate drawing or by material specifications. This is accomplished by means of various types of instruments, all of which enable the operator of the instrument to determine the tensile strength of the material.

Hardness testing is usually the function of the process laboratory in a manufacturing plant; however, there are times when a repairman may be required to determine the hardness of a material to find out whether it is satisfactory for a particular repair. Hardness testing is also a method for the identification of metals and alloys.

Brinell hardness test

The **Brinell hardness tester** shown in Fig. 5·5 is an instrument commonly used on aluminum-alloy castings, forgings, and billets before machining. The check is made by forcing a steel ball of a known diameter into the material by a specified and known pressure, as suggested by Fig. 5·6. Three distinct pressures are provided for ferrous, nonferrous, and soft materials. The reading is taken by measuring the width of the impression made by the steel ball in the material, by means of a microscope. The reading thus obtained is compared with an established comparison chart which gives the tensile strength for each reading.

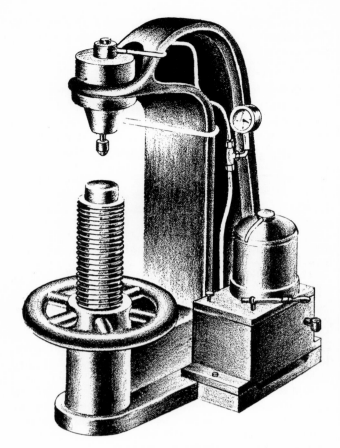

Figure 5·5   Brinell hardness tester.

Before testing any material with the Brinell instrument, the operator must make sure that the surface of the material is clean, free from scale, flat, and fairly smooth, in order to obtain an accurate reading. The work must be adequately supported to avoid twist or movement when applying the test load. A decarbonized surface might cause a low reading even though the hardness is correct. If the reading is much lower than expected, the surface should be filed or ground to

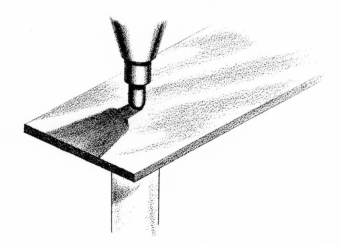

Figure 5·6   Forcing the steel ball into the surface of metal.

remove decarbonization, and another test made. The instrument is never used where excessive vibration is present or on thin material where the indentation will show through.

The Rockwell hardness test

The **Rockwell hardness tester** shown in Fig. 5·7 is another instrument used in examining the hardness of metals. Its operation is similar to that of the Brinell instrument because the test is made by the depth of penetration of a diamond point, or of a ball of fixed size, under predetermined load. The reading is made directly from a calibrated dial showing a given number for depth of penetration. This number is then checked against the comparison chart to find the tensile strength. Table 5·5 gives readings of both Brinell and Rockwell instruments for a wide range of hardness values.

There are three ranges of material covered by the diamond point, or "brale," as it is called on the Rockwell instrument, each using a specified pressure. Other ranges of softer material are checked by means of a given-size steel ball and predetermined pressure. Each range, for both ball and brale, is covered by an alphabetically designated scale shown on the calibrated head.

When testing with the Rockwell instrument, the operator must be certain that the surface of the material is clean and smooth. The material should be held square, as shown in Fig. 5·8, and in all cases where the material is large or heavy it should be adequately sup-

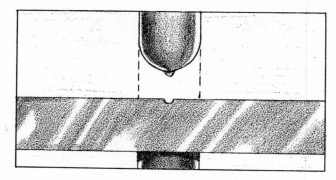

Figure **5·8** Position of material being tested for hardness.

ported to avoid any movement of the material while the reading is taken.

Figure 5·9 shows what will happen if too small a piece is tested with the Rockwell instrument. If the metal can flow away from the ball or brale as shown, a false reading will be obtained. False readings will also result from taking two readings too close together. This is illustrated in Fig. 5·10.

Other precautions must also be observed. The operator should not strike the penetrator when removing or replacing the anvil. He should not raise the jack-

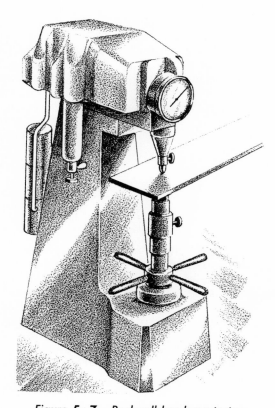

Figure **5·7** Rockwell hardness tester.

Figure **5·9** Result of testing too small a part.

Figure **5·10** Incorrect reading from tests too close together.

Table 5·5 Rockwell, Brinell, and Vickers hardness values

Rockwell hardness number				Vickers hardness number, diamond-pyramid penetrator	Brinell hardness number, 3000-kg load, 10-mm standard ball	Approx. tensile strength, 1000 psi
A scale 60-kg load, brale penetrator	B scale 100-kg load, 1/16-in. diam. ball	C scale 150-kg load, brale penetrator	D scale 100-kg load, brale penetrator			
78.5		55	66.9	595		287
78.0		54	66.1	577		278
77.4		53	65.4	560		269
76.8		52	64.6	544	500	262
76.3		51	63.8	528	487	253
75.9		50	63.1	513	475	245
75.2		49	62.1	498	464	239
74.7		48	61.4	484	451	232
74.1		47	60.8	471	442	225
73.6		46	60.0	458	432	219
73.1		45	59.2	446	421	212
72.5		44	58.5	434	409	206
72.0		43	57.7	423	400	201
71.5		42	56.9	412	390	196
70.9		41	56.2	402	381	191
70.4		40	55.4	392	371	186
69.9		39	54.6	382	362	181
69.4		38	53.8	372	353	176
68.9		37	53.1	363	344	172
68.4	(109.0)*	36	52.3	354	336	168
67.9	(108.5)	35	51.5	345	327	163
67.4	(108.0)	34	50.8	336	319	159
66.8	(107.5)	33	50.0	327	311	154
66.3	(107.0)	32	49.2	318	301	150
65.8	(106.0)	31	48.4	310	294	146
65.3	(105.5)	30	47.7	302	286	142
64.7	(104.5)	29	47.0	294	279	138
64.3	(104.0)	28	46.1	286	271	134
63.8	(103.0)	27	45.2	279	264	131
63.3	(102.5)	26	44.6	272	258	127
62.8	(101.5)	25	43.8	266	253	124
62.4	(101.0)	24	43.1	260	247	121
62.0	100.0	23	42.1	254	243	118
61.5	99.0	22	41.6	248	237	115
61.0	98.5	21	40.9	243	231	113

* Values in parentheses are beyond normal range and are given for information only.

screw with the anvil in place and force it against the penetrator. He should not overrun the set point in applying the minor load, and he should not back off to the set point if it has been overrun and then attempt a reading. The jackscrew, anvil seat, and penetrator seat should be clean to avoid a "cushioning" effect.

The Scleroscope hardness test

The **Scleroscope hardness tester,** shown in Fig. 5·11, is another instrument used for testing the hardness of metals. This instrument does not test by indentation, but by rebound. It has a diamond-pointed ball that drops through a glass tube onto the material being tested. This tube is mounted with a graduated scale, and the rebound of the ball, or point, is caught by the eye at its peak, and the corresponding graduation is then read. The instrument is also made with a direct-reading head which records the amount of rebound. A soft ball is provided for the testing of nonferrous metals and readings are taken from the same scale.

When using the Scleroscope, the surface of the material must be clean and smooth. The glass must be perpendicular, and the material square with the glass. The hammer must not be dropped twice in the

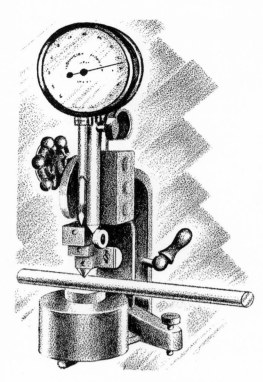

Figure 5·11   The Scleroscope.

Figure 5·12   The Shore durometer.

same place because this may chip the diamond point and would give a false reading.

Calibration of hardness testers

The accuracy of the readings on the hardness testers already described should be checked frequently, the frequency of checking depending upon the extent of their use. Checking for accuracy, or calibration, is done by means of test blocks supplied by the manufacturers of the instruments. These blocks have been tested to positive readings against master blocks. The Brinell instrument should have a calibration check twice a day when working continuously with the same pressures. Continuous work with the Rockwell tester requires a calibration check at least twice in any 8-hr shift. The Scleroscope, on production testing, should have a calibration at least once each hour. An erratic reading on any machine always calls for a calibration check. Any change of materials, beyond the scale range, requires a change in the machine setup, such as penetrators and loads. Such changes are made by authorized personnel who are directly responsible for the care and upkeep of the instruments.

The Shore durometer for plastics and rubber

The **Shore durometer,** shown in Fig. 5·12, is used to determine the hardness of treated or molded rubber, plastics, and allied materials. Readings are taken directly from a reading head, actuated by the upward movement of a calibrated pin that is forced against the material to be tested. The pin is spring-mounted under a predetermined pressure; hence its travel is governed by the degree of hardness of the material being tested.

Until this pressure is reached by the resistance of the material, the pin will penetrate the material up to the point where the spring pressure is overcome.

The Webster hand-type hardness tester

The **Webster hand-type hardness tester** is shown in Fig. 5·13. This is a simple pliers-type unit with an anvil on one jaw and a series of inclined indenters of increasing crest area on the other jaw. This instrument is used for testing aluminum and its alloys. When the indenters are forced into the metal by the action of the pliers, the number of indentations appearing on the surface is an indication of the hardness. An improved type of Webster instrument has a dial indicator that is read directly during the plier action, thus eliminating the necessity of looking at the part to count the indentations. Care must be taken in applying the indenter jaw to be sure it is at right angles to the surface being tested because any inclination or rotation will give inaccurate readings.

The Barcol hardness-testing machine

Like the Webster tester, the Barcol machine is used for testing aluminum and its alloys. This machine is shown in Fig. 5·14. It has a small spring-loaded needle point extending from the face of a small housing. The dial registers the amount the spring is compressed in forcing the needle into the material until the housing face contacts the material. As more pressure is exerted in forcing the needle into harder metal, the dial registers the increased pressure exerted. The instrument may be used as a production test for heat treating, after obtaining direct readings with the Rockwell instrument.

The Barcol tester may be adjusted for any homogeneous material to give an identical "one-point" reading equivalent to any Rockwell scale reading made on the same material. On clad aluminum and other nonhomogeneous materials where the coating thickness varies with materials, the Barcol tester must

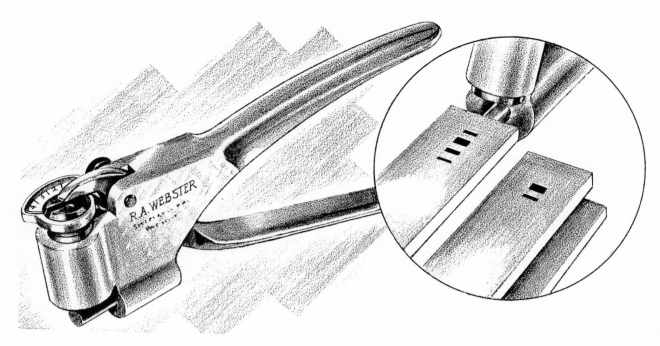

Figure 5·13 Webster hand-type hardness tester.

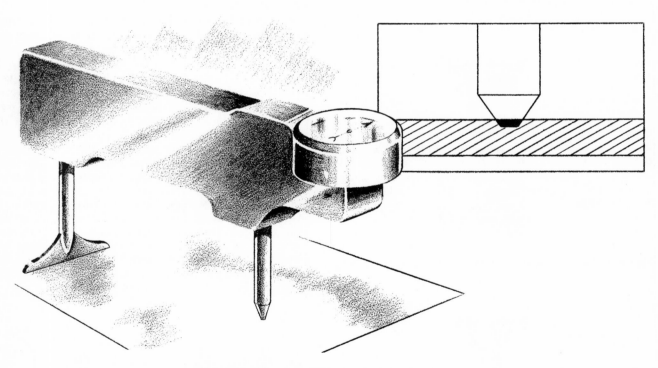

Figure 5·14 Barcol hardness-testing machine.

be calibrated against the Rockwell tester for each gage tested. The penetrating needle on the Barcol tester is very hard and brittle. It must be applied at right angles to the surface being tested, with no sliding force, or it will break. Broken, flattened, or bent needles must be replaced at once. Replacement is made only by the authorized personnel, because it requires disassembly and resetting of the spring. Resetting consists of

preloading the spring so that the instrument will be centered to give direct readings over the entire aluminum-alloy range. In either the Webster or the Barcol machine, the indicator must be periodically examined to detect whether or not soft material is adhering to the jaws.

Figure 5·15 shows the proper method for testing hollow tubing. Testing without an internal support,

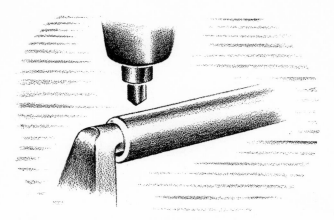

Figure 5·15   Testing hollow tube for hardness.

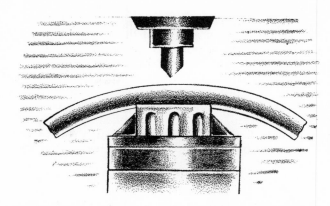

Figure 5·18   Improper method for testing a curved rod.

as shown in Fig. 5·16, will result in a false reading, because the tubing will tend to flatten and permit increased movement of the testing needle.

When a curved rod is tested for hardness, the rod must be placed as shown in Fig. 5·17. If the rod is placed in the convex position as in Fig. 5·18, a certain amount of give will take place with the result that a false reading will be obtained.

NONDESTRUCTIVE TESTING

Magnetic Inspection

The purpose of magnetic inspection is to render visible to the naked eye defects in magnetic metals, such as cracks, inclusions, and miscellaneous faults. This type of inspection can be used only on ferrous materials which are magnetic.

A thorough inspection is required on machined parts and welded structures made from magnetic materials, except on those subjected to very low stresses or those excepted by the specifications in effect at the time the job is done. Parts that require such inspections are so noted on the drawing or specification. The percentage of bolts, nuts, etc., requiring magnetic inspection is determined by the specifications for the job.

To prepare for a magnetic inspection, the parts must be thoroughly cleaned and freed from dirt, grease, and foreign matter that might produce erroneous indications.

In performing a magnetic inspection, the part to be inspected is placed between the faces of the testing machine and clamped tight by means of air pressure. Figure 5·19 shows a part in place for testing. The switch for current is pressed, thus sending a strong current through the part. This current produces magnetic lines of force around the part as shown in

Figure 5·16   Improper method for testing hollow tubing.

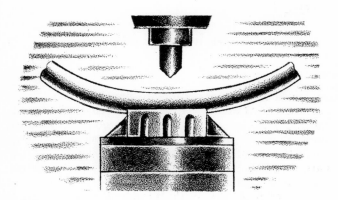

Figure 5·17   Correct method for testing a curved rod.

Figure 5·19   A part in position for magnetic inspection.

Fig. 5·20. These lines of force flow within and around the part in a uniform manner if there is no defect. If the part is cracked or otherwise damaged, the lines of force will be broken. This is indicated by the drawings of Fig. 5·21. Where the crack or other discontinuity exists, the lines of force will leave the part and form a local field near the surface. When iron oxide powder, either dry or in a liquid, is applied to the part, the magnetic field around the cracked area will attract the magnetic particles and reveal the location of the crack.

To detect cracks which are approximately perpendicular to the longitudinal axis of a part, it is best to magnetize the part by means of a coil. The field of a coil is shown in Fig. 5·22. When a part is placed in the coil as shown in Fig. 5·23, the magnetic lines of force will pass through the part from end to end as shown in Fig. 5·24. A crack will distort the lines of force, and this in turn will cause magnetic particles of iron oxide powder to collect in the cracked area. This, of course, makes the position of the crack visible.

Magnaflux

The name **Magnaflux** is a copyrighted word used to denote the magnetic process and equipment developed by the Magnaflux Corporation. Equipment is leased or sold to shops and inspection agencies whose operators are trained in the use of the Magnaflux process.

Many shops whose operations require the magnetic inspection of parts will send the parts to certified or

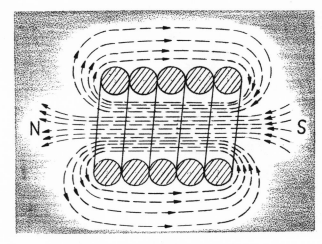

Figure 5·22   Magnetic field of a coil.

Figure 5·23   Parts being magnetized in a coil.

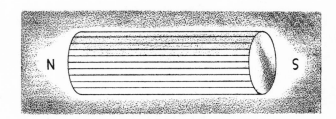

Figure 5·24   Magnetic field passing through a rod.

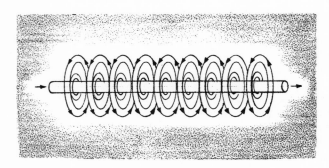

Figure 5·20   Magnetic field around a conductor.

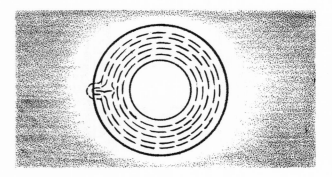

Figure 5·21   How a defect affects the magnetic field.

approved Magnaflux stations to have the inspections performed. After the parts are inspected and found satisfactory, they are indelibly stamped or marked to show that the inspection has been performed. An inspection certificate is usually issued to show that the parts have been subjected to approved Magnaflux inspection. In the case of aircraft or aircraft engine parts, the Magnaflux certificate should be retained with the overhaul records.

Dye-penetrant inspection

The **dye-penetrant process** involves the use of a highly penetrating dye which seeps into cracks or other defects. A white developer is applied, and the dye coming out of the defect through the film of developer reveals the defect as a bright red spot or line.

Before applying the dye, the part must be thoroughly cleaned to remove oil, rust, scale, and other extraneous material. The part to be inspected must be dry and at a temperature of over 70°F when the dye is applied. This is done by dipping the part in the dye, brushing, or spraying. The dye is allowed to "soak" on the part for 2 min or more to be sure it has penetrated all possible cracks or fissures. It is then washed off with a special cleaner or with warm water, after which the part is dried. The developer is an extremely fine white powder suspended in a solvent, and is sprayed or brushed on the part. The part can also be dipped in the developer liquid. The developer is allowed to dry, and the dye penetrant will then reveal defects as red spots or lines. After inspection, the developer is washed off with solvent.

Other nondestructive inspections

X-ray inspection, or **radiography,** is often used for the inspection of metal parts. A very powerful x-ray machine is used to produce the rays necessary to penetrate metal. The rays pass through the metal and impinge upon a photographic plate. Flaws in the metal will be revealed as shadows in the picture of the part.

Ultrasonic inspection utilizes high-frequency sound waves to reveal flaws in metal parts. The element transmitting the waves is placed on the part and a reflected wave is received and registered on an oscilloscope. If there is a flaw in the part, the reflected wave will show a "blip" on the oscilloscope trace. The position of the blip indicates the depth of the flaw.

REVIEW QUESTIONS

1. Name some common structural materials used for aircraft.
2. From what source is aluminum obtained?
3. Why is aluminum alloy a good material for aircraft construction?
4. What is the principal alloying element for 2024 aluminum alloy?
5. Describe the aluminum alloy 7075-T8.
6. What is a clad alloy and why is cladding done?
7. What are the principal advantages of titanium as a structural material for aircraft?
8. Why is titanium used for the skin of a supersonic airplane?
9. Discuss the methods for working titanium. What other materials require similar handling?
10. What precaution must be taken in heating titanium above 1000°F or in welding the material?
11. What is meant by *"stainless" steel?*
12. What alloying elements are commonly used in 18-8 steel?
13. Discuss high-temperature alloys and the metals most commonly used in their composition.
14. What are the principal characteristics desired in high-temperature alloys?
15. What type of alloy is Haynes Stellite?
16. What are the functions of heat treating?
17. What is meant by annealing?
18. What is the purpose of tempering steel?
19. Explain three methods for case hardening.
20. Describe a common heat-treating process.
21. What may occur if parts are not properly supported in a heat-treating furnace?
22. How should 2024 aluminum alloy be heat-treated?
23. What is meant by *precipitation heat treating?*
24. Give the advantages and disadvantages of a salt bath for heating metal.
25. How are heat treating and intergranular corrosion related?
26. Describe the basic principle of Brinell hardness testing.
27. Compare Rockwell and Brinell hardness testing.
28. What problem may be experienced if a Rockwell test is made on a very small part?
29. How are hardness testers calibrated or checked?
30. Briefly explain magnetic inspection.
31. How is dye-penetrant inspection accomplished?
32. Explain x-ray inspection.

Gas Welding Equipment

The aircraft maintenance technician will in some cases be called upon to repair important aircraft parts by welding, but if he is ignorant or careless the failure of a weld may cause the destruction of an airplane and everyone aboard. It is therefore essential that he be well acquainted with the approved welded repairs, techniques for welding, and the operation of welding equipment. If the technician is not sufficiently skilled to perform an airworthy welded repair himself, he should call upon a qualified welder to do the job for him.

Welding processes

Welding is a process used for joining metal parts by either fusion or forging. **Forge welding** is the process used by a blacksmith when he heats the ends of wrought iron or steel parts in a forge fire until the ends are in a plastic state and then unites them by the application of mechanical pressure or blows. **Fusion welding** is the process used by welders in the aircraft and other industries whereby enough heat is applied to melt the edges or surfaces of the metal so that the molten (melted) parts flow together, leaving a single, solid piece of metal when it cools. In both forge and fusion welding, the process is described as a **thermal metal-joining process** because heat is required. Only the fusion type of welding is used in aircraft work.

The principal types of welding in which metal parts are joined by the fusion process are **oxyacetylene welding,** commonly called **gas welding,** and electric-arc welding. **Gas welding** is one of the most frequently used of all welding processes in aviation. It produces heat by burning a properly balanced mixture of oxygen and acetylene as it flows from the tip of a welding torch. Since the temperature of the flame at the tip point of the torch is about 6300°F, it is apparent that it is hot enough to melt any of the common metals.

The heat required for the fusion of metal parts can be produced by electricity also. The principal types of electric welding are **electric-arc welding** and **electric-resistance** welding. In **electric-arc welding,** the heat of an electric arc is used to produce fusion of the parts. The arc is formed by bringing together two conductors of electricity and then separating them. **Electric-resistance welding** is a process whereby a low-voltage high-amperage current is brought to the work through a heavy copper conductor offering very little resistance to its flow. The parts are placed in the path of the current flow where they set up a great resistance to it. The heat generated by the current flow through this resistance is great enough to fuse the parts at their point of contact.

A special type of arc welding is called **inert-gas welding** in which an inert gas such as helium or argon blankets the weld area to prevent oxidation of the heated metal.

Details of the oxyacetylene-welding process

When the oxyacetylene flame is applied to the edges of metal parts, they are soon raised to a molten (melting) state, and flow together to form one solid piece after cooling and solidifying. To build up the seam to a greater thickness than the base metal, some additional metal is added to the weld in the form of a wire or rod. When very light sheet is to be welded, the edges may be flanged so that the weld metal will have the necessary thickness after the flanged edges are melted down.

This extra thickness in a weld is required to obtain the necessary strength in the joint, because the weld is cast metal that usually does not have a grain structure and fiber so strong as that of the base metal.

The strength of a weld in any metal depends principally upon the skill and knowledge of the welder. If he prepares the metal correctly in advance, and then uses the correct flame, he will obtain a dependable weld.

Oxyacetylene-welding equipment

The oxyacetylene-welding equipment may be either portable or stationary. A **portable apparatus** can be fastened on a hand truck, or cart, and pushed around from job to job. It consists of one cylinder containing oxygen; one cylinder containing acetylene; acetylene and oxygen pressure regulators complete with pressure gages and connections; a welding torch with a mixing head, tips, and connections; two lengths of colored hose, with adapter connections for the torch and regulators; a special wrench; a pair of welding goggles;

a safety flint and file gas lighter; and a fire extinguisher. Figure 6·1 shows a portable welding outfit.

Stationary equipment is similar to a portable set except that the acetylene and oxygen are piped to several welding stations from a gas supply. The welder does not have to bother with the oxygen and acetylene cylinders because they are connected to a manifold having a master regulator for each group of cylinders. In a typical installation, such as the one in Fig. 6·2, a **manifold** is a long horizontal pipe immediately above the cylinders, into which the short pipe from each cylinder feeds. Master regulators are used to control the flow of gas and maintain a constant pressure at each welding station. In some shops, the acetylene does not come from cylinders. Instead, it is piped directly from an acetylene generator, an apparatus used for producing acetylene gas by reaction of water upon calcium carbide.

Acetylene

Acetylene is a flammable, colorless gas with a distinctive odor that is easily detected, even when strongly diluted with air. It is a compound of carbon and hydrogen having the chemical symbol C_2H_2, which means that two atoms of carbon are combined with two atoms of hydrogen. Since carbon has an atomic weight of 12 and hydrogen an atomic weight of 1.008, acetylene is actually 92.3 percent carbon and 7.7 percent hydrogen by weight.

When acetylene is mixed with air or oxygen, it forms a highly combustible gas. Since the range of explosive mixtures is very wide (from 97 percent air with 3 percent acetylene to 18 percent air with 82 percent acetylene) it can be very dangerous unless carefully handled. It has a flame spread of 330 ft per sec. To prevent it from burning back to the source of supply during

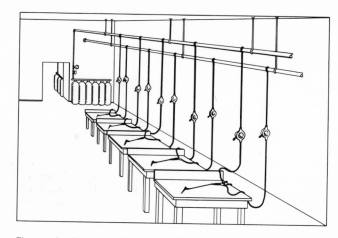

Figure 6·2 A stationary welding system with manifolds.

welding, the acetylene, when mixed with air or oxygen, must flow from the torch at a velocity greater than the flame spread, or the absorption of heat by the torch tip must be sufficient to prevent the flame from entering the tip.

Under low pressure at normal temperature, when free from air, acetylene is a stable compound; however, when it is compressed in an empty container to a pressure greater than 15 psi, it becomes unstable, and at 29.4 psi pressure it becomes self-explosive, and only a slight shock is required to cause it to explode even when it is not mixed with air or oxygen.

Although this gas is highly explosive, it is shipped great distances in cylinders under high pressure with a relatively high degree of safety. This is possible because the manufacturers place a porous substance inside the acetylene cylinder and then saturate this substance with **acetone**, which is a flammable liquid chemical which absorbs many times its own volume of acetylene. A cylinder containing a correct amount of acetone can be charged to a pressure of more than 250 psi with safety, under normal conditions of handling and temperature.

Acetylene is a manufactured gas. An **acetylene generator** is a device in which acetylene is produced by the direct combination of carbon and hydrogen, resulting from the reaction of water upon calcium carbide.

Calcium carbide is a compound of carbon and calcium (CaC_2), which is prepared by fusing limestone and coal in an electric furnace. When calcium carbide comes into contact with water, it absorbs the water rapidly and decomposes. The carbon combines with the hydrogen to form acetylene, and the calcium combines with the oxygen to form calcium hydrate (slacked lime). One pound of pure, clean carbide will supply about 5 cu ft of acetylene, but it is customary to figure only 4½ cu ft per lb to allow for impurities. Acetylene gas is sold by weight and contains 14.5 cu ft per lb.

An acetylene cylinder is a welded steel tank provided with a valve in the neck for attaching the pressure regulator and drawing off the acetylene. The cylinder is filled with a porous material saturated with acetone. Safety-fuse plugs, which release the gas from the cyl-

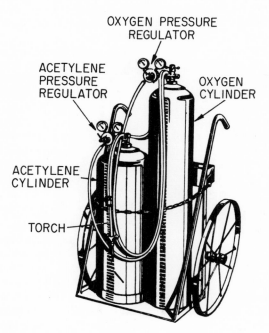

OXYGEN PRESSURE REGULATOR

ACETYLENE PRESSURE REGULATOR

OXYGEN CYLINDER

ACETYLENE CYLINDER

TORCH

Figure 6·1 A portable welding outfit.

inder in case of fire, are provided. Since the escaping gas is flammable, the holes in the plug are made so small that they will not allow the flame to burn back into the cylinder.

Acetylene cylinders are available in several sizes, holding up to 300 cu ft of gas at a maximum pressure of 250 psi. The cubic feet of acetylene gas in a cylinder may be found by weighing the cylinder and subtracting the tare weight stamped on the cylinder from the gross weight; that is, the weight of an empty cylinder is subtracted from the weight of a charged cylinder. The difference is in pounds; hence this figure is multiplied by 14.5 to obtain the number of cubic feet in the cylinder. Figure 6·3 is an exterior view of an acetylene cylinder.

Oxygen

Oxygen is a tasteless, colorless, odorless gas that forms about 23 percent by weight and about 21 percent by volume of the atmosphere. Water is a chemical compound of 2 parts hydrogen and 1 part oxygen by volume.

Oxygen is an extremely active element. It will combine with almost all materials under suitable conditions, sometimes with disastrous results. For example, grease and oil are highly combustible in the presence of pure oxygen; hence it is important to avoid bringing pure oxygen into contact with oil or grease. Such a mixture of oxygen and oil can produce a violent explosion. There are recorded cases of welders killing themselves by turning a stream of pure oxygen into a can of grease. Even grease spots on clothing may lead to explosions if they are struck by a stream of oxygen.

Everyone is familiar with the fact that rust on ferrous metals, the dark discoloration of copper, and the corrosion of aluminum are caused by the action of oxygen in the air.

Oxygen is necessary to support human life, and it is also necessary to make acetylene burn at a temperature high enough to melt metal in welding. In technical language, oxygen supports the combustion of the gas used in producing the welding flame.

The standard cylinder for storing and shipping oxygen gas for welding and cutting purposes is a seamless, steel, bottle-shaped container like the one shown in Fig. 6·4. It is made to withstand exceedingly high pressures. Although an acetylene cylinder is normally charged at a pressure of 250 psi at a temperature of 70°F, an oxygen cylinder is initially charged at the plant to a pressure of 2200 psi at a temperature of 70°F.

Two sizes of oxygen tanks are generally available. The standard size is a cylinder having a capacity of 220 cu ft, and the small cylinder has a capacity of 110 cu ft. Since the weight of oxygen is 0.08926 lb per cu ft, 11.203 cu ft equal 1 lb. To find the quantity of oxygen in a cylinder, simply subtract the weight of an empty cylinder from the weight of a charged cylinder, and multiply the number of pounds by 11.203 to obtain the cubic feet of oxygen in the cylinder.

Figure 6·5 shows the construction of an oxygen-cylinder valve assembly. A safety device (bursting disk) is contained in the nipple at the rear of the valve and consists of a thin copper-alloy diaphragm.

The valve in Fig. 6·5 is a needle type. The valve stem is in two parts, and the two sections are connected by a slide joint that allows the lower section to move up and down in opening and closing the valve. The lower section is threaded and contains a valve-seat needle made of Monel metal. Connected to the upper section of the stem is a hand wheel that is used for operating the valve. A rubber or synthetic compression washer around the valve stem provides a gastight seal, and is held in place with a bonnet nut. When the valve is completely open, the lower section exerts pressure against the upper section of the stem and compresses the gasket, thus preventing leakage. When the cylinder is not in use, the valve is covered with a protector cap.

PROTECTING CAP

Figure 6·3   An acetylene cylinder.

Figure 6·4   An oxygen cylinder.

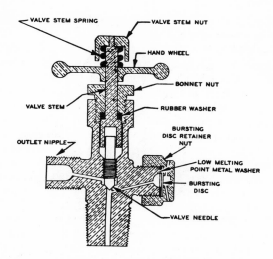

Figure **6·5**   An oxygen-cylinder valve.

This is an important feature in preventing the valve from being broken in handling.

Acetylene and oxygen regulators

Acetylene and **oxygen regulators** are mechanical instruments used to reduce the high pressure of the gases flowing from their containers and to supply the gases to the torch at a constant pressure and volume as required by the torch tip or nozzle.

Almost all regulators are either of the nozzle or the stem type and are available for either single-stage or two-stage pressure reduction. Figure 6·6 is a sectional drawing of a single-stage pressure regulator. Figure 6·7 shows how a single-stage pressure regulator works. Figure 6·8 is a sectional drawing of a two-stage pressure regulator, and Fig. 6·9 shows its operation. The two-stage pressure regulator is preferred for operation at the individual welding stations where stationary equipment is used.

Regulators on cylinders are usually equipped with

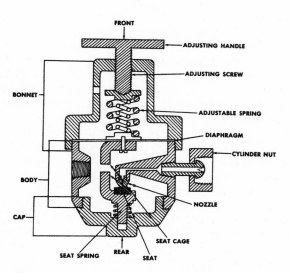

Figure **6·6**   A single-stage pressure regulator.

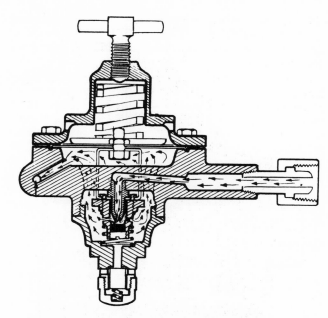

Figure **6·7**   Operation of a single-stage regulator.

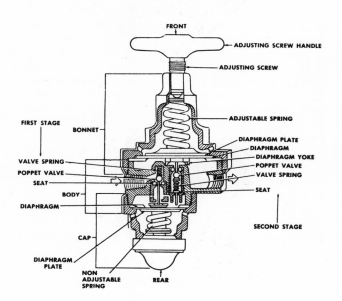

Figure **6·8**   A two-stage regulator.

two pressure gages. A high-pressure gage shows the pressure of the gas in the cylinder and a low-pressure gage indicates the pressure of the gases flowing to the torch. The high-pressure gages on oxygen regulators are graduated in pounds per square inch from 0 to 3000. The low-pressure, or working, gage for oxygen-welding regulators is usually graduated in pounds per square inch from 0 to 100, 0 to 200, or 0 to 400. Figure 6·10 shows oxygen-pressure gages mounted on a pressure regulator.

Figure 6·11 shows **acetylene-pressure gages** mounted on a pressure regulator. Acetylene regulators are designed in a manner similar to oxygen regulators, but they are not required to withstand such high pres-

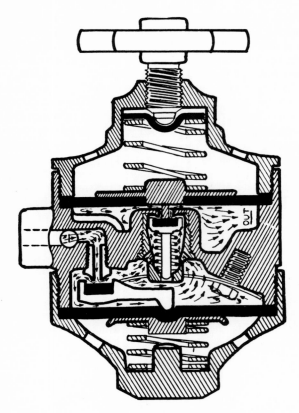

Figure 6·9   Operation of the two-stage regulator.

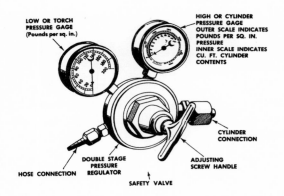

LOW OR TORCH
PRESSURE GAGE
(Pounds per sq. in.)

HIGH OR CYLINDER
PRESSURE GAGE
OUTER SCALE INDICATES
POUNDS PER SQ. IN.
PRESSURE
INNER SCALE INDICATES
CU. FT. CYLINDER
CONTENTS

CYLINDER
CONNECTION

DOUBLE STAGE
PRESSURE
REGULATOR

ADJUSTING
SCREW HANDLE

HOSE CONNECTION

SAFETY VALVE

Figure 6·10   Oxygen pressure gages on the regulator.

sures. The high-pressure gage for acetylene indicates pressures up to a maximum scale value of only 400 psi. The maximum scale values on various low-pressure or working gages range from 30 to 50 psi and the dial graduations have values of ½ to 2 psi, depending upon the purpose for which the gage is to be used.

In an installation where the gases are piped to the individual welding stations, only one gage is required for each welding station, because it is necessary only to indicate the pressure of the gas flowing through the hose to the torch.

It should be kept in mind that the principal purpose of the regulator is to reduce the pressure of the gases as they flow from the containers, from the high pressure

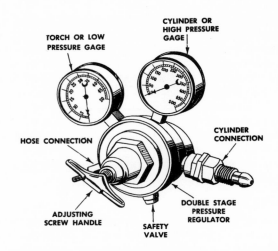

TORCH OR LOW
PRESSURE GAGE

CYLINDER OR
HIGH PRESSURE
GAGE

HOSE CONNECTION

CYLINDER
CONNECTION

ADJUSTING
SCREW HANDLE

SAFETY
VALVE

DOUBLE STAGE
PRESSURE
REGULATOR

Figure 6·11   Acetylene pressure gages on the regulator.

at the source to the desired safe working pressure at the torch. When the welder opens the tank valve, the gas enters the regulator through the inlet connection and flows into the passage leading to the high- and low-pressure chambers. The high-pressure gage shows the pressure in pounds per square inches in the cylinder. An adjusting screw on the regulator is turned to the right to permit the gas to enter the low-pressure chamber. This compresses the diaphragm control spring and forces the diaphragm against the yoke, or pin, which in turn connects with the seat holder. The pressure moves the seat away from the nozzle and allows the gas to flow into the low-pressure chamber. From there it flows through the hose to the torch. The gas pressure established in the low-pressure chamber is the result of a balance between the adjustable spring on one side of the control diaphragm and the low-pressure gas acting against the opposite side of the diaphragm as shown in Figs. 6·6 and 6·7. The working-pressure gage attached to the low-pressure chamber indicates the pressure of the gas flowing through the regulator to the torch.

When the welder closes the torch valves, pressure builds up in the low-pressure chamber and forces the diaphragm back to its original position. This increase is actually quite small because it requires but little change to affect the balance of the diaphragm. The pressure increase compresses the control spring a small amount and relieves the pressure against the seat holder, thus allowing the valve spring to move the seat against the nozzle and to shut off the gas.

When the welder opens the torch valves, the pressure of gas against the diaphragm is lowered, and the pressure adjusting spring forces the diaphragm against the yoke, or spacer pin. This, in turn, forces the seat away from the nozzle and allows the gas to flow through the regulator. In this manner, a constant volume and steady pressure of the gases is obtained by the welder for the adjustment he makes. Pressure to the torch is increased by turning the adjusting handle to the right and decreased by turning the handle to the left.

The two-stage regulators are preferred for the regulation of oxygen pressure direct from the cylinders to the torch because it is possible to obtain a more accurate adjustment and to lessen the possibility of the flame change after the first adjustment has been made. The two-stage regulator automatically reduces the initial cylinder pressure to about 200 psi in the first stage of reduction by means of an additional valve controlled by a diaphragm built into the regulator body. The final stage of pressure required at the torch is obtained by turning the adjusting handle as explained previously.

Welding torches

The **welding torch** is the device used to mix oxygen and acetylene together in the correct proportions and to provide a means of directing and controlling the quality and size of the flame. Welding torches may be divided into two principal types: (1) the **balanced-pressure type,** sometimes called the **equal-pressure type,** illustrated in Figs. 6·12 and 6·13 and (2) the **injector type,** illustrated in Figs. 6·14 and 6·15. These torches are available in different styles and sizes and they are obtainable for use with several sizes of tips which are interchangeable. The selection of the style and size of the torch depends upon the class of work to be done. The selection of the tip size depends upon the amount of heat and the size of the flame required for the kind and thickness of the metal to be welded.

In Fig. 6·12, the **needle valves** for the oxygen and acetylene are shown. They are placed like guards at the point where the oxygen and acetylene tubes enter the **torch head.** These valves are used to regulate the volumes of acetylene and oxygen that flow into the **mixing head.** The torch head is usually located at the forward end of the handle. The mixing head is seated in the torch head and extends beyond the torch head. As its name indicates, the purpose of the mixing head is to provide for the correct mixture of the gases for the best burning conditions. The mixture of oxygen and acetylene flows from the mixing head into the *tip* of the torch and then emerges at the end of the tip where it is ignited and burns to provide the welding flame.

Figure 6·13 shows a balanced-pressure torch with a cross-section drawing to illustrate internal construction. It will be noted that the oxygen is passed through the handle of the torch in a coil, thus helping to reduce the temperature of the handle.

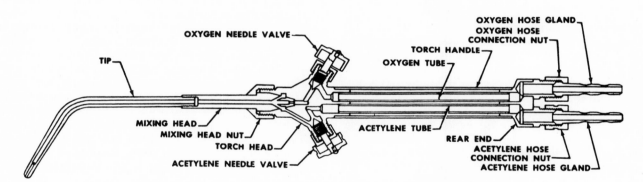

Figure **6·12**   *A balanced-pressure welding torch.*

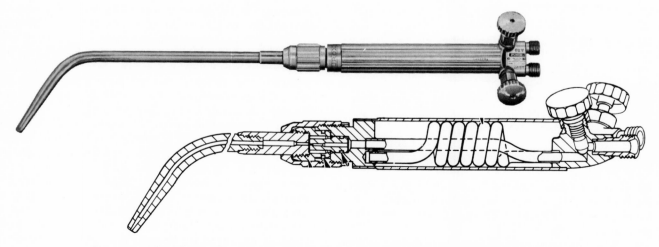

Figure **6·13**   *Photo of balanced-pressure torch and cross-section view. (Linde Div., Union Carbide Corp.)*

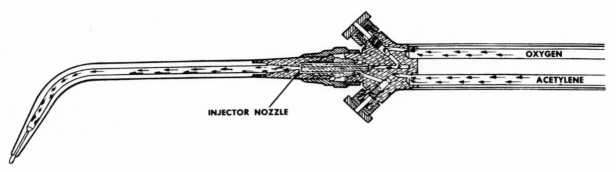

Figure **6·14**   *Injector-type welding torch.*

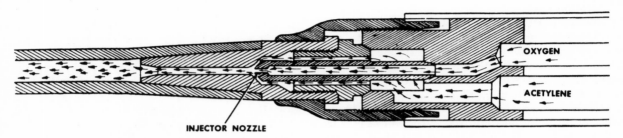

Figure **6·15**   *Mixing head for injector-type torch.*

Figures 6·14 and 6·15 show the construction of low-pressure acetylene injector-type torches. Figure 6·14 is a typical injector-type aircraft welding torch, and Fig. 6·15 shows the details of the mixing head. These torches operate with an acetylene pressure that is much lower than the oxygen pressure. The torch operates on a uniform oxygen pressure of about 20 psi for all sizes of tips because the pressure needs to be only great enough to overcome friction within the hose (line friction) until the acetylene gas reaches the injector nozzle. Here the velocity of the oxygen causes a low-pressure effect that draws the necessary amount of acetylene into the mixing chamber where the acetylene and oxygen are thoroughly mixed and directed to the tip.

The balanced-pressure type of welding torch is generally better suited to modern aircraft welding repair than the injector-type torch because of the ease of adjustment and maintenance. In using the injector-type torch, difficulty is experienced in maintaining the extremely low acetylene pressure. When the balanced-type torch is used, the operator merely adjusts the regulator pressures to supply a sufficient quantity of gases to operate the largest tip required for his work.

Some makes and models of welding torches are designed with an individual mixing head for each size of tip while others have only one mixing head for several sizes of tips.

Tip nozzles may have a one-piece hard copper tip or they may have a two-piece tip that includes an extension tube to make the connections between the mixing head and the tip.

As indicated previously, welding tips are made in a variety of sizes and styles. Removable tips are made of either hard copper or of an alloy, such as brass or bronze. Tip sizes are designated by numbers and each manufacturer has his own system of numbering. Some manufacturers designate tip sizes by 0, 1, 2, 3, 4, etc., and others start with a higher number such as 20, 21, 22, etc. The tip sizes differ in the diameter of the orifice to provide the correct amount of gas mixture at a velocity which will produce the heat necessary to do the job. It must be remembered that both the velocity and volume of gases are important. Too low a velocity will allow the flame to burn back into the tip and cause a "pop" which will blow the flame out. This is called a **backfire.** The same event will take place if the tip gets too hot. The manufacturer of the welding equipment supplies a table giving the approximate pressure of acetylene and oxygen for the various size tips for an equal-pressure torch and a similar table for an injector-type torch.

The torch tips should be of a proper size for the thickness of the material and the type of intersection involved. The commonly used sizes for working on steel butt welds are given in Table 6·1.

Table 6·1   **Typical torch-tip sizes**

Thickness of steel, in.	Diameter of hole in tip, in.	Drill size
0.015–0.031	0.026	71
0.031–0.065	0.031	68
0.065–0.125	0.037	63
0.125–0.188	0.042	58
0.188–0.250	0.055	54
0.250–0.375	0.067	51

For any given thickness of steel or steel alloys, the heat required varies according to the angle of intersection. For example, the heat required for two pieces of metal of the same thickness intersecting at an angle of 30° is different than the heat required for welding the same two pieces intersecting at an angle of 90°.

It is important to select a small tip for light work and a larger tip for heavy work because the size of the tip determines the amount of heat applied to the metal. If a small tip is used for heavy work, there is not enough heat to fuse the metal at the right depth. If the tip is too large, the heat is too great, and holes will be burned in the metal.

Welding hose

The **welding hose** is a rubber tube, especially made for the purpose, attached to the torch at one end and to a pressure regulator at the other end. It is used to carry the gases from their containers to the torch.

Acetylene hoses are usually red or maroon and are provided with left-hand threaded fittings. Oxygen hoses are green and are provided with right-hand threaded fittings. In addition, the name of the gas is printed on the hose. The nut with the left-hand thread used on the acetylene hose connection is usually identified with a groove around its center but the oxygen connection nut has no groove. Figure 6·16 illustrates typical acetylene- and oxygen-hose connections to show the difference.

Welding hoses and fittings should be examined regularly to see that the hoses are in good condition and that the fittings are not worn or damaged to the extent that they allow leakage of gases.

Safety equipment

Welding goggles, like the pair shown in Fig. 6·17, are fitted with colored lenses to keep out heat and the ultraviolet and infrared rays produced during welding. Clear lenses are provided to protect the colored lenses from injury. The cups of the goggles should hug the eye sockets so closely that sparks and tiny pieces of hot metal cannot hit the eyes.

Figure 6·18 shows a pair of **welding gloves,** commonly described as the **gauntlet style.** The material, workmanship, and fit must be such that the gloves protect the hands and wrists from burns and flying sparks. They are usually made of asbestos or of chemically treated canvas.

Figure **6·17**   Welding goggles.

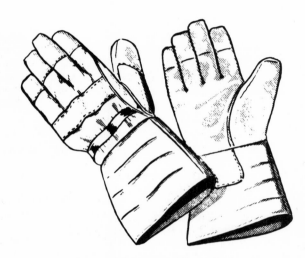

Figure **6·18**   Welding gloves.

Figure 6·19 shows a device which has several names. It may be called an **igniter, friction lighter, safety lighter,** or **spark lighter.** It is a hand-operated device used to light a gas torch safely. It consists of steel, a flint, a shield, and a spring. The steel, usually placed in a cup-shaped shield, resembles a **file** and is attached to one end of the spring. The replaceable **flint** is attached to the other end of the spring. The technician grasps the spring in his hand, and compresses and releases the spring, forcing the flint to rub across the steel and thus producing sparks that light the gas coming out of the torch. This device is safe because it is composed of noncombustible material, the spark burns only for a

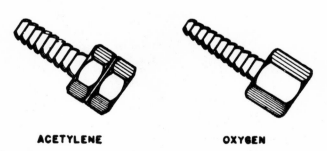

ACETYLENE   **OXYGEN**

Figure **6·16**   Acetylene and oxygen hose connections.

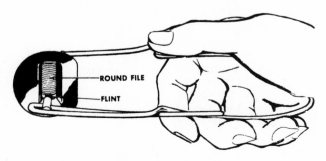

ROUND FILE

FLINT

Figure **6·19**   A friction lighter for welding torches.

second, and the lighter is long enough to protect the welder's hand from burns.

Never use matches. Always use the spark lighter described above. If matches are used, the puff of the flame from the torch may burn the hand.

One or more portable **fire extinguishers** are kept at hand to be used if the flame from the welding torch, flying sparks, or flying pieces of hot metal set fire to anything. **Carbon dioxide** is generally the fire-extinguishing medium used because it is effective in combating gasoline or oil fires and may be used on wood and fabric fires. Carbon dioxide is often combined with a chemical powder which aids in extinguishing fires.

Setting up the apparatus

The first step in setting up portable welding apparatus is to fasten the cylinders to the cart, or hand truck. The purpose of this step is to prevent the cylinders from being accidentally pulled or knocked over. The protecting cap that covers the valve on the top of the cylinder is not removed until the welder is ready to make a connection to the cylinder.

The second step in setting up the apparatus is to "crack" the cylinder valves. The welder stands at the side of, or behind, the cylinder outlet, as shown in Fig. 6·20, and opens the cylinder valve slightly for a moment and then quickly closes it. The purpose of this step is to clear the valve of dust or dirt that may have settled in the valve during shipment or storage. Dirt will cause leakage if it gets into the regulator and it will mar the seat of the regulator inlet nipple even if it does not actually reach the regulator.

The third step is to connect the regulators to the cylinders. The welder uses a tight-fitting wrench to turn the union nut as shown in Fig. 6·21, and he makes certain that the nut is tight so that the gas will not leak.

The fourth step is to connect the hoses to their respective regulators. The green hose is connected to the oxygen regulator and the red hose is connected to the acetylene regulator. The regulator adjustment handles should be turned clockwise a sufficient amount to blow gas through the hoses and clear any dust or dirt. The handles are then turned counterclockwise until there is no pressure on the diaphragm spring.

The fifth step is to connect the hoses to the torch, as shown in Fig. 6·22. The acetylene fitting, identified by the groove around the nut, has a left-hand thread and is connected to the acetylene fitting on the torch. A tight-fitting wrench should be used to avoid damage to the nuts.

The sixth step in setting up the welding equipment is to test for leaks. This should not be done by using a lighted match at the joints. No open flame should be allowed in the vicinity of welding equipment except for the flame of the torch. There are several ways to test

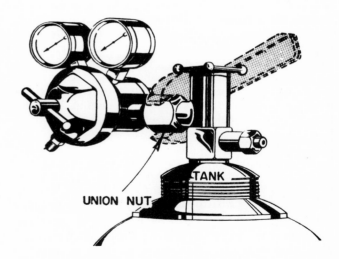

Figure 6·21 Wrench in position for tightening union nut.

Figure 6·20 Correct position for operator when opening cylinder valve.

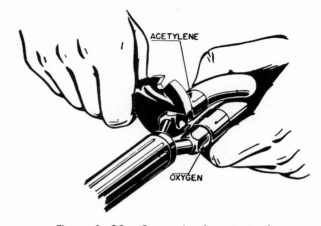

Figure 6·22 Connecting hose to torch.

for leaks but the best method is to apply soapy water to the joints with a brush. Before making this test, the oxygen and acetylene needle valves on the torch are closed. The cylinder valves are opened and then the regulator adjusting screws are turned to the right (clockwise) until the working gages show only a low pressure. The brush is dipped in soap suds, and the suds are spread evenly over the connections. If there is a leak, it is betrayed by a soap bubble.

If the welder finds a leak, he should close the cylinder valves and search for the source of trouble. It is generally sufficient to tighten the connecting unit slightly in order to stop the leak. Less common sources of trouble are dirt in the connection, which must be cleaned out, or marred seats or threads in the connection. If the seats or threads are damaged, the connection should be replaced. Having removed the trouble causing a leak, the welder must again test for leaks to be absolutely certain that none exist.

Ordinarily, the welder knows the correct tip size for the work he is to do, a small opening for thin metal or a larger opening for thick metal being provided. On the assumption that the apparatus is set up, the next job is to adjust the working pressure of the gases.

Setting the pressure

Figure 6·20 shows a welder in the correct position for opening the cylinder valve, regardless of whether the cylinder has a regulator attached or not. In the illustration the operator is in the position he would take if he were testing the operation of the cylinder valve.

When a regulator is installed on the cylinder, the operator stands behind or to the side of the regulator and opens the valve slowly. If the regulator is defective, pressure may build up behind the glass and cause it to burst. This would be likely to inflict injury on anyone standing in the area immediately in front of the regulator.

When the welder is ready to open the cylinder valves, he should open the acetylene cylinder valve about one complete turn and open the oxygen valve all the way, slowly in both cases. He sets the working pressure for the oxygen and the acetylene by turning the adjusting screw on the regulator to the right (clockwise) until the desired pressure reading is obtained on the gage. As mentioned before, the exact pressure required for any job primarily depends upon the thickness of the metal, and this determines the size of the welding tip used.

Lighting the torch

To light the torch, the welder opens the acetylene needle valve on the torch three-quarters of a turn, and then uses his spark lighter to light the acetylene as it leaves the tip. He should do this as quickly as possible in order to save gas. The flame should be large, very white, and smoky on the outer edges. If the flame produces much smoke, he "cracks" the oxygen needle valve very slightly. As soon as the flame appears to be under control, he continues slowly to open the **oxygen needle valve** until a well-shaped white cone appears near the tip of the torch. This white cone is surrounded

by a second, bluish cone, which glows faintly and is from 1/16 to 3/4 in. long, depending upon the size of the welding tip being used. This is known as a **neutral flame** and is represented by the upper drawing in Fig. 6·23.

Oxyacetylene flames

A welding flame is called **neutral** when the gas quantities are adjusted so all the oxygen and acetylene are burned together. Theoretically, 2½ volumes of oxygen are required to burn 1 volume of acetylene in order to produce this neutral flame, but actually it is only necessary to provide 1 volume of oxygen through the torch for 1 volume of acetylene consumed, because the remainder of the required oxygen is taken from the atmosphere. The carbon monoxide and hydrogen gas that come out of the first zone of combustion combine with oxygen from the air to complete the combustion, thus forming carbon dioxide and water vapor.

The neutral flame produced by burning approximately equal volumes of acetylene and oxygen oxidizes all particles of carbon and hydrogen in the acetylene, and it has a temperature of about 6300°F. This neutral flame should have a well-rounded, smooth, clearly defined, white central cone. The outer cone, or envelope, flame should be blue with a purple tinge at the point and edges.

A neutral flame melts metal without changing its properties and leaves the metal clear and clean. If the mixture of acetylene and oxygen is correct, the neutral flame allows the molten metal to flow smoothly, and few sparks are produced. If there is too much acetylene, the carbon content of the metal increases, the molten metal boils and loses its clearness, and the resulting weld is hard and brittle. If too much oxygen is used, the metal is burned, there is a great deal of foaming and sparking, and the weld is porous and brittle.

A neutral flame is best for most metals. However, a slight excess of one of the gases may be better for welding certain types of metal under certain conditions. For example, an excess of acetylene is commonly

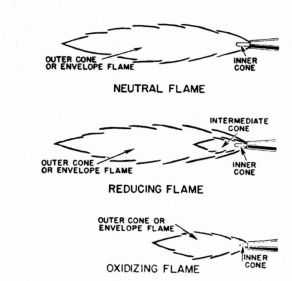

Figure 6·23 Neutral, reducing, and oxidizing flames.

used with the nickel alloys, Monel and Inconel. On the other hand, an excess of oxygen is commonly used in welding brass.

A **carbonizing,** or **reducing, flame** is represented by the middle drawing of Fig. 6·23. This occurs when there is more acetylene than oxygen feeding into the flame. Since the oxygen furnished through the torch is not sufficient to complete the combustion of the oxygen, carbon escapes without being burned. There are three flame zones instead of the two found in the neutral flame. The end of the brilliant white inner cone is not as well defined as it was in the neutral flame. Surrounding the inner cone is an intermediate white cone with a feathery edge, sometimes described as greenish-white and brushlike. The outer cone, or envelope, flame is bluish and similar to the outer cone, or envelope, flame of the neutral flame.

An **oxidizing flame** is represented by the lower drawing of Fig. 6·23. It is caused by an excess of oxygen flowing through the torch. There are only two cones; but the inner cone is shorter and more pointed than the inner cone of the neutral flame, and it is almost purple. The outer cone, or envelope, flame is shorter than the corresponding portion of either the neutral flame or of the reducing flame, and is of a much lighter blue color than the neutral flame. In addition to the size, shape, and color, the oxidizing flame can be recognized by a harsh, hissing sound, similar to the noise of air under high pressure escaping through a very small nozzle.

The **oxidizing flame** is well-named. It oxidizes, or burns, most metals, and it should not be used unless its use is definitely specified for some particular purpose. Since an oxidizing flame is generally objectionable, the welder must examine his flame every few minutes to be sure he is not getting an oxidizing flame. He does this by slowly closing the torch oxygen valve until a second cone or feathery edge appears at the end of the white central cone. He then opens the oxygen valve very slightly until the second cone disappears.

Figure 6·24 is a picture of a neutral or oxidizing flame with an irregular-shaped outer cone, or envelope, flame produced by an **obstructed tip.** Whenever a flame of this appearance is discovered, the welder should immediately shut down his welding apparatus, and either clean the tip or replace it with a new one.

Cleaning the tip

Small particles of carbon, oxides, and metal can be removed from the tip of a welding torch with a soft copper wire, a drill of the correct size, a tip cleaner manufactured for the purpose, or any other suitably shaped device which will not damage the tip. Care must be taken to maintain a smooth, round orifice through which the gases can emerge.

Figure 6·24 Flame produced by obstructed tip.

98

If the tip becomes worn to the extent that the opening of the orifice flares out or is bell-shaped, the end of the tip should be ground square on a piece of fine emery cloth held flat against a smooth surface. The tip should be held perpendicular to the surface of the emery cloth and moved back and forth with straight strokes.

The ouside surface of the tip can be cleaned with fine steel wool to remove carbon, oxides, and particles of metal. After cleaning the outside, the orifice should be cleaned to remove any material which may have entered.

Soft and harsh flames

When the welder has learned to adjust his flame so that the proportions of oxygen and acetylene are correct, he must then learn how to obtain a **soft flame.** This is a flame produced when the gases flow to the welding tip at a comparatively low speed. If the gases flow to the welding tip at a comparatively high speed, under too much pressure, they produce a **harsh flame** that is easily recognized because it is noisy. A harsh flame destroys the weld puddle and causes the metal to splash around the edges of the puddle. It is very difficult to get the metal parts to fuse properly with a flame of this kind.

On the assumption that the welder has the correct mixture of acetylene and oxygen, and is operating with the correct pressure, he may still fail to obtain a soft neutral flame if the welding tip is dirty or obstructed in any manner. An obstructed welding tip does not permit the gas mixture to flow evenly, and it restricts the source of heat required to melt the metal; therefore, a good weld is very difficult to produce.

If there is any fluctuation in the flow of the gases from the regulators, the mixture will change, regardless of other conditions; hence a good welder watches his flame constantly and makes any necessary adjustments to keep it neutral and soft. If he hears a popping noise, he knows that insufficient gas is reaching the tip and immediately delivers a little more oxygen and acetylene by opening both needle valves slightly more.

Backfire

A **backfire** is a momentary backward flow of gases at the torch tip, causing the flame to go out and then immediately to come on again. A backfire is always accompanied by a snapping or popping noise. Sometimes the word *backfire* is used loosely to mean a **flashback,** but a true backfire is not as dangerous as a flashback because the flame does not burn back into the torch head and does not require turning off the gases.

There are five common causes of backfires: (1) there may be dirt or some other obstruction in the end of the welding tip; (2) the gas pressures may be incorrect; (3) the tip may be loose; (4) the tip may be overheated; or (5) the welder may have touched the work with the tip of the torch.

If the tip is dirty or obstructed, it is removed and cleaned with a soft copper wire, or it is replaced. If the gas pressures are wrong, they are adjusted. If the tip is loose, the torch is turned off and the tip tightened. If the tip is overheated, the torch is turned off and allowed to cool. If the welder touched his work with the tip, he merely avoids repeating the error.

Flashback

Flashback is the burning back of the flame into or behind the mixing chamber of the torch. Where flashback occurs, the flame disappears entirely from the tip of the torch and does not return. In some instances, unless either the oxygen or the acetylene, or both, are turned off, the flame may burn back through the hose and pressure regulator into the gas supply (the manifold or the cylinder) causing great damage. Flashback should not be confused with **backfire**, as explained before. The welder must always remember that if a flashback occurs he will hear a shrill hissing or squealing, and his flame will burn back into the torch. He must quickly close the acetylene and oxygen needle valves to confine the flash to the torch and let the torch cool off before lighting it again. Since a flashback extending back through the hoses into the regulators is a symptom of something radically wrong, either with the torch or with the manner of its operation, the welder must find the cause of the trouble and remedy it before proceeding.

How to shut down the welding apparatus

The procedure for shutting down the welding apparatus is as follows:

1. Close the acetylene needle valve on the torch to shut off the flame immediately.
2. Close the oxygen needle valve on the torch.
3. Close the acetylene cylinder valve.
4. Close the oxygen cylinder valve.
5. Remove the pressure on the regulators' working-pressure gages by opening the acetylene valve on the torch to drain the acetylene hose and regulator.
6. Turn the acetylene-regulator adjusting screw counterclockwise (to the left) to relieve the pressure on the diaphragm, and then close the torch acetylene valve.
7. Open the torch oxygen valve, and drain the oxygen hose and regulator.
8. Turn the oxygen-regulator adjusting screw counterclockwise to relieve the pressure on the diaphragm; then close the torch oxygen valve.
9. Hang the torch and hose up properly to prevent any kinking of the hose or damage to the torch.

REVIEW QUESTIONS

1. What is meant by *fusion welding?*
2. Why is it usually necessary to add metal in the form of a welding rod while making a weld?
3. List the items necessary for a complete portable welding outfit.
4. Briefly describe *acetylene gas* and explain why it is used in gas welding.
5. At what pressures does acetylene gas become unstable and in danger of exploding?
6. What material is placed inside an acetylene cylinder to absorb the gas and thus assure safe handling?
7. What is the maximum pressure of the gas in an acetylene cylinder?
8. Why is it necessary to keep oxygen equipment free from oil or grease?
9. To what pressure is an oxygen cylinder charged?
10. How can you determine the volume of gas in an oxygen cylinder?
11. Discuss the importance of a protector cap over the valve on an oxygen cylinder.
12. Describe a gas pressure regulator and explain its function.
13. Why are two pressure gages used on a cylinder gas regulator?
14. List the main differences between an oxygen pressure regulator and an acetylene pressure regulator.
15. How does a welder adjust the gas regulator to increase pressure?
16. Name the two principal types of welding torches.
17. Which type is generally preferred for aircraft welding? Why?
18. Explain the function of the *mixing head.*
19. What determines the size of tip to be used in a welding torch?
20. How are oxygen and acetylene torch hoses identified?
21. How is the danger of connecting the hoses incorrectly avoided?
22. What are the two principal functions of welding goggles?
23. Why should a friction lighter be used to ignite the gas at the tip of a welding torch?
24. Briefly describe the steps for setting up welding apparatus.
25. What method should be used in testing for leaks?
26. In lighting a welding torch, what gas should be turned on first?
27. Explain how to adjust the torch for a *neutral flame.*
28. Why is the neutral flame best for welding steel?
29. Describe the appearance of a neutral flame.
30. What is the effect of using an oxidizing flame?
31. Compare the carbonizing (carburizing) flame with the oxidizing flame.
32. What is the effect of a damaged or obstructed tip orifice?
33. Explain how a tip can be cleaned properly.
34. Why is a *soft flame* better then a *harsh flame* for welding?
35. What are some of the causes for popping at the welding tip?
36. Give the procedure for shutting down the welding apparatus.

CHAPTER 7

Gas Welding Techniques

Skill in welding may be considered as both a skill and an art. An expert welder needs technical understanding of the processes with which he is working and many hours of practice to develop the manual dexterity necessary to produce a quality weld. Although the certificated aircraft maintenance technician is not always expected to be an expert welder, he still needs to know a good weld when he sees one, and he should be able to perform a satisfactory welding job when it becomes necessary. Furthermore, he should know his own abilities and whether a welding specialist should be called in to do a particular repair job.

Holding the torch

Figure 7·1 shows one method for holding the torch when welding light-gage metal. In this method, the torch is held as one might hold a pencil. The hose drops over the outside of the wrist, and the torch is held as though the welder were trying to write on the metal.

Figure **7·1** *Holding torch for welding light metal.*

Figure 7·2 shows how the torch can be held for welding heavier work. In this method, the torch is held as one would hold a hammer; the fingers are curled underneath and the torch balanced easily in the hand so that there is no strain on the muscles of the hand. A good way to describe the grip of the torch is to say that it should be held like a bird, tight enough so that it cannot get away but loose enough so it will not be crushed.

Forehand welding

Forehand welding, sometimes called **forward welding,** is a welding technique in which the torch flame is pointed forward in the direction the weld is progressing. In other words, it is pointed toward the unwelded portion of the joint, and the **rod** is fed in from the front of the torch, or flame. Figure 7·3 shows how this is done.

The torch head is tilted back from the flame to allow it to point in the direction that the weld is progressing. The angle at which the flame should contact the metal depends upon the type of joint, the position of the work, and the kind of metal being welded, but the usual angle is from 30 to 60°.

This forehand, or forward, technique must not be

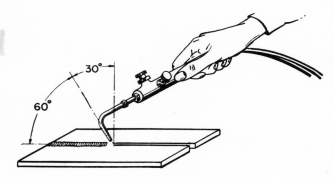

Figure **7·2** *Holding torch for welding heavy metal.*

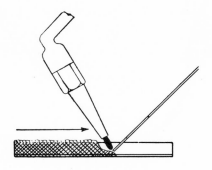

Figure **7·3** *Forehand welding.*

confused with the backhand, or backward, technique shown in Fig. 7·4 and explained in detail later in this chapter. The two techniques are distinctly different.

The welding, or filler, rod

The **welding rod,** sometimes called a **filler rod,** is filler metal, in wire or rod form, drawn or cast, used to supply the additional metal required to form a joint. During welding, the rod is melted into the joint, where it fuses with the molten base metal, the metal from the rod forming a large proportion of the actual weld metal. Welding rods are usually composed of only one metal or alloy, although rods known as **composite rods** contain more than one metal. If a rod has a very small diameter it is usually known as a **wire.**

When a rod is used in making a weld by the forehand method, it should be added to the pool of melting metal in front of the torch flame. The angle of the rod in relation to the torch must vary for different operations, but it is always necessary to add it to the weld by holding the end of the rod down into the molten pool of base metal formed by the fusing of the joint edges. If the rod is held above the pool and permitted to melt and drop into the weld, impurities floating on the surface of the molten metal will be trapped and a poor joint will be produced.

In using the rod, it can be kept straight, or it can be bent to form a right angle near the end, as shown in Fig. 7·5.

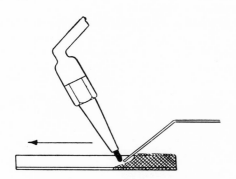

Figure 7·4   Backhand welding.

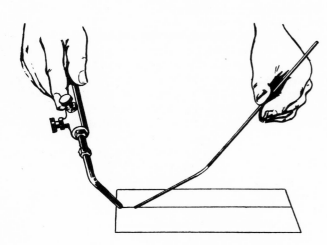

Figure 7·5   Welding rod bent at the end.

The welding torch is brought down until the white cone of the flame is about ⅛ in. from the surface of the base metal. It is held there until the flame melts a small puddle of metal. The tip of the rod is then inserted in this puddle and as the rod melts the molten pool is gradually worked forward.

The torch is never moved ahead of the puddle. Instead, it is worked along the edges of the seam so slowly that the heat will have an opportunity to break down the edges. If the welder hurries and moves the flame ahead too rapidly, the heat will not penetrate deep enough and the metal will not melt properly. If the welder is too slow in moving the flame along, or if it is held in one place too long, the flame burns a hole through the metal.

As the welder advances his torch, he continues to dip the filler rod in the pool of molten metal. He does not hold the rod too high because that would cause the molten metal to fall, a drop at a time, from the end of the rod into the pool. This is sometimes called the "raindrop" technique. It produces a poor weld that is full of pinholes.

The welder ordinarily does not place the rod directly under the flame. Instead he keeps the flame concentrated on the base metal. The rod is melted by the heat of the molten puddle.

In selecting welding rod for a particular application in the repair of aircraft structures, the operator must make certain that the rod he uses is satisfactory for the job. On structures which must be heat-treated after welding, the rod must be of a type or alloy which will heat-treat to the strength required.

Torch motions

The welder may use either the **semicircular motion** shown in Fig. 7·6 or the continuous **circular motion** shown in Fig. 7·7. Regardless of which motion he uses, he keeps the motion of the torch as uniform as possible so that he will have smooth even-spaced ripples. These **ripples** are the small, wavelike marks left on the surface

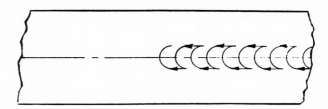

Figure 7·6   Semicircular welding motion.

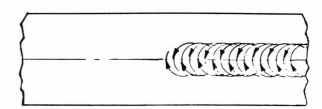

Figure 7·7   Circular welding motion.

of the completed weld by the action of the torch and welding rod.

A very slight circular motion of the torch is preferred in welding very thin material because the thin metal heats rapidly. Using a slight circular motion of the torch allows the welder to travel along the work faster and avoid burning holes in the metal.

Figure 7·8 shows the use of the forward, or forehand, technique in welding thin-walled tubing or light-gage metal. The torch is held so that it is inclined at an angle of from 50 to 60° to the surface of the work. Notice that the filler rod is being held so that it is added to the little pool of molten metal in front of the torch flame.

Backhand welding

Backhand welding, sometimes called **backward welding,** is a technique in which the flame is directed back toward the finished weld, away from the direction the weld is progressing, and the rod is fed in from the back of the torch, or the flame. This is the method illustrated in Fig. 7·4. Figure 7·9 also illustrates this technique and shows that the torch flame is pointed toward the finished weld (the shaded part of the bar) at an angle of about 60° to the surface of the work. The welding rod is added *between* the flame and the finished weld. In this backhand technique, the semicircular motion is directed so that the base of the arc falls toward the finished weld. Thus, in welding a seam like that in Fig. 7·9, the welder uses a right-to-left, or counterclockwise, motion.

Whether the forehand or the backhand technique is used, the end of the filler rod is always held in the pool and given a slight alternating or back-and-forth rocking movement as metal is added from the rod to the pool. This movement of the rod must not be made too energetically. It must be controlled so that the melted metal from the pool is not shoved over onto the metal which is not yet hot enough to receive it.

The backhand technique is preferred by most welders for metals having a heavy cross section. The

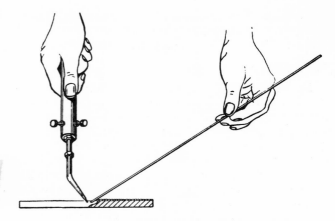

Figure **7·9**   Backhand welding technique.

metal being welded may be held in any position except for welding seams that run vertically. By using the backhand technique, the large pool of melting metal that must be kept up at all times is more easily controlled, and the required depth of fusion in the base metal is easier to obtain.

In backhand welding, the torch head may be tilted toward the unfinished weld at an angle varying from 60 to 70° with the seam, with the flame pointing toward the finished weld. The welding rod is added between the flame and the finished weld, the welder holding the end of the rod in the pool and giving it the slight alternating movement with the flame while metal is added to the weld. As already indicated, if the rod movement is not controlled properly, the melting metal from the pool will be pushed over on metal that is not yet in a proper state of fusion to receive it and to form a good weld.

The flame is moved back and forth across the seam with the semicircular motion previously described, thus breaking down the edges and the side walls of the base metal in order to fuse them to the necessary depth.

Welding positions classified

The four **welding positions** are **flat-position welding, vertical-position welding, horizontal-position welding,** and **overhead-position welding.** The welder must be able to make a good weld in any one of these four positions. A **welding position** refers to the plane (position) in which the work is placed for welding.

Two of the terms refer to welding the top or bottom surface of a work in a horizontal plane (flat work); overhead position is used when the underside of work is welded and flat position when the topside of work is welded. The other two refer to welding work in a vertical plane, but make a distinction according to the direction of the line of weld. Thus horizontal position is used when the line runs across from side to side; vertical position when the line runs up and down from top to bottom. The **line of weld** is simply the path along which the weld is laid.

Figures 7·10 to 7·12 illustrate the four positions as seen from different viewpoints.

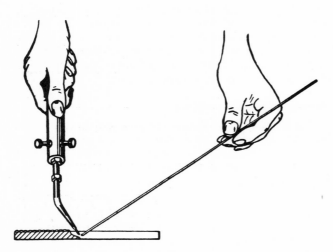

Figure **7·8**   Forehand technique in welding thin-walled metal.

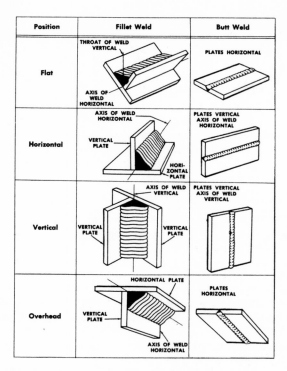

Figure 7·10   The four positions for welding.

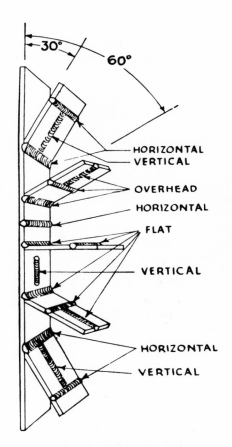

Figure 7·11   Welding positions as viewed from the side.

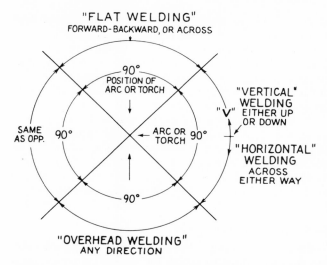

Figure 7·12   Torch directions for different welding positions.

Flat-position welding

The **flat position** is the position used when the work is laid flat or almost flat and welded on the topside with the welding torch pointed downward toward the work. Thus, if a weld is made with the parts to be welded laid flat on the table, or inclined at an angle less than 45°, it is designated as being flat. The weld may be made in this position by the forehand or by the backhand technique, depending upon the thickness of the metal. The seam runs horizontally.

Vertical-position welding

The **vertical position** is the position used when the line of the weld runs up and down (vertically) on a piece of work laid in a vertical, or nearly vertical, position. The welding torch is held in a horizontal, or almost horizontal, position. Thus, when the parts are inclined at an angle of more than 45°, with the weld running vertically, it is described as a vertical weld. The weld should be made from the bottom with the flame pointed upward at an angle of from 45 to 60° to the seam for welding in this position. The rod is added to the weld in front of the flame as it is in ordinary forehand welding. Figure 7·13 shows how the filler rod is added to the weld in front of the flame while making a weld in the vertical position.

Horizontal-position welding

The **horizontal position** is the position used when the line of weld runs across (horizontally) on a piece of work placed in a vertical, or almost vertical, position; the welding torch is held in a horizontal, or almost horizontal, position. Thus, when a weld is made with the parts in a vertical position, or inclined at an angle of more than 45° with the seam running horizontally, it is called a **horizontal** weld. The seams in this horizontal position may be welded by either the forehand or the backhand technique; in either case, the flame should point slightly upward in order to aid in keeping the

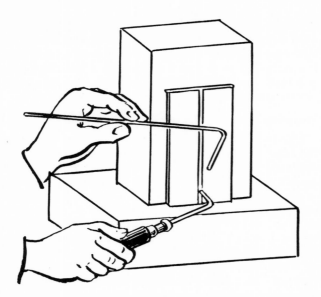

Figure 7·13   Adding rod when making a vertical weld.

melting metal from running to the lower side of the seam. The welding rod should be added to the weld at the upper edge of the zone of fusion, since it dissipates some of the heat and lowers the temperature enough to help in holding the melting metal in the proper place. Figure 7·14 shows the hands of the welder holding the torch and the rod in this position.

Overhead-position welding

The **overhead position** is the position used when work is flat (horizontal), or almost flat, and is welded on the lower side with the welding torch pointed in an upward direction toward the work. Thus, when a weld is made on the underside of the work with the seam running horizontally, or in a plane that requires a flame to point upward from below, it is described as an overhead weld.

Either the forehand or the backhand technique can be used in welding seams in an overhead position. In either case, the flame must be pointed upward and held at about the same angle as it is for welding in a flat position. The volume of flame used for overhead welding should not be permitted to exceed that required to obtain a good fusion of the base metal with the filler rod. Unless the welder avoids creating a large pool of melting metal, the metal will drip or run out of the joint, thus spoiling the weld. Figure 7·15 shows a welder's hands holding the rod and torch correctly for this type of weld.

Preparation of the metal

The elements to be welded should be properly held in place by welding jigs, or fixtures, that are sufficiently rigid to prevent misalignment due to expansion and contraction of the heated material. These jigs, or fixtures, must also positively locate the relative positions of the pieces to be welded.

The parts to be welded should be cleaned before welding by sandpapering or brushing with a wire brush or by some similar method. If the members to be welded have been metallized, the surface metal should be removed by careful sandblasting.

All mill scale, rust, oxides, and other impurities must be removed from the joint edges or surfaces to prevent them from being included in the weld metal. The edges, or ends, to be welded must be prepared so that fusion can be accomplished without the use of an excessive amount of heat, and the amount of heat radiation into the base metal from the weld can be reduced

In addition to cleaning the surfaces, the edges must be **beveled** down with a grinding wheel or a file so that they will fuse with the smallest possible amount of heat. Whether or not a welder must bevel the edges is determined by the thickness of the metal. For example, if a welder has two pieces of steel 1-in. thick to be welded, he should **bevel,** or "V out," the joint in order to prepare the metal so that the weld will extend all the way through.

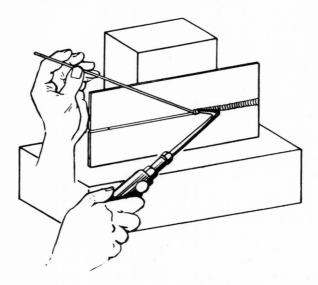

Figure 7·14   Positions of hands and torch for a horizontal weld.

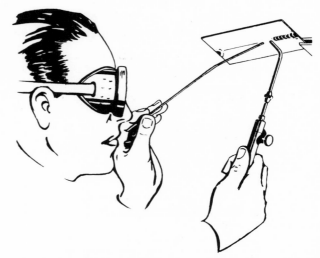

Figure 7·15   Positions of hands and torch for an overhead weld.

It is apparent that the use of too much heat will burn the metal. In addition, an excessive amount of heat will radiate from the weld into the base metal and will cause it to expand at first and to contract later; this will result in warping if the metal is "soft" or in cracking if the metal is brittle.

Types of joints

Five different types of joints are used to weld the various forms of metal. These are (1) butt joints, (2) tee joints, (3) lap joints, (4) corner joints, and (5) edge joints.

Factors governing preparation of metal

Important factors to be considered in the preparation of the metal are (1) form, (2) thickness, (3) kind of metal, (4) available facilities for preparing the edges to be formed, and (5) the load stress that the weld must support.

Butt joints

A **joint** is that portion of a structure where separate base-metal parts are united by welding. The word **weld** is often used to refer to a **joint**. For example, a **butt weld** is a welded butt joint. The word **seam** is often used to refer to a welded joint, especially in the case of tanks and containers.

A **butt joint** is a joint made by placing two pieces of material edge to edge in the same plane so that there is no overlapping. It is called a **butt joint** because the two edges, when joined, are abutted together.

Butt joints are used in welding to join all kinds of metal forms, such as sheet, bar, plate, tube, and pipe; in aircraft welding, however, butt joints are not generally used for joining tubing, because such joints are not strong enough for aircraft purposes.

Figure 7·16 shows **flange butt joints.** These can be used for sheet metal up to 0.0625 in. thick. The edges to be welded are turned up to 80 or 90°, from one to three times the thickness of the metal, and the flanges are melted down and fused together to form the weld. Since the flanges supply enough metal to fill the seam, a filler rod is not used.

Figure 7·17 shows two drawings of a **plain butt joint.**

This can be used for thickness up to ⅛ in. when the weld is made with the oxyacetylene flame. Where the thickness is greater, other types of welding are used. It is necessary to use a filler rod when a plain butt joint is formed by gas welding in order to obtain a sufficiently strong weld.

Preparing thick metal edges

Figure 7·18 includes four drawings that show how the edges of metals with heavy cross sections should be prepared. The four types are the single V, and the double V, the single U, and the double U.

The joint with a single-V bevel is known as a **single-V butt joint.** It is used for metal ⅛ to ½ in. thick where the joint can be welded from one side only. The joint with a double-V bevel is used for solid shapes that can be welded from both sides. The angle of bevel for both of these joints should be 45° for the oxyacetylene process. The double-V joint requires about one-half the amount of welding rod required for the single V, but it is more expensive to prepare.

The single-U butt joint and the double-U butt joint are widely used for solid shapes of great thickness because they require less welding rod than the V-type joints.

All butt joints are suitable for any kind of load stresses if they are made so that there is full penetration, good fusion, and proper reinforcement.

Tee joints

Figure 7·19 shows how the metal is prepared for various types of tee joints. A **tee joint** is a form of joint made by placing the edge of one base part on the surface of the other base part so that the surface of the second part extends on either side of the joint in the form of a T.

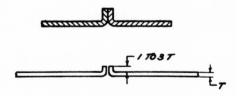

Figure 7·16   Flange butt joints.

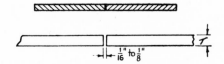

Figure 7·17   A plain butt joint.

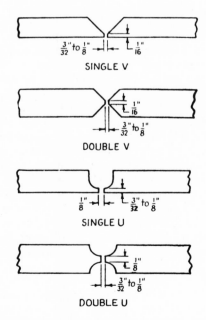

Figure 7·18   Four ways in which edges of metal can be prepared for welding.

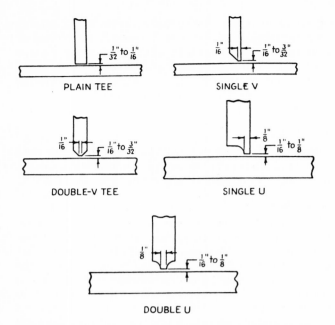

PLAIN TEE SINGLE V

DOUBLE-V TEE SINGLE U

DOUBLE U

Figure **7·19** *Preparation of metal for welded tee joints.*

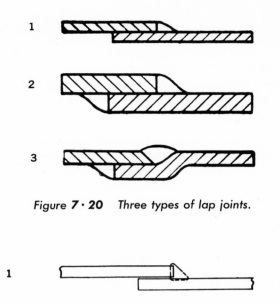

Figure **7·20** *Three types of lap joints.*

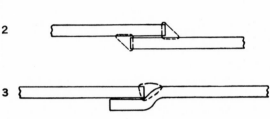

Figure **7·21** *Lap joints in detail.*

The **plain tee joint** is acceptable for most metal thickness in aircraft work and also may be used for heavier metals where the weld can be located so that the load stresses will be transverse (perpendicular) to the longitudinal dimensions of the weld. The only preparation required is cleaning the surface of the horizontal member and the end of the vertical member. The weld is then made from each side with penetration into the intersection. This results in a **fillet weld** having a general triangular cross-sectional shape.

The **single-V tee joint** is widely used for plates and shapes where the joint can be welded from only one side and where the thickness is ½ in. or less. This joint is acceptable for normal loading if there is full penetration with fusion into both members.

The **double-V tee joint** is used for welding heavy plates and shapes where the joint can be welded from both sides. It is suitable for all types of loading if the weld metal is fused together at the end of the branch member and if the penetration exists in both members. In both the single-V tee joint and the double-V tee joint, a welding rod is used.

The single-U joint is used for plates 1 in. thick or thicker, where the weld can be made from only one side. The double-U joint is suitable for all plates and other solid shapes of heavy cross section where the joint can be welded from both sides. Generally, the aircraft mechanic will not be required to use the single-U and double-U joints because most aircraft welding is done on plates thin enough for the other types of joints.

Lap joints

Figure 7·20 shows three types of **lap joints.** Figure 7·21 presents three drawings of the same joints but are drawn with a little more attention to detail.

A weld securing a lap joint is called a **lap weld.** A lap

joint is a joint made by lapping one base over the other, and is used in plate, bar, tubing, and pipe. These joints are widely used in the construction of articles fabricated from plate and sheet metal (flat, wrought metals), but a lap joint is not as efficient as a butt joint for distributing load stresses. When the weld can be placed so that the load stress will be transverse (perpendicular) to the line of weld, the lap joint is stronger.

The **single-welded lap joint,** shown in drawing 1 of Fig. 7·20 and also in drawing 1 of Fig. 7·21, is used for sheet, plate, and structural shapes where the loading is not severe. The same type of joint can be used for telescope splices in steel tubing, and in that application it is better than a butt joint.

The **double-welded lap joint,** shown in drawing 2 of Fig. 7·20 and also in drawing 2 of Fig. 7·21, is used for sheet and plate where the strength required is greater than that which can be obtained when a single weld is used. This type of joint provides for great strength, when properly made, in all ordinary thicknesses of sheet and plate. The **offset,** or **joggled, lap joint,** shown in drawing 3 of Fig. 7·20 and in drawing 3 of Fig. 7·21, is used for sheet and plate where it is necessary to have a lap joint with one side of both plates or sheets in the same plane; that is, on one side the surface is flush. This type of joint provides for a more even distribution of load stresses than either the single or double lap joint, but it is more difficult to prepare.

In all three types of lap joints, a welding rod must be used.

Edge joints

Figure 7·22 shows types of edge joints for plate and sheet. An **edge joint** is a form of joint made by placing a surface of one base part on a surface of the other base part in such a manner that the weld will be on the outer surface planes of both parts joined. This type of joint is not used where a high joint strength is required, but it is widely used for fittings composed of two or more pieces of sheet stock where the edges must be fastened together. This use is acceptable because the joint is not subjected to high stresses. Edge joints can be used also for tanks that are not subjected to high pressures. In Fig. 7·22, drawing 1 shows a joint used for thin sheets, and drawing 2 shows a joint adaptable to thick sheets.

Edge joints are usually made by bending the edges of one or both parts upward at a 90° angle, placing the two bent ends parallel to each other, or placing one bent end parallel to the upright unbent end, and welding along the outside of the seam formed by the two joined edges.

Corner joints

A **corner joint** is made by placing the edge of one part at an angle on an edge or a surface of another part so that neither part extends beyond the outer surface of the other, the structure resembling the corner of a rectangle.

Figure 7·23 shows three types of corner joints for plate and sheet. The **closed type of corner joint,** shown in drawing 1 of Fig. 7·23, is used on the lighter-gage metals, where the joint is subjected to moderate stresses only. It is made without adding much, if any, filler rod because the edge of the overlapping sheet is melted and fused to form the bead.

The **open type of corner joint,** shown in drawing 2 of Fig. 7·23, is used on heavier sheet for the same purpose as a closed type of corner joint. It is made by fus-ing the two edges at the inside corner and adding enough welding rod to give a well-rounded bead of weld metal on the outside. If such an open joint is required to bear a fairly heavy load, an additional weld must be made on the inside corner to provide the necessary strength, as shown in drawing 3 of Fig. 7·23, where a light concave bead has been laid on the inside.

Fillet welds

Any weld which joins two parts which are at right angles to each other may be called a **fillet weld.** Corner joints, lap joints, and edge joints require fillet welds.

The parts of a weld

Figure 7·24 shows the names of the parts of a weld. The **face** is the exposed surface of the weld. The **root** is the zone at the bottom, or base, of the weld; in other words, it is the depth that fusion penetrates into the base metal at the joint. The **throat** is the distance through the center of the weld from the root to the face; that is, it is the minimum thickness of the weld along a straight line drawn through the root. The **toe** is the edge formed where the face of the weld meets the base metal; that is, it is the edge of the fusion zone in the base metal on each side of the weld. The **reinforcement** is the quantity of weld metal added above the surface of the base metal (the metal in the parts being joined) to give the weld a greater thickness in cross section. Other terms not illustrated in Fig. 7·24 are the following: (1) The **leg** is the dimension of the weld metal extending on each side of the root of the joint and (2) the **fusion zone** is the width of the weld metal, including the depth of fusion in the base metal on each side of the joint.

In Fig. 7·24, the **bead** is shown. This is the metal deposited as the weld is made. In order to have good penetration, the base metal at the joint must be melted throughout its thickness; hence a bead of weld metal should be visible on the under side of a butt joint, as shown in Fig. 7·24. A good indication of penetration in the case of a fillet weld is the presence of scale on the lower side.

Figure 7·25 consists of three drawings that illustrate the meaning of width of fusion, reinforcement, throat, root, leg, and toe.

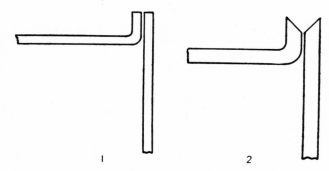

Figure **7·22**   Edge joints for plate and sheet.

Figure **7·23**   Three types of corner joints.

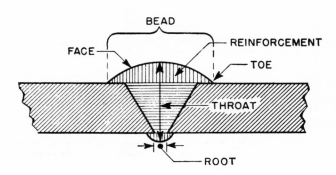

Figure **7·24**   Nomenclature of a weld.

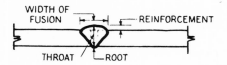

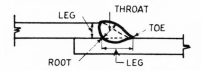

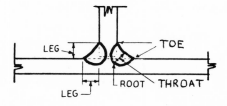

Figure 7·25　Details of weld nomenclature.

The proportions of a weld

The three most important proportions of a weld are (1) the **depth of penetration,** which should be at least one-fourth the thickness of the base metal; (2) the **width of the bead,** which should be two to three times as great as the thickness of the base metal; and (3) the height of the reinforcement, which should be not less than one-half the thickness of the base metal.

In Fig. 7·26, the butt weld shown in drawing 1 has a bead that is twice the thickness of the base metal. In attaching an aircraft fitting by means of a lap weld, as in drawing 2 of Fig. 7·26, the width of the fillet bead is 1½ times the thickness of the upper sheet. In making a tee joint, as in drawing 3, the weld bead has a thickness through the throat that equals the thickness of the vertical member. The penetration of the weld into the sides of the joint is one-fourth the thickness of the base metal, and the height of the reinforcement meets the requirements given before.

The correct formation of a weld

A weld must be formed correctly to provide strength and to resist fatigue in a joint. If it is not made properly, the weld may have less than 50 percent of the

strength for which the joint was designed. Figure 7·27 shows correct lap joints; Fig. 7·28 shows correct tee joints; Fig. 7·29 shows good corner joints; and Fig. 7·30 illustrates properly formed butt joints.

The usual causes of improperly formed weak welds are (1) undercutting of the base metal at the toe of the weld; (2) not enough penetration; (3) poor fusion of the weld metal with the base metal; (4) trapped oxides, slag, or gas pockets in the weld; (5) overheating of the weld; and (6) overlap of the weld metal on the base metal. These incorrect conditions are due to lack of experience, wrong technique, or carelessness. Figure 7·31 shows a large number of faults commonly found in the weld-metal formation of various joints. Any weld which has an appearance similar to one of the drawings in this illustration should be rejected.

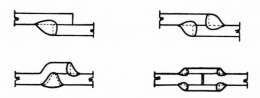

Figure 7·27　Properly made lap joints.

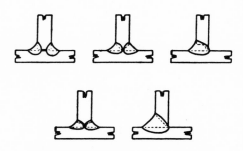

Figure 7·28　Correct tee joints.

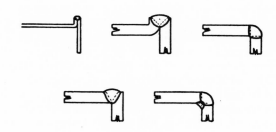

Figure 7·29　Good corner joints.

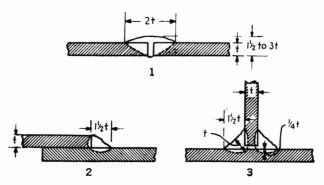

Figure 7·26　Dimensions of a weld.

Figure 7·30　Properly formed butt joints.

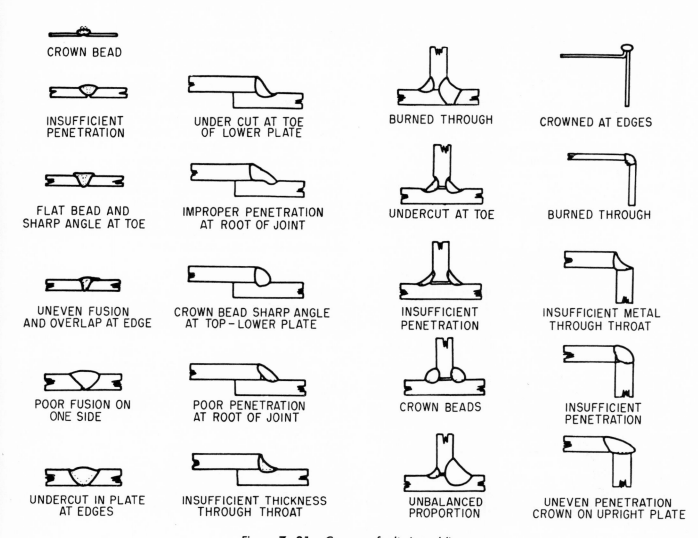

CROWN BEAD

INSUFFICIENT
PENETRATION

FLAT BEAD AND
SHARP ANGLE AT TOE

UNEVEN FUSION
AND OVERLAP AT EDGE

POOR FUSION ON
ONE SIDE

UNDERCUT IN PLATE
AT EDGES

UNDER CUT AT TOE
OF LOWER PLATE

IMPROPER PENETRATION
AT ROOT OF JOINT

CROWN BEAD SHARP ANGLE
AT TOP – LOWER PLATE

POOR PENETRATION
AT ROOT OF JOINT

INSUFFICIENT THICKNESS
THROUGH THROAT

BURNED THROUGH

UNDERCUT AT TOE

INSUFFICIENT
PENETRATION

CROWN BEADS

UNBALANCED
PROPORTION

CROWNED AT EDGES

BURNED THROUGH

INSUFFICIENT METAL
THROUGH THROAT

INSUFFICIENT
PENETRATION

UNEVEN PENETRATION
CROWN ON UPRIGHT PLATE

Figure 7·31   Common faults in welding.

Chemical changes produced by welding

A **chemical change** occurs when a substance is added to the metal or taken away. The great heat of the oxyacetylene flame will cause the loss of one or more of the chemical constituents of a piece of metal if the flame is turned on the metal for any length of time; this loss usually will result in a reduction of such physical properties of the metal as tensile strength, ductility, and yield point. Also, if some element is added to the metal by the welding process, or if there is some material change in one or more of the chemical constituents, the change will usually lower the strength of the metal.

Physical changes produced by welding

A **physical change** is a change of any kind that takes place without affecting the chemical structure of a metal. Some of the physical changes most important in welding are changes in the melting point, heat conductivity, and rate of expansion and contraction.

Melting point

The melting point is the degree of temperature at which a solid substance becomes liquid. Pure metals have a melting point, but alloys have a **melting range.** The welder should know the approximate melting point of the various metals with which he works because he must often weld together metals which have widely different melting points. However, melting points above 2000°F are not known exactly and may vary 5 or 10° one way or the other from the reading in a table of melting points. If a metal includes an alloyed element, the melting point is lowered; hence the melting points given in tables for alloyed metals vary according to the proportion of alloying elements present, and should be considered with this fact in mind.

Expansion

Expansion is an increase in dimensions (length, width, thickness) of a substance under the action of heat. If a metal structure is unevenly heated, there will be an uneven expansion and this will produce distortion (warping) and possibly breakage. On the other hand, if the temperature is raised progressively throughout the whole mass of the object, the action is uniform and there is no distortion or breakage.

Applying this to welding, it can be understood that if the heat from the welding flame is concentrated at one point on a metal object, the metal in the heated area tends to expand where the heat is applied, and the portion which opposes this expansion may be distorted, cracked, or severely strained.

Coefficients of expansion

Tables giving the properties of metals usually include the coefficients of expansion. A **coefficient of expansion** of any metal is the amount that the metal will expand per inch for each degree rise in temperature. For example, aluminum has a coefficient of expansion of 0.00001234 while steel has a coefficient of expansion of 0.00000636. This shows that aluminum expands more than steel for each degree rise in temperature. In both these cases, the coefficient refers to a rise of 1°F.

To apply this knowledge, a simple formula can be used. Let A represent the length in inches of the piece of metal, B the temperature in degrees Fahrenheit, and C the coefficient of expansion. Then, expansion in inches $= A \times B \times C$. Thus, if a piece of aluminum is 1 in. long and is raised in temperature 1°F, and its coefficient of expansion is 0.00001234, then the expansion is $1 \times 1 \times 0.00001234$, or 0.00001234 in.

Contraction

Contraction is the shrinking of a substance when cooled from a high temperature. It is the reverse of expansion. Unless there is some restraint, materials contract as much when cooled as they expanded when they were heated, assuming that the temperature is uniform throughout.

In a trussed frame, whether it is in an airplane or a bridge, there is a restriction of the free movement of the metal parts. When such restrictions are present and the metal is malleable (capable of being worked into shape by hammering, rolling, or pressing), warping will take place. If the metal is brittle, it will usually crack.

If the piece of metal is "open," that is, if no obstructions or restrictions hinder its free expansion and contraction, there is no danger of its being damaged from expansion and contraction. An example of open metal occurs in the case of an ordinary bar of metal, a length of unattached tubing, or some similar detached piece of metal.

If the metal is "closed," as in Fig. 7·32, there is danger from expansion and contraction. The bar that was formerly free and unattached is now the center section in Fig. 7·32, and it is fastened rigidly to a solid frame. If the break marked with the letters A and B in Fig. 7·32 is welded, provision must be made for expansion and contraction. Since the crosswise and lengthwise members of the frame are rigid, they do not permit the ends of the bar in the center to expand;

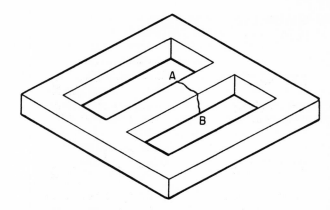

Figure 7·32 Welding a closed section requires heating of entire assembly.

hence the only place where expansion can take place while the metal is heated during the welding process is at the point of the weld. When this portion begins to cool, the center bar contracts and shortens, while the frame in which it is placed refuses to surrender to the inward pull of the ends of the center bar. Warping occurs along the line of weld, or possibly a break occurs.

To avoid this damage, a trained welder heats the whole object before he attempts to weld the break in the center piece. The whole object expands equally, pulling apart the edges of the break. The welder makes his weld and allows the object to cool. All of it cools to the same extent, contracts equally, and suffers neither warpage nor breakage. Figure 7·33 shows examples of shrinkage in welded metal objects.

Conductivity

Conductivity is the physical property of a metal that permits the transmission of either an electric current or heat through its mass. The **rate of conductivity** is the speed at which a metal body will transmit either an electric current or heat through its mass. The rate of conductivity varies among metals. Radiation (heat loss) influences both the rate and the distance of heat conductivity. Thus, metals which are good heat

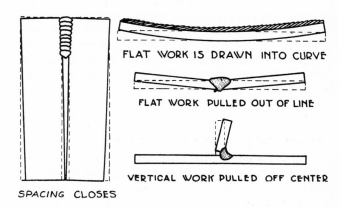

SPACING CLOSES

FLAT WORK IS DRAWN INTO CURVE

FLAT WORK PULLED OUT OF LINE

VERTICAL WORK PULLED OFF CENTER

Figure 7·33 Warping of metal caused by welding.

conductors may be poor radiators, and those which are good radiators may be poor conductors.

In welding, it should be understood that a considerable amount of heat is carried away from the point of application and is lost to the surrounding atmosphere. For this reason, metals which have a high conductivity require more heat in welding than those with a low conductivity, other things being equal.

Another thing to remember in welding is that the higher the conductivity, the more extensive and the hotter will become the heated area around the weld. Therefore more expansion can be expected with metals of high conductivity, other things being equal.

Effect of high temperatures on strength of metals

Some metals have absolutely no strength, or almost no strength, when they are raised to extremely high temperatures. In some cases, this temperature may be far below the melting point of the metal. For example, aluminum alloys, brass, bronze, copper, cast iron, and certain alloy steels become very brittle at high temperatures near their melting points. If such metals are strained while at these high temperatures, they will break, or check, in the area that has been heated.

For example, the melting point of aluminum is 1218°F. At 210°F, it has 90 percent of its maximum strength; at 400°F, it has 75 percent; at 750°F, it has 50 percent; at 850°F, it has 20 percent; and at 930°F, it has only 8 percent of its maximum strength. Yet at 930° it is still far below the melting point.

How to reduce distortion and residual stress

To reduce distortion and residual stress produced by welding, the expansion and contraction of the metal should be controlled. The distortion is especially noticeable in welding long sections of thin sheet metal because the thinner the metal being welded, the greater the distortion.

Four things a welder can do to control the action of those forces which adversely affect the finish weld are the following: (1) He can distribute the heat more evenly; (2) he can put a smaller amount of heat into the weld; (3) he can use special jigs to hold the metal rigidly in place while it is being welded; (4) he can provide a space between the edges of the joint. The nature of each welding job will determine whether only one or all four of these methods should be used.

In discussing Fig. 7·32, the even distribution of heat was explained. Preheating the entire metal object before welding sets free the stored-up forces and permits a more uniform contraction when the welding job is completed.

Putting a smaller amount of heat into a weld is difficult for a beginner, although an experienced welder can estimate accurately the amount of heat required. This is an example of the skill that comes from experience. One of the "tricks of the trade" is to use a method called **stagger welding,** shown in Fig. 7·34. The operator welds briefly at the beginning of the seam, skips to the center, then jumps to the end, comes back to where the first weld ended, and repeats this

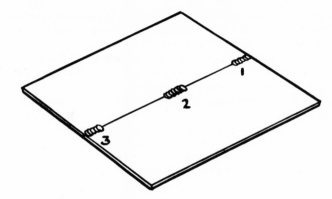

Figure **7·34** Stagger, or skip, welding.

staggered process until he has finished his weld.

Another term for stagger welding is **skip welding,** which is defined as a welding technique in which alternate intervals are skipped in the welding of a joint on the first pass and completed on the second pass or successive passes. The purpose is to prevent any one area of the metal from absorbing a great deal of heat, thus avoiding buckling and the tendency toward cracking.

When a welder uses special jigs to hold the metal rigidly in place while it is being welded, excessive movements of the metal are hindered and the severe distortion resulting from expansion and contraction is prevented.

A **jig** is any rigid structure or mechanism, either wood or metal, which holds parts while they are being worked on (drilled, sawed, welded, etc.) before assembly, or which holds the component parts while they are being assembled or disassembled. Therefore, a welding jig is simply a contrivance that holds the metal sections rigidly in place while a seam is welded. Jigs are fastened tightly, but not so tightly that they will hinder the normal expansion and contraction of the metal at the ends of the joints. If a jig is fastened too tightly, it causes internal stresses in the metal that lower its ability to carry heavy loads.

The fourth method for reducing distortion and residual stresses is the **careful spacing** of the pieces to be welded. Figure 7·35 shows how a **tapering space** is allowed between the pieces that are to be welded together. This tapering space is a distance equal to the thickness of the metal for every foot of seam length. For example, if a welder is to make a joint between two pieces of metal which are both ½ in. thick and 1 ft long, the space between them should be ½ in. at the

Figure **7·35** Tapering space to allow for metal contraction.

ends opposite the starting point. If these same two pieces were 2 ft long, then the space at the wider ends would be twice as much, or 1 in.

Figure 7·36 shows a method of providing for contraction in butt joints. The edges are set parallel and tack-welded. A **tack weld** is one of a series of small welds laid at intervals along a joint to hold the parts in position while they are being welded. This method is used for making short, straight seams or the curved seams on tubing, cylinders, tanks, etc.

Figure 7·37 shows how the edges for butt joints may be set and spaced, the amount of spacing depending upon the kind of metal being welded, usually ranging from ⅛ to ⅜ in. for each foot of the seam length. This method is better for flat sheets and longitudinal seams of cylindrical shapes.

Figure 7·38 is a welding jig for sheet-metal butt joints. It is useful for both flat sheets and longitudinal seams of cylindrical shapes.

Figure 7·39 shows a jig consisting of four pieces of angle iron, used for welding butt joints in sheet metal. The angles for supporting the work on the lower side may be bolted or welded together. A recess of ⅟₃₂ to ³⁄₆₄ in. deep and from ½ to ¾ in. wide is machined in the center. This is labeled "milled groove" in the illustration.

The jig shown in Fig. 7·40 is used for welding corner joints. It consists of three pieces of angle iron. The edge of the piece used to support the work on the lower side is ground- or machined-off to provide about ⅟₁₆-in. clearance for the joint. This enables the fusion to penetrate the base metal all the way through at this point. These jigs are held in place on the metal by means of C-clamps.

In welding plate stock where the shape of the part permits, the butt joints may be set up as illustrated in Fig. 7·37, but if the shape of the work is such that the joint edges must be parallel, either the skip-welding procedure, previously explained, or the **step-back method** should be used for welding the joint. Either of these methods will lower the heat strains because the heat is more evenly distributed over the whole length of the seam, thus causing the expansion and contraction to be uniform.

The **step-back method,** also called the **back-step method,** is a welding technique in which the welder welds and skips intervals between tack welds with each successive pass until the joint is completely

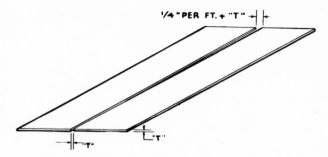

Figure 7·37   Spacing of metal parts for welding.

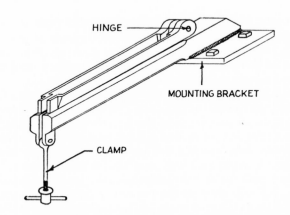

Figure 7·38   A welding jig for sheet-metal butt joints.

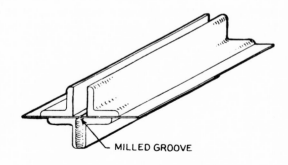

Figure 7·39   Use of a welding jig.

welded. As each pass is completed, the welding is "back-stepped" or "stepped-back" to the next unwelded interval near the beginning of the weld. Figure 7·41 illustrates the step-back method. This should be studied and compared with the stagger welding shown in Fig. 7·34 and a more detailed drawing of this same "skip" method shown in Fig. 7·42.

Figure 7·43 shows that when it is not possible to design a jig for the work, and the metal is held in such a manner that normal expansion and contraction are restrained, the edges of the sheet may be bent up at the joint, as shown in the upper drawing, or a bead may be formed in each sheet, paralled to the seam, ⅝ to 1 in. from the joint, as shown in the lower drawing of Fig. 7·43. Normally, either of these forms will straighten sufficiently on cooling to relieve the strain of the weld;

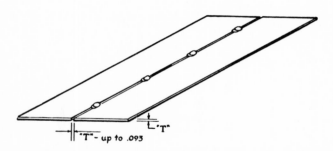

Figure 7·36   Tack welding to hold metal in position.

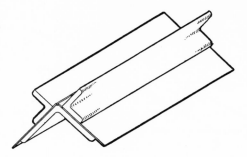

Figure 7·40   *Welding jig for corner joints.*

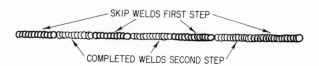

Figure 7·42   *Detailed drawing of skip welding.*

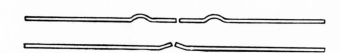

Figure 7·43   *Use of bend or bead to restrain distortion.*

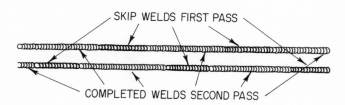

Figure 7·44   *Reducing stresses in welded tee joint.*

however, if for any reason bends of this type are not practical, the welder may place chill plates or a cold pack of wet asbestos on the metal near the joint and parallel to the seam to reduce the flow of heat and the expansion that follows.

Figure 7·44 shows the welding procedure for reducing stresses in tee joints. The welding in this case alternates from one side to the other. If the plate is heavy, the tee joints are heated to a dull red on the opposite side from the side on which the weld is being made. A separate torch is used for this purpose. If done carefully, this heating causes a uniform expansion on both sides of the plate and produces an even contraction that prevents the parts from being pulled out of their correct alignment.

There are several methods for providing for the expansion in the welding of castings. The one selected in each case depends upon the type, kind, and shape of the casting and also on the nature of the break being welded. If the welder has mastered the principles and techniques already described, he should have no trouble in selecting the correct procedure for each job. For example, the entire casting might require preheating to a temperature that will prevent expansion strains on one job, while on another job it might be enough to apply local preheating, that is, heat applied only in the vicinity of the welding zone.

When preheating is applied, the parts preheated must be cooled evenly and slowly. Depending upon the design and other factors, the opposing parts or sections may be preheated to relieve the strains that come from welding. Mechanical devices, such as screw jacks, may be used as an additional precautionary measure. Figure 7·45 shows the application of methods of providing for expansion in the welding of

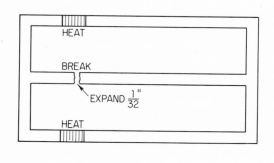

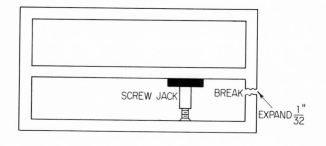

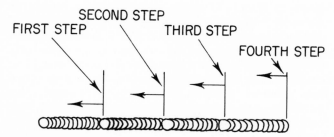

Figure 7·41   *The step-back method of welding.*

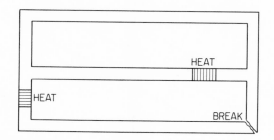

Figure 7·45   *Providing for expansion in welding rectangular castings.*

rectangular castings, and Fig. 7·46 shows the method of providing for expansion in the welding of circular castings.

When parts are fabricated or repaired by welding, there is usually some stress which remains. This stress should be relieved to obtain the full strength of the weld and the base metal. **Heat treatment,** which is discussed in considerable detail elsewhere in this text, is the most reliable method of relieving stress, provided that the part can be heated in a furnace to the stress-relieving temperatures and then cooled slowly and evenly. For example, aluminum and aluminum alloys require a temperature of from 700 to 800°F; gray cast iron, 900 to 1000°F; nickel-chromium-iron alloy (Inconel), 1400°F; carbon steels up to 0.45 percent carbon, 1000 to 1200°F; chrome-molybdenum-alloy steel, 1150 to 1200°F; and chrome-nickel stainless steel (18-8), from 1150 to 1200°F.

Local heating with the welding flame may be used to relieve or eliminate distortion in structures fabricated of steel tubing, angle iron, and similar materials by bringing the metal to a red heat at the proper locations. Figure 7·47 shows a tube pulled out of alignment by weld shrinkage being given this treatment, and Fig. 7·48 shows an angle iron pulled out of alignment by weld shrinkage being given a similar application of local heat.

Identification of metals

The mechanic must be able to identify various metals before he can attempt to weld them. In some organizations, metals may be marked with painted bands of different colors on tubes and bars or by means of numbers on sheet stock. Where there are no colored bands or numbers on the metal, three types of tests are commonly used: (1) the **spark test,** (2) **chemical tests,** and (3) the **flame test.**

In the identification of metals by means of the spark test, **ferrous metals** may be recognized by the characteristics of the spark stream generated by

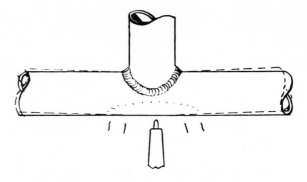

Figure **7·47** Application of heat to straighten a tube.

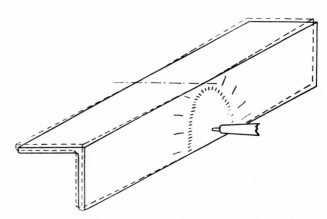

Figure **7·48** Use of heat to straighten an angle section.

grinding with a high-speed grinding wheel. A ferrous metal is one that contains a high percentage of iron. In general, nonferrous metals cannot be identified by the spark test because they do not produce a large shower of sparks and may produce almost none.

In applying the spark test, the most sensible procedure is to obtain samples of various metals and to grind these samples to compare them with the piece of metal being identified. When a known sample produces the same spark characteristics as the unknown piece of metal, identification is accomplished. The characteristics to be observed are (1) the volume of the spark stream, (2) the relative length of the spark stream (in inches), (3) the color of the spark stream close to the grinding wheel, (4) the color of the spark streaks near the end of the stream, (5) the quantity of the sparks, and (6) nature of the sparks.

In volume, the stream is described as extremely small, very small, moderate, moderately large, and large. The relative length may vary from 2 to 70 in., depending upon the metal. For example, cemented tungsten carbine produces an extremely small volume of sparks and the stream is usually only about 2 in. long. On the other hand, machine steel produces a large volume and may be about 70 in. long. These particular figures apply when a 12-in. wheel is used on a bench stand. The actual length in each case depends upon the size and nature of the grinding wheel, the pressure applied, and other factors.

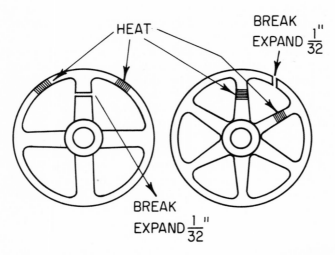

Figure **7·46** Providing for expansion in welding circular castings.

In color, the stream of sparks may be described as red, white, orange, light orange, or straw-colored. The quantity of sparks may be described as none, extremely few, very few, few, moderate many, or very many. The nature of the sparks may be described as forked-, or fine-, repeating. In some cases, the sparks are described as curved, wavy, or blue-white, but in most instances the terms previously given apply.

Some handbooks for mechanics include tables showing these characteristics of the sparks, but all the terms used to describe the spark stream are only comparative. One man will describe the color as orange, while another man will refer to the same stream of sparks as light orange or even straw-colored. Because of this situation, the use of the known samples saves time and promotes accuracy.

A chemical test for distinguishing between **chrome-nickel corrosion-resisting steel (18-8 alloy)** and **nickel-chromium-iron alloy (Inconel)** should be known by welders. A solution consisting of 10 g cupric chloride dissolved in 100 cu cm hydrochloric acid is used. One drop is applied to the unknown metal sample and allowed to remain on the metal for about 2 min. At the end of this time, three or four drops of water are slowly added with a medicine dropper. The sample is then washed and dried. If the metal is stainless steel, the copper in the cupric chloride solution has been deposited on the metal, leaving a copper-colored spot. If the sample is Inconel, the spot left is white.

A **flame test** is used to identify **magnesium alloys.** The welding flame is directed on a small sample until the metal is brought to the melting point. If the metal sample is magnesium alloy, it will ignite at once and burn with a bright glow.

Characteristics of a completed weld

The completed weld should have the following characteristics:

1. The seam should be smooth and of a uniform thickness.
2. The weld should be built up to provide extra thickness at the seam.
3. The weld metal should taper off smoothly into the base metal.
4. No oxide should be formed on the base metal at a distance of more than ½ in. from the weld.
5. The weld should show no signs of blowholes, porosity, or projecting globules.
6. The base metal should show no signs of pitting, burning, cracking, or distortion.

Simple tests for welds

There are many reliable tests for welds, but at this stage of a mechanic's training he should be able to apply one or two very simple tests to judge his progress. One of these is usually called the **bend test.** The welder allows the metal to cool slowly, and then he picks it up with a pair of pliers and clamps the metal in a vise with the weld parallel to the top of the jaws of the vise and slightly above the top of the vise, as shown in Fig. 7·49. He strikes the top of the metal with a

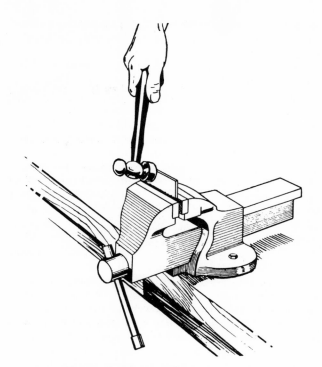

Figure 7·49 Bend test for a weld.

hammer so that the metal is bent along the line of the weld. The weld should be bent in on itself, that is, bent so the bottom of the weld is in tension and the top is in compression. If the weld breaks off very sharply and shows a dull, dirty break and the presence of blowholes, the weld is unsatisfactory. If the weld has been made properly, the metal will not break off short. Instead, it is distorted under the blows of the hammer until it forms an angle of at least 90° without cracking under repeated hammering.

A **visual inspection** is another simple test. The welder examines the smoothness of the bead, the amount of reinforcement (making certain that the same is at least 25 to 50 percent thicker than the base metal), and the cleanliness of the completed weld. The contour should be even. It should extend in a straight line, and its width and height should be even all the distance. No pits should be present.

It should be understood that a clean, smooth, fine-appearing weld is not necessarily a good weld, because it may be dangerously weak inside. However, the opposite is true; that is, if the weld is rough pitted, uneven, and dirty looking, the weld is almost always unsatisfactory inside.

Welds should not be filed to present a smooth-appearing job, since such treatment deprives the weld of part of its strength. Welds must not be filled with solder, brazing metal, or any other filler. When it is necessary to reweld a joint that was previously welded, all old weld material must be thoroughly removed before the new welding job may be accomplished. Never weld over a weld if it can be avoided, because continual heating in the welding process causes the material to lose its strength and to become brittle. All these are practices to be guarded against constantly.

115

REVIEW QUESTIONS

1. Discuss the knowledge of welding necessary for the aircraft maintenance technician.
2. How should the welding torch be held for heavy welding?
3. Explain the difference between *forehand* and *backhand* welding.
4. Explain the purpose of the *filler rod*.
5. Approximately how far should the welding flame cone be held from the base metal?
6. Describe the application of welding rod to the weld.
7. Explain *circular* and *semicircular* motion of the torch.
8. At what angle is the torch flame applied to the metal?
9. Name the four common positions of a weld.
10. Describe how metal is prepared for welding.
11. Why are the edges of the metal beveled in many cases?
12. Describe a *butt joint* in welding.
13. Why is it not necessary to use filler rod for a flange butt joint?
14. Under what conditions is a *double-V tee joint* used?
15. Describe a *single-welded lap joint*.
16. Name the various parts of a weld.
17. What are the three most important proportions of a weld?
18. What should be the width of the welding bead?
19. What should be the depth of penetration in welding?
20. What are the usual causes of improperly formed weak welds?
21. Describe the chemical changes which may take place during gas welding.
22. What is the effect of expansion in welding?
23. Explain *coefficient of expansion*.
24. What precautions must be taken in welding a *closed* metal assembly?
25. Discuss the effect of high temperatures on the strength of metals.
26. What actions can a welder take to reduce the effects of distortion and residual stresses?
27. Explain *stagger* welding and *skip* welding.
28. What is the purpose of a welding jig?
29. When welding heavy plate, how may welding stresses be reduced?
30. How is *preheating* accomplished?
31. Explain *stress relieving*.
32. What is meant by the *spark test* for the identification of metals?
33. Describe a good quality completed weld.
34. What is meant by the *bend test* for a weld?

CHAPTER 8

Arc Welding

Arc welding of various types is quite common in modern manufacturing and repair processes and should be understood by the certificated technician even though he may not be an expert welder himself. A good knowledge of the types of arc welding and how arc welding can be employed in the repair of metal structures is important because the technician will from time to time encounter parts which have been joined by arc welding and he must be able to recognize such construction. Primary structures in aircraft which have been arc-welded must be repaired by approved processes, and it is the responsibility of the repairman to determine the nature of these processes.

Essentially, arc welding consists of utilizing an electric arc to heat and melt metal parts so they may be fused together. An electric arc is concentrated on the edges of two pieces of metal, causing the metal to melt and flow together. Additional metal may be added to the weld by means of wire rods called **electrodes,** or **filler rods.**

A number of different types of arc welding have been developed; however, we may consider the most important types to be the common arc method used for welding heavy steel and the **inert-gas** method employed for the welding of lighter metals which are particularly subject to oxidation and heat distortion. The inert-gas welding technique is divided into different types depending upon the type of gas used and the type of electrical power employed to make the arc. The most common term for inert-gas welding is called **heliarc,** because the original process involved the use of helium as the insulating gas (see Heliarc Inert-gas Welding, page 119, for a more detailed discussion of this process).

A rather sophisticated welding method developed in recent years is **electron-beam welding.** In this process, a powerful beam of electrons is "shot" from an electron gun inside a vacuum chamber. The parts to be welded are placed in the chamber before it is evacuated, and the operator watches and controls the work from outside the chamber. The electron beam is directed to impinge upon the joint to be welded and creates an extremely hot but very small spot where the metal is melted. As the joint fuses, the operator moves the beam until the two parts are joined completely. Since the welding occurs in a near-vacuum, there is no oxidation of the molten metal.

ELECTRIC-ARC WELDING

The term **electric-arc welding** is used here to denote the standard arc process which utilizes an electrode filler rod and is generally employed for welding heavy steel. This method requires a special generator to produce a low-voltage, high-amperage current for the arc. The power supply may be an electric, motor-driven generator, an engine-driven generator, or a special transformer.

The electric arc is made between the tip end of a small metal wire, called the **electrode,** which is clamped in a holder held in the hand, and the metal being welded. A gap is made in the welding circuit by holding the tip of the electrode ¹⁄₁₆ to ⅛ in. away from the work. The electric current jumps the gap and makes an arc which is held and moved along the joint to be welded. The heat of the arc melts the metal. The arc is first caused ("struck") by touching the electrode to the metal, and then the electrode is withdrawn slightly to establish the correct gap across which the arc flows.

The welding circuit

The operator's knowledge of arc welding must go beyond the arc itself. He must know how to control the arc, and this requires a knowledge of the welding circuit and the equipment which provides the electric current used in the arc. Figure 8 · 1 is a diagram of the welding circuit. The circuit begins where the electrode cable is attached to the welding machine and ends

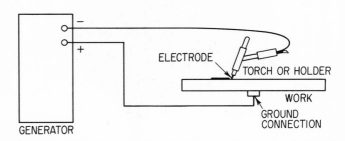

Figure 8 · 1   An arc-welding circuit.

where the ground cable is attached to the welding machine. Current flows through the electrode cable to the electrode holder, through the holder to the electrode, and across the arc. From the work side of the arc, the current flows through the base metal to the ground cable and back to the welding machine. The circuit must be complete for the current to flow, which means that it is impossible to weld if the cables are not connected to the machine or to either the electrode or the work. All connections must be firm so the current can flow easily through the entire circuit.

The several types of welding machines include motor generators, engine-driven generators, transformers, rectifiers, and combination transformers and rectifiers. Figure 8·2 illustrates a typical arc-welding power supply. Each type has its place and purpose but the basic function of each is the same, that is, to provide a source of controlled electric power for welding. This controlled electric power has the characteristic of high amperage at low voltage. The high amperage is required to provide sufficient heat at the arc to melt the metal being welded. The voltage must be low enough to be safe for handling and yet high enough to maintain the arc. The welding machine permits the operator to control the amount of current he uses. This, in turn, controls the amount of heat at the arc. Some welding machines permit the operator to select either a forceful or soft arc and to control its characteristics to suit the job.

The welder's job

A good welder does more than simply hold the arc. He must, first of all, be able to select the correct size and type of electrode for each job. He must know which machine to use for the job and be able to set the current and voltage controls properly. He must be able to manipulate the electrode and arc to make a satisfactory weld under varying conditions. In addition, the welder must have a knowledge of joint preparation, positioning the work, distortion, and many other factors which enter into the final result of a good weld. He must be a mechanic and a craftsman. Nearly anyone can "stick two pieces of metal together," but becoming a good welder requires study, training, and practice.

The welding arc

The action which takes place in the arc during the welding process is illustrated in Fig. 8·3. The "arc stream" is seen in the middle of the picture. This is the electric arc created by the current flowing through air between the end of the electrode and the work. The temperature of this arc is about 6000°F which is more than enough to melt the metal. The arc is very bright, as well as hot, and cannot be looked at with the naked eye without risking painful, though temporary, injury.

The arc melts the plate, or base, metal and actually digs into it, even as the water flowing through a nozzle on a garden hose digs into the earth. The molten metal forms a pool or "crater" and tends to flow away from the arc. As it moves away from the arc, it cools and solidifies. A slag forms on top of the weld to protect it during cooling. The slag comes from the flux coating on the electrode.

The electrode or rod

Arcs for welding are produced by different kinds of power supplies and the various types of power produce arcs with different characteristics. The power supply may be designated dcsp, dcrp, or a-c. Dcsp means **direct current, straight polarity.** Straight polarity is the condition when the electrode is negative and the base metal or work is positive. Dcrp means **direct current, reverse polarity,** where the electrode is positive. The direction of current will have a pronounced effect on the depth and penetration of the weld.

A-c power, of course, means alternating current. With a-c power the order in which the leads from the power source are connected will make no difference.

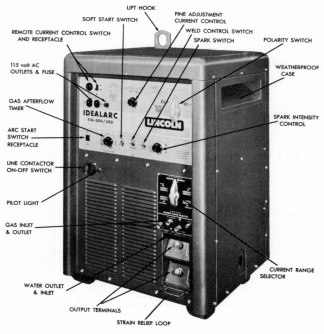

Figure **8·2** Power supply unit for arc welding. (Lincoln Electric Co.)

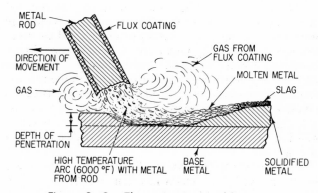

Figure **8·3** The action in a welding arc.

118

In preparing to perform arc welding, the operator should seek to determine the best power source and type of welding rod for the welding being done. Very often, however, only one source of power is available, and the only choice the operator has is the direction of welding current and type of rod.

The function of the electrode is much more than simply to carry current to the arc. The electrode is composed of a core of metal wire around which a chemical coating has been extruded and baked. The core wire melts in the arc, and tiny droplets of molten metal shoot across the arc into the pool. The electrode provides filler metal for the joint to occupy the space or gap between the two pieces of the base metal. The coating also melts or burns in the arc and serves several functions. It makes the arc steadier, increases the arc force, provides a shield of smokelike gas around the arc to keep oxygen and nitrogen in the air away from the molten metal, and provides a flux for the molten pool, which picks up impurities and forms the protective slag. The principal differences between various types of electrodes are in their coatings. By varying the coating, it is possible to alter greatly the operating characteristics of electrodes.

The electrode to be used in any arc welding operation depends upon the material being welded, the type of power being used, and the type of weld. The operator must make certain that the rod chosen will supply the strength required of the weld. When alloy steels and stainless steels are being arc-welded, the rod must be of a composition similar to that of the base material.

HELIARC INERT-GAS WELDING

Heliarc welding is an arc-welding process which employs an inert gas to shield the welding area, thus preventing contamination of the weld from the oxygen and nitrogen. The process originally employed helium to prevent air from reaching the arc and the molten pool of metal, hence the name **heliarc.** The gas most commonly used for inert-gas welding at present is argon, because it is more suitable for a wide variety of metals. Furthermore, argon is used at a lower gas-flow rate and makes the welding operation easier because heat input to the weld puddle is affected less by variations in arc length.

Heliarc welding is accomplished by means of a torch with an unconsumable tungsten electrode. A filler rod is usually fed into the arc to supply the metal necessary to fill the gap and develop the required bead. Inert gas is fed to the weld area through the gas cup on the torch which surrounds the electrode. Heliarc welding using the tungsten electrode is also referred to as **tungsten inert gas** (TIG) welding.

Advantages of inert-gas welding

Inert-gas welds, because of 100 percent protection from the atmosphere, are stronger, more ductile, and more corrosion-resistant than welds made with ordinary metal-arc processes. In addition, the fact that no flux is required makes welding applicable to a wider variety of joint types. Corrosion due to flux entrapment cannot occur, and expensive postwelding cleaning operations are eliminated. The entire welding action takes place without spatter, sparks, or fumes. Fusion welds can be made in nearly all metals used industrially. These include aluminum alloys, stainless steels, magnesium alloys, titanium, and numerous other metals and alloys. The inert gas process is also widely used for welding various combinations of dissimilar metals, and for applying hard-facing and surfacing materials to steel.

Heliarc equipment

The equipment used for heliarc or inert-gas welding consists primarily of the power supply, the torch, and the gas supply, together with connecting hoses and cables. For torches which require cooling, a water system must be included.

A typical torch for inert-gas welding is illustrated in Fig. 8·4. This is the Linde HW-17 torch, suitable for thin-to-medium metal thicknesses. The torch consists of the collet and collet body to hold the tungsten electrode, the gas lens for controlling and directing the gas flow, the gas cup, the handle through which current and gas flow, and supporting structures.

The power supply for inert-gas welding can be the same as that employed for standard arc welding or it may be especially designed for inert-gas welding. A portable power-supply unit for heliarc welding is shown in Fig. 8·5. This is the Linde HDA 300 welder which can supply 300 amp for a 60 percent duty cycle. The unit also includes the argon cylinder, argon regulator, and tow cart. When purchased as a complete welding unit, the torch, connecting lines and other accessories are included.

Type of power for TIG welding

As mentioned previously, tungsten inert-gas welding can be accomplished with direct current, straight polarity (dcsp); direct current, reverse polarity (dcrp); or with alternating current, high-frequency stabilized (achf). Achf power is generally recommended for magnesium and aluminum alloys and castings while

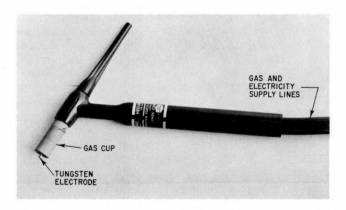

GAS AND
ELECTRICITY
SUPPLY LINES

GAS CUP

TUNGSTEN
ELECTRODE

Figure 8·4   A heliarc torch.

Figure 8·5 A portable power-supply unit. (Anderson Equipment Co.)

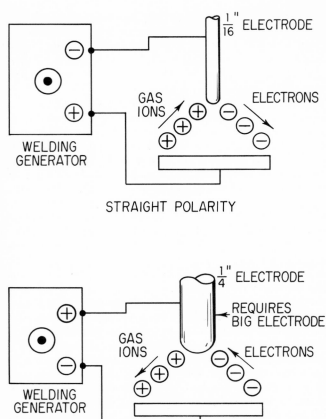

Figure 8·6 Action of different types of welding current.

dcsp power is recommended for stainless steel, copper alloys, nickel alloys, titanium, low-carbon steel, and high-carbon steel. Achf or dcrp provides the best results with beryllium-copper alloys or copper alloys less than 0.040 in. thick.

The effects of different types of current may be understood by studying the diagrams of Fig. 8·6. In direct-current welding, the welding current may be hooked up as either sp or rp. As previously explained, the machine connection for dcsp welding is with the electrode negative and the work positive. The electrons will then flow from the electrode to the work as shown in the illustration. For dcrp welding, the connections are reversed and the electrons flow from the work to the electrode.

In straight-polarity welding, the electrons hitting the plate at a high velocity exert a considerable heating effect on the plate. In reverse-polarity welding, just the opposite occurs; the electrode acquires this extra heat which then tends to melt the end. Thus, for any given welding current, dcrp requires a larger-diameter electrode than dcsp. For example, a ¹⁄₁₆-in.-diameter pure-tungsten electrode can handle 125 amp of welding current under straight-polarity conditions. If the polarity were reversed, however, this amount of current would

melt off the electrode and contaminate the weld metal. Hence, a ¼-in.-diameter pure-tungsten electrode is required to handle 125 amp dcrp satisfactorily and safely.

These opposite heating effects influence not only the welding action but also the shape of the weld obtained. Dcsp welding will produce a narrow, deep weld; dcrp welding, because of the larger electrode diameter and lower currents generally employed, gives a wide, relatively shallow weld. The difference is illustrated in Fig. 8·7.

One other effect of dcrp welding should be considered here, namely, the so-called **cleaning effect.** Although the exact reason for this surface cleaning action is not known, it seems probable that either the electrons leaving the plate or the gas ions striking the plate tend to break up the surface oxides, scale, and dirt usually present.

Inert-gas welding with alternating current

Theoretically, straight a-c welding is a combination of dcsp and dcrp welding. This can be explained by showing the three current waves visually. As illustrated in Fig. 8·8, half of each complete a-c cycle is dcsp and the other half is dcrp. Actually, however, moisture,

120

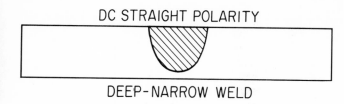

DC STRAIGHT POLARITY

DEEP-NARROW WELD

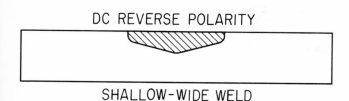

DC REVERSE POLARITY

SHALLOW-WIDE WELD

Figure 8 · 7   Effects of different polarities on the weld.

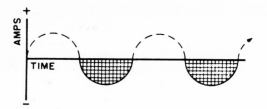

Figure 8 · 9   Rectified a-c wave: two complete cycles of a-c with reverse polarity completely rectified. (Linde Div., Union Carbide Corp.)

Figure 8 · 10   Comparison of achf weld with dcsp and dcrp welds. (Linde Div., Union Carbide Corp.)

oxides, scale, and other materials on the surface of the work tend to prevent the flow of current in the reverse-polarity direction. This effect is called **rectification.** For example, if no current at all flows in the reverse-polarity direction, the current wave will look something like the curve in Fig. 8 · 9.

To prevent the effects of rectification, it is common practice to introduce into the welding current a high-voltage, high-frequency, low-power additional current. This high-frequency current jumps the gap between the electrode and the workpiece and pierces the oxide film, thereby forming a path for the welding current to follow. Superimposing this high-voltage, high-frequency current on the welding current provides the following advantages:

1. The arc may be started without touching the electrode to the workpiece.
2. Better stability is obtained.
3. A longer arc is possible. This is particularly useful in surfacing and hard-facing operations.
4. Welding electrodes have a longer life.
5. The use of wider current ranges for a specific diameter electrode is possible.

A typical weld contour produced with high-frequency stabilized alternating current is shown in Fig. 8 · 10, together with both dcsp and dcrp welds for comparison.

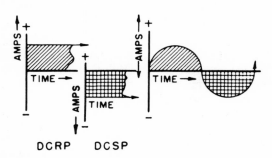

Figure 8 · 8   Illustration of a-c wave: one complete cycle of a-c. (Linde Div., Union Carbide Corp.)

Welding joint design

Although there are innumerable welding joint designs possible, the basic types are **butt joint, lap joint, corner joint, edge joint,** and **tee joint.** Almost any heliarc weld will be one or a combination of two or more of these basic types. Selection of the proper design for a particular application depends primarily on the following factors:

1. Physical properties desired in the weld
2. Cost of preparing the joint and making the weld
3. Type of metal being welded
4. Size, shape, and appearance of the part to be welded

Filler metal in the form of welding rod need not be used if proper reinforcement and complete fusion of the edges can be obtained without it. The joint designs described in this section are but a few of the many that can be successfully welded with the inert-gas method.

No matter what types of joint is used, proper cleaning of the work prior to welding is essential if welds of good appearance and physical properties are to be obtained. On small assemblies, manual cleaning with a wire brush, steel wool, or a chemical solvent is usually sufficient. For large assemblies, or for cleaning on a production basis, vapor degreasing or tank cleaning may be more economical. In any case, it is necessary to remove completely all oxide, scale, oil, grease, dirt, rust, and other foreign matter from the work surfaces.

Precautions should be taken when using certain chemical solvents such as carbon tetrachloride, trichlorethylene, and tetrachlorethylene, which break down in the heat of an electric arc and form a toxic gas. Welding should not be done when these gases are present and the solvents should not be exposed to the heat of the welding torch. Inhalation of the fumes can be dangerous; hence proper ventilation equipment should be provided to remove fumes and vapors from the work area.

The square-edge **butt joint** shown in Fig. 8·11 is the easiest to prepare, and it can be welded with or without filler metal, depending on the thickness of the pieces being welded. Joint fit for a square-edge butt joint should always be true enough to assure 100 percent penetration with good fusion. When welding light-gage material without adding filler metal, extreme care should be taken to avoid low spots and burn-through. The heavier thickness will generally require filler metal to provide adequate reinforcement.

The single-V butt joint, shown in Fig. 8·12, is used where complete penetration is required on material thicknesses ranging between ⅜ and 1 in. Filler rod must be used to fill in the V. The included angle of the V should be approximately 60°; the nose will measure from ⅛ to ¼ in., depending on the composition and thickness of the pieces being welded.

The double-V butt joint of Fig. 8·13 is generally used on stock thicker than ½ in., where the design of the assembly being welded permits access to the back of the joint for a second pass. With this type of joint, proper welding techniques will assure a sound weld with 100 percent fusion.

A flange-type butt joint such as that illustrated in Fig. 8·14 should be used in place of the square-edge butt joint where some reinforcement is desired. This joint is practical only on relatively thin material, about 0.065 to 0.085 in.

A **lap joint** has the advantage of eliminating entirely the necessity for edge preparation. Such a joint is shown in Fig. 8·15. The only requirement for making a good lap weld is that the plates be in close contact along the entire length of the joint and that the work be thoroughly cleaned as explained previously. On material ¼ in. thick or less, lap joints can be made with or without filler rod. When no filler metal is used, care must be taken to avoid low spots or burn-through. The lap-type joint is not usually recommended on material thicker than ¼ in. except for rough fitup. When so used, filler rod must always be added to assure good fusion and buildup. The number of passes

Figure **8·11**   Square-edge butt joint. (Linde Div., Union Carbide Corp.)

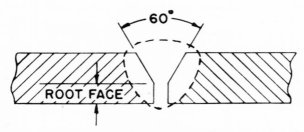

Figure **8·12**   Single-V butt joint. (Linde Div., Union Carbide Corp.)

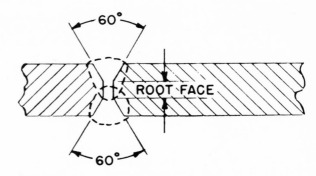

Figure **8·13**   Double-V butt joint. (Linde Div., Union Carbide Corp.)

Figure **8·14**   Flange joint. (Linde Div., Union Carbide Corp.)

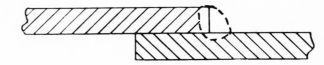

Figure **8·15**   Lap joint.

required depends on the thickness of the pieces being joined.

Corner joints are frequently used in the fabrication of pans, boxes, and all types of containers as well as for other heavier purposes. The type *A* corner joint, shown in Fig. 8·16, is used on material thicknesses up to ⅛ in. No filler metal is required, as the amount of base metal fused is sufficient to assure a sound, high-strength weld. Type *B*, as shown in the illustration, is used on heavier material that requires filler rod to provide adequate reinforcement. Type *C* is used on very heavy material where 100 percent penetration is impossible without the beveled-edge preparation. The nose should be thick enough to prevent burn-through on the first pass. The number of passes required depends on the size of the V and thickness of the members being welded. On all corner joints, the pieces must be in good contact along the entire seam.

All **tee joints** require the addition of filler rod to provide the necessary buildup. Such a joint is shown in Fig. 8·17. The number of passes on each side of the joint depends upon the thickness of the material and the size of the weld desired. When 100 percent penetration is required, the welding current must be adequate for the thickness of the web material.

A typical **edge joint** is shown in Fig. 8·18. Such joints are used solely on light-gage material and require no filler rod. Preparation is simple, and the

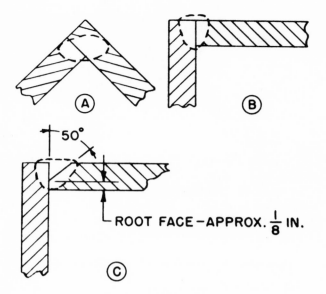

Figure 8 · 16   Corner joint.

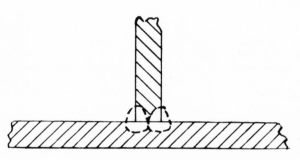

Figure 8 · 17   Tee joint.

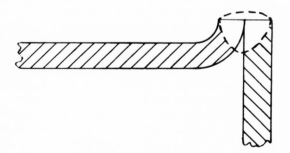

Figure 8 · 18   Edge joint.

joint is economical to weld. This type of joint should not be used, however, where direct tension or bending stresses will be applied to the finished joint because it will fail at the root under relatively low stress loads.

Weld backup

On many heliarc welding applications, the joint should be backed up. This is done for several reasons. On light-gage material, backing is usually used to protect the underside of the weld from atmospheric contamination resulting in possible weld porosity or poor surface appearance. In addition to these func-

tions, weld backup prevents the weld puddle from dropping through by acting as a heat sink and drawing away some of the heat generated by the intense arc. The backup also can physically support the weld puddle. A heliarc weld can be backed up by (1) metal backup bars, (2) introducing an inert-gas atmosphere on the weld underside, (3) a combination of the first two methods, or (4) use of flux backing, painted on the weld underside.

Flat, metal backup bars are generally used on joints like the flange type shown in Fig. 8 · 19, where the bar does not actually touch the weld zone. If the bar comes in contact with the underside of the weld, nonuniform penetration may occur and the weld underside may be rough and uneven.

A type of backup bar more commonly used is that shown in Fig. 8·20, where the surface is cut or machined-out directly below the joint. On square-edge butt joints, for example, where fitup is not too accurate and filler rod is required, a bar of this sort will protect the bottom of the weld from excessive contamination by the atmosphere and will draw the heat away from the weld zone.

Apparatus check

Before starting to weld, the entire welding setup should be thoroughly checked. It is most important to use the proper-size electrode, gas cup, etc. All components must be functioning properly to realize the full advantage of this type of welding. The following instructions can be used as a guide:

1. Check all connections in the argon supply line for tightness. Be sure that good seals are obtained between the torch body, the cap, and the gas cup, because any air leakage into the argon stream will contaminate both the weld and the electrode. Be sure any gaskets required are in good condition and firmly in place. After welding, the electrode should have a clean, silvery appearance upon cooling. A dirty, rough electrode surface usually signifies air leakage in the torch or argon supply system.
2. Check the welding current and argon-flow settings. They should be present to the approximate values recommended for the material being welded.
3. Select the proper gas cup and electrode size.

Figure 8 · 19   Use of a backup bar.

Figure 8 · 20   Use of backup bar with a cutout.

4. Check the rate of water flow through the torch if it is the water-cooled type. Flow rates lower than those recommended decrease torch efficiency and may result in damage to the torch, particularly if the torch is being used at or near its maximum capacity.
5. Check the ground connection to be sure it is securely clamped to the workpiece. The workpiece should be cleaned at the point of contact, preferably by grinding, to assure good contact.

HELIARC WELDING TECHNIQUES

Starting an arc

There is nothing difficult about starting an arc in the proper manner. The procedure explained in this section should ensure a good start and maximum protection of the work from atmospheric contamination at the start of the welding operation.

In a-c welding, the electrode does not have to touch the work to start the arc. The superimposed high-frequency current jumps the gap between the welding electrode and the work thus establishing a path for the welding current to follow. To strike an arc, the torch is held in a horizontal position about 2 in. above the work or starting block, as shown in Fig. 8·21. The end of the torch is then swung quickly down toward the work so the end of the electrode is about ⅛ in. above the metal. The arc strikes at this distance. The downward motion should be made rapidly to provide the maximum amount of gas protection to the weld zone. The position of the torch when the arc strikes is shown in Fig. 8·22.

In d-c welding, the same motion is used for striking the arc. In this case, however, the electrode must actually touch the work in order to start the arc. As soon as the arc is struck, the torch is withdrawn so the electrode is about ⅛ in. from the work. This prevents contamination of the electrode in the molten pool. High-frequency a-c is sometimes used to start a d-c arc. This eliminates the need for touching the workpiece. The high-frequency current is automatically

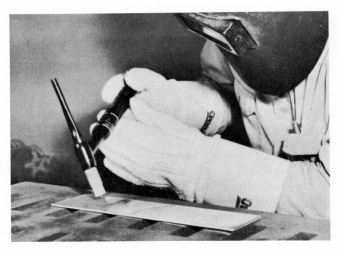

Figure 8·22   Torch position when arc is struck.

turned off by means of a current relay when the arc is started.

The arc can be struck on the workpiece itself or on a heavy piece of copper or scrap steel, and then carried to the starting point of the weld. A carbon block should not be used for striking the arc because it is likely to contaminate the electrode and cause the arc to wander. When starting to weld with a hot electrode, the action must be very rapid because the arc tends to strike before the torch is in the proper position.

To stop an arc, the torch is merely snapped quickly back to the horizontal position. This motion must be made rapidly so the arc will not mar or damage the weld surface or work.

Arc wandering

With the heliarc torch held stationary, the points at which an arc leaves the electrode and impinges upon the work may often shift and waver without apparent reason. This is known as **arc wandering** and is generally attributed to one of the following causes: (1) low-electrode-current density, (2) carbon contamination of the electrode, (3) magnetic effects, and (4) air drafts. The first two causes are distinguished by a very rapid movement of the arc from side to side, generally resulting in a zigzag weld pattern. The third cause, magnetic effect, usually displaces the arc to one side or the other along the entire length of the weld. The fourth causes varying amounts of arc wandering, depending upon the amount of air draft present.

When current density of the electrode is at a sufficiently high level, the entire end of the electrode will be in a molten state and completely covered by the arc. When too low a current density is used, only a small area of the electrode becomes molten resulting in an unstable arc which has poor directional characteristics and is difficult for the operator to control. Too high a current density results in excessive melting of the electrode.

When a carbon block is used to strike the arc,

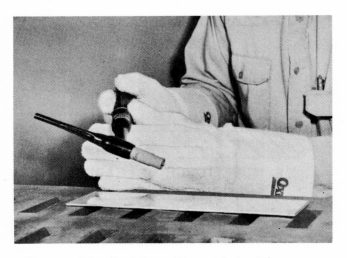

Figure 8·21   Torch in position ready to strike an arc.

electrode contamination will often result. As the electrode touches the carbon, the molten tungsten on the tip of the electrode forms tungsten carbide. This has a lower melting point than pure tungsten and forms a large molten ball on the end of the electrode. This, in effect, reduces the current density at the electrode end and arc wandering occurs. The electrode can also be contaminated by touching it to the workpiece or filler rod. When electrode contamination occurs in any form, it is best to clean the electrode by grinding, breaking off the end, or using a new electrode.

Magnetic effects are not generally encountered and are too complex to be discussed fully in this text. The most common magnetic action on the arc, however, results from the magnetic field set up by the current flowing in the work. This field may tend to attract or repel the arc from the normal path. One method for remedying this condition is to alter the position of the ground connection on the work until the effects are no longer noticed.

Making a butt weld

After the arc has been struck, as previously explained, the torch should be held at about a 75° angle to the surface of the work. The starting point of the weld is first preheated by moving the torch in small circles, as shown in Fig. 8·23, until a small molten pool is formed. The end of the electrode should be held approximately ⅛ in. above the work. When the puddle becomes bright and fluid, the torch is moved slowly and steadily along the joint at a speed that will produce a bead of uniform width. No oscillating or other movement of the torch, except for the steady forward motion, is required.

When filler metal is required to provide adequate reinforcement, the welding rod is held at about 15° to the work and about 1 in. away from the starting point. The starting point is then preheated as explained previously to develop the molten pool. When the puddle becomes bright and fluid, the arc is moved quickly to the rear of the puddle and filler rod is added by quickly touching the leading edge of the puddle.

The rod is removed and the arc is brought back to the leading edge of the puddle. As soon as the puddle becomes bright again, the steps are repeated. This sequence is continued for the entire length of the weld. Figure 8·24 illustrates the steps as described. The rate of forward speed and the amount of filler rod added depend on the desired width and height of the bead.

For making **butt joints** on a vertical surface, the torch is held perpendicular to the work and the weld is usually made from top to bottom. When filler rod is used, it is added from the bottom or leading edge of the puddle in the manner described previously. Figure 8·25 shows correct positioning of the rod and torch relative to the work.

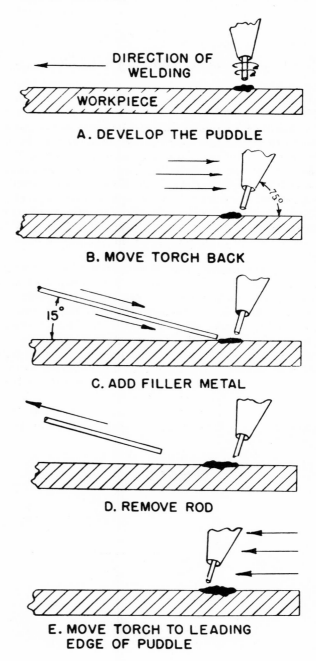

A. DEVELOP THE PUDDLE

B. MOVE TORCH BACK

C. ADD FILLER METAL

D. REMOVE ROD

E. MOVE TORCH TO LEADING EDGE OF PUDDLE

Figure **8·24** *Steps in starting a weld.*

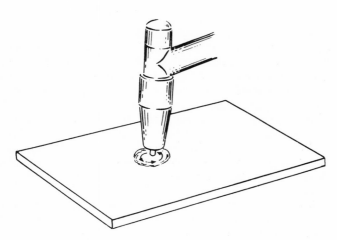

Figure **8·23** *Forming the molten puddle.*

125

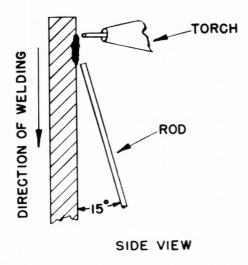

SIDE VIEW

Figure 8·25 Position of torch and filler for vertical weld.

Making a lap weld

A **lap weld,** or **joint,** is started by first developing a puddle on the bottom sheet. When the puddle becomes bright and fluid, the arc is shortened to about ¹⁄₁₆ in. The torch is then oscillated directly over the joint until the sheets are firmly joined. Once the weld is started, the oscillating movement is no longer required. The torch is merely moved along the seam with the electrode held just above the edge of the top sheet.

In lap welding, the puddle developed will be boomerang- or V-shaped as shown in Fig. 8·26. The center of the puddle is called the **notch,** and the speed at which this notch travels will determine how fast the torch can be moved forward. Care must be taken to see that the notch is completely filled for the entire length of the seam. Otherwise, it is impossible to get 100 percent fusion and good penetration.

When filler metal is used, faster welding speeds are possible because the rod helps to fill the notch. Complete fusion must be obtained rather than allowing bits of filler rod to be laid into the cold, unfused base metal. The rod should be alternately dipped into the puddle and withdrawn ¼ in., as illustrated in Fig.

DIRECTION OF WELDING

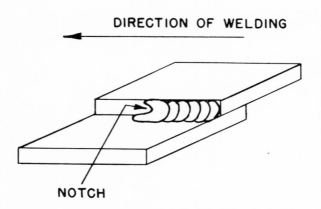

NOTCH

Figure 8·26 Shape of puddle in lap welding.

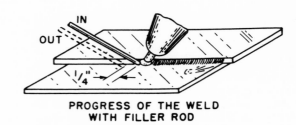

PROGRESS OF THE WELD
WITH FILLER ROD

Figure 8·27 Procedure for lap welding. Move filler rod in and out about ¼ in.

8·27. By carefully controlling the melting rate of the top edge, and by adding just enough filler metal where needed, a good uniform bead of correct proportions can be obtained.

Making a corner or edge weld

The **corner,** or **edge, weld** is the easiest type to make. A puddle is developed at the starting point and the torch is then moved straight along the joint. Rate of travel is regulated to produce a uniform bead. Too slow a welding speed will cause molten metal to roll off the edges. Irregular or too-high speeds will produce a rough, uneven surface. No filler metal is required.

Multipass heliarc welding

Multipass welding is generally required for welding material over ¼ in. thick. The number of passes required depends upon the thickness of the material, the current-carrying capacity of the equipment involved, and the assembly being fabricated. The first pass should be a **root weld** and provide complete fusion at the bottom of the joint. Subsequent passes can be made at higher currents due to the backup effect of the root weld. Care should be taken to prevent inclusions between weld layers. On heavy work, it is sometimes advantageous to carry all the beads along simultaneously in a staggered arrangement to utilize the residual heat of preceding passes.

CONCLUSION

In this section we have explained two common types of electric-arc welding. The plain electric-arc system is commonly used for heavy industrial construction in steel. Inert-gas welding, on the other hand, is used in a wide variety of precision welding on many different types of metals and alloys. For this reason it is particularly well adapted for welding structures and parts for aerospace vehicles.

There are many other types of arc welding, some of which are **submerged-arc, plasma, metal-inert-gas** (MIG), and **electron-beam welding.** These are specialties and are usually practiced by highly skilled welders. They are not usually done by the average airframe and powerplant maintenance technician; hence, detailed descriptions of these processes are considered beyond the scope of this text.

REVIEW QUESTIONS

1. Describe the process of electric-arc welding.
2. Describe the electrode for arc welding.
3. What are two functions of the electrode?
4. What is the purpose of the coating on the electrode?
5. Describe the welding circuit.
6. What is the nature of the power used for electric-arc welding with respect to voltage and amperage?
7. What type of devices supply power for arc welding?
8. Describe what takes place in the welding arc.
9. What temperature is developed in the arc?
10. Explain the three types of current which may be used for arc welding.
11. Describe heliarc inert-gas welding.
12. What is the nature of the electrode used with heliarc?
13. Give the advantages of inert-gas welding.
14. What equipment is necessary for heliarc welding?
15. What types of power are used with heliarc welding?
16. What is the difference in the effects of dcsp and dcrp current?
17. Why is a larger electrode required with dcrp welding?
18. What are the advantages of achp current?
19. Name five basic joints for heliarc welding.
20. How should metal be prepared before starting to weld?
21. Why is a weld backup used with some joints?
22. List the checks that should be made before starting to weld.
23. Describe the process of striking an arc.
24. Why is it undesirable to strike the arc on a carbon block?
25. What is meant by *arc wandering?*
26. What are principal causes of arc wandering?
27. Describe the process of starting a weld.
28. What is meant by *multipass* welding?

Aircraft Construction and Repair by Welding

WELDING OF AIRCRAFT METAL PARTS

As mentioned in other sections of this text, a rather wide variety of welding processes have been developed for joining various types of metals for aircraft. Oxyacetylene welding is still practiced extensively for the manufacture and repair of steel aircraft structures; however, inert-gas welding (heliarc) is more commonly used for the welding of aluminum, stainless steels, titanium, and magnesium alloys.

This chapter deals with the conventional methods used for the repair of steel structures which are easily performed by the technician either in the shop, or in the field with portable equipment.

MONO-COQUE

Modern metal airplanes are designed so that the skin of the airplane, rather than the interior structures of steel tubing, carries a large part of the loads and stresses during flight. As a result, there is a smaller amount of tubing in the newer airplanes, but there are still many parts of structures built with steel tubing, especially in some of the smaller aircraft.

AIRCRAFT TUBING REPAIR

Types of steel tubing

The steel tubing used most extensively for aircraft structures, engine mounts, and similar parts, is **chromium-molybdenum,** also called **chrome-molybdenum** or **chrome-moly.** It is usually designated by the SAE number 4130. The above descriptive terms refer to a group of steels included under the general classi-

fication of molybdenum steels that contain **chromium** as well as molybdenum. The principal properties of these steels are resistance to impact fatigue, abrasion, and high-temperature stress. They are capable of deep-hardening when given a suitable heat treatment, they have good machinability, and they are easily welded by gas and electric-arc methods.

The SAE 4130 steel is designated by the American Iron and Steel Institute (AISI) as A4130. This alloy steel is available in both sheet and tubing forms and, like the other steels in its class, it is very shock-resistant, and it has great initial strength.

Steel tubing is adaptive to aircraft construction because it is strong for its weight and can be repaired easily. In making repairs, either steel tubing or sheet stock having code numbers 1025 (carbon steel), 4130 (chrome-moly), or 4330 (nickel-chromium-molybdenum) can be used. In any case, if replacements are being made, the replacement material should be the same as the original. Repairs can be made with little equipment. All that is required is a welding apparatus, a short section of steel to replace the damaged section, and the tools to cut and prepare the metal for welding.

Procedures for weld repairs (TEST)

The parts to be welded should be cut to the proper dimensions and secured in place with clamps or jigs to assure correct alignment. In the case of a major rework of a fuselage, it is likely that the entire fuselage must be placed in a jig to keep it properly aligned while the repair is being made.

The areas to be welded must be thoroughly cleaned by wire brushing, filing, or by some other method to assure a weld free of such defects as inclusions or contamination. A brass brush should never be used because the small amount of brass left on the surface will weaken the weld.

The torch flame should be adjusted for a reasonably soft condition; that is, the force of the flame should not be such that it will tend to blow the molten pool of metal away from the weld. For comparatively thin tubing, the inner cone would not be more than ⅛ in. long.

The size of the welding torch tip is primarily governed by the thickness of the metal. Table 6·1 gives typical tip sizes.

The tip should be large enough to permit rapid welding but small enough to avoid overheating and burning the metal. Burning weakens the metal and causes it to crack when it contracts because of cooling. Rewelding is objectionable for the same reason; that is, it tends to overheat the metal, and thus might lead to structural failure in flight. In preheating metal, the flame is pointed in the direction of welding.

The **welding (filler) rod** usually is made of mild steel for welding chrome-moly steel because it flows smoothly and contributes to a uniform, sound weld. Flux is not required. Some welders recommend the use of a welding rod made of alloy steel but the disadvantages of alloy steels sometimes appear to outweigh the advantages. In any event, if the repaired part requires heat treating, it is necessary that the welder use heat-treatable filler rod.

Welds made in aircraft tubing must not be dressed to produce a smoother appearance. Such treatment will weaken the weld. In welding thin tubing, which usually means tubing less than 0.040 in. thick, the weld should be no wider than ¼ in.

All steels tend to be weak when very hot but strong and tough when cold. This is especially true in the case of chrome-moly steel; hence it may crack if placed under a comparatively light stress while it is still very hot. One way to avoid trouble is to use welding jigs that will not restrict the expansion and contraction of the welded members. Another precaution is to avoid overheating the metal while it is being welded at or near an edge. The reason for this is that an edge gets hot very fast and may crack before the welder realizes the condition. He can reduce losses from this source by drawing the welding flame away slightly whenever he approaches an edge.

Welders are cautioned against filing welds in an effort to make a smooth-appearing job, because such treatment reduces the strength of the part. Likewise, it is forbidden to fill a weld with solder, brazing, metal, or any other filler. When it becomes necessary to reweld a joint that was previously welded, all the old weld material is thoroughly removed before rewelding. A weld should not be made over an old weld because the repeated heating weakens the material and makes it brittle.

Welding should never be done over a brazed area or where the brazing has been removed. If a repaired area were covered with a corrosion-resistant material before the repair were made, this material should be replaced after the repair is completed. (MECALIZATION)

For standard steel-tubing repairs, it is good practice to sandblast the welded area after welding to provide a good clean metal base for the application of primer such as zinc chromate. The weld should be primed before corrosion has had a chance to start, and the clean surface should be protected from any contamination before it is primed.

Controlling distortion (TEST)

When steel-tube structural units and steel fittings are constructed or repaired, the welder can expect the usual expansion, contraction, and shrinkage of the weld metal. In addition, he must prevent any extraordinary loss of metal thickness from excess scaling during welding. If he applies the correct procedure, these factors may be controlled within satisfactory limits.

Cracking can be prevented by reducing the strains on the weld and hot-base metal caused by weight or restriction of the normal processes of expansion and contraction. For example, one end of a web member may be welded to the flange member of a truss and permitted to cool before the opposite end of the web member is welded. Also, joints of a tubular assembly in which several members terminate should be welded first and allowed to cool before the opposite ends are welded. This is done because the additional time required to weld such joints permits the heat to flow from the weld into the members, and this heat flow causes them to expand. If the members are connected to similar joints at the opposite end, it is advisable to apply heavy clamps, chill plates, or wet asbestos to the members, close to the weld, in order to restrict this heat flow and thus reduce the expansion.

When fittings are welded, shrinkage strains and their accompanying tendency to cause cracking can be reduced greatly by beginning the weld at the fixed end and working toward the free end of the opening or seam. Cold-rolled alloy-steel forms or heat-treated forms are annealed before welding to reduce the brittleness. Another recommended practice is to relieve the stresses of alloy-steel parts after welding by heating the whole part uniformly to a temperature between 1150 and 1200°F, and then allowing the part to cool very slowly. (NORMALIZING)

If a joint is held together by both riveting and welding, the rivet holes are lined up and the welding is completed before the rivets are driven. This procedure prevents the shearing stress on the rivets and the elongation of the holes caused by the expansion and contraction of the metal.

Warpage is controlled by using enough clamps and correctly constructed jigs. **Progressive welding,** which is welding progressively along the joint from the beginning to the end, either continuously from start to finish, or in sections with each section tied in or joined to the next, is another method for reducing strains. A third method is to heat the member on the opposite side from which the weld is made.

Shrinkage is provided for by making the required allowance for normal shrinkage as indicated by a trial weld under similar conditions. An allowance of ½₂ in. at each end of a truss or web member is often enough. This allowance is a rough, general one for both steel-tube structural units and fittings built up of sheet metal, but it is not a substitute for careful work.

SIMPLE Minor operations

Most repairs on aircraft tubing require the cutting out and welding in of a partial replacement tube, or the replacement of a whole section of tubing, but some repairs are relatively ~~minor~~ SIMPLE. An example is the straightening of a piece of fuselage tubing which has become slightly bent or buckled. If the bent or buckled part is not made of a heat-treated steel, it should be stronger after straightening because the cold working which the metal receives in the straightening process adds to its strength.?

One device useful for straightening bent or buckled tubing is a heavy-duty C-clamp as shown in Fig. 9·1. Three blocks of hardwood are required for use with the

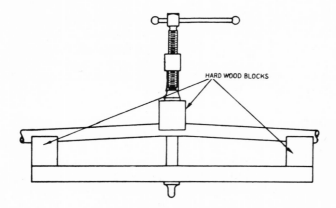

HARD WOOD BLOCKS

Figure 9 · 1   C-clamp used to straighten bent tubing.

C-clamp. These blocks are cut to fit the shape of the tubing and the tubing grooves are lined with a soft material such as leather or heavy cloth. Another unit of required equipment is a steel bar, sufficiently strong to withstand the bending stress applied when the tubing is straightened. One of the grooved blocks is placed at each end of the bent section of tubing and the blocks are held in place by the C-clamp and bar, the latter spanning the bent area and backing up the wooden blocks as shown in the illustration. The third block is placed under the jaw of the clamp to bear against the tubing at the point of greatest bend. Since the C-clamp jaws apply pressure to force the tubing toward the steel bar, the tubing is straightened as the clamp is tightened. The handle of the C-clamp should be turned until the tubing is bent slightly past the straight position. The clamp and blocks are removed and the tubing is tested by placing a straightedge on both the side and the top of the tube. If the tube is straight, the job is completed; however, if a bend is still apparent the operation must be repeated until the desired result is obtained.

Whenever a bent tube is straightened, the adjoining welded joints must be examined for cracks. If cracks are found, they must be repaired. They usually occur at the point where the maximum bend was corrected. Briefly, the repair is made by drilling a hole at each end of the crack and welding a split steel sleeve over the crack, but the details of such a repair are given later in this chapter. Remember that the tube straightening procedure illustrated and described above is done only if the tube is not dented, crushed, or kinked.

Another minor local defect in tubing is one in which a section of tubing has been slightly flattened; that is, it has become slightly oval-shaped or out-of-round. This defect is remedied by first drilling a steel block to the diameter of the tube to be re-formed. This block, which is usually about 4 in. square, is sawed in half lengthwise through the center of the hole, and the two sections are separated. A small quantity of cup grease or oil may be applied to the blocks on the surfaces that will come into contact with the tube. The two grooved steel blocks, obtained by sawing through the original block, are clamped into position over the out-of-round portion of the tube. The clamp is gradually tightened

and pressure is applied, as shown in Fig. 9 · 2, and the assembly is rotated around the tube until it assumes its original, normal shape. Heating the tubing to a dull red makes this procedure easier. If the out-of-round portion of the tube is longer than the length of the two steel blocks, the procedure is repeated throughout the length of the out-of-round area until the whole length has resumed its original round shape.

If the defect is a minor, smooth dent in tubing, not deeper than one-twentieth the tube diameter, and is clear of the middle third of the tube section, it may be disregarded. If the dent is large enough to require removal, and the tubing is not out-of-round for any considerable distance, the dent may be pushed out by air pressure. One of the self-tapping screws provided at the ends of the main steel tubes is removed so that an air pressure of about 75 psi or more can be applied inside the tubing. The dented area is heated with the welding torch until it is dull red, and the air pressure is maintained until it forces out the dent and restores the tubing to its original shape. In order to apply air pressure to the inside of the tubing, it will be necessary to install a suitable fitting to which an air source can be attached.

In some cases the combination of heat and air pressure is not sufficient to straighten the tube. Under these conditions, a welding rod is tack-welded to the center of the dented area and pulled while the area is heated. When the dent has been pulled out in this manner, the welding rod is removed, the heated area is allowed to cool, and then the air pressure is released. Finally the self-tapping screw is replaced.

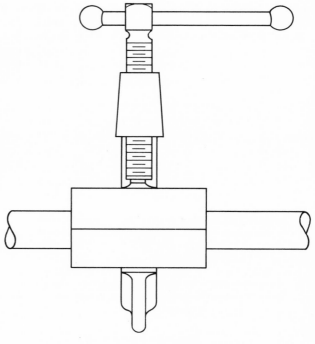

Figure 9 · 2   Use of grooved steel block to re-form steel tubing.

To find small cracks at a joint, the dye-penetrant method can be employed. This method has been explained in a previous chapter. After a crack is located, all finish must be removed with a wire brush, steel wool, or by sand blasting. If the crack is in an original weld bead, the existing bead is carefully removed by chipping, filing, or grinding. When this has been done, the crack is welded over along the original weld line. A common error in following this procedure is to remove some of the tubing or the reinforcing material while taking off the weld bead.

The small crack may be near a cluster joint but not on the weld bead. In this case, the finish is removed and a No. 40 (0.098 in.) hole is drilled at each end of the crack to prevent the crack from spreading. A split reinforcement tube is welded in place completely around the tubing over the cracked area. The repair tubing in this case should have an inside diameter approximately the same as the outside diameter of the tubing being repaired. The repair section is cut at an angle of 30° as shown in Fig. 9·3 before being split so it will fit over the repaired section. The repair tubing should extend a distance of at least 1½ times the diameter of the tubing being repaired beyond each end of the crack. This is shown in the illustration. When the weld is completed and cooled, a coat of zinc chromate primer is applied to the area where the finish was removed in the beginning. Finally, the area is given finishing coats to match the adjoining surfaces.

Under certain conditions, a dent or hole in tubing can be repaired by an external patch which does not completely surround the tubing. If a dent is not deeper than one-tenth the tube diameter and does not encompass more than one-quarter the tube circumference; if it is free from cracks, abrasions, and sharp corners; and if the tube can be substantially re-formed without cracking before the application of the patch, then a patch such as that shown in Fig. 9·4 can be used. A

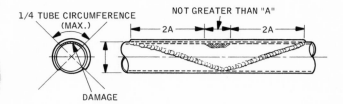

Figure **9·4** *Welded patch repair for dent or hole.*

hole in tubing which is not longer than the tube diameter and does not involve more than one-quarter the tube circumference can be patched in this manner. Such a patch is not permitted in the middle third of the tube section and must not overlap a tube joint.

Heat-treated compression members can be returned to their original strength, if the dents are minor, by means of a split tube clamped in place over the damaged section, as shown in Fig. 9·5, where the split tube is called a **splint tube** because it serves as a splint for an injured section. This type of repair should be considered only for temporary purposes, and a suitable permanent repair should be made as soon as possible. For this temporary repair, the split tube should have a wall thickness equal to that of the tube being repaired, and it must be clamped tight enough to prevent both the split tube and the clamps from becoming loose in service. Such a repair should be inspected frequently until the time it is replaced.

If the dents occur in tubular members which are not heat-treated, such dents may be reinforced by welding repairs illustrated in Fig. 9·3. The reinforcement tube is clamped in place and welded along two sides and at the ends as explained previously. This method of repair is satisfactory for short struts or dents in long members near the center of the span because such members are under greater bending stress near the center of the span and their full strength must be retained.

The **split sleeve** reinforcement illustrated in Fig. 9·3 is suitable for repairing cracks, dents, gouges, and other types of damage in structural tubing. In many cases it is necessary to straighten the member because of the bend that occurred at the time of the damage. After the member has been straightened it is necessary that the structure, especially at the welded joints, be thoroughly inspected to detect any possible secondary damage which may have occurred. The dye-penetrant method of inspection lends itself well to this inspection. Cracks in welds must be repaired by removing the old weld and rewelding the joint.

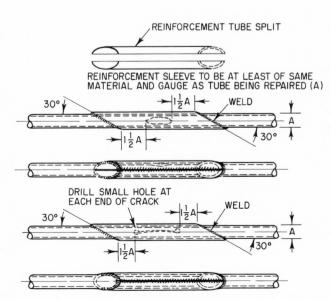

Figure **9·3** *Split-sleeve reinforcement.*

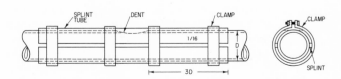

Figure **9·5** *Clamped tube reinforcement for heat-treated tube.*

131

Patch repairs at stations

Where damage has occurred at a station, a patch repair is often desirable. If tubular members, such as fuselage longerons, have sustained local damage at a station, they are repaired by welding on a **patch plate,** also called a **finger plate.** Such a repair is illustrated in Fig. 9·6. The patch must be of the same material and thickness as the injured tube and of a size sufficient to cover the damage. The fingers that extend onto the truss members should have a width equal to the diameter of the brace tube and a length equal to at least 1½ times that of the diameter. The ends of the fingers should be rounded or pointed to prevent heating the tube to an annealing temperature in a direct cross section at these spots. Rounding the ends of the fingers helps to distribute the load, thus reducing stress concentrations. Figure 9·7 shows additional details of finger plate repairs.

To prepare a patch for the repair of damage at a cluster, it is well to make a template by cutting a piece of heavy paper in the shape of the required patch. The paper is fitted around the cluster to be repaired and marked for correct size. It is then cut out and tested by placing it in the position of the patch. The paper tem-

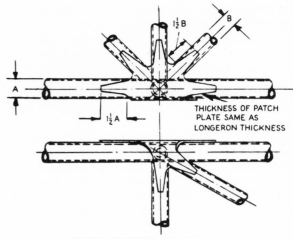

THICKNESS OF PATCH PLATE SAME AS LONGERON THICKNESS

PATCH PLATE BEFORE FORMING AND WELDING

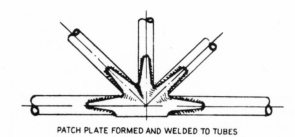

PATCH PLATE FORMED AND WELDED TO TUBES

Figure 9·7   Details of finger patch repair.

plate is placed on a piece of sheet steel of the correct type and thickness and the steel is marked for cutting.

Chrome-molybdenum, SAE 4130, sheet steel that has a thickness equal to or thicker than the wall of the damaged tube is suitable for the patch. The patch should be trimmed so that it will extend past the dent in both directions and have fingers as wide as the brace members. All the existing finish on the part to be repaired must be removed by rubbing with steel wool or fine emery cloth. The patch is clamped into position and tack-welded in several places where its edges touch the tubing. It is heated and light hammer blows with the ball end of a ball peen hammer are applied to form the patch around the repair area. The patch should not be overheated, but it must be softened enough so it can be formed to the tubing with a gap of not more than ¹⁄₁₆ in. between the tubing and the patch. The patch is then fused to all the tubes involved by welding around all the edges. When the weld is completed and cooled, the surface around the joint is refinished.

Major welded repairs (TEST)

Unless the damage to the member of a steel-tube structure is comparatively slight, it is usually better to remove the injured section and to weld in either a partial replacement tube or an entirely new section of tubing. Any tube cutting is done with a hacksaw and not by the oxyacetylene-flame cutting process. The manner of removing tubes and the number to be removed are determined by the location and extent of

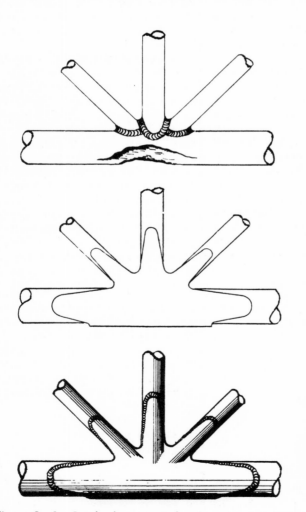

Figure 9·6   Patch plate repair for damage at a station.

the damage. Any tubes inserted as replacements are joined at their ends by means of a splice.

Splicing in the case of partial tube replacements may be done by using an external replacement tube of the next larger diameter, in which case the replacement tube is spliced to the stub ends of the original tubing, or it may be done by using a replacement tube of the same diameter together with either internal or external reinforcing sleeves.

If the original damaged tube includes fittings or castings that have been made especially to fit the tube, the spliced replacement tube must be of the same diameter as the original tubing, and this calls for either internal or external **reinforcing sleeves** under or over the splices.

If no fittings or castings are attached to the original tubing, it is possible to use an **external replacement tube.**

The two principal types of splice welds permitted in the repair of aircraft tubing are the **diagonal (scarf) weld** and the **fishmouth weld.** A splice is never made by butt welding. The best form is the **fishmouth weld,** sometimes called a **fishmouth joint.** It is a tubular joint used in joining two pieces of tubing end to end, which in the edges are cut to resemble a fish's mouth. For pieces of equal diameter, a butt joint with the joining ends of both pieces cut in matching fishmouths is used; while for pieces of unequal diameter, a reduction joint with only the end of the larger piece fishmouth cut is used. A **scarf joint** is a joint between two members in line with each other, in which the joining ends of one or both pieces are cut diagonally at an angle of about 30° from a center line (scarf cut). In welding aircraft tubing, for example, scarf joints are used both as butt joints and reduction joints.

A **reduction joint** is the joint made between two members of unequal diameter or width, both members being on the same general plane, that is, not at an angle to each other. Reduction joints are used, for example, in the welding of aircraft tubing for joining tubes end to end for greater length, as in the construction of longerons, to repair defective sections of tubing, or to brace a section of a piece of tubing. When additional length is the main purpose, the end of the smaller tube is telescoped into the end of the larger tube, far enough for adequate bracing. A welded joint of this nature is sometimes called a **telescope joint.** When repair or bracing of a central section is the main purpose, a short section of larger tubing is slipped over the smaller tube like a sleeve. Scarf joints and fishmouth joints are usually used in welding reduction joints on aircraft tubing, but occasionally a plain reduction joint with unshaped edges is used.

Figure 9·8 shows a **scarf-butt joint.** Figure 9·9

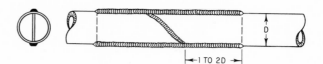

Figure 9·9   A scarf-butt splice with reinforcing plate.

shows a **scarf-butt splice** reinforced with a steel gusset plate. This splice is sometimes used to join the ends of the circular member of a radial engine mount. The ends of the tube are prepared with a slot to receive the gusset plate which extends from one to two diameters on each side of the weld between the tube ends. The gusset plate should be ¼ in. wider than the exterior diameter of the tube and the cut for the scarf splice should be made at an angle of 30°.

Figure 9·10 is a **fishmouth reduction splice** having the end of the telescoping tube cut to give a fishmouth shape. The length of the cut on the outside measurement of the tube is from one to two diameters of the smaller tube. This joint has a greater length of welded seam than a butt or scarf splice and does away with heating the tube to a welding temperature in a direct cross section. It is used for splicing continuous members of steel-tube fuselages and members of other units where tube splices of different diameters are required by the construction.

Figure 9·11 is a **scarf reduction splice** having the end of the telescoping tube cut diagonally at an angle of 30°. This joint is used for splicing members of different diameters and resembles the fishmouth splice to the extent that the tube is not heated to a welding temperature in a direct cross section.

The fishmouth weld is stronger than the scarf (diagonal) joint because of its resistance to bending stresses. There is no single straight line of weld through the structure where a fishmouth weld is used; hence a straight-line break cannot occur if the part is subjected to vibration or shock. However, in some aircraft repairs it will be found that the location of the damage and its extent are such that a diagonal type of weld must be used to the exclusion of the fishmouth type.

The following precautions must be observed in splicing:

1. A cut for splicing purposes must not be made in the middle third of a section of tubing because aircraft tubing must withstand high bending stresses.
2. Only one partial replacement tube can be inserted in any one section of a structural member, because more than one would weaken the member too much. If more than one tube in a joint is injured, the entire

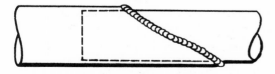

Figure 9·8   A scarf-butt joint.

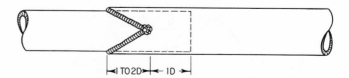

Figure 9·10   A fishmouth reduction splice.

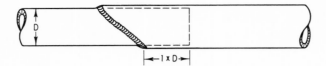

Figure 9·11   A scarf reduction splice.

joint must be removed and a new, preassembled, welded joint of the correct design must be inserted.

3. If a web member is damaged at a joint so badly that it is not possible to retain at that location a stub long enough to permit the splicing of a replacement, an entirely new web member must be installed.

4. If a continuous longeron is damaged at a joint, the replacement-tube splices must be at locations far enough past the joint on each side to avoid the necessity of locating the splice weld too close to the joint weld. The reason is that a welded joint is weaker than the metal it joins; hence the placing of a weld close to another weld increases the already existing weakness. The correct procedure is first to cut loose the web member at the damaged joint and to remove the damaged section of longeron tubing. The replacement tubing is then spliced to the stub ends of the original longeron section. Finally, the web member is welded to the new section of longeron tubing.

5. Wooden braces are used to keep the tubes in alignment while repairs are being made. The bent or damaged tubes having been replaced by new ones, it is then important to examine the original alignment of the corresponding tubes on an undamaged airplane of the same make and model to be sure that no error exists.

Inner reinforcements

Figure 9·12 shows a partial replacement tube spliced to the original tubing by means of **inner reinforcing sleeves.**

There is a very small amount of welding to be done; hence there is little possibility of weakening or distorting the tubing. In addition, a smooth outer surface is obtained for the repaired section.

Diagonal cuts are made in the damaged tubing to remove the injured portion. The cuts are located away from the middle third of the damaged section. When the part has been removed, any burr or roughness is removed from the edges of the cuts by filing. A

replacement tube that matches the damaged original tubing in both wall thickness and diameter is obtained; from this tubing, a length ¼ in. less than that of the removed section is cut by means of diagonal cuts on the ends. This gives a ⅛-in. gap between the original tubing and each end of the replacement tubing.

The next step is to cut two reinforcing sleeves. Tubing for this purpose must have the same wall thickness as the original tubing and an outside diameter equal to the inside diameter of the original tubing. The sleeves are cut across the tubing, and not diagonally. Each sleeve must fit snugly inside the original tubing, leaving a clearance between sleeve and tubing of not more than 1/16 in. These inner sleeves are cut long enough so that each end of a sleeve is not less than 1½ tube diameters from the diagonal cuts in the original tubing and the replacement tubing, as shown in Fig. 9·13.

The two reinforcing sleeves having been cut, the next task is to start splicing. The sequence given below should be followed to do a good job:

1. Set up a jig or brace arrangement to support the structure while the welding is done. Figure 9·14 shows how a brace takes the place of the damaged

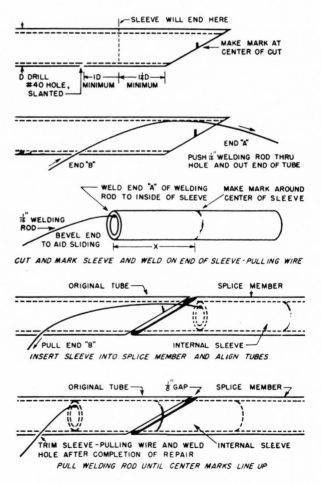

Figure 9·13   Details of construction for inner reinforcing sleeve repair.

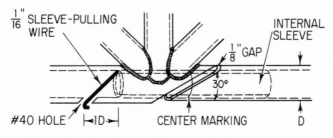

Figure 9·12   Splice with inner reinforcing sleeve.

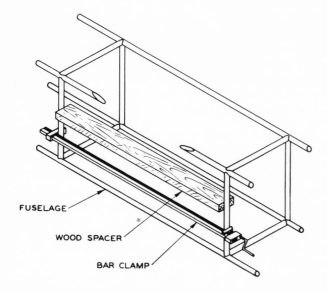

Figure **9 · 14** *Bracing of structure to maintain alignment.*

tubing in holding the vertical members in line during welding.

2. On the stub end of the original tube, halfway along the diagonal cut, make a small mark on the outside.

3. Measure a distance 2½ tube diameters long, starting at the nearest end of each diagonal cut on the original tubing. Center-punch the tube at these locations, and begin drilling holes, No. 40 size, using a drill held at a 90° angle to the surface of the tubing. When the hole is started far enough to keep the drill from jumping out, slant the drill toward the cut and continue drilling at a 30° angle. Then, file off the burr from the edges of the holes, using a round needlepoint file.

4. Insert one end of a length of 1/16 in. welding wire through the hole just drilled and push it out through the diagonally cut-open end of the original tubing. Repeat the process at the other stub end, using another wire. These wires are used to draw the sleeves into the tubing.

5. Weld the end of each wire which sticks out of the open end of the tubing to the inside of one of the inner sleeves as shown in Fig. 9 · 13. The sleeve can be drawn into the tube easier if the ends of the sleeves to which the wires are welded are first beveled.

6. Using thin paint, metal dye, or emery paper, place a narrow mark around the centers of the reinforcing sleeves.

7. Push the inner sleeve into the replacement tube so that the place where the wire is welded to the sleeve is 180° from the drilled hole. If the drilled hole is at the bottom of the tubing, the inner sleeves are located so that the place at which the wire is welded is at the top. If the inner sleeve fits too snugly in the replacement tube, cool the sleeve with dry ice or cold water. If the sleeve continues to stick, polish it with emery cloth.

8. Line up the stub ends of the original tube with the replacement tube.

9. Begin to pull the end of the wire that protrudes from the drilled hole. Pull the sleeve along until the center mark on the sleeve is directly in line with the center mark on the diagonal cut. When these two marks are in line, the sleeve is centered under the joint, as illustrated in Fig. 9 · 13. Repeat the same procedure for the other sleeve at the opposite end of the replacement tube.

10. Bend the pulling wire over the edge of the hole to hold the sleeve in position. Weld the inner sleeve to the original tube stub and replacement tube at one end. This takes up the gap between the replacement tube and the original tube at one end, as shown in Fig. 9 · 13. A weld bead must be formed over the gap. After the joint is welded, the pulling wire is snipped off flush with the surface of the tube. Weld over the drilled hole.

11. When this weld over the drilled hole is cool, adjust the brace arrangement to provide for contraction and shrinkage. Having adjusted the brace, pull the sleeve into position and tack-weld the gap at the other end of the replacement tube. This holds the joint in alignment. Remove the brace to eliminate any restraint on the contraction forces at the joint. Complete the weld around the gap that has been tack-welded.

12. Weld the replacement tube in place, reinforced as it is with the sleeves at the joints.

13. Apply a similar method to any splicing described elsewhere, except that sleeve-pulling wires are not needed if external reinforcing sleeves are used or where sleeves are omitted and a simple replacement tube of a larger diameter is used for splicing.

Figure 9 · 15 illustrates a typical longeron splice using the same diameter replacement tube. In this

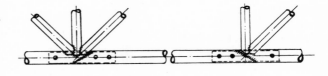

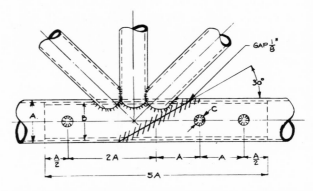

Figure **9 · 15** *Longeron splice using tubing of same diameter as original.*

drawing, A is the original tube, B is the insert tube, and C is one-quarter the diameter of tube A (six rosette welds for each splice on the drilled outside tube only). It is shown that a partial replacement tube is spliced to the original tubing by means of inner reinforcing sleeves. This is a very efficient method. There is a minimum amount of welding to be done; hence there is little danger of weakening and distorting the tube from the heat of welding. In addition, this method has the advantage of presenting a smooth outside surface for the repaired section.

Another excellent method for repairing a damaged section of tubing between stations is illustrated in Fig. 9·16. In this method a replacement tube large enough to telescope over the original tubing is used. The replacement tubing should fit snugly over the original tube. This method can be used only where there is sufficient undamaged tubing at each end of the section to allow for the necessary stub lengths. On one end a minimum of 2½ tube diameters of length should be allowed; on the other end, a minimum of 4½ diameters of tube length is necessary. The original tubing is cut square across at each end as shown in the drawing.

The replacement tube must have the same wall thickness as the original tube and should have an inside diameter just large enough to slip over the stub ends of the original; in any case, it should not be more than 1/16 in. larger than the outside diameter of the original tube. A fishmouth end should be cut on each end of the replacement tube with an angle of 30° from the center line. The tube should be of such a length that each end will extend a minimum distance of 1½ tube diameters over the stub at each end.

To install the replacement tube, the long stub of the original tube is sprung sufficiently to permit the replacement tube to be slipped over the stub. The other end of the replacement tube is then aligned with the short stub and pushed over it to a distance of at least 1½ tube diameters. When the replacement tube is in the correct position, the edge of the fishmouth is welded to the original tube.

Rosette welds (TEST) TUBULAR TACK WELDS

In the description of the above welding job, the phrase **rosette welds** is used. A rosette weld is one of the types of welds classified as **plug welds**. A plug weld is a weld holding two lapped pieces. It is laid as a plug in a hole (slot) cut through the top piece or cut through both pieces. A rosette weld is a round plug weld. Rosette welds are generally used to fuse an inner reinforcing tube (liner) with the outer member. Where a rosette

weld is used, the holes should be made in the outside tube only and be of a sufficient size to ensure fusion of the inner tube. A hole diameter of about one-quarter the tube diameter of the outer tube is adequate. If the sleeves or inner liners fit tight, the rosettes may be omitted.

Outside-sleeve reinforcement

There are three principal methods of repairing an injured tube, as suggested before. One is the use of an inner-sleeve splice, another is the use of a larger-diameter replacement tube, and the third is the use of a partial replacement tube of the *same diameter* as the original, reinforced by an **outside sleeve.** The latter method requires more welding than the other two, there is greater danger of distortion from the heat of welding, and hence it is usually the least desirable repair method. However, if neither of the other two methods can be used for any reason, this method must be employed.

Figure 9·17 shows the use of a tube of the same diameter as the original. In this method, the new section of tube is the same size as the longeron forward (left) of the fitting. The rear end (right) of the tube is cut at 30°, and it forms the outside sleeve of a scarf splice. A sleeve is centered over the forward joint as illustrated.

Figure 9·18 illustrates a satisfactory method for repairing tubing in a bay with outside-sleeve reinforcements and an outer sleeve. The fishmouth sleeve is shown; however, a 30° scarf sleeve is also satisfactory. Remember that the fishmouth slope is cut 30° from horizontal.

To make the repair shown, the damaged portion of tubing is cut out by sawing straight across the tubing at a distance of four times the tube diameter from the adjacent welded fittings or tubes. Before the tube is removed, it is well to brace the fuselage section to make sure that it remains in correct alignment.

A new section of tube, having the same diameter and wall thickness as the original, is cut at such a length that there is a gap of about 1/32 in. when it is installed, to allow for expansion. For the outer reinforcing sleeves, the inside diameter should be such that they will fit snugly over the other tubes and in any case the maximum diameter difference between the inner tubing and the sleeve should be not more than 1/16 in.

The outer sleeves are cut with fishmouth ends or diagonally, preferably fishmouth, the length being such

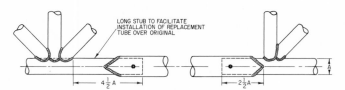

LONG STUB TO FACILITATE INSTALLATION OF REPLACEMENT TUBE OVER ORIGINAL

Figure **9·16** *Replacement of tubing between stations with larger tube over stubs of original.*

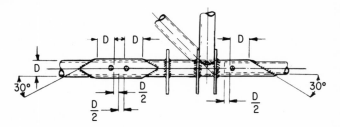

Figure **9·17** *Fishmouth sleeve repair for splice at a station with fittings.*

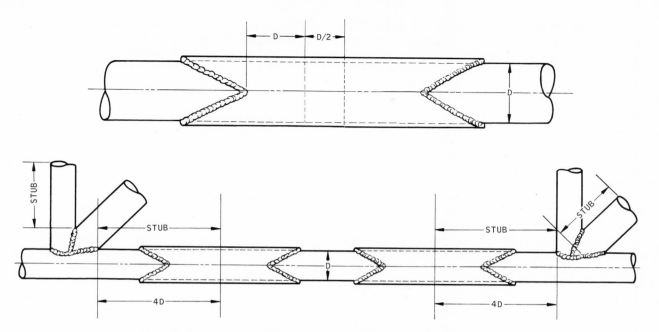

Figure 9·18   Fishmouth sleeves for replacement tube between stations.

that the nearest portion of the sleeve end cut is at least 1½ tube diameters from the ends of the original tube. The two sleeves are slipped over the replacement tube, and the tube is then aligned with the stubs of the original tubing. The sleeves are slipped out over the centers of the joints and adjusted to provide the maximum reinforcement. They are then tacked in place by welding. To reduce warpage, one sleeve is welded in place and allowed to cool before the other is welded. Rosette welds should be employed for further reinforcement unless the sleeves fit tightly.

Replacement of a cluster at a station

Figure 9·19 illustrates a suitable method for replacing a damaged cluster weld by means of welded outer sleeves. The structure is braced to hold it in correct alignment and then the original cluster is sawed out as shown by the dotted lines. The longeron section is cut squarely across and a new section of tubing with the same wall thickness and diameter is cut to fit the space where the old tube was removed. Two sleeve sections with dimensions as shown are cut to fit over the joints

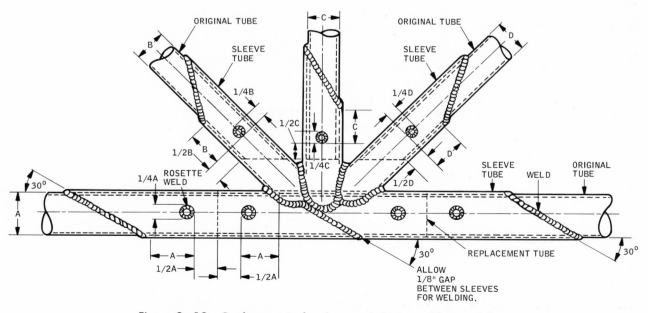

Figure 9·19   Replacement of a damaged cluster weld at a station.

and are welded together at the center and at the outer ends with 30° diagonal welds. Rosette welds are also employed to reinforce the assembly. Sleeves are also cut to fit the truss members, and these sleeves should be slipped over the ends of the truss members before the longeron weld is made. Otherwise, assembly will be impossible.

Finally the truss member sleeves are welded into place, first at the cluster and then to the original tubes. It is important to remember that one weld should be made at a time and allowed to cool before making the next in order to reduce warping.

Repair at built-in fuselage fittings

When a welded structure has steel fittings built in at a cluster, the repair is somewhat more complicated than those previously described, but the same principles apply. Figure 9·20 shows a tube (sleeve) of larger diameter than the original. This makes it necessary to ream the fitting holes (at the longeron) to a larger diameter. The sleeve should extend about 6 in. forward (left of fitting) of the joint and 8 in. aft (right of fitting). The forward splice should be a 30° scarf splice. The rear longeron (right) should be cut off about 4 in. from the center line of the joint and a spacer 1 in. long fitted over the longeron. This spacer and the longeron should be edge-welded. A tapered V cut about 2 in. long is then made in the rear end of the outer sleeve. The end of the outer sleeve should be swaged to fit the longeron and then welded.

When the longeron tubing on each side of the station and fittings is the same size, a simpler type of repair is possible as shown in Fig. 9·21. The sleeve is cut and welded in place as shown and then the fittings are welded in the correct positions.

For the condition where there is a large difference in diameter of the longeron on each side of the fitting, the repair shown in Fig. 9·22 can be used. In this repair, a section of tubing forms an inner sleeve for the section on the left of the fitting and an outer sleeve for the section on the right of the fitting. Standard welding procedures are employed with dimensions as shown.

Welded repair of fabric-covered steel fuselage (TESG)

When it is necessary to make a repair of a fabric-covered, steel-tubing fuselage without the removal of large sections of fabric, care must be taken to see that the fabric is not damaged by heat or set afire. Fabric

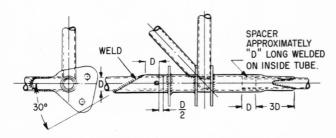

Figure 9·20 Repair of station with fittings using repair sleeve of larger diameter than original.

138

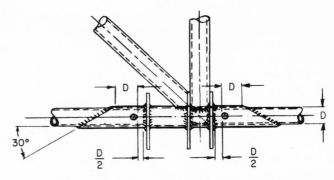

Figure 9·21 A simple sleeve repair at a station with fittings.

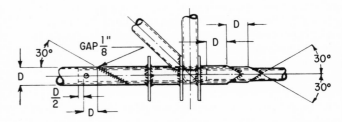

Figure 9·22 Repair where there is a large difference in diameter of the longeron on each side of the station.

covering is often very flammable; hence it should not be exposed to the sparks from welding, and heat conducted through the tubing should be stopped before it reaches the fabric.

To protect the fabric, it is cut and laid back away from the area to be welded. This usually requires a cut along the longeron and perpendicular to the longeron on each side. When the fabric is rolled back it should not be creased or folded because this will crack the dope and possibly weaken the fabric. Wet cloths are then wrapped around the tubing on all sides of the area to be repaired. These cloths will prevent the heat from being conducted to the fabric. Additional wet cloth is placed over the fabric where sparks from the welding process could reach to the fabric.

After the welding is completed and the tubing refinished, the fabric is sewed, reinforced, and doped as has been described earlier in this text.

Repair of engine mounts (TESG)

Welded engine mounts are particularly vulnerable to damage by cracking, largely because of the vibration to which they are subjected. Landing loads on such mounts are also particularly severe because the weight effect of the engine is multiplied several times during a hard landing. For these reasons the materials used in the manufacture of engine mounts should be of high quality and the welded joints must be uniform and strong. Engine-mount repairs are accomplished in the same manner as other tubular-steel repairs; however, replacement tubes should be large enough to slip over the original tubing. A fishmouth joint is recommended although a 30° scarf may be used if necessary. Rosette welds are used to assure a completely rigid joint.

Repairs to engine mounts must be governed by accurate means of checking the **alignment.** When new tubes are used to replace bent or damaged tubes, the original alignment of the structure must be maintained. This is done by measuring the distance between points of corresponding members that have not been distorted and by reference to the drawings furnished by the manufacturer.

If all members are out of alignment, the engine mount must be replaced by one supplied by the manufacturer; the method of checking the alignment of the fuselage or nacelle points should be requested from the manufacturer.

Minor damage, such as a crack adjacent to an engine attachment lug, may be repaired by rewelding the ring and extending a gusset or a mounting lug past the damaged area. Engine-mount rings that have been extensively damaged should not be repaired, but should be replaced unless the method of repair is approved by an authorized agency.

Attachment and repair of welded fittings

Aircraft fittings of interest to welders are principally small attachments or connections that are fastened to tubing members. They may be built up of one or more thicknesses of sheet metal, or they may be forged or machined from bars or billets. The method of welding fittings to tubular members depends upon the load stress they will carry in operating conditions.

Moderately stressed fittings that are not subjected to vibrating stresses are generally made of a single thickness of sheet steel and are welded to only one wall of the tube as shown in Fig. 9·23.

Fittings or lugs for transmitting high stresses are welded to the supporting members at more than one point. High-stressed fittings attached to the main member of a structural unit halfway between station points are welded to both walls of the tube as shown in Fig. 9·24, where the tube is slotted and the fitting is inserted.

Fittings attached to the main members of tubular structures where brace members terminate are also welded to the brace members in most cases. The main members and ends of the brace members may be slotted and the fitting welded in, as shown in Fig. 9·25, or the fitting may be built up of two or three sections with fingers extending to the brace members, as shown in Fig. 9·26.

Figure 9·27 shows a representative male fitting for round struts. It consists of a bearing sleeve or bushing

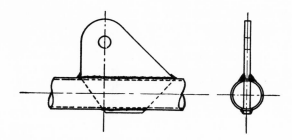

Figure **9·24**   Inserted fitting where stresses are high.

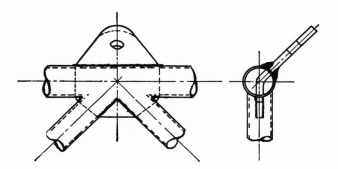

Figure **9·25**   Inserted fitting at a station.

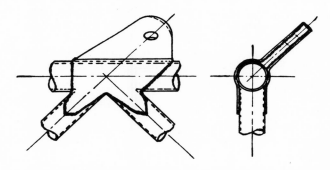

Figure **9·26**   Fitting reinforced with welded fingers.

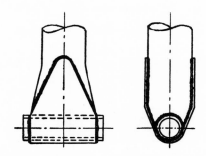

Figure **9·27**   Male fitting for the end of a round strut.

welded to the strut end, which is reinforced with a steel plate formed around the bearing. The plate is welded to the bearing sleeve and strut with a fillet weld.

The fitting in Fig. 9·28 is a typical female strut-end connection used for round struts. This is forged and machined to fit into the strut end and is attached to the strut with a combination riveted and welded joint.

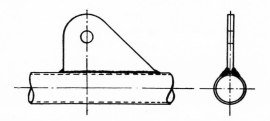

Figure **9·23**   Simple fitting where stress is moderate.

139

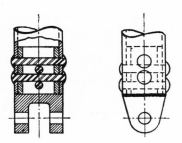

Figure **9·28** *Female fitting for the end of a round strut.*

The fitting illustrated in Fig. 9·29 is a forged and machined male fitting for elliptical or streamlined struts. This fitting is inserted by slotting the strut end to receive its tang, and the attachment is made by means of a fillet weld.

The fitting shown in Fig. 9·30 is a typical female fitting for streamlined or elliptical struts, and it also may be used for round sections. It is built up of sheet steel and bearing sleeves. The strut end is slotted and formed to receive the fitting.

When the fitting welded to a structural member is discovered to be broken or worn, it is removed and a new fitting installed. The new fitting must have physical properties at least equal to those of the original part or unit. In removing the damaged fitting, care must be taken that the tube to which it is attached is not damaged, and the new fitting must be installed in the same manner as the original. If a damaged fitting attached to a main member, where truss members terminate,

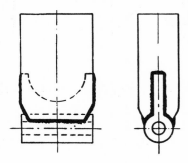

Figure **9·29** *Forged and machined fitting for the end of a streamline strut.*

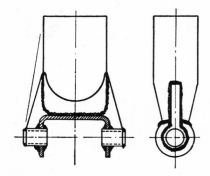

Figure **9·30** *Female end fitting for streamline strut.*

cannot be removed without weakening the structural members, the part of the tubing having the damaged fitting attached to it should be removed, and a new section and fitting should then be installed.

Devices for holding tubular structures in alignment

Figure 9·31 is a drawing of a jack and a tube. Figure 9·32 is a drawing of a fixture for holding tubular structures in alignment during repair, showing the jack set up between struts and the clamp on the outside of the struts. This clamp is adjustable and is placed on the outside of the members directly over and parallel to the jack to prevent the assembly from spreading apart.

The original dimensions are obtained from drawings or by measuring the corresponding member of the airplane that is not distorted. If the latter method is followed, the main member is lightly prick-punched, in line with the center of the brace member intersections, and the dimensions are then taken with trammel points and a bar. These measurements are applied to the structure being repaired and the clamps are used to bring the members into the correct position.

Repair of streamline tubing (TEST)

Although streamline tubing can be repaired in many ways using standard welding practices, there are four methods which have been proved reliable and are approved by the Federal Aviation Agency for certificated aircraft.

The method illustrated in Fig. 9·33, recommended for landing gear, utilizes a section of round tubing which is one gage thicker than the original tube to serve as the splicing reinforcement. The streamline tubes to be spliced are cut with a 30° scarf and the ends to be joined are slotted according to the approved specifications shown in the table. The combined slots are three times the length of the major axis of the streamline tubing. A gap of ⅛ in. is established between the

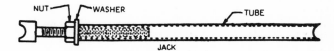

Figure **9·31** *Jack and tube used for alignment.*

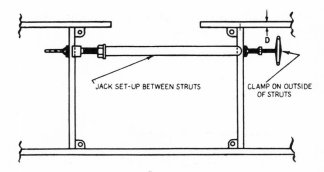

Figure **9·32** *Fixture with jack and tube holding structure in alignment.*

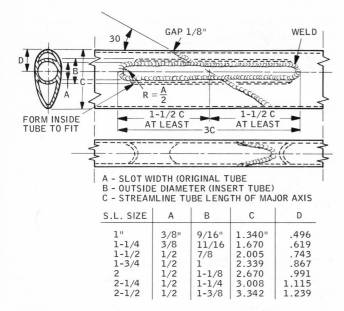

A - SLOT WIDTH (ORIGINAL TUBE
B - OUTSIDE DIAMETER (INSERT TUBE)
C - STREAMLINE TUBE LENGTH OF MAJOR AXIS

S.L. SIZE	A	B	C	D
1"	3/8"	9/16"	1.340"	.496
1-1/4	3/8	11/16	1.670	.619
1-1/2	1/2	7/8	2.005	.743
1-3/4	1/2	1	2.339	.867
2	1/2	1-1/8	2.670	.991
2-1/4	1/2	1-1/4	3.008	1.115
2-1/2	1/2	1-3/8	3.342	1.239

Figure 9·33 A streamline tube splice using an inner round tube.

scarfed ends of the streamline tubes to provide for full penetration of the weld. The round tubing section is fitted in the slots as shown and welded in place.

Figure 9·34 illustrates the approved splice for streamline tubing where a split sleeve is welded over the original tube to reinforce the splice. This repair is applicable to wing-and-tail-surface brace struts and similar members. In this method the original tubing is cut squarely across and the split sleeve is scarfed at 30°. The outer sleeve is cut along the trailing edge and then opened up to fit over the original tubing. It is then

welded at the trailing edge to the inside tubing and along the end scarfs. The dimensions are given in the table.

The splice shown in Fig. 9·35 utilizes an inside sleeve of streamline tubing as a reinforcement. This tubing is the same as the original; however, the size is reduced by cutting off the trailing edge and rewelding. The reinforcing tube is inserted in the ends of the original tubing which has been cut with a 45° scarf. A gap of ⅛ in. is allowed for welding the two ends together and to the inner sleeve. Rosette welds are used as shown to secure the inner sleeve.

Figure 9·36 illustrates the splicing method where steel plates are used to reinforce the splice. The steel plates are twice the thickness of the tubing wall. Slots are cut in the streamline tubing according to the dimensions given in the table and the plates are welded into the slots. The ends of the streamline tubing are scarfed at 30° and welded together. A gap of ⅛ in. is allowed to facilitate the weld.

Repairable and nonrepairable types of ~~axle~~ assemblies LANDING GEAR

Figure 9·37 shows three types of landing-gear axle assemblies formed from steel tubing. These may be repaired by any standard method shown in the previous illustrations of this chapter. However, it is always necessary to find out whether or not the members are heat-treated. It must be remembered that all members which depend on heat treatment for their original physical properties should be re-heat-treated after the welding operation. If it happens that the heat-treat value cannot be obtained from the manufacturer, some

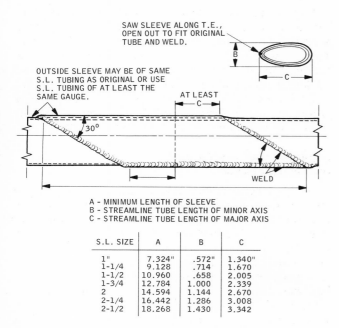

A - MINIMUM LENGTH OF SLEEVE
B - STREAMLINE TUBE LENGTH OF MINOR AXIS
C - STREAMLINE TUBE LENGTH OF MAJOR AXIS

S.L. SIZE	A	B	C
1"	7.324"	.572"	1.340"
1-1/4	9.128	.714	1.670
1-1/2	10.960	.658	2.005
1-3/4	12.784	1.000	2.339
2	14.594	1.144	2.670
2-1/4	16.442	1.286	3.008
2-1/2	18.268	1.430	3.342

Figure 9·34 A streamline tube splice using a split sleeve.

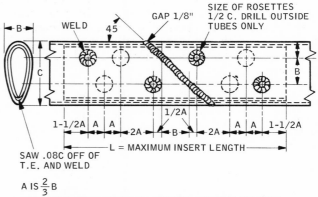

A IS $\frac{2}{3}$ B

B IS MINOR AXIS LENGTH OF ORIGINAL STREAMLINE TUBE
C IS MAJOR AXIS LENGTH OF ORIGINAL STREAMLINE TUBE

S.L. SIZE	A	B	C	L
1"	.382	.572	1.340	5.16
1-1/4	.476	.714	1.670	6.43
1-1/2	.572	.858	2.005	7.72
1-3/4	.667	1.000	2.339	9.00
2	.763	1.144	2.670	10.30
2-1/4	.858	1.286	3.008	11.58
2-1/2	.954	1.430	3.342	12.88

Figure 9·35 A streamline tube splice using an inside streamline tube reinforcement.

141

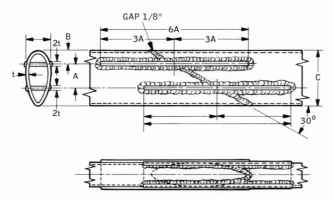

A - STREAMLINE TUBE LENGTH OF MINOR AXIS, PLATE WIDTHS.
B - DISTANCE OF FIRST PLATE FROM LEADING EDGE, 2/3A.
C - STREAMLINE TUBE LENGTH OF MAJOR AXIS.

S.L. SIZE	A	B	C	6A
1"	.572	.382	1.340	3.43
1-1/4	.714	.476	1.670	4.28
1-1/2	.858	.572	2.005	5.15
1-3/4	1.000	.667	2.339	6.00
2	1.144	.762	2.670	6.86
2-1/4	1.286	.858	3.008	7.72
2-1/2	1.430	.954	3.342	8.58

Figure 9·36 A streamline tube splice using steel-plate inserts.

test must be made, such as the Brinell or Rockwell hardness tests applied in several places of the member being tested. Welding must be done with a rod which can be heat-treated.

Figure 9·38 shows an axle assembly which is not generally regarded as repairable for the following reasons: (1) The axle stub is usually made from a highly heat-treated nickel-alloy steel and carefully machined to close tolerances; hence such stubs are generally replaceable and should be replaced if damaged; (2) the oleo portion of the structure is usually heat-treated after welding, and is perfectly machined to make certain that the shock absorber will function properly. These parts would be distorted by welding after machining.

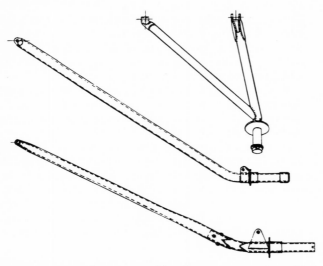

Figure 9·37   Three types of landing-gear axle assemblies.

Figure 9·38   An axle assembly not repairable by welding.

Damaged ski pedestals which are constructed of welded tubular steel can be repaired according to the methods described previously in this chapter. Care should be taken to note whether the pedestals are heat-treated; and if they are, they should be welded with a heat-treatable rod and re-heat-treated after the repair is made.

Wing- and tail-surface repairs (TEST)

Built-up tubular wing- or tail-surface spars may be repaired by using any of the standard splices and methods of repair described in this chapter if the spars are not heat-treated. If they are heat-treated, the entire spar assembly must be re-heat-treated to the manufacturer's specifications after the repair is completed. This is usually less practicable than replacing the spar with one furnished by the manufacturer of the airplane.

Damaged wing brace struts made either from round or streamlined tubing are usually replaced by new members bought from the original manufacturer. There is no objection from an airworthiness viewpoint to repairing such members in any correct manner. Brace struts must be spliced only adjacent to the end fittings. When making repairs to wing- and tail-surface brace members, particular attention must be paid to the proper fit and alignment.

Steel parts which must not be welded

Airplane parts that depend for their proper functioning on strength properties developed by cold working must not be welded. These parts include (1) streamlined wires and cables; (2) brazed or soldered parts (the brazing mixture or solder will penetrate hot steel and weaken it); (3) steel parts, mostly of nickel-alloy steels, which have been heat-treated to improve their physical properties, particularly aircraft bolts, turnbuckle ends, axles, and other heat-treated steel-alloy parts.

Inspection after welding and corrosion protection

Hollow steel structures may be filled with hot linseed oil or petroleum-base oils, under pressure, in order to coat the inside surface and discourage corrosion. This also helps to detect weld cracks because the hot oil will seep through cracks that are not visible to the eye otherwise. This is not applicable in all cases, but it is recommended where a large portion of the structure has been rewelded. Carefully examining all joints with a medium-power magnifying glass, at least 10 power, after first removing all scale, is an acceptable method of inspection for repaired structures.

Final inspection of a welded structure is easily accomplished by means of dye-penetrant inspection. As explained previously, the dye penetrates any small cracks or fissures and then seeps out when the developer is applied to the joint. Thus the crack is revealed as a bright red line.

Magnetic inspection by means of magnetic powder, such as magnaflux and black rouge, is an efficient, practical, and nondestructive method that will indicate the presence of tiny cracks or small blowholes. The surface to be examined should be reasonably smooth and free from scale because it is difficult to find cracks in the irregular surface of the weld metal deposited. Sandblasting gives good results but only when done by experienced mechanics.

X-ray inspection was limited in value in the past because of the inaccessibility of many joints and the necessity of taking exposures from several angles to make certain that all defects were found. However, the results are very satisfactory; the recent developments in this field have reduced the cost and time. The use of radioactive cobalt "bombs" has made it possible to x-ray joints at almost any location.

Since all steel parts and welded joints in the various aircraft units are covered with paint, scale, or rust that must be removed before finishing, sandblasting is used as the most efficient means of removing such coatings. If sandblasting is not used, the scale, rust, and dirt should be removed with fine emery cloth before applying a standard metal cleaner. As soon as the metal has been cleaned, it should be finished immediately and not touched by ungloved hands until at least a priming coat has been applied. If this precaution is not observed, corrosion will set in later.

A very satisfactory protection for finishing the exterior of tubing is obtained by spraying or brushing two coats of zinc chromate primer with 4 oz of aluminum-bronze powder per unthinned gallon in the second coat of primer. This finish provides excellent protection against corrosion and is very dopeproof. Any equivalent finish using oil-base primers and enamels is acceptable. The portions of the structure coming in contact with doped fabric should be given a protecting strip of tape or a coat of dopeproof paint if the base finish is not already dopeproof. Adhesive tape is another satisfactory means of protective covering for the same purpose.

Corrosionproofing the interior steel-tube structures can be done satisfactorily by filling the structures with hot linseed oil, lionoil, or petroleum-base oil under pressure and draining the oil before sealing. Sealing the members only, without the use of oil, by permanently closing all openings to prevent air from circulating through them is also considered an acceptable method for protecting the interior of repaired structures.

Construction of steel-tube assemblies by welding

A suitable jig must be used in the construction of aircraft steel-tube assemblies by welding. This jig is used to support and to hold the various members of the assembly in their proper positions until they are permanently fastened. Jigs should be rigid enough to withstand the usual strains without losing their shape when the parts are being assembled.

In some factories, the jigs for welding flat assemblies are made of boiler plate $\frac{3}{8}$ to $\frac{1}{2}$ in. thick. These plates are fitted with suitable clamps, or blocks, to receive and hold the members of the assembly.

In a case where only one unit is to be built, the jig for the construction of flat assemblies may be entirely made of wood on the same general plan as a mass-production jig made of metal. A flat-top table may be used as the base, and wood blocks grooved to receive the members fastened to this base with nails, or screws. A piece of reasonably heavy iron or steel plate, or heavy sheet asbestos, is placed under the joint to protect the wood during welding.

If the tubular structure is not flat, such as a steel-tube engine mount, a more complicated jig is required. It may have a heavy steel-base plate and a top plate of a lighter gage, supported with angle-iron vertical members that are welded to plates to obtain the greatest amount of rigidity. Holes and clamps are provided for holding the members to be welded and the assembly is left in the jig after welding until it has cooled.

Repair of engine exhaust units

Exhaust manifolds for reciprocating engines and exhaust cones and noise suppressors for turbine engines are usually constructed of stainless steel, Inconel, or other high-temperature alloy. Welding of cracks in these parts is most satisfactorily accomplished by means of heliarc or some other type of inert-gas welding. It is important for the technician to determine what the alloy is and to use the correct type of filler rod for the weld.

A strong jig is required for holding the parts of an exhaust manifold in position during construction and for maintaining the correct alignment during assembly. The typical unit may have a heavy bedplate with fittings for locating and holding the parts in position while welding is done, making allowance for the expansion and contraction of the parts in a longitudinal direction without permitting them to get out of line.

The repair of exhaust manifolds usually consists of welding cracks or breaks, patching worn parts, and replacing broken or worn fittings.

When a damaged fitting is replaced, the old fitting, including the weld-metal deposit, must be ground off and the section cleaned inside before the new fitting is made and welded in place.

It is often necessary to repair sections of the exhaust manifold that telescope together because they are subjected to considerable wear. The worn portion is removed and replaced with a new section made of sheet stock of the same gage and kind of metal as the original portion. In gas welding, a heavy coat of flux is applied to the edges on the lower side to prevent oxidation of the weld metal and the base metal.

Before repairing a crack or break, the metal on the inside and outside must be clean and bright, and there must be a ¹⁄₁₆- to ³⁄₃₂-in. hole drilled at each end of the crack to prevent it from spreading. If the crack is more than 2 in. long, the break is tacked at 2-in. intervals. When gas welding is used for the repair of exhaust units distortion and cracking on cooling are reduced by preheating the part to between 400 and 600°F. In repairing stainless-steel exhaust units, if much welding has been done, the units are preheated to between 1900 and 2000°F; they are then cooled slowly and evenly to relieve the residual stresses caused by welding and to restore the metal to its original condition.

Repair of fuel and oil tanks (JTC 80)

Pg 316
ADDITIONAL INFO

When fuel and oil tanks are repaired, either by heliarc or gas welding, it is most important that the tank be thoroughly purged of any fuel or oil fumes before the weld is begun. Even though a fuel tank has been empty for a long time and appears to be dry inside, it is still likely that enough fumes can be released by the heat of welding to create an explosive mixture. The correct procedure in such cases is to wash the tank with hot water and a detergent and then allow live steam to flow through the tank for about ~~30 min.~~ This treatment will vaporize and remove any residual fuel or oil that may be in the tank.

NOTE—
GAS) - STM
OIL 1 HR.

The welding of tanks, whether they be constructed of aluminum, stainless steel, or titanium should be done by heliarc if possible. As previously explained, this method produces a smooth weld with a minimum of distortion due to heat and also eliminates oxidation and burning of the metal.

There are several types of welded seams used in the construction of aluminum tanks for aircraft. These include butt joints, corner joints, edge joints, and lap joints. When baffle plates are riveted to the shell, the rivets are headed by welding to make them liquidtight.

Corrugated beads, formed into the sheet, adjacent and parallel to the seams, provide for expansion and contraction. These beads, acting as expansion joints, close up slightly when the metal expands under the heat of welding and straighten out on cooling enough to relieve the strains of contraction. In addition, they add stiffness to the metal and help to prevent buckling.

Figure 9·39 shows a riveted joint between the shell and baffle plate with a rivet headed to the shell by welding.

Figure 9·40 shows a joint used to secure the baffle plates to the shell in some types of tank construction. The plates either extend through a slot and are welded to the shell, or they are located at the seams in the shell and are welded to the shell when the seams are made.

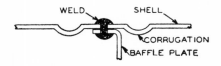

Figure **9·39** *Welded joint with rivets to secure baffle plates.*

144

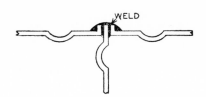

Figure **9·40** *Welded joint to secure baffle plate in a tank.*

Figure 9·41 shows a mechanical lock seam sealed by welding in the construction of some types of shells.

Figure 9·42 shows a joint adaptable for small seams. The turned edges provide stiffness to the sheet at the joint, tend to maintain alignment during welding, and supply additional metal for the weld.

Figure 9·43 shows how edge joints may be used for corner seams in making a tank and for welding hand-hole cover plates into the shell.

Figure 9·44 shows a corner seam widely used in tank construction. It is welded like a flanged butt joint.

Figure 9·45 shows a butt-type joint with a stiffener strip between the butt ends that is extended above the plates. Fillet welds are used to secure the whole assembly.

If a tank is repaired by gas welding, it is extremely important to remove all welding flux after a repair in order to prevent corrosion. As soon as welding is completed, a tank is washed inside and outside with great quantities of hot water and is then drained. It is then either immersed in 5 percent nitric or sulphuric acid or filled with this solution and also washed on the outside with the same solution. The acid is left in contact with the weld about 1 hr and then rinsed carefully with clean, fresh water. The efficiency of the cleaning process is tested by applying some acidified 5 percent silver nitrate solution to a small quantity of rinse water that has been used for the last washing of the weld. If a

HNO₃
H₂SO₄

Figure **9·41** *A welded lock seam.*

Figure **9·42** *Welded seam with turned-up edges.*

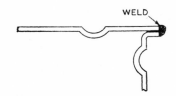

Figure **9·43** *Corner-seam edge joint.*

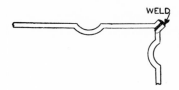

Figure 9·44   Flanged corner-seam joint.

Figure 9·45   A butt-type joint with a stiffener strip.

heavy white precipitate is formed, the cleaning has not been done thoroughly, and the washing must be repeated.

Cowlings (TESO)

Aluminum and aluminum-alloy **cowlings** are usually repaired by patching worn spots; welding cracks, or breaks, caused by vibration; and replacing worn or broken fittings.

A crack, or break, is repaired by welding the fracture. Heliarc should be used if possible but a skilled operator can make suitable repairs by gas welding. All welds must have enough penetration to provide a small bead on the lower side. In repairing cracks that extend into the sheet from a hole in the cowl or from the edge, the cracks are lined up, tacked, and welded progressively, starting from the end of the crack toward the edge or opening. A cowling having been repaired by welding must be finished on the outside to provide a smooth surface. (NON-STRUCTURAL)

Worn spots may be repaired by removing the worn section and replacing it with a new piece that is cut to fit the removed portion and then formed to the required shape before installation. It is then placed in position and tack-welded at intervals of 1 to 2 in. around the edges before the actual welding.

REVIEW QUESTIONS

1. What type of steel is commonly used for tubular steel structures in aircraft?
2. If major repair work is done on a welded steel tubular fuselage, what precaution must be taken?
3. What principal factor governs the size of a welding tip?
4. When welding a structure which will require heat treating, what type of filler rod must be used?
5. When welding a section of tubing into a structure, why is it a good practice to allow one end to cool after welding before welding the other end?
6. Describe a method for straightening a bent section of tubing in a fuselage.
7. Under what conditions is it permissible to ignore a dent in structural tubing?
8. Describe a method for removing a dent from steel tubing.
9. Before welding a reinforcing sleeve or patch over a crack in tubing, what should be done with respect to the crack?
10. Describe the installation of a *finger plate patch*.
11. At what angle is the scarf for a repair sleeve cut?
12. Describe a *fishmouth* cut for a sleeve.
13. Why is a fishmouth joint stronger than a scarf joint?
14. When cutting a length of replacement tubing which is to be spliced with inner sleeve reinforcements, how much clearance must be allowed for each end of tubing?
15. How are inner splice sleeves placed into position for welding a replacement tube between stations?
16. What are the lengths of the original tube stubs required when splicing in a new replacement section between stations and the replacement section is telescoped over the original stubs?
17. Describe a *rosette weld*.
18. What is the maximum clearance between an outer reinforcement sleeve and the tube inside it?
19. Describe the replacement of a cluster weld with the use of outside reinforcement sleeves.
20. What precautions must be taken when making a welded repair on a fabric covered fuselage?
21. What special care must be taken with the inspection and repair of welded engine mounts?
22. Describe three methods for welding steel-attachment fittings to tubular structures.
23. Explain how a fuselage structure can be held in alignment while making welded repairs.
24. Describe three methods for splicing streamline tubing.
25. What type of landing gear axle structures are not repairable by welding?
26. Why is it not permissible to weld a steel structure which has been brazed?
27. What types of nondestructive inspections can be performed to assure that welds have been made properly?
28. How can the interior of welded steel tubing be protected against corrosion?
29. Discuss the weld repair for exhaust parts.
30. What precaution must be taken before welding fuel and oil tanks?
31. What should be done to welds which are made on the outside surface of cowlings?

CHAPTER 10

Aircraft Sheet-metal Tools, Machines, and Methods

A wide variety of tools has been devised for use in working sheet metal. Some of these tools are used primarily for the forming and cutting of sheet metal and similar metals for commercial purposes; others are particularly useful for working aircraft sheet metals such as aluminum alloy, stainless steel, and titanium sheet. In this section we shall discuss a number of commonly employed tools with which the aircraft technician may become familiar when he is involved with sheet-metal repairs.

FLOOR AND BENCH TOOLS

Squaring shears

Squaring shears, shown in Fig. 10 · 1, are used to cut and square sheet metal. The mechanism consists of two blades operated either by foot or motor power. The lower blade is attached securely to the bed which has a scale graduated in fractions of an inch for measuring the sheet being cut. The other blade is mounted on the upper crosshead and is moved up and down to cut the metal stock. The upper blade is set at angle to the lower blade so the cut will take place at only one point on the metal at a time. The cut then takes place progressively across the width of the sheet.

Foot-power squaring shears usually cut mild-carbon steel up to 22 gage. Aluminum alloys up to 0.050 in. and above can be cut without difficulty. To operate, the long bed gage is set parallel to or at an angle with the blades according to the shape desired. The metal is placed on the bed of the machine and is trimmed off

from ¼ to ½ in. to make a straight edge on the sheet. The trimmed edge is held against the gage, and the sheet is sheared to size. To square the sheet, the end that has been cut last is held against the side gage, and from ¼ to ½ in. is trimmed off. The sheet is turned over, holding the straight edge against the long gage that has been set to the required distance, and then the other edge is sheared.

The parts numbered in Fig. 10 · 1 are as follows: (1) housing and leg, (2) lower crosshead, (3) foot treadle, (4) turnbuckle for adjusting blade, (5) T slot for gage bolt, (6) upper crosshead, (7) upper blade, (8) bed, (9) side gage, and (10) bolt for extension arm.

Gap-squaring shears

Gap-squaring shears, shown in Fig. 10 · 2, resemble the regular squaring shears except that the housing is constructed so that the sheet may pass completely through the machine, thus making possible the cutting of any desired length. The gap-squaring shears are used where the regular squaring shears are too narrow to split long sheets.

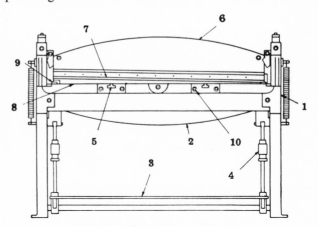

Figure 10 · 1 Squaring shears.

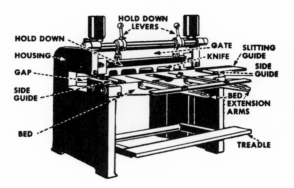

Figure 10 · 2 Gap squaring shears.

146

Slitting shears

Slitting shears, shown in Fig. 10·3, are used to slit sheets in lengths where the squaring shears are too narrow to accommodate the work. Slitting shears of the lever type, for cutting heavier grades of sheet metal, are commonly used and are known as lever shears. The parts numbered in Fig. 10·3 are: (1) base, (2) lower blade, (3) upper blade, (4) die, (5) punch, and (6) handle. Such shears should not be used to cut rods or bolts unless fitted with a special attachment. Some lever shears have a punching attachment on the end (opposite the blades) for punching heavy sheets, as shown in Fig. 10·4.

Throatless shears

Throatless shears are shown in Fig. 10·5. They are usually made to cut sheet metal as thick as 10 gage in mild-carbon steel and 12 gage in stainless steel. For aluminum-alloy stock they can cut much heavier sheets. The frame of the throatless shear is made so that sheets of any length may be cut and the metal may be turned in any direction, allowing irregular lines to be followed or notches to be made without distorting the metal.

Rotary slitting shears

Rotary slitting shears are shown in Fig. 10·6. The numbered parts of the drawing are (1) shank for bench standard, (2) frame, (3) back gear, (4) hand crank, (5)

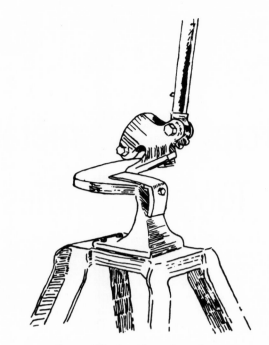

Figure 10·5   Throatless shears.

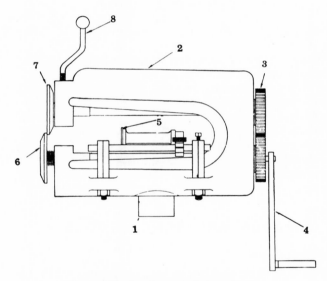

Figure 10·6   Rotary slitting shears.

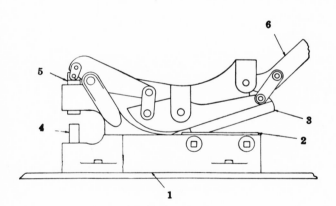

Figure 10·3   Slitting shears.

Figure 10·4   Lever shears with punching attachment.

adjustable gage, (6) lower rotary cutter, (7) upper rotary cutter, and (8) cutter adjusting screw.

Rotary slitting shears consist of a frame with a deep throat fitted with circular, disk-shaped cutters fastened to parallel shafts and connected with gears. The cutting wheels are operated by a crank or by a power-driven wheel. Such shears are used for slitting sheet metal and cutting irregular curves and circles. The edge of the sheet is held against the gage, and the end of the sheet is pressed against the cutting wheel. The handle is turned until the full length of the strip has been cut. For irregular curves, the gage is slid back out of the way and the handle turned slowly; and at the same time

147

the operator keeps the cutting wheels on the line to be cut.

Unishears

A portable **Unishear** is shown in Fig. 10·7. Unishear is merely a trade name for a type of power shear similar to a nibbling machine. It has a high-speed, narrow, reciprocating shearing blade and adjustments of vertical and horizontal clearances, depending on the thickness of the metal to be cut. It is especially useful in cutting internal curved patterns where the radius is small. A machine for the same purpose is also made in the stationary form.

Nibbling machine (nibbler)

A **nibbling machine (nibbler),** shown in Fig. 10·8, is a machine that has a die and a vertical cutting blade that travels up and down at a relatively high speed. The stroke is longer than that of the Unishear, and it is adjustable. This machine is used for cutting mild steel up to a thickness of ½ in. and to cut circles and curves of complex shapes in heavy sheets. The machine operates on the shearing principle and leaves rough edges.

Folding machines

A **bar-folding machine,** or **bar folder,** is a tool commonly used to turn (bend over) narrow edges and to turn rounded locks on flat sheets of metal to receive stiffening wires. A stop gage is set to the width of the fold desired, the sheet metal is held against the stop, and the bending leaf of the machine is turned over by lifting the bending handle. As the bending leaf swings over, it folds the sheet. The bar-folding machine is shown in Fig. 10·9.

A **pipe-folding machine** is illustrated in Fig. 10·10. This is a machine designed to bend flanges either on flat sheets or on stock that has previously been formed into a cylindrical shape. Bar-folding and pipe-folding machines are not commonly used in aircraft sheet-metal repair.

Cornice brake

The **cornice brake,** also called a **leaf brake,** is a machine used to make simple bends in flat sheet-metal stock. A drawing illustrating this type of brake is shown in Fig. 10·11. The cornice brake can form locks and seams, turn edges, and make bends through a wide range of angles. It operates like a bar-folding machine except that a clamping bar takes the place of the stationary jaw of the latter. The bar is raised so that the sheet of metal can be pushed in to any desired distance. A stop gage is set at the angle or amount of bend to be made, and then the bending leaf is raised until it strikes the stop. When it is desired to make a bend having a given radius, a **radius bar** having the correct radius for the bend is secured to the clamping bar. Figure 10·12 shows the relative positions of the parts when making the bend.

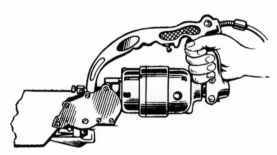

Figure 10·7   A portable Unishear.

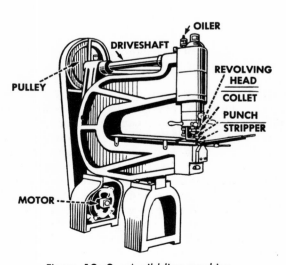

Figure 10·8   A nibbling machine.

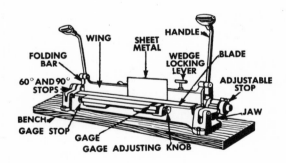

Figure 10·9   Bar-folding machine.

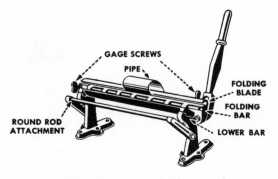

Figure 10·10   A pipe-folding machine.

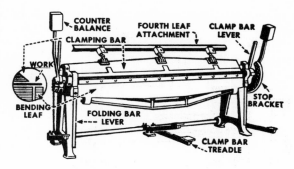

Figure 10·11   A cornice brake.

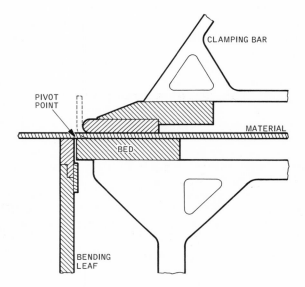

Figure 10·12   Positions of parts in making a bend.

Forming roll

The **forming roll,** shown in Fig. 10·13, is used to form sheet metal into cylinders of various diameters. It consists of right-end and left-end frames, between which are mounted three solid-steel rolls which are connected with gears and operated either by means of a power drive or a hand crank. The front rolls can be adjusted to the thickness of the metal by two thumbscrews located either on the bottom or the top of each end frame. These rolls grip the metal when it is started in the machine, and carry it to the rear, or forming, roll, which is adjusted in the same manner as the front pair. The forming roll is called a **slip-roll** former. The top roll in this type is so arranged that one end can be loosened and raised, permitting the work to be slipped out at the end to prevent distortion of the metal. Small cylinders and pipes can be formed on the slip-roll former.

Turning machine

A **turning machine** is a short-throated rotary device used on circular work to turn a narrow edge (flange) or to score a crease. The upper roll die is disk-shaped with a round edge. The lower roll is cylindrically shaped with a semicircular groove running around its side near

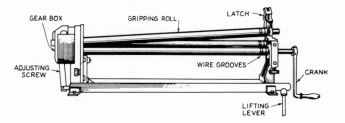

Figure 10·13   A forming roll.

the outer end. This machine is sometimes referred to as a **burring, turning,** and **wiring machine,** since it performs all these functions, provided the correct attachments are available.

A turning machine with a variety of attachments is shown in Fig. 10·14. In this drawing the parts are (1) turning rolls, (2) elbow-edging rolls, (3) burring rolls, (4) wiring rolls, (5) elbow-edging rolls, (6) elbow-edging rolls, and (7) burring rolls. The letter A refers to a small crank screw, and the letter B refers to the crank that controls the rolls.

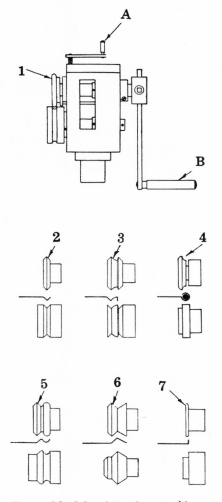

Figure 10·14   A turning machine.

Beading machines

The **beading machine,** shown in Fig. 10·15, is used to turn beads on pipes, cans, buckets, etc., both for stiffening and for ornamental purposes. It is also used on sheet-metal stock that is to be welded to prevent buckling and breaking of the metal. The numbers in the drawing refer to (1) single-beading roll, (2) triple-beading roll, (3) double-beading roll, and (4) ogee-beading roll. This machine was used extensively for aluminum oil lines on early aircraft to provide beads for holding clamped rubber tubing.

Crimping machine

The **crimping machine,** shown in Fig. 10·16, is used to make one end of a pipe joint smaller so that several sections may be slipped together. The mechanism is similar to that of the beading machine but the rolls are corrugated longitudinally. The parts numbered in the drawing are (1) vertical adjustment handle, (2) crank, (3) crimping rolls, and (4) adjustable gage.

Combination rotary machine

The **combination rotary machine** is a three-speed, motor-driven combination of the burring, turning, wiring, elbow-edging, beading, crimping, and slitting machines. This machine is illustrated in Fig. 10·17 with numbers indicating the following types of rollers: (1) thin forming rolls, (2) thick forming rolls, (3) burring rolls, (4) wiring rolls, and (5) elbow-edging rolls. This machine is supplied with a spanner wrench for quickly changing the different rolls. It is most useful where a variety of operations are to be performed.

Drop hammer

Drop hammers are used to form sheet-metal parts between a punch and die which have previously been constructed to provide the required shape. Since expen-

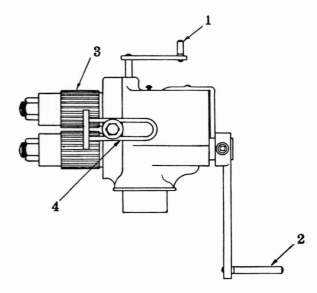

Figure 10·16   A crimping machine.

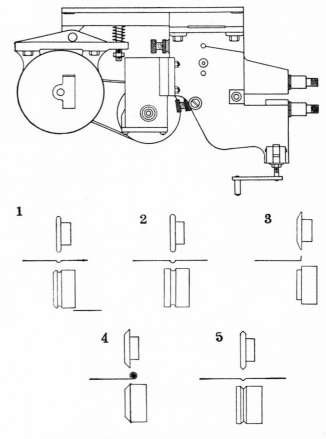

Figure 10·17   Combination rotary machine.

sive matching dies are required, the drop hammer is economical only for large quantities of standard production parts. The weighted hammer is generally the male portion of a forming die that is raised and then allowed to drop freely between vertical guides onto the stock, which forces it into the matching portion of the

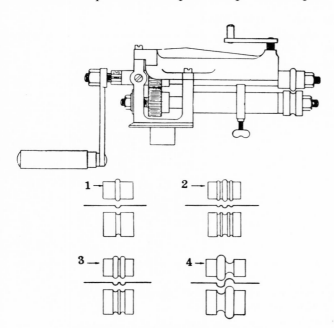

Figure 10·15   A beading machine.

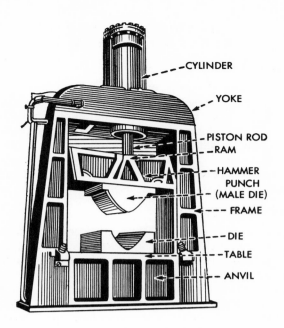

Figure 10·18 A drop hammer.

die. The hammer may be raised by a rope running over a drum, by a vertical board running between two opposed cylinders, or by air, steam, or hydraulic mechanism. The drop hammer is illustrated in Fig. 10·18.

Metal-cutting band saw

The metal-cutting band saw is similar to a wood-cutting band saw in construction. Because of the different properties of metals which may be cut, the saw must be adjustable in speed. The metal cutting blades must have hard-tempered teeth which will cut through hard metal without excessive wear or breakage. A metal-cutting band saw is shown in Fig. 10·19.

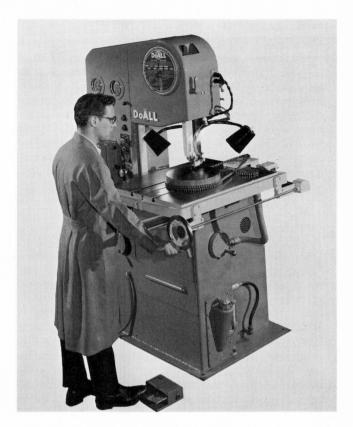

Figure 10·19 Metal-cutting bandsaw. (DoAll Co.)

In using a band saw to cut metal, the operator should refer to a chart to determine the type of blade and the blade speed for any particular metal. Table 10·1 gives blade speeds.

Table 10·1   Pitch and velocity settings for carbon-steel saw blades

Material	Blade pitch, teeth per in.			Blade velocity, ft per min		
	½ in. thick	1 in. thick	3 in. thick	½ in. thick	1 in. thick	3 in. thick
Carbon steels	10	8	4	175	175	150
Manganese steels	10	8	4	125	100	80
Nickel steels	10	10	4	100	90	80
Nickel-chrome steels	10	8	4	100	90	75
Molybdenum steels:						
4017–4042	10	4	4	135	125	110
4047–4068	10	8	4	125	100	75
Chrome-molybdenum steels	10	8	4	100	75	50
Corrosion-resistant steels 303, 416	10	8	4	100	80	60

Note:

For complete information on the operation of a power saw for metal cutting, the manufacturer's chart should be consulted.

For some types of materials a high-speed steel blade or a tungsten-carbide blade should be used.

When cutting many types of materials, cutting fluids or lubricants should be used.

To prevent tooth stripping and breaking of teeth, at least two teeth should be in contact with the work.

Stakes

A **stake** is a type of small anvil having a variety of forms, as shown in Fig. 10·20. It can be set in a bench plate and used to bend and shape sheet metal to the desired form by hand or by hammering. Its variety of shapes provides a convenient means for backing up or supporting otherwise inaccessible portions of intricately shaped pieces. Stakes are not machines, but they are usually classed with bench machines and tools. In order to hold these stakes, a flat, iron plate with square, tapered holes is fastened to the bench, and the stakes are set in these holes so as to be held securely while the work is being done.

Metal-spinning lathes

A **metal-spinning lathe** (shown in Fig. 10·21) is used to form sheet metal into shapes which have a circular cross section, such as hemispheres or nosecones for propellers. The machine differs from other metal lathes in that it has no back gears, carriage, or lead screws. It is rigid, and the spindle is usually driven by a step-cone pulley. Speed is important; hence the machine is adjustable over a wide range. In general, the thicker the metal, the slower must be the speed. Forms are constructed to provide the shape required for the finished product, and the metal is shaped by spinning over these forms.

HAND TOOLS FOR SHEET-METAL WORK

Hammers

Figure 10·22 shows two types of hammers often used by aircraft mechanics in the repair and forming of sheet-metal aircraft parts. The hammers shown are used for smoothing and forming sheet metal and are commonly called **planishing hammers.** The hammer with the square face is used for working in corners. When it is necessary to work in the radius of a bend, a hammer with a cross peen is used.

Hand snips and shears

Several types of **hand snips** and **shears** are shown in Fig. 10·23. These are named as follows: (1) right-hand straight snips, (2) left-hand straight snips, (3) double-cutting shears, (4) circular-cutting shears, (5) bench shears, and (6) aviation snips. The latter are especially made for cutting heat-treated aluminum alloy, stainless steel, and titanium. The blades have small teeth on their cutting edges and the handles are made to give great leverage. Aviation snips are shown in Fig. 10·24.

Mallets

Soft mallets (see Fig. 10·25) are of particular importance in the forming of sheet-metal parts to prevent damage to the metal. The mallet may be made of wood,

Figure 10·20   Stakes.

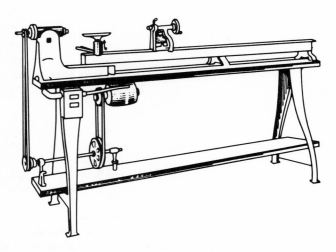

Figure 10·21   Metal-spinning lathe.

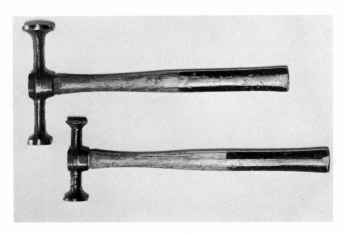

Figure 10·22   Planishing hammers for hand use.

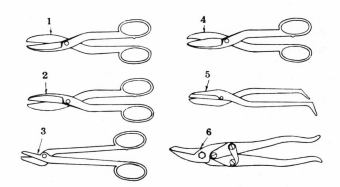

Figure 10·23   Hand snips and shears.

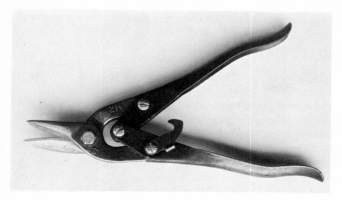

Figure 10·24   Aviation snips.

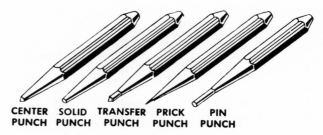

CENTER SOLID TRANSFER PRICK PIN
PUNCH PUNCH PUNCH PUNCH PUNCH

Figure 10·26   Hand punches.

rawhide, rubber, or plastic and is used in forming sheet metal over stakes or forms. Soft hammers or mallets should be used in any case where there is a possibility of causing damage by the use of a steel hammer.

Punches

Hand punches, usually called simply **punches,** are shown in Fig. 10·26. The center punch is used to produce a small conical indentation in metal to help center a drill and hold it in position while starting a hole. It is also used to mark a point on metal for reference in measuring. The **solid punch** is for general use wherever such a tool is appropriate. A **transfer punch** provides a means for transferring the position of a drilled hole from one part to another. When using the transfer punch, the size of the shank must be the same as that of the hole being transferred. The **prick punch** is used primarily for marking a point in metal. The **pin punch** is useful for installing or removing metal pins from cylindrical shafts or other parts. The punch diameter must be slightly less than the diameter of the pin.

Figure 10·27 is one type of hand-lever punch. This punch is designed to produce great force such that a hole may easily be punched through aluminum or other soft metal. A rotary-lever punch is shown in Fig. 10·28.

Hand-rivet set

A **hand-rivet set** is shown in Fig. 10·29. This type of set is used in commercial sheet-metal work and is also used for some hand-riveting operations in aircraft work. The holes in the hand-rivet set are for the purpose of drawing rivets through the metal before riveting. A rivet is inserted through a drilled hole in the metal, and the hole in the set is placed over the protruding shank of the rivet. With the head of the rivet held against a suitable backing block, the set is struck lightly with a hammer. This draws the sheets of metal together and causes them to fit snugly against the inside of the head of the rivet. The shank of the rivet may then be headed with the hammer.

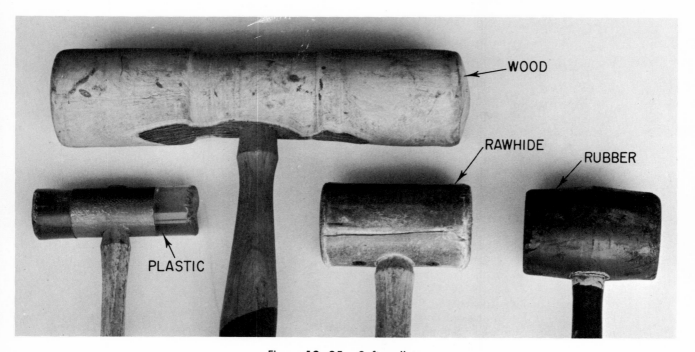

WOOD

RAWHIDE

RUBBER

PLASTIC

Figure 10·25   Soft mallets.

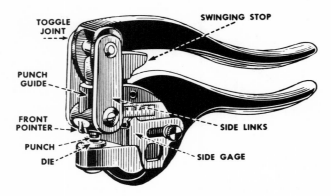

Figure 10·27   A hand-lever punch.

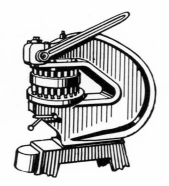

Figure 10·28   A rotary-lever punch.

Figure 10·29   A hand-rivet set.

Chisels

Chisels are merely steel bars provided with cutting edges for the purpose of cutting metal. They are made in many sizes and shapes; however, the chisels shown in Fig. 10·30 are usually sufficient for the aircraft technician. The common **cold chisel** is shown at the top and the **cape chisel** is at the bottom of the picture. The cold chisel is used for cutting any reasonably soft metal, including iron or steel that has not been hardened. The cape chisel is especially shaped for cutting grooves and keyways; however, its use is sometimes recommended for cutting rivet heads when removing rivets from aircraft sheet-metal structures. When this is done, great care must be exercised to avoid damaging the metal. The proper method for drilling and removing rivets is described in another section of this text.

Dividers

A pair of extension **dividers** is shown in Fig. 10·31. One leg can be lengthened or shortened, as desired, or removed and used as a scratch awl for marking. The divider is used primarily for transferring dimensions scribing circles, and striking arcs in layout work. These functions are explained in the section covering sheet-metal layout.

Pliers

Pliers are manufactured in a variety of designs to meet particular requirements. Figure 10·32 illustrates (1) common, automotive **slip-joint pliers,** (2) **electrician's pliers,** (3) **diagonal-cutting pliers,** (4) **duckbill pliers,** and (5) **needle-nose pliers.**

Slip-joint pliers are used for general use in gripping and holding parts where the possibility of damage is not critical. These pliers should not be used to turn nuts and bolts when there is any other possible method for doing this. The teeth in the jaws will scratch and mar the part being gripped; hence the pliers should only be used where no other tool will serve. Sometimes the jaws can be wrapped with tape to prevent damage. Electrician's pliers are generally used by commercial electricians for holding, pulling, twisting, and cutting electrical wire, usually of the commercial type. Fre-

Figure 10·30   Common chisels.

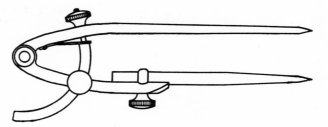

Figure 10·31   Dividers.

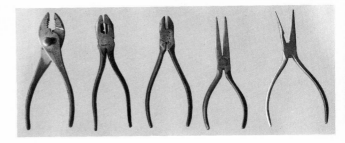

Figure 10·32   Common types of pliers.

quently the handles are insulated to avoid the possibility of shock in case a "hot" wire should be contacted.

Diagonal-cutting pliers ("dikes") are most useful for the airframe and powerplant technician, primarily for cutting safety wire, cotter pins, aircraft electrical wire, and similar purposes. The technician should have large and small sizes available in his tool kit.

Duckbill pliers, as the name indicates, have flattened jaws suitable for holding safety wire while twisting it. These pliers may also be used for any general purpose where their size and shape make them useful.

Needle-nose pliers are used for reaching into small openings where larger pliers cannot be placed. They are particularly useful in the assembly of small motors, magnetos, and other accessories to hold small washers, nuts, and other parts which cannot be handled by a wrench or other tool.

Rules

A **rule** or **scale** is a most essential item in the kit of a technician who is to perform sheet-metal work. Figure 10·33 shows a **circumference rule** on the left. This rule is made of high-grade steel and is graduated in eighths of an inch. The exact circumference of a cylinder can be found on the lower edge by referring to the diameter mark on the upper edge. On the opposite side of the rule are measurements for various objects encountered in sheet-metal work. The small drawing on the right of Fig. 10·33 represents the corner of a **steel square.**

The 6-in. scale shown in Fig. 10·34 is useful for general measuring and is available in a variety of calibrations. Scale markings on the edges may be as small as $\frac{1}{100}$ in. Because of its size and utility this scale is considered a basic tool for the aircraft maintenance technician.

Another essential measuring tool for the technician is the **combination square** shown in Fig. 10·35. This tool includes a 12-in. steel rule and a square head as shown. It is also possible to obtain the combination square with a **protractor head** and a **center head.** The protractor head is used for measuring angles and the center head is used for finding the exact center of round stock. A combination square with a center head and protractor head is shown in Fig. 10·36.

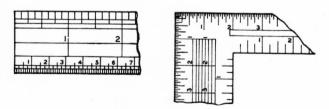

Figure **10·33**   Circumference rule and square.

Figure **10·34**   A 6-inch scale.

Figure **10·35**   Combination square.

Figure **10·36**   Combination square with protractor and center heads.

Wire and sheet-metal gages

Wire and sheet-metal gages are used for measuring the diameter of wire and the thickness of sheet metal. Figure 10·37 shows one form of this type of gage. It is simply a circular disk with slots cut around its circumference and numbered to indicate dimensions and measurements obtained by inserting the wire or sheet metal into the slot.

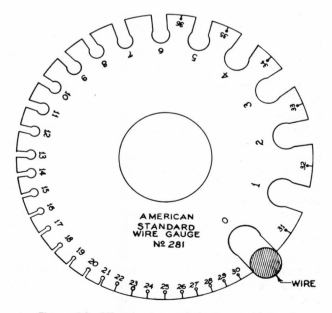

Figure **10·37**   A wire and sheet-metal gage.

SOLDERING

The soldering method

Soldering is the sealing and securing of a joint between two metal pieces by applying **solder,** a low-melting-point metal such as an alloy of lead and tin, to the joint in a melted condition. The melted solder is spread over the adjoining surfaces with a soldering "iron" (copper) or a jet of flame. The solder does not actually fuse with the metals being joined but bonds to them on the surface. Soldering produces a relatively weak joint but is satisfactory for many purposes. It is especially useful in making airtight joints of sheet metal that do not have to withstand much pull or vibration, and it is also used to seal electrical connections. Where soldering is attempted, it is necessary to employ flux to clean the surfaces to be soldered so the solder can adhere to the metal.

The metals commonly soldered are iron, tin, copper, brass, galvanized iron, and terneplate. Aluminum, stainless steel, titanium, and other metals can be soldered under the proper conditions and with the right materials. Ordinary lead-tin solder cannot be used for all soldering. Special fluxes are available, however, which make possible a broad application of such solder.

Sweat soldering

Sweat soldering, also called **sweating,** is a method of soldering in which the parts to be soldered are first tinned and then the melted solder is drawn between the surfaces to be soldered by capillary attraction with the application of heat. Sometimes a soldering iron is used and sometimes a neutral gas flame (torch) is used to melt and flow the solder in the joint. The torch is particularly useful in silver (hard) soldering.

Soldering copper

The **soldering copper** is the solid, pointed block of copper alloy forming the head (tip) of a soldering tool (soldering iron or soldering copper). It is attached to the handle by means of an iron shank with a tang. The copper is heated, usually in a flame, and then used to melt and spread the solder on the surfaces to be joined. It must be emphasized that the soldering copper must be clean and well-tinned and the correct flux must be applied.

Soldering coppers are manufactured in many sizes and shapes. Figure 10·38 shows four common shapes used in commercial sheet-metal work.

It is common practice to employ electric soldering coppers because of their convenience where electric power is available. The electric tool contains a resistance heating element inside the hollow copper head. An electric soldering copper is shown in Fig. 10·39.

As explained previously, a soldering copper must be tinned before it can be used. If the copper is not tinned, the solder will not adhere to it and the heat will not be conducted in sufficient quantity to melt the solder and heat the joint. To tin the copper, the tip is

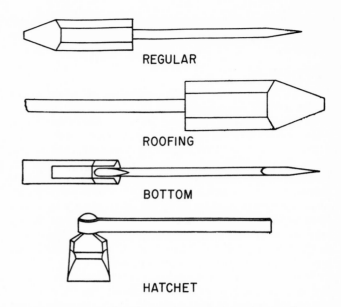

Figure **10·38** *Four common soldering coppers for commercial work.*

Figure **10·39** *An electric soldering copper.*

first filed clean and in the correct shape. After being filed to shape the copper is heated and then filed again slightly to remove any oxide which has formed. When bright and clean the tip is dipped into a flux before solder is applied. If rosin-core solder is used, it is not necessary to dip the tip in flux. When the entire point is covered with melted solder the copper is ready for use.

Flux

Flux is, in general, any chemical compound, such as borax, ammonium chloride, sodium carbonate, zinc chloride, rosin, or stearic acid which unites with oxides and other impurities in molten metal and floats them to the surface. In soldering, the most common fluxes are acid (hydrochloric acid in which zinc has been dissolved), rosin, and paste fluxes. The use of acid fluxes is not approved for aircraft work because of the corrosive effects of such fluxes. The fluxes recommended for aircraft work are rosin and non acid paste flux. Excess paste flux should be wiped off after the soldering is completed.

Fluxes for hard soldering (silver soldering, brazing, and eutectic welding) are (1) powdered borax, (2) powdered borax and carbonate of soda, and (3) special patented fluxes designed for specific types of hard soldering.

Soft soldering

The technique for **soft soldering** involves clean parts, proper fit, and correct flux. Scraping, filing, or wire brushing are the usual cleaning methods. Scale, dirt, and oxides are thoroughly removed. The cleaned surfaces are then fitted in place, coated with the proper flux, and the hot soldering copper applied with the solder to the adjoining parts. A small additional amount of flux is often necessary to remove any oxides that may form and to help the melting of the solder that is already applied. It is essential that the soldering copper be kept in contact with the work until the solder is thoroughly sweated into the joint. Poor solder joints are often the result of insufficient heat.

When soldering a seam such as that shown in Fig. 10·40, the parts to be soldered should be tacked with drops of solder unless they are otherwise fastened together. The solder is picked up with the soldering copper and transferred to the metal where it is deposited along the seam. Flux should be used as required to cause the solder to adhere to the metal.

To finish the seam, a hot, well-tinned soldering copper is applied with the point extending over the seam on the single thickness of metal; the heel or back of the copper is over the seam itself, at an angle of about 45°. The bar of solder or wire solder is touched to the copper while it is in this position. As the solder melts, the copper is drawn slowly along the work, keeping it at an angle and permitting it to sweat the solder into the entire width of the seam.

Hard soldering

Hard soldering is the process of soldering with a composition of copper, zinc, silver, and tin. Since soft-soldered gasoline- and oil-pipe joints, and similar

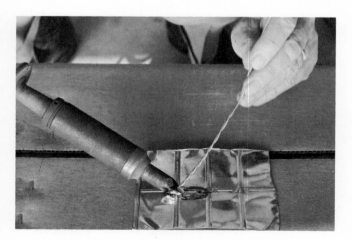

Figure 10·40   Soldering a seam.

joints fracture with repeated vibration, this composition of solder is used. It is suitable for bronze parts, copper, and brass. Since the solder cannot be melted with a soldering copper, it is necessary to use a neutral torch flame for heating the solder and the joint. It is usually necessary to heat the parts and the solder to a red heat in order to melt the solder and cause it to flow into the joint.

The process called **brazing,** in which a brass-type rod is used for "soldering" the joint, is also a form of hard soldering. Still another process is called **eutectic welding.** The term **eutectic** describes low-melting-point metals. Eutectic welding is a form of welding akin to hard soldering in which the welding material has a lower melting point than the metal being welded, thus this type of welding can be classed as hard soldering and is similar to brazing or silver soldering.

Application of soldering to aircraft

The use of soft or hard soldering for the repair of aircraft parts is strictly limited. Generally these processes should not be employed for any stressed (load-bearing) part. In certain instances, silver soldering or brazing may be employed but the repair must be approved and passed by proper government authority if it is used on a certificated aircraft.

REVIEW QUESTIONS

1. Describe *squaring shears* and their purpose.
2. For what special purpose is the *gap-squaring shear* used?
3. Explain the use of *slitting shears.*
4. Describe *rotary slitting shears.*
5. For what purpose is the *nibbling machine* useful?
6. Explain the operation of the *cornice brake.*
7. What is the function of the *radius bar* on the cornice brake?
8. For what special purpose is the *forming roll* or *slip-roll former designed?*
9. How is a power hammer useful in aircraft sheet-metal work?
10. Explain the purpose of a *drop hammer.*
11. In operating a metal-cutting band saw, what determines the blade speed to be used?
12. Explain how a *hand planishing hammer* is used.
13. What features of aviation snips make them useful for cutting tough sheet metal?
14. Under what conditions should a soft mallet be used?
15. Describe two common types of chisels used in metal work.
16. What is the function of the *protractor head* when used with a *combination square?*
17. Of what metals is ordinary solder made?
18. Why is it necessary to use flux in welding?
19. Explain *sweat soldering.*
20. How is heat applied for *silver soldering?*
21. Describe the method for preparing the tip of a soldering copper to obtain good results in soldering.
22. What types of soldering flux are required for aircraft work?
23. What types of joints should not be soldered on an aircraft?

CHAPTER 11

Aircraft Layout Work

LAYOUT TOOLS

The purpose of layout work

To take the punishment encountered in flight and on the ground, an airplane must be manufactured, maintained, and repaired correctly. This means that the engineers, technicians, inspectors, foremen, and supervisors connected in any manner with aircraft work must be able to read and follow blueprints. The subject of reading blueprints is covered in the text *Basic Science for Aerospace Vehicles,* one of the books in this series. The purpose of this discussion is to explain how to transfer or lay out blueprint drawings in marking material so that the flat shapes, or pattern, of a part can be drilled, cut, bent, or formed by following the lines and marks on the material.

In aircraft work, it is common to keep within limits of 0.010 in., hardly more than the width of a pencil point. The technician must use the best precision tools that he can obtain in order to meet the specifications. He uses layout tools to get the design from the blueprint, or drawing, and to transfer it to the material with which he is working. If he can read a blueprint and do layout work, and if he has the skills normally required for certificated technicians, he can make an aircraft part, make a repair, and make other changes in the aircraft.

In experimental aircraft design and construction, layout work is essential and is used continuously. For repairs and modifications, it is used frequently. The technician makes modifications on airplanes already in service to ensure that they will conform to modern requirements and to eliminate weaknesses which may have been found through experience. In addition, the technician must conform to the instructions issued by the manufacturers of aircraft and equipment, and the bulletins, airworthiness directives, and other repair or maintenance orders applicable to the aircraft upon which he is working.

When it is necessary for a technician to make a number of similar parts, he uses a **template.** The template is a metal pattern used in transferring the required dimensions to a number of pieces of material or stock. The purpose of working from a template is to provide a high degree of uniformity and a great saving of time. However, the technician should not expect that he will always be able to work from templates. In some cases he will find it necessary to make his own templates in order to perform a job satisfactorily.

Whether or not a template is available, the technician must use layout tools in checking the accuracy of his finished product. Wherever he works—with a commercial air line, in a repair shop, or for a private operator at an airport—he is expected to know how to use layout tools.

The pencil

The technician should not use the first pencil he happens to pick up. Instead, he should carefully select the correct pencil and then be sure that it has the right kind of a point on it. This is especially important if he is later to cut, file, or bend material along pencil marks. There is no advantage gained by using a dull-pointed pencil and then having to guess at the proper width of a line.

Lead pencils actually contain graphite, not lead. A typical drawing pencil is graded according to hardness, starting with the B grades and going up to 6H, which is the hardest grade in ordinary use.

A **file** is a convenient device for sharpening pencils in a workshop. In the drafting room, a combination lead-pencil file and tack lifter is sometimes used. The most common device used by the draftsman is the pencil pointer which consists of sheets of abrasive paper made into a block.

Figure 11 · 1 shows three views of a pencil that has been sharpened correctly for ordinary layout work.

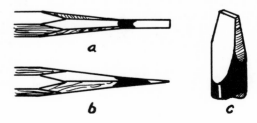

Figure 11 · 1 Pencil point correctly sharpened for layout work.

This pencil has been sharpened to a **chisel point.** In the illustration, the drawing marked with the letter *A* shows the wide portion, *B* is a side view, and *C* is a perspective view illustrating the fact that all four sides should be sharpened.

A chisel point is best for line work because it leaves a clean-edged line, since more of the pencil touches the material than is the case when a needle point is used. Also, it is not necessary to sharpen a chisel-pointed pencil as often as one with a needle point. In drawing circles, the compass lead should always have a chisel point.

A **needle point** is obtained when a pencil is sharpened in the common pencil-sharpening machine. It is better than the chisel point for some types of work, but it is necessary to rotate the pencil slowly in the hand while it is being used in order to keep the sharpest possible point in continuous contact with the surface of the material.

The scriber

Pencils are used in layout work when the technician wants to avoid marring the work, but no kind of pencil will leave as clean and narrow a mark as the scratch of a well-sharpened instrument. Figure 11·2 is a drawing of a double-pointed **scriber.** This is merely a sharp, hard steel pick, used when laying out work on metal as a pencil is used when drawing on paper. It is not used on Alclad aluminum or aluminum alloy where the scribed line will not be cut off later. It is important to emphasize the fact that a scribe line should never be permitted on a structural aircraft part. A scratch, nick, or similar defect on a structural part is likely to produce a stress concentration which eventually leads to a crack and ultimate failure of the part.

Note that the scriber in the illustration is a slender piece of tool steel tapered to a point at each end, with one point set at a 90° angle. This is sometimes called a **plain machinist's scriber.** It is long enough so that it can be gripped in the middle.

A **pocket scriber** is smaller and has only one point. There is a chuck mechanism for holding the point and this enables the technician to remove the point so he can carry the scriber in his pocket without worrying about injury to himself because of the point. Both types of scribers have knurled handles or grips so they can be held without slipping.

The scriber must be sharp to make the clean, narrow lines required for marking metal properly. Before using a scriber, the technician examines the point. If it is not sharp and evenly ground, he sharpens the point with an India oilstone.

In drawing a straight line, a scriber is held in the hand at an angle, tilted slightly in the direction of the

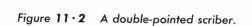

Figure 11·2 A double-pointed scriber.

line. Regardless of the kind of guiding edge used, the scriber must touch the lower surface at all times, and it must be applied with an even pressure. If this is not done, the line will be broken and crooked. Finally, a good technician draws an accurate line at the first attempt. He does not retrace.

The machinist's steel rule

The **machinist's steel rule,** such as the one illustrated in Fig. 11·3, is made from spring steel to a high degree of accuracy. This tool was mentioned in the previous chapter as the 6-in. scale. This rule is a precision instrument with the usual lengths being 4, 6, or 12 in., but there are other standard lengths up to 48 in. The usual graduations in the United States are ⅛, ¹⁄₁₆, ¹⁄₃₂, and ¹⁄₆₄ in. or decimal graduations as fine as ¹⁄₅₀ or ¹⁄₁₀₀ in.

When the total length of a measurement is not too great, the rule is used rather than a measuring tape because the rule is more accurate and is easier to read. Since the rule is a precision measuring instrument, it should not be used as a screwdriver, scraper, or putty knife.

The technician should examine his rule every time he starts to use it. The graduations should be perfect, and there should be no nicks or scratches. When not in use it should be carried in a leather or plastic case. If the case is slightly oiled it will help to keep the rule from rusting; if it is too oily, however, it will pick up dirt, which acts as an abrasive that will cause the rule to wear.

In using the rule, if the technician measures ½ in. from the inside to the inside of the engraved lines (graduations) on the rule, he will have what is commonly called a **scant half-inch.** If he measures from outside to outside he will get what is commonly called a **full half-inch.** Neither is accurate. He should measure from center to center of the graduation markings.

In measuring, it is best to take the measurement from the 1-in. mark to avoid wear and tear on the ends of the scale and to obtain greater accuracy. The only danger is that the technician sometimes forgets to subtract the 1 in. from the measurement indicated on the scale.

Figure 11·4 shows how a slot is measured, and Fig. 11·5 shows how to measure the diameter of a hole. The beginner soon discovers that it is not as easy to mark off a measurement as it appears. The scale is made from flat stock, and it does not have a beveled edge; hence

Figure 11·3 Machinist's steel rule.

159

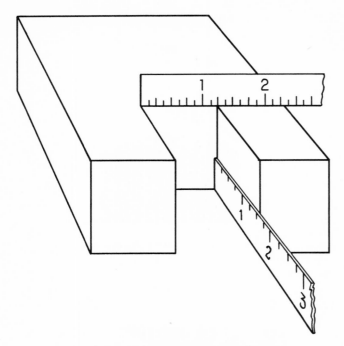

Figure 11·4 Measuring a slot.

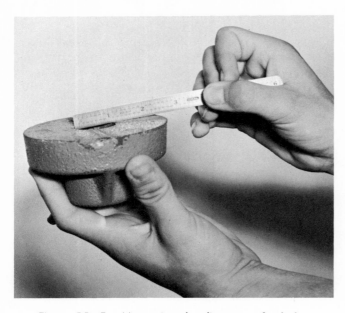

Figure 11·5 Measuring the diameter of a hole.

it is not possible to get the scale graduations close to the work. In ordinary rough layout work, this is not an obstacle, but in working to close tolerances it presents a problem. The solution is to tilt the scale on its edge, thus bringing the graduations closer to the work, reducing the light reflections on the scale, and making it easier to read. By sliding the scriber point down the graduations, the technician can mark the metal exactly at the right points.

If a technician has trouble gripping the rule firmly when he tilts it, or if there is danger of slipping, he should use it flat on the work, even though the graduations are harder to see in this position. The danger here is that the measurements may be recorded larger than they actually are. The solution to this problem is to close one eye, move the head so that the open eye is vertically above the graduation from which the measurement is taken, and move the head as the scriber is moved along to the next graduation, thus keeping the open eye vertically above any graduation.

Tapes

There are several kinds and lengths of **tapes.** The type commonly used by aircraft technicians is 6 ft long, made of flexible steel, and coiled in a circular case. One end may or may not be permanently fastened to the case. The tape may be drawn out or pushed back into the case. It is graduated on one side only in $\frac{1}{16}$- and $\frac{1}{32}$-in. divisions. There is a small lip at one end, which is used to make it easy for a technician to line up the end of the tape with the end of a piece of stock. The steel tape is shown in Fig. 11·6.

The straightedge

The **straightedge** is a long, straight, flat, square-edged strip of steel, ground to close tolerances, but not graduated. It is used for layout work where the line to be scribed or drawn is longer than that which can be produced with the ordinary rule or scale. The straightedge should be protected from dirt, grit, bends, dents, and other sources of inaccuracy. When not in use it should be stored carefully, preferably in a case or box, and it should be lightly oiled at all times to prevent rust.

Straightedges used for determining the accuracy of woodwork are often made of hardwood. Such a tool can be trued periodically on a jointer or a belt sander, thus keeping it in accurate alignment.

The ordinary straightedge should not be confused with a timing straightedge. The latter is a thin strip of steel about 6 in. long, the edges of which are straight. This tool is used for timing a magneto equipped with a step-cut timing collar.

Dividers

Dividers were mentioned in the previous chapter as a sheet-metal tool. In this section we shall specifically consider them in connection with layout. A pair of dividers is shown in the drawing of Fig. 11·7. The point on the dividers are the parts that do the work;

Figure 11·6 A steel measuring tape.

Figure 11·7 Dividers.

Figure 11·8 Using the dividers.

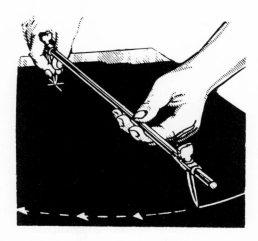

Figure 11·9 Trammel points used in layout work.

hence they should be kept sharp and protected against bending.

The most accurate dividers are those known as **toolmaker's dividers.** They are strong and have little weave or spring in their legs. However, the ordinary technician's dividers are satisfactory for rough layout work. Regardless of the type used, the technician must know how to use and care for his dividers. For example, in setting spring dividers to scale, he does not simply turn screws. Instead, he is careful to handle the spring tension so the dividers will not unexpectedly work loose and creep open while he is making a delicate measurement.

The dividers are placed on a rule with one point in the 1-in. mark, and then they are adjusted until the other point is at the required dimension; the technician should remember to subtract 1 in. to allow for the first point being at the 1-in. mark. Then the dividers are set by turning the adjusting screw. While the dividers are being set, the legs should be grasped between the thumb and fingers to relieve the spring tension and to protect the threads from unnecessary wear.

In ordinary layout work, it is sufficient to check the setting of the dividers by measuring the laid-off distance with the rule, or scale, but for very close tolerances this is not enough. With the setting of the dividers being used, a circle is drawn on any scrap metal or paper, and then the diameter of the circle is measured with the rule. If the diameter is twice the setting, the dividers are set correctly.

When an arc or a circle is scribed with the dividers, to keep the dividers from bumping along the metal, they should be tilted in the direction of the arc that is being drawn. In drawing that part of a circle which is closest to him, the technician tilts the dividers toward his body. In drawing that part which is away from him, he tilts the dividers away from his body as shown in Fig. 11·8.

Trammel points

Figure 11·9 shows **trammel points** being used to lay out a job of such large dimensions that dividers cannot be used. The points are attached to an extension bar by means of lockscrews. There must be no bend or sag in the extension bar and the screws must be tight, or the work will be inaccurate. In the words of the shop, the "radius walks away."

In using trammel points, the trammel should be inclined in the direction of the arc, just as the dividers are inclined when swinging an arc. The angle of inclination must be constant through all the arc, or circle.

Trammel points are used for rigging the alignment of wings and other parts when assembling aircraft. In these cases the primary function of the trammel points is to transfer dimensions accurately.

Squares

Three types of squares are generally used in layout work: (1) the ordinary **steel square,** shown in Fig. 11·10, which has one leg 16 in. long and the other leg 24 in. long; (2) the **diemaker's square,** shown in Fig. 11·11, which can be adjusted to form angles of 30 and 45°, as well as one of 90°; and (3) the **combination square,** mentioned in the previous chapter.

Punches

Punches have been described previously; however, it is well to describe how they are used in layout work. The two used for this purpose are the **center punch** and the **prick punch.**

The plain center punch shown in Fig. 11·12 is made

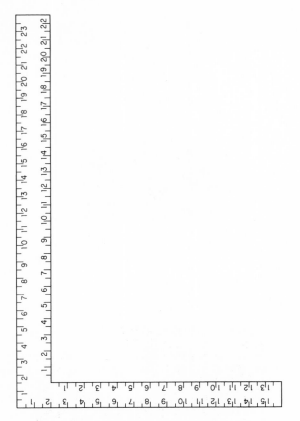

Figure **11·10**   The steel square.

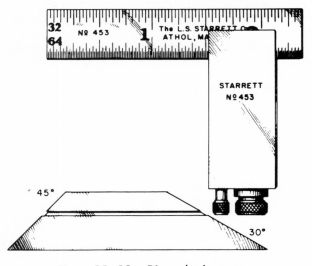

Figure **11·11**   Die maker's square.

from tempered tool steel. It is usually between 2 and 6 in. long, and its point is ground to a 60° to 90° angle. Center punches used for making large indentations in metal, such as those necessary to start a twist drill, are usually ground to a point with an angle of 60°, and are larger than the type used for layout work.

The prick punch illustrated in Fig. 11·13 has a point ground to approximately a 60° angle and is used to

Figure **11·12**   A center punch.

Figure **11·13**   A prick punch.

place a reference mark on metal. Some prick punches are tapered to a point of about 30° if they are intended for rough work.

To keep the punches sharp, a grinding wheel and an India oilstone are used. The correct angle having been determined for the point, this angle should be maintained by constant measurement and grinding when necessary.

The prick punch is used to identify the location of a hole; the center punch is used to make a cone-shaped impression large enough for a drill point to start and be able to remain in the correct position.

A prick punch can be used to make a depression in which one leg of a pair of dividers is placed for striking arcs or for laying out accurate distances by means of the dividers.

Hole centers and centers for arcs are always established first by the intersection of two scribed lines. The prick punch is accurately centered by placing the point in one of the scribed lines and running it along the groove until it is stopped by the burr thrown up by the other scribed line that intersects the first. Then, the punch is held perpendicular (at right angles) to the work, with the technician resting his fingers against the material to steady the punch, and the punch is struck a very light blow with a small hammer.

The work must be inspected constantly for accuracy. If the punch mark is off-center, the prick punch is held at an angle, and then it is struck a light tap with the hammer to move the punch mark into position.

Technicians who do a great amount of layout work use an **automatic center punch.** This punch works by a spring action which permits an adjustment of the blow to be struck and eliminates the use of a hammer.

Finally, regardless of the type of punch used, either a machinist's scale or a pair of dividers is used to check for accuracy immediately after the blow is struck.

Spline and duck weights

A **spline** is a long, thin, flexible, grooved rod made of wood, metal, or plastic, that can be bent to any desired curve. **Duck weights,** made of lead or iron, with a hook that fits into the groove of the spline, are used to maintain the curve and to hold the spline against the work. Figure 11·14 shows a spline with the duck weights. With this arrangement, a curved line can be drawn on metal or paper as desired.

A spline with duck weights is especially useful when the technician must scribe an irregular curve that has been established by a series of points. In a lofting room,

Figure 11·14   Using a spline with duck weights.

a spline with duck weights is an absolutely essential instrument for laying out curves to actual size.

Ship curves

Ship curves are club-shaped outlines with two expanding curves as illustrated in Fig. 11·15. They are made in a great variety of sizes and different curvatures, and are usually made of some transparent material. To meet all conditions, a complete set usually consists of about 120 curves, packed in a special chest that has a tray divided into compartments. In the aircraft industry, these are usually supplied to the employees by the employer; in the shipbuilding industry, however, the employee generally furnishes his own set of curves.

When an aircraft layout job requires connecting a number of points with a ship curve, the first step is to observe the direction in which the curve is expanding. The radius of the beginning curve is normally rather small and expands or flattens as it develops. The second step is to move the ship curve around until it expands in the same direction as the direction of the curve to be drawn. Third, the ship curve is aligned with three or more points that are to be connected, and the points are connected with a pencil or scriber. Fourth, the operator moves on to the next series of points, being careful that the part of the curve being scribed or drawn at any moment flows smoothly into the next portion of the curve.

When ship curves or a spline with duck weights are not available, a long strip of thin wood, cut evenly and free from weak spots, can be bent into the desired shape and used in an emergency. If no weights are available they can be improvised, or the operator can have another man hold the strip in position while he draws or scribes the curve.

French curves

French curves serve a function similar to that described for ship curves, however the French curves are used for drawing curved lines with sharper bends. Both ship curves and French curves are usually made from a transparent plastic material, thus making it possible for the operator to see both sides of his scribing. The difficulty is that plastic curves are easily nicked and scratched; hence they must be inspected carefully before being used to avoid errors in the work. French curves are illustrated in Fig. 11·16.

Figure 11·15   Ship curves.

Figure 11·16   French curves.

GEOMETRIC CONSTRUCTION

The words **geometric** and **geometrical** come from geometry, which is the branch of science which deals with space and its relations, such as the relative positions of surfaces, lines, and points. A related branch of science is **mensuration,** which deals with the measurement of length, area, and volume. An aircraft technician does not have to be a mathematician to do layout work, but he does have to have an understanding of geometrical figures.

It may not be immediately apparent why **geometrical construction** is useful to the aircraft technician; however, when the time comes that he must layout sheet metal for the construction of original or of repair parts, he will then realize the value of this skill. The examples of geometric construction given in this section are those which are found to be most useful to the person concerned with laying out angles, curves and dimensions to develop sheet-metal patterns of particular shapes.

To bisect a line

To bisect (divide into two equal parts) the given line *AB*, shown in Fig. 11·17, use the points *A* and *B* as center and with a radius greater than ½ *AB*, draw arcs that intersect at *C* and *D*. Then draw the line *CD*. The point *E* where *CD* intersects line *AB* is the center of *AB*.

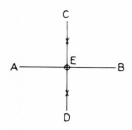

Figure 11·17   Bisecting a line.

If the foregoing construction is done with a compass on paper, the steel point of the compass is placed on point *A* and an arc is struck with the pencil point passing through both *C* and *D*. The steel point is then placed on point *B* and arcs are again struck through the arcs previously drawn. The intersections of the arcs establish the precise locations for points *C* and *D*. Figure 11 · 18 shows how the compass is used for the construction.

To bisect an arc

In Fig. 11 · 19 is the given arc *AB*. Taking *A* and *B* as centers, with a radius greater than ½ *AB*, draw arcs intersecting at *C* and *D*. Draw *CD*. Then the point *E* at the intersection of the straight line *CD* and the arc is the center of the arc. It will be observed that this construction is essentially the same as that used for the bisection of a straight line.

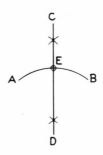

Figure **11 · 19**   Bisecting an arc.

To bisect an angle

In Fig. 11 · 20, *ABC* is a given angle. Using *B* as a center and with any convenient radius, draw an arc cutting the sides of the angle at *E* and *D*. Then, take *E* and *D* as centers, and with a radius greater than one-half the distance between *E* and *D*, draw arcs that intersect, in this case at point *F*. Then draw the line *FB*. Angle *ABF* will be equal to angle *CBF*; hence angle *ABC* has been bisected or divided into two equal angles.

To erect a perpendicular from a given point on a line

In the diagram of Fig. 11 · 21, *AB* is a given line, and *C* is the given point from which a perpendicular line is to be drawn to the line *AB*. From any suitable point, such as *D*, and with a radius of *CD*, draw the arc *ECF*. Through *E* and *D*, draw a line cutting the arc at *F*. Then draw the line *CF*, which is perpendicular to the line *AB*.

To draw a line perpendicular to a given line from a given point

In Fig. 11 · 22, a perpendicular line is to be drawn from point *C* to the line *AB*. Establish any two points on the line *AB*, such as *D* and *E*. With *E* as a center and

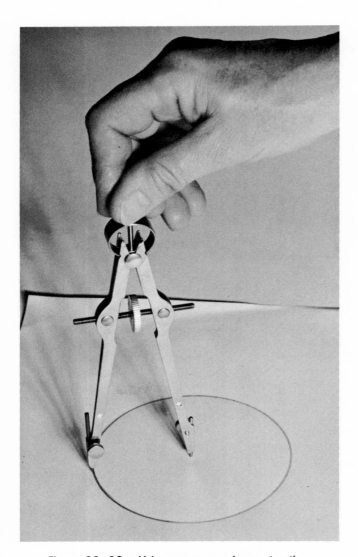

Figure **11 · 18**   *Using a compass in construction.*

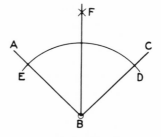

Figure **11 · 20**   Bisecting an angle.

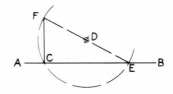

Figure **11 · 21**   *Erecting a perpendicular from a line.*

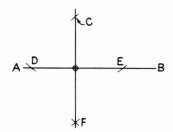

Figure 11·22   Constructing a perpendicular from a point to a line.

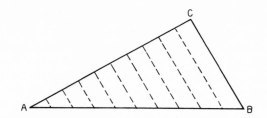

Figure 11·24   Dividing a line into equal parts.

with a radius of *EC*, draw an arc at a point near *F*. Then with *D* as a center and a radius of *DC* (the same length as *EC*), draw another arc through the first one near *F*. Then, from this intersection (*F*), draw *FC* which will be perpendicular to *AB*.

To draw an angle equal to another angle

Figure 11·23 shows two angles. *ABC* is the given angle, and it is required to draw another angle *FDE* equal to *ABC*. Draw the line *DE*. Then from points *B* and *D*, draw arcs *AC* and *FE* using the same radius. With *E* as a center and with a radius equal to *AC*, draw an arc that intersects the arc *EF* at *F*. Then draw the line *DF*. The angle *FDE* is equal to the angle *ABC*.

To divide a line into any number of equal parts

In Fig. 11·24, line *AB* is to be divided into 10 equal parts. Another line, *AC*, is drawn from *A* at any convenient angle and at a length *AC* which is 10 units in length. Each unit is marked with a point. Then from the points on line *AC*, lines parallel to *CB* are drawn to intersect *AB*. To make the lines parallel to *CB*, it is necessary that each divider line form an angle with *AC*

equal to the angle *ACB*. Line *AB* will then be divided into 10 equal parts.

To divide a circle into six equal parts

Figure 11·25 shows a circle with points on its circumference marked from *A* to *F*. If an unmarked circle is to be divided into six equal parts, start at any convenient point, such as *A*, and draw arcs using a compass radius equal to the radius of the circle. From point *A*, arcs can be struck through the circumference of the circle at *B* and *F*. Then from point *B* an arc can be struck through point *C*, and from point *F* an arc can be drawn through the point *E*. Finally, an arc can be drawn through *D* from either *C* or *E*. For accuracy it is necessary to use a very sharp compass or divider point and take great care in striking the arcs. The principle to be noted here is that *the radius of a circle is equal to the side of the inscribed hexagon.* See Fig. 11·26.

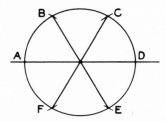

Figure 11·25   Dividing a circle into six equal parts.

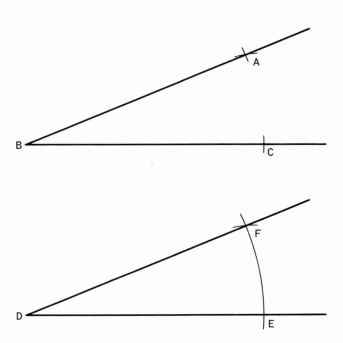

Figure 11·23   Drawing an angle equal to a given angle.

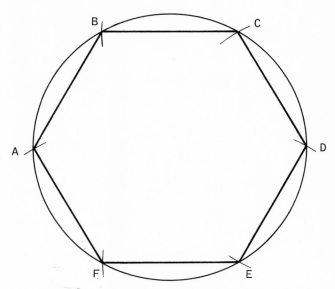

Figure 11·26   A hexagon inscribed in a circle.

To find the center of a given circle

The method for finding the center of a circle utilizes the principles already explained. In the diagram of Fig. 11 · 27, locate any three points, such as *A*, *B*, and *C* on the circumference. Connect the points with chords *AB* and *BC*. **Chords** are straight lines joining the ends of an arc. Now, bisect the chords as explained in the section "To bisect a line," and extend the bisecting lines to intersect in the circle. The point of intersection, *D*, is the center of the circle.

To draw an ellipse when the long and short diameters are given

Figure 11 · 28 shows two circles, one within the other, both having a common center. The diameter of the inside circle is the short diameter of the desired ellipse. The diameter of the outside circle is the long diameter of the ellipse. Divide the circumference of the circles into a number of equal divisions as shown. From the intersections of the division lines and the circumferences of the circle, draw pairs of lines perpendicular to each other. A curved line passed uniformly through the intersections of these lines will describe the ellipse.

To find the circle determined by three points not on the same straight line

In Fig. 11 · 29 are three points, *A*, *B*, and *C*, not located on the same straight line. To determine the size and position of the circle passing through the three points, connect *A* and *B* with a straight line and connect *B* and *C* with a straight line. Bisect the lines *AB* and *BC* with perpendicular lines, and permit the bisecting lines to intersect at a point *D*. This point is the

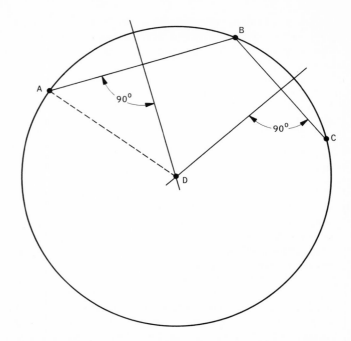

Figure 11 · 29   Constructing a circle from three points not on the same straight line.

center of the circle which passes through the three points. With *DA* as a radius, draw the circle.

To construct angles without a protractor

A technician may find it necessary to construct an angle when he has no protractor available. There is nothing difficult about it if he remembers there are 360° in a circle. If he knows the radius of the circle with which he is working, he can find the circumference.

Figure 11 · 30 shows how to determine a given angle. In view *A*, the upper diagram in Fig. 11 · 30, the radius of the circle involved is 10½ in. The circumference is found by multiplying the radius by 2π; hence $2 \times 10.5 \times 3.1416 = 65.9736$ in., the circumference of the circle. Since there are 360° in a circle, the arc for each degree is found by dividing 65.9736 by 360. From this division we obtain 0.1832 in., which is slightly less than

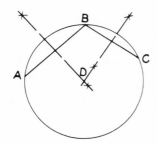

Figure 11 · 27   Finding the center of a circle.

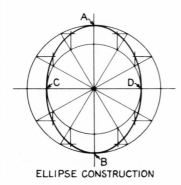

ELLIPSE CONSTRUCTION

Figure 11 · 28   Constructing an ellipse.

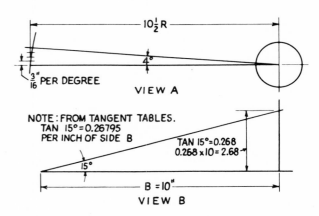

Figure 11 · 30   Determining a given angle when the radius of a circle is known.

166

3⁄16 in. After drawing the arc with a radius of 10½ in. in Fig. 11·30, the dividers are used to step off 3⁄16 in. for each degree, or four steps if the angle is to measure 4°, as in the illustration.

If an angle of 10° is to be constructed, more accuracy can be obtained by using the original measurement for 1°, that is, 0.1832 in. For 10 in. we multiply 0.1832 by 10, and obtain 1.832 in. as the length of the arc for 10°. This is approximately 1⅞ in.

Another means for obtaining accuracy for large angles is to use geometric methods to lay out a known large angle, and then add the smaller measurement to obtain the desired angle. For example, if it is desired to obtain an angle of 49° the technician can bisect a right angle to find a 45° angle and then add 4° to it as explained above.

Another method for constructing a given angle without a protractor is shown in view *B* of Fig. 11·30. This is called the **tangent-offset method** and is one of the most accurate methods for constructing angles. For this method a table of **natural trigonometric functions,** such as Table 11·1, is required. A similar table can be found in any good textbook on trigonometry or in manuals for engineers and technicians.

Assume that the technician is required to construct an angle of 15°. He looks up the tangent for 15° in the table and finds that it is 0.26795. If he is doing rough work, he can call this 0.268 without much loss in accuracy.

If a right triangle has a base line 1 in. long, the height of the triangle will be 0.268 in. when the angle at *A* is 15°. Let us assume that the technician decides to have a base line of 10 in. Then the height of the triangle will be 10 × 0.268 or 2.68 in. Therefore, to construct an angle of 15° he draws a base line 10 in. long and a vertical line at one end 2.68 in. long. When he draws a line from the end of the vertical line to the end of the base line, an angle of 15° is formed.

PREPARATION FOR LAYOUT WORK

Working surface

Before beginning aircraft layout work, the technician should find a good working surface, such as a smooth, flat bench or table. A good surface plate is ideal if a small sheet of material is to be used for the layout. In working with a large sheet of material, it is important to avoid bending it; hence it is a good practice to have a helper in laying the sheet on the working surface. To protect the under surface of the material from any possibe damage, it is often advisable to place a piece of heavy paper, felt, or plywood between the material and the working surface.

Layout fluids

Layout fluids of various kinds are applied to a metal surface for layout work so that the pattern will stand out clearly while the technician is cutting along the drawn or scribed lines. Among the fluids or coatings used are **zinc chromate, bluing fluid, flat white paint, and copper sulfate solution.** The coatings used should be easily scratched away with a scriber or other marking instrument so the mark will show clearly.

Zinc chromate is a metal primer which can be sprayed on a metal surface in a thin coat. It serves not only as a good background color for the pattern used in layout work but also acts as a protection for the surface during the layout work. It tends to prevent corrosion and helps to prevent scratches. Zinc chromate need not be removed from a part after the layout and forming are completed.

Bluing fluid, also called **Dykem blue,** is brushed on the metal surface. Although both scribed lines and pencil work show up clearly on a metal surface coated with zinc chromate, this is not the case with bluing fluid. The scribed lines will be clearly visible against the dark background but pencil work is difficult to see. Chemically, bluing fluid is merely a blue or purple dye dissolved in alcohol or a similar solvent. It does not protect metal against corrosion or serve as a binder for paint; hence it must be removed from the part with alcohol or other suitable solvent.

Flat white paint, soluble in water, can be used for some types of layout work. To be sure that it will come off when water is applied, a small sample area can be painted on a piece of scrap metal.

Another layout fluid is a **copper sulfate solution.** Scribed lines on iron or steel stand out clearly when this solution is brushed on the surface. Through a chemical action, a coating of copper is deposited on the iron or steel. The scribed lines show as a bright steel

Table 11·1   Natural trigonometric functions

Degrees	Tangents							Cotangents
	0'	10'	20'	30'	40'	50'	60'	
0	0.00000	0.00291	0.00582	0.00873	0.01164	0.01455	0.01746	89
1	0.01746	0.02036	0.02328	0.02619	0.02910	0.03201	0.03492	88
2	0.03492	0.03783	0.04075	0.04366	0.04658	0.04949	0.05241	87
3	0.05241	0.05533	0.05824	0.06116	0.06408	0.06700	0.06993	86
4	0.06993	0.07285	0.07578	0.07870	0.08163	0.08456	0.08749	85
5	0.08749	0.09042	0.09335	0.09629	0.09923	0.10216	0.10510	84
6	0.10510	0.10805	0.11099	0.11394	0.11688	0.11983	0.12278	83
7	0.12278	0.12574	0.12869	0.13165	0.13461	0.13758	0.14054	82
8	0.14054	0.14351	0.14648	0.14945	0.15243	0.15540	0.15838	81
9	0.15838	0.16137	0.16435	0.16734	0.17033	0.17333	0.17633	80
10	0.17633	0.17933	0.18233	0.18534	0.18835	0.19136	0.19438	79
11	0.19438	0.19740	0.20042	0.20345	0.20648	0.20952	0.21256	78
12	0.21256	0.21560	0.21864	0.22169	0.22475	0.22781	0.23087	77
13	0.23087	0.23393	0.23700	0.24008	0.24316	0.24624	0.24933	76
14	0.24933	0.25242	0.25552	0.25862	0.26172	0.26483	0.26795	75
15	0.26795	0.27107	0.27419	0.27732	0.28046	0.28360	0.28675	74
16	0.28675	0.28990	0.29305	0.29621	0.29938	0.30255	0.30573	73
17	0.30573	0.30891	0.31210	0.31530	0.31850	0.32171	0.32492	72
18	0.32492	0.32814	0.33136	0.33460	0.33783	0.34108	0.34433	71
19	0.34433	0.34758	0.35085	0.35412	0.35740	0.36068	0.36397	70
20	0.36397	0.36727	0.37057	0.37388	0.37720	0.38053	0.38386	69
21	0.38386	0.38721	0.39055	0.39391	0.39727	0.40065	0.40403	68
22	0.40403	0.40741	0.41081	0.41421	0.41763	0.42105	0.42447	67
23	0.42447	0.42791	0.43136	0.43481	0.43828	0.44175	0.44523	66
24	0.44523	0.44872	0.45222	0.45573	0.45924	0.46277	0.46631	65
25	0.46631	0.46985	0.47341	0.47698	0.48055	0.48414	0.48773	64
26	0.48773	0.49134	0.49495	0.49858	0.50222	0.50587	0.50953	63
27	0.50953	0.51320	0.51688	0.52057	0.52427	0.52798	0.53171	62
28	0.53171	0.53545	0.53920	0.54296	0.54674	0.55051	0.55431	61
29	0.55431	0.55812	0.56194	0.56577	0.56962	0.57348	0.57735	60
30	0.57735	0.58124	0.58513	0.58905	0.59297	0.59691	0.60086	59
31	0.60086	0.60483	0.60881	0.61280	0.61681	0.62083	0.62487	58
32	0.62487	0.62892	0.63299	0.63707	0.64117	0.64528	0.64941	57
33	0.64941	0.65355	0.65771	0.66189	0.66608	0.67028	0.67451	56
34	0.67451	0.67875	0.68301	0.68728	0.69157	0.69588	0.70021	55
35	0.70021	0.70455	0.70891	0.71329	0.71769	0.72211	0.72654	54
36	0.72654	0.73100	0.73547	0.73996	0.74447	0.74900	0.75355	53
37	0.75355	0.75812	0.76272	0.76733	0.77196	0.77661	0.78129	52
38	0.78129	0.78598	0.79070	0.79544	0.80020	0.80498	0.80978	51
39	0.80978	0.81461	0.81946	0.82434	0.82923	0.83415	0.83910	50
40	0.83910	0.84407	0.84906	0.85408	0.85912	0.86419	0.86929	49
41	0.86929	0.87441	0.87955	0.88473	0.88992	0.89515	0.90040	48
42	0.90040	0.90569	0.91099	0.91633	0.92170	0.92709	0.93252	47
43	0.93252	0.93797	0.94345	0.94896	0.95451	0.96008	0.96569	46
44	0.96569	0.97133	0.97700	0.98270	0.98843	0.99420	1.00000	45
Tangents	60'	50'	40'	30'	20'	10'	0'	Degrees
			Cotangents					

color through the copper-colored coating. Copper sulfate solution must not be used on aluminum or aluminum-alloy surfaces.

Planning the work

Having examined a blueprint from which a design is to be transferred to material, the technician should plan his job carefully. If the part to be made is small, it may be possible to make it from scrap metal that is found to be sound after having been examined carefully to make sure it has no scratches or nicks. If there is no suitable scrap available, it may be advisable to cut the part from a corner of a large sheet of metal, thereby avoiding the waste that would occur if it were cut from the center. Fitting the work to the available material correctly but without waste of material is simply a matter of ordinary common sense.

In some cases it may be advisable to do the layout on a piece of cardboard or stiff paper before marking the metal for cutting. This is particularly true where the shape is complex and there is considerable danger of mistakes.

Reference edges and reference lines

When a technician "trues up" one edge of a sheet of metal on a squaring shear, or if he receives the sheet with one edge already straight, that edge can be used as a **reference edge.** A reference edge provides a line from which various measurements can be made, thus increasing the uniformity and accuracy of the work. If there are two such reference edges at right angles to each other, it is even better, for then the operator can obtain a much greater degree of accuracy in layout. When possible, these reference edges should be edges of the finished part; however, if the finished part is to have an irregular outline, it may be advisable to prepare one or two reference edges even though they will disappear when that portion of the material is cut away in finishing the part.

When cutting tools are not available, or when it is not practical to establish a reference edge, **reference lines** should be drawn or scribed, preferably two lines at right angles. These may be established only temporarily and have no relation to other lines except as reference lines, or they may be center lines for holes. In a like manner, the center line for the completed part may serve as one of the reference lines. In this case, the technician merely erects a perpendicular to the center line of the part, thus obtaining the two desired lines.

Reference edges and reference lines may be better understood if they are regarded as **base lines** used in the construction of angles, parallel lines, and intersecting lines required in the layout. However, in the strict sense of the term, a base line is the horizontal reference line, as viewed by the observer; hence it is technically correct to speak of reference lines and edges as previously explained.

Care of material during layout

We have already mentioned the importance of not wasting material by cutting a part from the center of the sheet. It is likewise a matter of good judgment to avoid making cuts that extend into the center. A good technician tries to do his layout work along existing edges, leaving as much material intact and usable as possible.

If the technician wears a wristwatch or rings, he should be careful to see that these do not scratch the material. Leaving tools and instruments on the material is another source of damage. When weights are used to hold a pattern, or template, on the material, they should be smooth on their lower surface or be padded with felt. They should also be free from sharp corners or projections that might accidentally injure the material.

When a scriber is used in layout work, the lines are sharper, cleaner, and more accurate than they are when made with a pencil, but there is always a danger that the technician will make an unnecessary scratch, especially on aluminum sheet. When a scratch is left on Alclad or any other similar corrosion-resisting sheet, trouble is likely to occur. Since Alclad is made up of two layers of pure aluminum and a harder aluminum-alloy core, scratching the surface permits any exposed aluminum alloy to corrode. For this reason, the finished part should have no scratches or nicks whatsoever.

Since there are conditions of stress and vibration present in the operation of an airplane, any scratched metal surface, whether it is aluminum or some other metal, may develop cracks from the scratches. This, of course, would result in failure of the part and the possible loss of an airplane. This does not mean that the scriber should not be used in layout work. It means simply that scratched layout marks should be cut away from the finished part.

BEND ALLOWANCE AND SETBACK

Factors in bending

Bending is a forming operation extensively used in aircraft work. The **bend allowance,** abbreviated BA, is the length of sheet metal required to make a bend over a given inside radius (that is, it is the distance from the beginning to the end of the bend), measured perpendicular to the axis of the bend and along the neutral axis. The distance of the bend allowance depends upon the thickness of the metal, the type of metal, the radius of the bend, and the degree of the bend.

A technician generally encounters a curve where there is a bend line on a blueprint. Unless he knows how to handle curves in bending metals, he cannot succeed with layout work. He must realize that a curved corner requires less metal than a square corner and that he must decide how to cut the stock correctly before he bends it.

Characteristics of a bend

When a piece of sheet metal is bent, the material on the outside of the bend is in **tension** and stretches; the material on the inside of the bend is in **compression** and shrinks. Where the two forces of tension and compression meet within the metal, there is a plane that neither stretches nor compresses. This plane remains the same length after bending as its length before bending and is called the **neutral axis.** It is approximately 44.5 percent of the thickness T of the metal, measuring from the inside of the bend.

A drawing giving the nomenclature of a bend is shown in Fig. 11·31. As shown in the drawing, the bend begins and ends at the **bend tangent lines** and the length of the neutral axis between the two lines is the **bend allowance.** Since the neutral axis does not change in length, the BA can be measured on the flat part before the metal is bent.

The **mold-line dimensions** of a part are given from the end of the metal part to the outer mold point. The **outer mold point** is the intersection of the outer mold lines after the part is bent. This point is shown in the drawing of Fig. 11·31. When the part is bent around a given radius the metal will not extend to the mold point, and the material required to make the part will be smaller in length than the sum of the mold-line dimensions. The amount of material saved by bending around a given radius is called **setback.**

To find the setback, both the BA and the X **distance** must be known. The X distance is shown in Fig. 11·31. For a 90°-angle bend the X distance is equal to the **bend radius** R plus the thickness T of the metal. As shown in the drawing, the X distance is the distance from the **bend tangent line** to the mold point and is measured on either side of the bend.

The X distance may be found by using a K chart, which is shown in Table 11·2. K is the tangent of one-half the bend angle, and the K chart will give the value of K for any angle of bend from 1 to 180°.

The formula for finding the X distance is $K \times (R + T)$

$$K = \tan \tfrac{1}{2} \text{ bend angle}$$
$$R = \text{inside bend radius}$$
$$T = \text{thickness of the metal}$$

To understand how the quantity K is derived, study Fig. 11·32. The tangent of an angle is determined by using one-half the angle of the bend as one of the acute angles in a right triangle and then finding the ratio of the length of the side opposite the angle to the length of the side adjacent to the angle. For example, in the triangle of Fig. 11·33, a/b is the tangent of the angle A. This is also expressed

$$\tan A = \frac{a}{b}$$

If $a = 2$ and $b = 1$, $a/b = 2/1$ and the tangent of angle A is therefore 2. From a table of tangents we find that the angle A is then equal to about 64°.

In the diagram of Fig. 11·32, the angle CAD is equal to one-half the angle BAD. The tangent of angle CAD is CD/AD. This can also be given $CD = \tan CAD \times AD$, which is merely another form of the same equation.

$$AD = AE + \text{ED} \quad \text{or} \quad R + T$$

Therefore, $\qquad \tan CAD = \dfrac{CD}{R + T}$

or $\qquad CD = \tan CAD \times (R + T)$

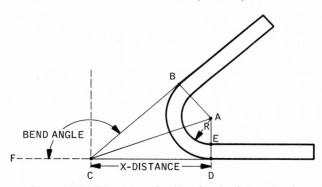

Figure **11·32**   *How the K value is determined.*

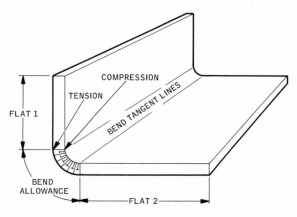

Figure **11·31**   *Nomenclature of a bend.*

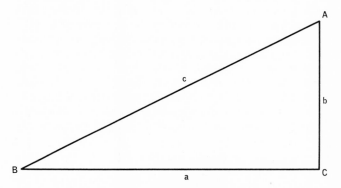

Figure **11·33**   *Triangle to illustrate the tangent of an angle.*

Table 11·2 *K* chart

Deg.	K	Deg.	K	Deg.	K	Deg.	K	Deg.	K
1	0.0087	37	0.3346	73	0.7399	109	1.401	145	3.171
2	0.0174	38	0.3443	74	0.7535	110	1.428	146	3.270
3	0.0261	39	0.3541	75	0.7673	111	1.455	147	3.375
4	0.0349	40	0.3639	76	0.7812	112	1.482	148	3.487
5	0.0436	41	0.3738	77	0.7954	113	1.510	149	3.605
6	0.0524	42	0.3838	78	0.8097	114	1.539	150	3.732
7	0.0611	43	0.3939	79	0.8243	115	1.569	151	3.866
8	0.0699	44	0.4040	80	0.8391	116	1.600	152	4.010
9	0.0787	45	0.4142	81	0.8540	117	1.631	153	4.165
10	0.0874	46	0.4244	82	0.8692	118	1.664	154	4.331
11	0.0963	47	0.4348	83	0.8847	119	1.697	155	4.510
12	0.1051	48	0.4452	84	0.9004	120	1.732	156	4.704
13	0.1139	49	0.4557	85	0.9163	121	1.767	157	4.915
14	0.1228	50	0.4663	86	0.9324	122	1.804	158	5.144
15	0.1316	51	0.4769	87	0.9489	123	1.841	159	5.399
16	0.1405	52	0.4877	88	0.9656	124	1.880	160	5.671
17	0.1494	53	0.4985	89	0.9827	125	1.921	161	5.975
18	0.1583	54	0.5095	90	1.000	126	1.962	162	6.313
19	0.1673	55	0.5205	91	1.017	127	2.005	163	6.691
20	0.1763	56	0.5317	92	1.035	128	2.050	164	7.115
21	0.1853	57	0.5429	93	1.053	129	2.096	165	7.595
22	0.1943	58	0.5543	94	1.072	130	2.144	166	8.144
23	0.2034	59	0.5657	95	1.091	131	2.194	167	8.776
24	0.2125	60	0.5773	96	1.110	132	2.246	168	9.514
25	0.2216	61	0.5890	97	1.130	133	2.299	169	10.38
26	0.2308	62	0.6008	98	1.150	134	2.355	170	11.43
27	0.2400	63	0.6128	99	1.170	135	2.414	171	12.70
28	0.2493	64	0.6248	100	1.191	136	2.475	172	14.30
29	0.2586	65	0.6370	101	1.213	137	2.538	173	16.35
30	0.2679	66	0.6494	102	1.234	138	2.605	174	19.08
31	0.2773	67	0.6618	103	1.257	139	2.674	175	22.90
32	0.2867	68	0.6745	104	1.279	140	2.747	176	26.63
33	0.2962	69	0.6872	105	1.303	141	2.823	177	38.18
34	0.3057	70	0.7002	106	1.327	142	2.904	178	57.29
35	0.3153	71	0.7132	107	1.351	143	2.988	179	114.59
36	0.3249	72	0.7265	108	1.376	144	3.077	180	Inf.

By former definition and demonstration it is known that CD is the X distance, and we therefore conclude that

$$X \text{ distance} = \tan CAD \times (R + T)$$

The angle BAD can be proved by geometry to be equal to the bend angle FCB, and the angle CAD is equal to ½ BAD or ½ FCB. It is clear then that

$$X \text{ distance} = \tan \tfrac{1}{2} FCB \times (R + T)$$
or $\qquad X \text{ distance} = K \times (R + T)$

Bend allowance

An empirical formula has been derived which is suitable for determining **bend allowance**. Remember that bend allowance is the distance between tangent lines before a bend is made, or we may say it is the amount of material needed for the bend. The empirical formula for bend allowance is

Bend allowance = $(0.01743R) + (0.0078T)$
$\qquad\qquad\qquad \times$ degrees in bend angle

When X distance and bend allowance are known, the **setback** is the difference between the sum of the two X distances and the bend allowance. That is,

$$\text{Setback} = 2X - \text{bend allowance}$$

The amount of material required to make the part is called the **developed width** (DW). Since material is saved by bending around a radius, the amount of metal required to make the bent part will be the difference between the sum of the mold-line dimensions and the amount saved at the bend. That is,

$$\text{DW} = \text{MLD}_t - \text{SB}_t$$

where DW = developed width
$\quad$ MLD$_t$ = total mold-line distance
$\qquad\qquad$ (sum of mold lines)
$\quad$ SB$_t$ = sum of setbacks

As an example problem, consider the diagram of Fig. 11·34. We proceed with the problem as follows:

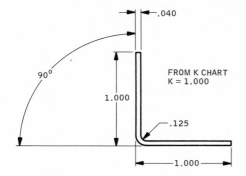

Figure 11·34   Determining values of a bend.

1. Find the X distance

$$X = K \times (R + T)$$
$$= 1.000 \times (0.125 + 0.040)$$
$$= 1.000 \times 0.165$$
$$= 0.165 \text{ in.}$$

2. Find bend allowance

$$BA = (0.01743R + 0.0078T) \times \text{degrees of bend angle}$$
$$= (0.01743 \times 0.125 + 0.0078 \times 0.040) \times 90$$
$$= (0.00217875 + 0.0003120) \times 90$$
$$= (0.00249075) \times 90$$
$$= 0.22416750$$
$$= 0.224 \text{ in.}$$

3. Find setback

$$SB = 2X - BA$$
$$= 2(0.165) - 0.224$$
$$= 0.330 - 0.224$$
$$= 0.106 \text{ in.}$$

4. Find developed width

$$DW = MLD_t - SB_t$$
$$= 1.000 + 1.000 - 0.106$$
$$= 2.000 - 0.106$$
$$= 1.894 \text{ in.}$$

The flat layout of the foregoing problem is developed from left to right on the material as illustrated in Fig. 11·35. To locate the bend tangent lines on the flat stock we must find the length of the unbent portion of each leg or flange and add the bend allowance

between the flat sections. To find the length of one **flat,** or **flange,** we subtract one X distance from one mold-line distance. That is,

$$1.000 - 0.165 = 0.835 \text{ in.}$$

The foregoing equation locates the first bend tangent line from the left edge. We add the bend allowance to find the second bend tangent line; that is,

$$0.835 + 0.224 = 1.059 \text{ in.}$$

This equation locates the second bend tangent line from the left edge of the metal. Now we find the length of the second flat section or flange by subtracting one X distance from the second mold-line distance.

$$1.000 - 0.165 = 0.835 \text{ in.}$$

We add this result to the former quantity, 1.059, to find the total developed width of the flat stock.

$$1.059 + 0.835 = 1.894 \text{ in.}$$

This is the developed width as shown in the drawing of Fig. 11·35.

When a part has more than one bend, the length of the flat section between the bends is found by subtracting the X distance of each bend from the mold-line distance. This is illustrated in Fig. 11·36 and the equation may be shown as

$$\text{Center flat} = MLD - (X_l + X_r)$$

where MLD = mold-line distance
X_l = X distance, left
X_r = X distance, right

Bending the part

In bending a sheet-metal section to produce a required bent accurately, reference lines must be used. The type and location of the reference lines depend upon the type of bending machine employed. The most common type of bending machine for aircraft sheet-metal work is the cornice brake, which was described previously.

Since a bend begins at the bend tangent line, this line will be positioned directly below the center of the radius bar on the brake as shown in Fig. 11·37. In this position the bend tangent line will be out of sight; hence another reference line must be established for visual reference. This is called the **sight line,** and its position is located the distance of the radius from the bend tangent line. This is shown in Fig. 11·37. When the part is placed in the brake, the sight line is directly

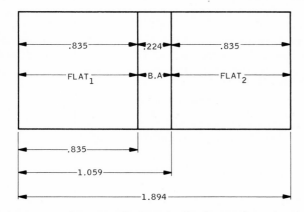

Figure 11·35   Developing the flat layout for a bend.

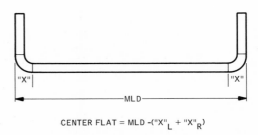

CENTER FLAT = MLD -("X"$_L$ + "X"$_R$)

Figure 11·36   A part with two bends.

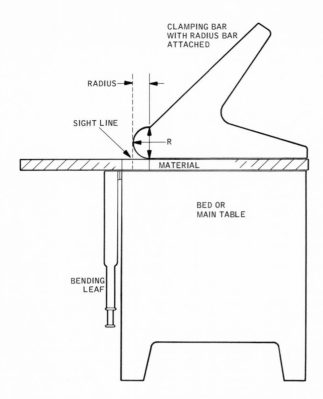

Figure 11·37 *Locating sheet metal in the brake.*

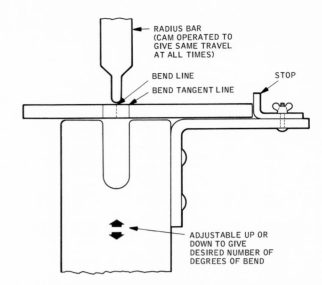

Figure 11·38 *Bending with a press or vertical brake.*

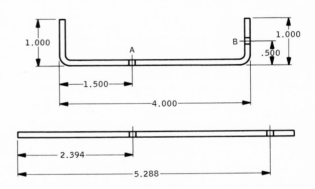

Figure 11·39 *Locating the positions of holes with reference to bends.*

below the nose of the radius bar. This, of course, will position the BTL directly below the center of the radius bar, and the bend will be formed between the bend tangent lines.

The sight line is the only line required on the flat layout and may be used with a cornice brake, bar folder, or finger (box) brake, since they all bend metal in the same manner.

If a production machine, such as a press brake is used, the reference line used to position the part is called a **bend line** and is located between the two bend tangent lines. The positioning of metal on a press brake is shown in Fig. 11·38.

It must be emphasized that great care is needed to produce an accurate bend. The placing of the metal, the setting of the brake, and the actual bending operation all require precision to assure that the bend will meet the specifications required.

When holes are to be drilled in any of the legs or flanges of a part before the part is bent, the hole center-line dimensions are treated the same as mold-line dimensions. This is illustrated in Fig. 11·39. To find the exact location of a hole center from the left edge of the part, the mold-line dimensions and the hole-center dimensions are added and then the set back of all bends between the left edge and the hole center are subtracted. In Fig. 11·39, it is necessary to determine the developed width of the metal to form the part illustrated.

To locate the center of hole *A* from the left edge, the mold-line dimension of the left leg is added to the mold-line dimension from the left leg to the center of

the hole and the setback of the left bend is then subtracted.

$$1.000 + 1.500 - 0.106 = 2.394 \text{ in.}$$

Next, to locate the center of hole *B*, all the mold-line dimensions from the left edge of the part to the center of hole *B* are added and the setback distances of both bends are subtracted.

$$1.000 + 4.000 + 0.500 - 0.212 = 5.288 \text{ in.}$$

The setback distance 0.212 is the sum of the setback distances for both bends.

Bend-allowance tables

When **bend-allowance tables** are available for the type of metal being used, it is possible to save calculation time. The values shown in Table 11·3 are suitable for nonferrous sheet metal such as aluminum alloy and are derived from the empirical formula mentioned earlier. Common alloys are designated 2024-T3, 2024-T4, 7075-T3, etc. These numbers are explained in Chapter 5 of this text.

If we desire to form a 60° bend in a sheet of alumi-

Table 11·3 Nonferrous sheet-metal bend allowances for 1° (thickness and radius in inches)

Thickness →	.016	.020	.022	.025	.028	.032	.040	.045	.051	.064	.072	.081	.091	.128	5/32	3/16	
Radius																	
1/32	.00067	.00070	.00072	.00074	.00077	.00079											
1/16	.00121	.00125	.00126	.00129	.00131	.00135	.00140	.00144	.00149	.00159	.00165						
3/32	.00176	.00179	.00180	.00183	.00186	.00188	.00195	.00199	.00203	.00213	.00220	.00226	.00234				
1/8	.00230	.00234	.00235	.00238	.00240	.00243	.00249	.00253	.00258	.00268	.00274	.00281	.00289	.00317			
5/32	.00285	.00288	.00290	.00292	.00295	.00297	.00304	.00308	.00312	.00322	.00328	.00335	.00343	.00372	.00394		
3/16	.00339	.00342	.00344	.00347	.00349	.00352	.00358	.00362	.00367	.00377	.00383	.00390	.00398	.00426	.00449	.00473	
7/32	.00394	.00397	.00398	.00401	.00403	.00406	.00412	.00417	.00421	.00431	.00437	.00444	.00452	.00481	.00503	.00528	
1/4	.00448	.00451	.00454	.00456	.00458	.00461	.00467	.00471	.00476	.00486	.00492	.00499	.00507	.00535	.00558	.00582	
9/32	.00503	.00506	.00507	.00510	.00512	.00515	.00521	.00526	.00530	.00540	.00546	.00553	.00561	.00590	.00612	.00636	
5/16	.00557	.00560	.00562	.00564	.00567	.00570	.00576	.00580	.00584	.00595	.00601	.00608	.00616	.00644	.00667	.00691	
11/32	.00612	.00615	.00616	.00619	.00621	.00624	.00630	.00634	.00639	.00649	.00655	.00662	.00670	.00699	.00721	.00745	
3/8	.00666	.00669	.00671	.00673	.00676	.00679	.00685	.00689	.00693	.00704	.00710	.00717	.00725	.00753	.00776	.00800	2024-O
13/32	.00721	.00724	.00725	.00728	.00730	.00733	.00739	.00743	.00748	.00758	.00764	.00771	.00779	.00808	.00830	.00854	
7/16	.00775	.00778	.00780	.00782	.00785	.00787	.00794	.00798	.00802	.00812	.00819	.00826	.00834	.00862	.00884	.00909	
15/32	.00829	.00833	.00834	.00837	.00839	.00842	.00848	.00852	.00857	.00867	.00873	.00880	.00888	.00917	.00939	.00963	
1/2	.00884	.00887	.00889	.00891	.00894	.00896	.00903	.00907	.00911	.00921	.00928	.00935	.00943	.00971	.00993	.01018	
17/32	.00938	.00942	.00943	.00946	.00948	.00951	.00957	.00961	.00966	.00976	.00982	.00989	.00997	.01025	.01048	.01072	
9/16	.00993	.00996	.00998	.01000	.01002	.01005	.01012	.01016	.01020	.01030	.01037	.01043	.01051	.01080	.01102	.01127	
19/32	.01047	.01051	.01051	.01055	.01057	.01058	.01065	.01070	.01073	.01083	.01091	.01098	.01105	.01133	.01157	.01181	2017-T3
5/8	.01102	.01105	.01107	.01109	.01112	.01114	.01121	.01125	.01129	.01139	.01146	.01152	.01160	.01189	.01211	.01236	
21/32	.01156	.01160	.01161	.01164	.01166	.01170	.01175	.01179	.01183	.01193	.01200	.01207	.01214	.01245	.01266	.01290	
11/16	.01211	.01214	.01216	.01218	.01220	.01223	.01230	.01234	.01238	.01248	.01254	.01261	.01269	.01298	.01320	.01345	
23/32	.01265	.01268	.01269	.01271	.01275	.01276	.01283	.01288	.01291	.01301	.01309	.01316	.01322	.01351	.01374	.01399	
3/4	.01320	.01323	.01324	.01327	.01329	.01332	.01338	.01343	.01347	.01357	.01363	.01370	.01378	.01407	.01429	.01454	
25/32	.01374	.01378	.01378	.01381	.01384	.01386	.01392	.01397	.01401	.01411	.01418	.01425	.01432	.01461	.01484	.01508	
13/16	.01429	.01432	.01433	.01436	.01438	.01441	.01447	.01451	.01456	.01466	.01472	.01479	.01487	.01516	.01538	.01562	2024-T3
27/32	.01483	.01486	.01487	.01490	.01493	.01494	.01501	.01506	.01509	.01519	.01527	.01534	.01540	.01569	.01593	.01617	
7/8	.01538	.01541	.01542	.01545	.01547	.01550	.01556	.01560	.01565	.01575	.01581	.01588	.01596	.01625	.01647	.01671	
29/32	.01592	.01595	.01596	.01599	.01602	.01604	.01616	.01615	.01619	.01629	.01636	.01643	.01650	.01679	.01701	.01726	2024-T6
15/16	.01646	.01650	.01651	.01654	.01656	.01659	.01665	.01669	.01674	.01684	.01690	.01697	.01705	.01734	.01756	.01780	
31/32	.01701	.01704	.01705	.01708	.01711	.01712	.01718	.01724	.01727	.01737	.01745	.01752	.01758	.01787	.01810	.01835	
1	.01755	.01759	.01760	.01763	.01765	.01768	.01774	.01778	.01783	.01793	.01799	.01806	.01814	.01843	.01865	.01889	

num alloy where the thickness of the metal is 0.040 in. and the radius of the bend is ³⁄₁₆ in., we locate the thickness of the metal from the row of figures at the top of Table 11·3. Under 0.040 we locate the value in the line opposite ³⁄₁₆ which is the radius dimension. In this case we find the value to be 0.00358. To find the bend allowance, we multiply 0.00358 (the bend allowance for 1°) by 60 to determine the bend allowance for 60°. Hence, the bend allowance we are calculating is 60 × 0.00358 or 0.21480 in. This is the amount of material required to make the bend desired.

Geometrical method

Another method for finding the bend allowance for a given bend is to solve the problem with **geometrical processes.** That is, we compute the length of the material in the bend by finding the circumference of a circle having the same radius as the bend neutral axis, and from this we find the length of the material represented by the bend as a part of the circle.

Refer to Fig. 11·40. The bend angle is 110° and the bend radius is ½ in. The thickness of the material is ³⁄₁₆ in. As mentioned previously, the neutral axis of the material is 0.445T from the inside of the bend. Since T is ³⁄₁₆ in., the neutral axis is 0.445 × ³⁄₁₆ or 0.0834 in. from the inside of the bend. Then, we compute the circumference of the circle where the dimensions given are

$$R = 0.50 + 0.0834 = 0.5834 \text{ in.}$$
$$\text{Cir} = 2\pi R$$
$$= 2 \times 3.1416 \times 0.5834$$
$$= 3.666 \text{ in.}$$

The distance for 1° on the circumference of the circle is 3.66/360 (number of degrees in a circle) or 0.01018 in.

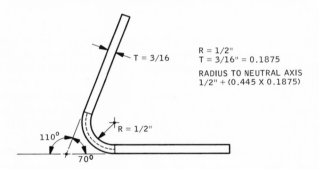

Figure 11·40   Determining bend allowance by geometrical computation.

When we multiply this by 110, the number of degrees in the bend we obtain 1.1198 in., the bend allowance. If we compare this with the figures in Table 11·3, we find that we have obtained the same value for the bend allowance that would have been obtained if we had used the table.

Open and closed angles

Figure 11·41 shows two angles. The angle on the left is 65° and is called a **closed angle** because it is less than 90°. The angle on the right is 140° and is called an **open angle** because it is greater than 90°. These terms are used in problems for determining setback. A 90° angle is neither open nor closed. In Fig. 11·41, notice that the closed-angle flange leans toward the leg. The angle is 65°, which is 25° less than 90°; hence it is said to be closed 25° or have a 25° closed bevel. The open-angle flange leans away from the leg. The angle in the illus-

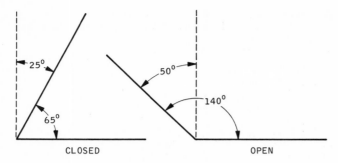

Figure 11·41 Closed and open angles.

tration is 140°, which is 50° more than 90°; hence it is said to be open 50° or have a 50° open bevel.

Setback development chart

Figure 11·42 shows a bend that has an angle of 140°. This is greater than 90° by 50°; hence the angle is described as being 50° open. The thickness of the material used for the bend is shown to be 0.064 in. The radius of the bend is ⅛ in. which is equivalent to 0.125 in. The leg is 6 in. long and the flange is 4 in. long. The problem is to find the length of stock to be cut.

Refer to Fig. 11·43. This is called a **setback development chart,** and it is also referred to as a J chart. To solve the problem stated in the previous paragraph, place a ruler or straightedge on the chart so that it lines up with a bend radius of 0.125 in the scale at the top of the chart and a thickness of 0.064 on the scale at the bottom of the chart. The heavy, horizontal line represents an angle of 90°. Everything above the line is for closed angles and everything below the line is for open angles. The degrees indicated on the scale at the right of the chart show the amount of closed bevel and open bevel for the various angles.

Since the angle we are using is 140° it is an open angle and has an open bevel of 50°. Therefore we locate the horizontal line for this bevel and follow it across the chart until it hits the ruler connecting the bend radius with the stock thickness value at a point on a curve. In this case we find that the intersection of the 50° bevel line and the ruler occurs near the curve for 0.030 in.; hence the setback is 0.030 in. If the intersection of the 50° bevel line and the ruler occurred between the curves we could estimate the position and interpolate the setback. For example, if the thickness of the material were 0.075 in., we would find that the intersection

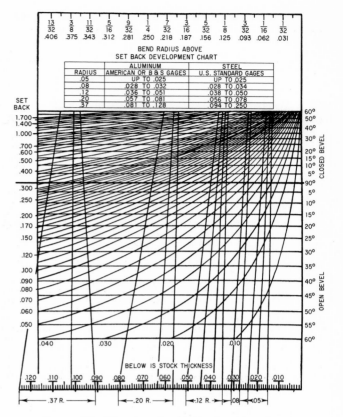

Figure 11·43 A setback development chart.

of the 50° line and the ruler would be about halfway between the 0.030 and the 0.040 curves. We would then call the setback 0.035 in.

In the problem illustrated in Fig. 11·42, the length of the leg has been given as 6 in. and the length of the flange as 4 in. These lengths add to a total of 10 in. To obtain the length of the stock to be cut we subtract the setback of 0.030 (¹⁄₃₂) in. from the 10 in. and obtain 9³¹⁄₃₂ in. This is the length to which the stock should be cut.

Note: The setback development chart should be used only for open bevels up to 60° and closed bevels up to 60°. Furthermore, the chart is subject to greater error than would be likely when using the other methods described; hence when great accuracy is required, it is best practice to avoid the use of the chart.

REVIEW QUESTIONS

1. What is meant by *layout?*
2. Under what conditions would a technician need to do layout work?
3. What is the purpose of a *template?*
4. How should a pencil be sharpened for layout work?
5. Explain the use of a *scriber.*
6. Why is it good practice to measure from the 1-in. mark on a steel rule?
7. Discuss the use of a *straightedge* in layout work.
8. Describe the adjustment of a pair of *dividers.*
9. What is the purpose of *trammel points?*
10. Name three types of *squares* useful in layout work.

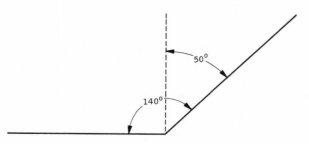

Figure 11·42 Example for determining setback.

11. What is the difference between a *prick punch* and a *center punch?*
12. Explain how a *spline* and *duck weights* are used.
13. Compare *ship curves* and *French curves.*
14. Explain how to bisect an angle.
15. Explain how to erect a perpendicular from a given point on a line.
16. How would you divide a circle into six equal parts?
17. Show how to draw a circle through three points not in a straight line.
18. How can you construct a given angle without a protractor?
19. What precautions must be used in handling sheet metal during layout?
20. What is the purpose of layout fluids?
21. Discuss the prevention of waste in laying out sheet-metal parts.
22. How are reference edges useful?
23. What precaution must be observed with reference to scribed lines on sheet-metal parts?

24. Define *bend allowance.*
25. With reference to a bend, define *mold line, setback,* and *bend tangent line.*
26. What is meant by *X distance?*
27. How would you find *X* distance using the *K* chart?
28. Give the *empirical formula* for bend allowance.
29. Compute the bend allowance for a 60° bend with a ¼-in. radius when the thickness is 0.050 in.
30. Compute the developed width of a piece of aluminum-alloy sheet which is to be formed into a Z section with two bends of 110° each around a radius of ⅜ in. when the thickness of the metal is 0.060 in., the mold-line distance for each flange is 2 in., and the mold-line distance for the inside flat section is 3 in.
31. In bending a part on a cornice brake, discuss the importance of *bend tangent line* and *sight line.*
32. Explain *closed* and *open* angles.

CHAPTER 12

Aircraft Sheet-metal Repairs

The need for repairs in metal aircraft structures may be the result of any one of a variety of causes. During the operation of an airplane the structure is subjected to all types of stresses and many damaging forces which cause wear, stretching, bending, twisting, and other types of undesirable conditions which result in a loss of strength and therefore require repair. Periodic inspections of the structure and attachments are made to reveal the need for both minor and major repairs.

Damage to an aircraft structure may be caused by corrosion, vibration, impact of rocks or other missiles, hard landings, excessive loads in flight, collision, and crash damage. In every case of such damage it is the duty of the technician to make a very careful inspection of all affected parts and assess the degree of damage. He must then determine the type of repair required and design the repair so that the strength of the structure will be returned to its original value or greater. This process requires a thorough knowledge of the structure, the materials of which it is constructed, and the processes employed in the manufacture.

Since metal aircraft are constructed largely of sheet metal, a good knowledge of standard approved sheet-metal repair practices will make it possible for the technician to analyze a repair problem and develop a suitable repair. In all cases he should consult the manufacturer's manual describing the structure if such a manual is available, and he should also refer to Federal Aviation Administration publications which give information regarding the type of repair which is to be made.

The parts of sheet-metal aircraft structures are usually fastened together by means of rivets. For this reason the repairman must understand the use of rivets, materials of which rivets are composed, methods for installing rivets, and the procedures for determining the number of rivets needed to develop the required strength of the repair.

RIVETING

A **rivet** is a metal pin or bar with a cylindrical shank, used for fastening two or more pieces of metal together. The metal pieces to be joined have holes of the proper size drilled through them. The shank of the rivet is inserted through one of these holes. One end of the rivet has a head formed previously by the manufacturer. The size and shape of the head are chosen to fit the requirements of the application. After the rivet is inserted through the holes in the metal, a **bucked head** is formed on the end opposite the manufactured head. This bucked head is formed by any of the various methods described in this chapter. Figure 12·1 illustrates popular head styles and standard head markings for aircraft rivets.

Types of rivets

In the past there have been many different types of rivets for aircraft construction. Because of standardization in the industry, two principal types have evolved. These are the **universal-head rivet** (AN470) and the **countersunk-head rivet** (AN426). There are other types in use, and these are described briefly in this text. In addition to the common types, there are special types of rivets which are used where the standard types cannot be used because of design or where special strength characteristics are required. A careful study of Fig. 12·1 makes it possible to identify the various common types of aircraft rivets.

The **universal-head rivet** (AN470 or MS20470) is used throughout the interior aircraft structure where special rivets are not required and in the exterior surfaces where skin friction is not critical. The head of the universal rivet is designed to combine the strength features of the old brazier-head, roundheaded and flat-headed rivets. The head of the universal rivet is about twice the diameter of the shank and is slightly flattened on the top.

A **countersunk-head rivet** (AN426 or MS20426) is one which has a head flat on the top and beveled toward the shank so that it may fit in either a countersunk or a dimpled hole. When it has been driven, the top of the head is flush with the surface of the skin. The bevel, or slope, of the underside of the head forms an angle of 100°. Countersunk-head rivets are used where it is necessary to provide a smooth surface. This may be where it is necessary to install other material over the heads of the rivets or on the outer skin of the airplane in order to reduce drag.

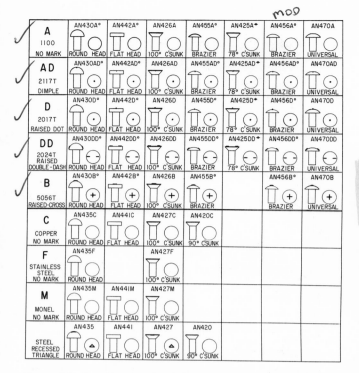

Figure 12·1   Head styles and markings for aircraft rivets.

The mechanic will undoubtedly encounter some aircraft structures where some of the older-type rivets have been used; hence it is deemed wise to discuss them here briefly.

The **brazier-head rivet** (AN455) is similar in appearance to the universal-head rivet, but the head has a greater diameter and is thinner near the edges, as shown in Fig. 12·1.

A **flatheaded rivet** (AN442) has a head which is flattened on both the top and the bottom. This rivet is normally used for internal structure where it does not affect the drag of the airplane.

A **roundheaded rivet** (AN430) has a head which includes approximately 144° of a sphere. This rivet is used internally and sometimes externally, where it is desired that the rivet absorb some tensile stress.

Rivet code

To identify rivets correctly and to identify the material from which they are made, certain code systems have been developed. The two methods used in the aircraft industry are (1) a number system and (2) a symbol system.

The letters and numbers which identify a rivet indicate the type, material, and size. For example, AN470AD-3-4 is interpreted as follows: AN denotes that the rivet meets the specifications set forth by the military services; 470 indicates a universal head; AD shows that the material is 2117T aluminum alloy; the figure 3 gives the diameter in thirty-seconds of an inch; and the figure 4 gives the length of the shank in sixteenths of an inch.

The following diagram explains the meaning of each portion of the AN number:

AN	"AN" standard part (indicates Air Force–Navy specifications)
426	Type (countersunk head in this example)
DD	Alloy (2024T in this example)
5	Diameter in thirty-seconds of an inch
5	Length in sixteenths of an inch

In the case of countersunk-head rivets, the length is given to include the head of the rivet. This is done because the top of the rivet head is flush with the skin when the rivet is driven.

The symbol code for the material of a rivet is illustrated in Fig. 12·1. The mechanic who uses aircraft rivets should memorize this code and should check the symbol on each rivet that he uses. By so doing, he will avoid the possibility of rivet failure in the aircraft structure.

Temper designations for aluminum rivets

Aluminum-alloy rivets can be made from any available aluminum alloy, but the strength requirements for various types of rivet joints and alloys have been satisfactorily met with the rivet alloys now in use. These are 1100, 2117T, 2017T, 2024T, 5053T, and 6061T. The alloys most commonly used for aircraft structures are 2117T, 2017T, and 2024T. 2117T rivets may be driven in the condition in which they are received from the manufacturer. 2017T and 2024T rivets are usually heat-treated and driven immediately, or they may be heat-treated and stored at subzero temperatures to prevent *(RETARD)* age hardening. Rivets which must be refrigerated in order to remain soft are called **icebox rivets** and must be driven within 5 to 10 min after removal from the icebox.

Icebox rivets will age-harden very quickly at ordinary temperatures but at −50°F they will remain soft enough for driving for several weeks. At 32°F, they will remain soft for only about 24 hr.

The aluminum-alloy and temper designation of a rivet or any aluminum alloy includes the alloy number, a letter, and usually a one- or two-digit number. As explained previously, the letter following the alloy number indicates condition of the alloy. The meanings of the letters are as follows:

—F	As fabricated (for wrought products)
—O	Annealed (for wrought products)
—H	Strain-hardened
—W	Solution heat-treated and aged at room temperature (used only with those alloys which are also furnished in the artificially aged temper)
—T	Heat-treated temper

—RT   COLD WORKED AFTER HEAT TREATMENT

The number following the letter indicates the type of heat treatment and other processes which have been applied to the alloy.

Commonly used aluminum-alloy aircraft rivets are

designated 2017-T4, 2117-T4, and 2024-T4. The T4 following the alloy number indicates that the rivets are solution heat-treated only. After the rivet is driven it is in the T3 condition because it has been cold-worked as well as heat-treated.

Installing rivets

The installation of common rivets consists of drilling holes slightly larger (0.001 to 0.003 in.) than the rivet shank in the parts to be joined, removing the burrs from the edges of the holes, inserting the rivet, and driving the rivet. A No. 40 drill is used for a 3/32-in. rivet and a No. 30 drill is used for a 1/8-in. rivet. The rivet is usually driven by means of a pneumatic hammer and a bucking bar to "back up" the rivet. Figure 12·2 shows how rivets can be installed to join two pieces of flat-sheet aluminum alloy.

The rivet gun, or riveting hammer, is the device most commonly used by the mechanic for driving rivets. The rivet gun is equipped with a **rivet set** designed to fit the head of the rivet being driven. The set is inserted into the **set sleeve** of the gun and is held in place by means of a retaining spring. The retaining spring must always be in place to prevent the set from flying out and causing injury to anyone who may be in the vicinity. During operation a piston in the gun is driven rapidly back and forth by compressed air which is alternately directed to one side of the piston and then the other. This causes the piston to strike the set rapidly, driving the rivet against the bucking bar and forming the bucked head. The cutaway drawing in Fig. 12·3 illustrates the construction and operating mechanism of a typical rivet gun. Various other designs for rivet guns are also shown in Fig. 12·3.

Rivet sets are made in many sizes and shapes to meet different requirements for riveting and to provide for the different types of rivets. The **shank** of a rivet set is the part inserted into the rivet gun. Shanks are made in uniform standard sizes to fit standard rivet guns. Figure 12·4 illustrates typical rivet sets for use with a rivet gun.

Rivet sets designed for use with universal- or brazier-head rivets have a cupped head to fit over the rivet head. The cup is curved with a slightly larger radius than that of the rivet head to assure that the maximum force of the gun is applied to the center of the rivet head, causing the rivet to draw the riveted materials together as the bucked head is being formed.

Installing countersunk rivets

To install countersunk rivets, it is necessary to provide a conical depression in the surface of the skin so that the head of the rivet will be flush with the surface. This depression is made by means of a countersink when the skin is sufficiently thick and by **dimpling** when

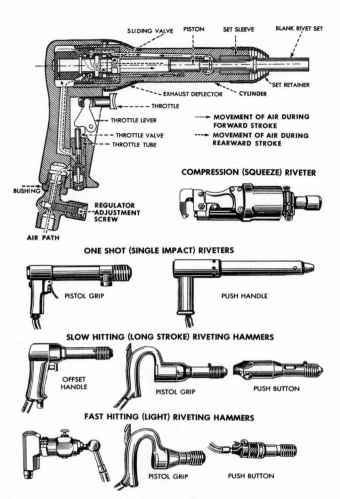

COMPRESSION (SQUEEZE) RIVETER

ONE SHOT (SINGLE IMPACT) RIVETERS

SLOW HITTING (LONG STROKE) RIVETING HAMMERS

FAST HITTING (LIGHT) RIVETING HAMMERS

Figure 12·3   Construction of a rivet gun.

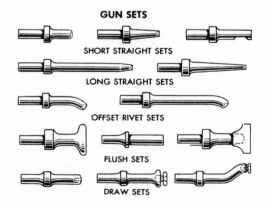

GUN SETS

SHORT STRAIGHT SETS

LONG STRAIGHT SETS

OFFSET RIVET SETS

FLUSH SETS

DRAW SETS

Figure 12·4   Rivet sets.

the skin is thin. The use of a machine countersink is limited by the size of the rivet and the thickness of the skin. Generally, sheet metal should not be machine-countersunk entirely through the sheet. For sheet metal of 0.040- to 0.051-in. thickness it is common practice to countersink not more than three-fourths the thickness of the sheet. For repairs on an airplane the specifica-

Figure 12·2   Rivets joining two pieces of sheet metal.

178

tions for use of machine countersinking usually may be determined from the rivets installed by the manufacturer.

Dimpling for countersunk rivets is a common practice when using a relatively thin skin such as 0.016 to 0.025 in. in thickness. **Dimpling** can be accomplished with a dimpling bar and flush set as shown in Fig. 12·5. The rivet head is the die which forms the dimple. When thin skin is attached to a heavier structural member, the heavy member is subcountersunk and the skin is dimpled into the countersunk depression, as illustrated in Fig. 12·6. For production work in a factory, dimpling often is accomplished with dimpling dies used in a pneumatic squeeze riveter.

It is sometimes necessary to dimple heavy sheet in a highly stressed part of the airplane in order to retain the maximum strength of the sheet. A process called **hot dimpling** has been developed for this purpose. Hot dimpling is performed with a special hot-dimpling machine consisting of heated dies which can be pressed together pneumatically to form a dimple as shown in Fig. 12·7.

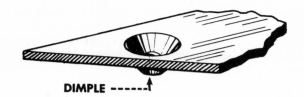

Figure 12·7 Dimple formed with heat.

Figure 12·8 shows an automatic hot-dimpling machine manufactured by Aircraft Tools, Inc. The operator sets the controls of the machine according to charts supplied by the manufacturer, which set forth the temperatures and pressures required for various types and thicknesses of materials.

The material, having been previously drilled, is placed over the stationary die with the pilot of the die projecting through the hole in the material. The operator then presses on the foot control of the machine. This brings upper and lower dies toward each other; thus they press on the material and their heat is transferred to the material. As the material becomes heated sufficiently, the pressure of the dies causes it to be formed. This pressure comes from a compressed-air system. The initial pressure on the dies is limited to prevent the material from being deformed before it has been heated sufficiently. After the material reaches the forming temperature, additional pressure is applied automatically to the dies to complete the forming operation. This pressure is maintained for a predetermined number of seconds, and then it is automatically released.

Another method for hot dimpling employs a resist-

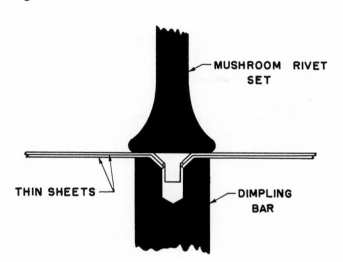

Figure 12·5 Use of a dimpling bar for dimpling.

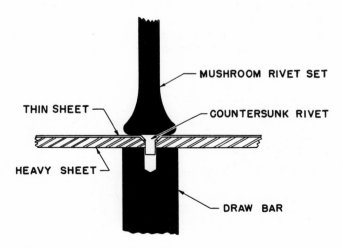

Figure 12·6 Dimpling thin skin into countersunk sheet.

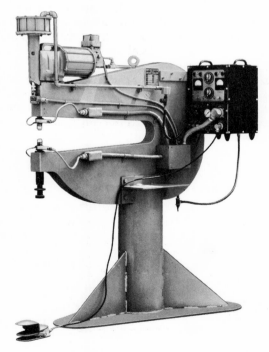

Figure 12·8 Automatic hot-dimpling machine.

ance-heating machine. The dies of the machine are electrodes which pass a current through the metal to be riveted and cause it to heat. When the metal has been heated sufficiently, full pressure is applied to the dies to form the dimple.

RIVETING PRACTICES

* Rivet sizes

In replacing rivets, the original size should be used if this size will fit and fill the holes. If not, the holes should be drilled or reamed for the next larger rivet. The rivet diameter for a sheet-metal joint should be approximately three times the thickness of the heavier sheet, or somewhat larger for thin sheets. NOTE

In determining the size of rivets to be used in any repair of aircraft, the mechanic must comply with the provisions of Federal Aviation Administration publications. These publications set forth the policies and regulations of the Federal Aviation Administration relative to the repair, maintenance, and overhaul of aircraft and engines. In the repair of military aircraft, the technician should follow military standards as set forth in technical orders and handbooks.

NOTE

* Rivet spacing

The spacing of rivets in a replacement or a repair of stressed sheet metal may be determined by observing the spacing in adjacent parts of the same aircraft. The minimum spacing for aircraft rivets is three times the diameter of the rivet shank. The minimum edge distance is two times the diameter of the rivet shank, as shown in Fig. 12 · 9. Although the minimum edge distance for rivets is given as two times the diameter of the rivet shank, it is recommended that the edge distance be not less than 2½ times the rivet shank diameter when the rivet is of the countersunk type. This will assure adequate strength of material along the edge of the sheet.

The space between rivets in a single row is called **pitch,** and the distance between rows of rivets is called **gage.** These terms are illustrated in Fig. 12 · 10. The spacing between any two rivets is measured from the center of the shank of one to the center of the shank of the other.

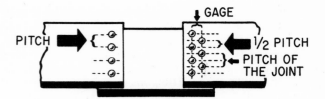

Figure 12 · 10   Pitch and gage.

DESIRED PITCH = 6D - 8D

It is general practice to limit the maximum pitch (space between rivets in a single row) to 24 times the thickness of the sheet metal. For example, if the thickness of the sheet metal is 0.083 in., 24 × 0.083 in. = 1.992 in., or 2 in. for practical purposes.

* Rivets required for a repair

The number of rivets required in any repair is determined by the strength necessary for the riveted joints. This strength is based upon two considerations. First, we must determine the **shear strength** of the rivets. The shear on a rivet is the load that tends to cut the rivet in two parts as shown in Fig. 12 · 11. Second, the **tensile strength** of the sheet metal must be determined. These two forms of strength, considered together, constitute the basis for determining how many rivets are needed.

The shear strength of rivets and the tensile strength of materials may be determined from engineering tables. When these values are known, it is possible to determine the number of rivets required in a repair by dividing the shear strength of one rivet into the required tensile strength of the joint. For example, if the shear strength of a ⅛-in. 2117-T3(AD) rivet is 344 lb and it is necessary to provide a tensile strength of 5600 lb to a joint, the number of rivets required would be 5600/344 = 16.03. To make sure that the strength is adequate, it would be best to use 17 rivets.

In making a riveted seam both the shear strength of the rivet and the bearing strength of the metal sheet must be taken into consideration. The **bearing strength** is the amount of force applied to a rivet installed in metal sheet which will cause the rivet to elongate the rivet hole in the sheet. If the bearing strength is greater than the shear strength of the rivet, the rivet will shear before the hole is elongated. If the shear strength of the rivet is greater than the bearing strength of the

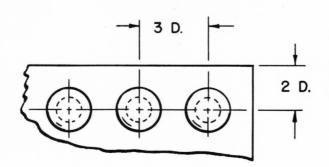

Figure 12 · 9   Minimum rivet spacing.

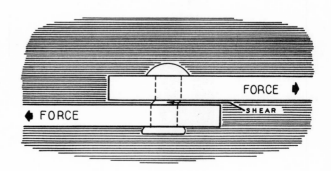

Figure 12 · 11   Shear on a rivet.

NOTE: - MIN. RIVET FOR STRUCTURAL USE - 3/32"

metal, the metal will yield and the rivet will pull through the metal.

Tables have been prepared to designate the number of rivets necessary to restore the strength to a given section of sheet aluminum alloy when using 2117-T3 rivets. Table 12·1 is an example for rivets from ³⁄₃₂ to ¼ in. in diameter and aluminum-alloy sheet thicknesses from 0.016 to 0.128 in. When such tables are available it is a simple matter to determine the number of rivets necessary for any particular repair.

If it is desired to repair a 2-in. break in a sheet of 0.025-in. aluminum-alloy skin on an airplane, the number of rivets would be determined as follows:

1. Select the size of rivet. Since the riveted sheet is 0.025-in. thick, the rivet diameter must be at least three times this amount. This requires a rivet of at least 0.075 in. in diameter. The next larger standard rivet is ³⁄₃₂ in., hence this is the size to be used.
2. Refer to Table 12·1 and note that when the thickness T of the sheet is 0.025 in., the number of ³⁄₃₂-in. rivets should be at least 8.6 per in. of width W of the repair. The break to be repaired is 2 in. long; hence 17.2 rivets are required. We therefore use 18 rivets on each side of the repair to restore the required strength.

The layout for the repair discussed above could appear as shown in Fig. 12·12. There can be variations in the design of a layout, provided the basic requirements of edge distance, rivet size, and rivet spacing are met. It will be observed in the illustration that rivets are spaced at a greater distance than the minimum.

If a rivet table is not available when a repair is to be made, the number of rivets can be determined by considering the strength of the rivets and metal in

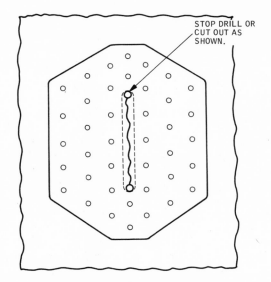

STOP DRILL OR CUT OUT AS SHOWN.

Figure 12·12   Layout for rivet repair.

accordance with a standard formula, as follows:

$$\text{No. of rivets} = \frac{\text{length of break} \times \text{thickness} \times 75{,}000}{\text{shear strength or bearing strength}}$$

In the formula, the figure 75,000 is based upon the tensile strength of aluminum alloy and is an indication of the strength to be restored. The shear or **bearing-strength value** must be that which is the lowest of the two values. For example, the shear strength of an AN470-AD-4 (⅛-in.) rivet is given as 388 lb in the ANC-5 manual, a government manual specifying standards for aircraft metals. The bearing strength for a ⅛-in. rivet in sheet aluminum alloy having a thickness of 0.040 in. is given as 514 lb for metal having a tensile strength of 100,000 psi. For aluminum alloy with a strength of 60,000 psi, the bearing strength in the above case would be 308.4 lb. Since this is less than 388 lb, we would use 309 lb for the value in the formula.

Dimensions of installed rivets

When rivets are installed in a standard repair, it is necessary that certain minimum dimensions be observed. Figure 12·13 shows the minimum dimensions for formed rivet heads and length of rivet. Although the drawing shows 0.65D as the desired height of the formed head, a minimum height of 0.50D will be accepted.

Table 12·1   Number of 2117-T3 protruding-head rivets required per inch of width W

| Aluminium-alloy sheet thickness T, in. | Rivet diameter, in. | | | | | No. of AN-3 bolts |
	³⁄₃₂	⅛	⁵⁄₃₂	³⁄₁₆	¼	
0.016	6.5	4.9				
0.020	6.9	4.9	3.9			
0.025	8.6	4.9	3.9			
0.032	11.1	6.2	3.9	3.3		
0.036	12.5	7.0	4.5	3.3	2.4	
0.040	13.8	7.7	5.0	3.5	2.4	3.3
0.051		9.8	6.4	4.5	2.5	3.3
0.064		12.3	8.1	5.6	3.1	3.3
0.081			10.2	7.1	3.9	3.3
0.091			11.4	7.9	4.4	3.3
0.102			12.8	8.9	4.9	3.4
0.128				11.2	6.2	4.2

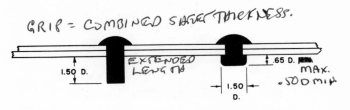

GRIP = COMBINED SHEET THICKNESS.

1.50 D.   EXTENDED LENGTH   .65 D. MIN. MAX.   .500 MIN.   1.50 D.

Figure 12·13   Minimum dimensions for a rivet.

Drilling holes for rivets

To make a good riveted joint, it is essential that the rivet hole be drilled properly. The first requirement for a perfectly drilled hole is the use of a drill that is ground accurately. New drills usually have a satisfactory point, but after they are worn they should be sharpened or discarded. The dimensions for a correctly ground point are shown in Fig. 12·14. Before a technician uses a drill, he should examine it to see that it is straight and that the point conforms to required standards.

The location of a hole to be drilled may be indicated by marking with a pencil or, in the case of heavy sheet stock, by making a slight indentation with a center punch. For holes which must be held within extremely close tolerances, a **drill jig** is normally used. This device holds the drill accurately in position while the hole is being drilled.

When the technician begins to drill a hole, he must be very careful to hold the drill perpendicular to the material being drilled. He must also steady the drill and motor so that the drill will not move away from the correct position and damage the adjacent material. It is common practice to start the drill by placing it in position and turning it by hand before turning on the electric or air power to operate the motor. By this method the hole will be started, and the drill will usually remain in the proper position. Figure 12·15 shows a technician holding the drill properly for starting to drill a hole.

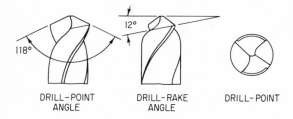

Figure 12·14 *Dimensions for a correctly ground drill point.*

DRILL-POINT ANGLE   DRILL-RAKE ANGLE   DRILL-POINT

118°   12°

Figure 12·15 *Proper method of starting a drill.*

Figure 12·16 illustrates properly and improperly drilled holes. The left and middle drawings show holes that are clean and in good alignment. The right drawing shows two holes which were drilled at an angle and would not be suitable for riveting.

A hole is not complete until it is both drilled and burred. **Burring** is the process of removing rough edges and chips from a newly drilled hole. It is usually done by hand with a drill larger than the hole, or it can be done with a special burring tool which is merely a piece of metal with sharp edges. When two or more sheets are drilled at the same time, it is necessary to remove chips and burrs from between the sheets. Figure 12·17 illustrates the results of leaving material between drilled sheets.

The use of the rivet gun

Rivet guns are available in various sizes, starting with 1X, the smallest, which is used for rivets of 1/16- and 3/32-in. diameter. The size of rivet guns increases progressively for rivets of larger diameter, the most commonly used size being the 3X, which is used for rivets of from 3/32- to 5/32-in. diameter. For larger-size rivets, 4X and 5X rivet guns may be used. There are several larger sizes of rivet guns used for even larger rivets than the ones we have mentioned.

The various rivet guns can be adjusted to deliver the required blow for each size of rivet. The most desirable practice is to adjust the gun so that the formed head of the rivet will be properly shaped, using as few blows of the rivet gun as possible. When the rivet gun is adjusted with too light a blow, the rivet may be work-hardened to such a degree that the head will not be formed properly without cracking the rivet.

The care of the rivet gun

Rivet guns and rivet sets perform better work and will last longer if they are properly handled and serviced; the latter meaning ordinary good care, including lubricating, cleaning, etc.

A rivet set should not be placed against steel or

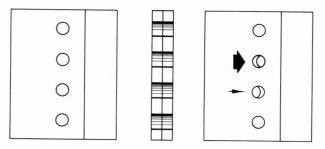

Figure 12·16 *Properly and improperly drilled holes.*

Figure 12·17 *Foreign material between sheets of metal.*

other hard metal when the air power is on; this practice will ruin the rivet set.

A rivet set can be a deadly weapon. If a rivet set is placed in a rivet gun without a set retainer and the throttle of the gun is open, the rivet set may be projected like a bullet out of the gun and cause either a severe injury to a person or the destruction of equipment.

A few drops of light machine oil should be placed daily in the air intake of the rivet gun. Periodically, depending upon use, the rivet gun should be disassembled and cleaned, worn parts replaced, and the gun reassembled and lubricated.

Bucking bars

A **bucking bar** is a smooth steel bar made up in a variety of special shapes and sizes and used to form a head on the shank of a rivet while it is being driven by a rivet gun. The edges are slightly rounded to prevent marring the material, and the surface is perfectly smooth. The face of the bar, placed against the shank of the rivet, is flat. Bucking bars are sometimes called **dollies, bucking irons,** or **bucking blocks.**

For best results, the mechanic should choose a bucking bar of the proper weight and shape for a particular application. A common rule of thumb is that the bucking bar should weigh approximately 1 lb less than the number of the rivet gun with which it is being used. For example, the bucking bar to be used with a 3X gun should weigh about 2 lb. Figure 12·18 illustrates a group of bucking bars.

Expanding bucking bars, shown in Fig. 12·19, are steel blocks whose diameters or widths can be adjusted. A bucking bar of this type is attached to the end

of a hollow steel shaft which contains a bar that can be twisted to expand or reduce the width of the block. It is used to buck (upset) rivets on the inside of tubular structures or in similar spaces that cannot be reached by regular bucking bars. The space must be small enough for one side of the partly expanded block to press against the tip of the rivet's shank and for the other side to press against a strong supporting surface. Expanding bucking bars speed up the process of riveting the skin on the wing section.

A bucking bar is used as shown in Fig. 12·20. The bar is held firmly against the shank of the rivet while the rivet gun with the correct set is applied to the manufactured head. It is essential that the bucking bar be placed against the shank of the rivet before the rivet is driven. If the operator of the rivet gun starts to drive the rivet before the bucking bar is in place, the sheet in which the rivet is being installed will be damaged.

The correct installation of a rivet is dependent upon the proper use of the bucking bar as well as the rivet gun. The face of the bucking bar must be held square with the rivet, or the rivet may "clinch"; that is, the bucked head will be driven off center. Sometimes the operator can control the formation of the bucked head by carefully tilting the bucking bar. Both the rivet gun and the bucking bar must be firmly in place against the rivet before the throttle of the gun is opened to drive the rivet. Figure 12·21 illustrates rivets improperly installed.

Sheet fasteners

Because of the necessity for holding sheets of metal close together during the riveting process, a fastener of some type is essential. Otherwise the rivet will tend to expand between the sheets and leave a gap which reduces the strength of the joint and promotes the accumulation of moisture between the sheets. This, of course, leads to corrosion. The tool designed to meet the need is called a **sheet fastener** and is quickly and easily installed.

Sheet fasteners have been designed and used in many styles and shapes; however, they are presently limited to relatively few designs.

One of the popular sheet fasteners, manufactured by the Wedgelock Company, is illustrated in Fig. 12·22. Figure 12·23 shows the internal construction of the fastener.

The fastener consists of a machined steel body in which is installed a plunger, coil spring, locking wires,

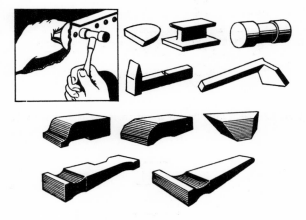

Figure 12·18   Bucking bars.

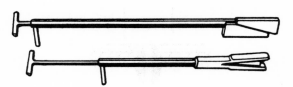

Figure 12·19   Expanding bucking bars.

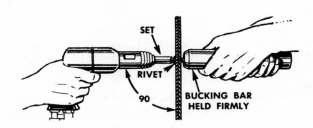

Figure 12·20   Bucking a rivet.

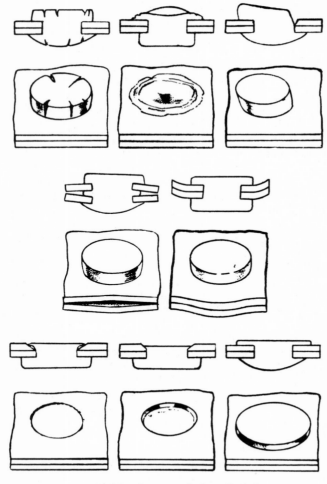

Figure **12·21**   Improperly installed rivets.

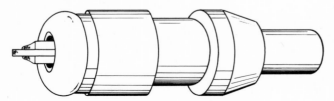

Figure **12·22**   A sheet fastener.

(CLECO)

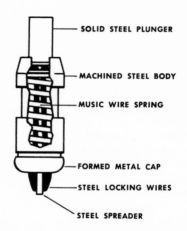

— SOLID STEEL PLUNGER
— MACHINED STEEL BODY
— MUSIC WIRE SPRING
— FORMED METAL CAP
— STEEL LOCKING WIRES
— STEEL SPREADER

Figure **12·23**   Construction of a sheet fastener.

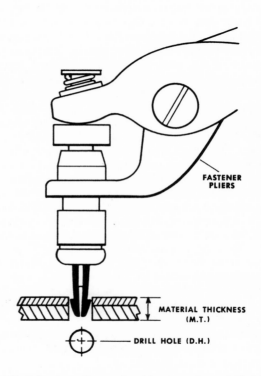

FASTENER PLIERS

MATERIAL THICKNESS (M.T.)

DRILL HOLE (D.H.)

Figure **12·24**   Inserting a sheet fastener in a drilled hole.

and a spreader. When the plunger is depressed with the fastener pliers, the locking wires extend beyond the spreader and "toe in," reducing the diameter. The locking wires can then be inserted in a drilled hole of the proper size as shown in Fig. 12·24. When the pliers are released, the locking wires are drawn back over the spreader. This causes the wires to separate and grip the sides of the drilled hole as in Fig. 12·25. Removal of the fastener is accomplished by reversing the process of installation.

CLECO COLOR CODE
SILVER - 3/32"
COPPER - 1/8"
BLACK - 5/32"
GOLD - 3/16"

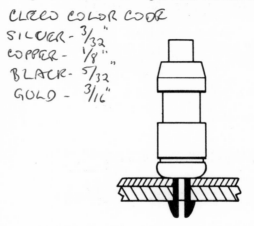

Figure **12·25**   Locking wires gripping sheet metal.

Shaved rivets   *NACA RIVETING*

On modern, high-speed aircraft, it is necessary to remove every possible cause of drag from the outer surface of the airplane skin. For many years it has

IN PLACE OF CLECOS, SMALLER SIZE SHEET METAL SCREWS CAN BE USED.

been the practice to install flush (countersunk-type) rivets in skin and other structural sections exposed to airflow. To obtain the most nearly perfect surface, shaved-riveting techniques were developed.

In preparation for shaved riveting, standard rivet holes are drilled in the metal to be riveted. This may be done by the manual method or by automatically programmed machines. On the outer surface of the metal the holes are countersunk with a 60° tool instead of the conventional 100° countersink.

Standard rivets are installed with the rivet head inside the metal skin and the shank of the rivet is driven to form a head in the conical depression on the outer surface. The forming to the rivet shank to fill the depression can be done with a standard rivet gun and smooth-faced bucking bar but, during production, it is often done with automatic machines.

After the rivet is driven sufficiently to fill the countersunk hole completely, the excess of rivet material projecting above the surface of the skin is shaved with a small rotary mill called a **rivet shaver.** With this tool, the surface of the skin and rivet is made extremely smooth so drag will be reduced to the minimum. For the manual process, the rivet shaver is held in the hand as one would hold a drill motor. It is prevented from cutting too deeply by means of a carefully adjusted stop.

Removing rivets

In the repair of sheet-metal aircraft it is often necessary to remove rivets. However, great care must be used, or damage may be done to the metal from which the rivets are removed. Rivets are removed by drilling through the manufactured head with a drill of approximately the same size as the shank of the rivet. The mechanic must make sure that the drill is started and held in the exact center of the rivet head. The drill should penetrate no further than the base of the rivet head, or the rivet hole may be enlarged by the drill. Usually the rivet head will come off as soon as the drill has penetrated the proper distance. After the head of the rivet is removed, the shank may be pushed or driven out with a pin punch.

When replacing rivets in a hole where a rivet previously has been installed, it is necessary to ascertain that the hole has not been enlarged beyond the correct tolerance for the rivet being installed. If the hole is too large, it should be drilled to the correct size for the next larger rivet.

SPECIAL RIVETS

The need for special rivets

Standard rivets cannot meet all the requirements of fabrication and strength in the construction of aircraft; hence it becomes necessary to use a wide variety of special rivets which are designed for specific purposes. This need for special rivets is so pronounced that some manufacturers have built large organizations devoted entirely to the design and production of special rivets.

Blind rivets

Blind rivets are rivets designed to be installed in places where it is impossible to use a bucking bar to form the bucked head. These rivets are so designed and constructed that they can be installed and expanded from one side of the material. Their use is generally confined to locations such as the trailing edges of airfoils (rudder, ailerons, flaps, etc.) and other places where one side of the material is inaccessible for riveting.

Cherry rivets are blind rivets which are manufactured by the Cherry Rivet Division of the Townsend Company. A Cherry rivet is a hollow rivet with an expanding stem inserted through the center, as illustrated in Fig. 12·26. The rivet is inserted in a carefully driven rivet hole and the stem is pulled into the rivet, causing it to expand and grip the material firmly.

There are two general types of Cherry rivets: the self-plugging and the pull-through hollow type. When the self-plugging type is installed, the stem breaks off when sufficient pressure has been exerted to expand the rivet completely. The remaining stub of the stem is then cut off and filed smooth. In the installation of the pull-through hollow rivet, the stem is completely pulled through the rivet. This type of rivet does not have the shear strength of the self-plugging type.

Cherry rivets must be installed according to the manufacturer's specifications and in accordance with pertinent government regulations.

The **standard Cherrylock rivet** is installed as shown in Fig. 12·27. The rivet is inserted into the correctly drilled hole as shown in view a. View b shows the action as the pulling head (not shown in the drawing) begins to pull the stem and form a blind head adjacent to the blind sheet. At this time the two sheets of metal are being drawn together. In view c the two sheets are firmly clamped together and the rivet head is seated. As the stem pulls into the hollow rivet, as shown in view d, the drilled hole is filled; when the breaknotch is flush with the rivet head and the hole is filled, view e, the locking collar is inserted by the installing tool and the stem breaks off flush with the top of the rivet head. The installed rivet is shown in view f.

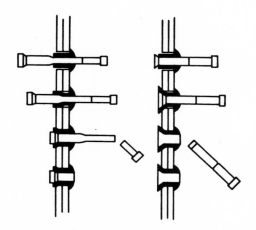

Figure 12·26 Installation of Cherry rivets.

185

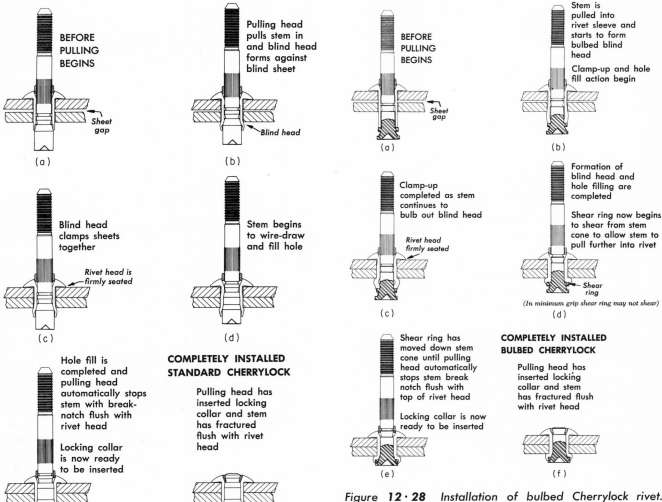

BEFORE PULLING BEGINS

Sheet gap

(a)

Pulling head pulls stem in and blind head forms against blind sheet

Blind head

(b)

Blind head clamps sheets together

Rivet head is firmly seated

(c)

Stem begins to wire-draw and fill hole

(d)

Hole fill is completed and pulling head automatically stops stem with break-notch flush with rivet head

Locking collar is now ready to be inserted

(e)

COMPLETELY INSTALLED STANDARD CHERRYLOCK

Pulling head has inserted locking collar and stem has fractured flush with rivet head

(f)

Figure **12·27** Installation of Cherrylock rivet. (Cherry Rivet Div., Townsend Co.)

BEFORE PULLING BEGINS

Sheet gap

(a)

Stem is pulled into rivet sleeve and starts to form bulbed blind head

Clamp-up and hole fill action begin

(b)

Clamp-up completed as stem continues to bulb out blind head

Rivet head firmly seated

(c)

Formation of blind head and hole filling are completed

Shear ring now begins to shear from stem cone to allow stem to pull further into rivet

Shear ring

(In minimum grip shear ring may not shear)

(d)

Shear ring has moved down stem cone until pulling head automatically stops stem break notch flush with top of rivet head

Locking collar is now ready to be inserted

(e)

COMPLETELY INSTALLED BULBED CHERRYLOCK

Pulling head has inserted locking collar and stem has fractured flush with rivet head

(f)

Figure **12·28** Installation of bulbed Cherrylock rivet. (Cherry Rivet Div., Townsend Co.)

The **bulbed Cherrylock rivet** installation is shown in Fig. 12·28. The action is similar to that described for the standard Cherrylock rivet; however, a different type head is formed.

The installation of Cherrylock rivets is accomplished with either hand guns or pneumatic power guns. The guns are manufactured with a provision for changing pulling heads to accommodate different styles and sizes of rivets. The technician must follow the specifications given by the manufacturer for the installation of the rivets. The *Cherry Rivet Process Manual* provides information on installation and the proper types of guns and pulling heads.

Cherry rivets are identified by numbers to indicate type, grip length, and shank diameter. For example, CR2163-6-4 indicates a 2017T aluminum-alloy rivet with a universal head, ⁵⁄₃₂ in. in diameter and having a maximum grip length of ⁴⁄₁₆ in.

Du Pont explosive rivets, manufactured by E. I. Du Pont de Nemours & Company, are blind rivets which are expanded by explosive material contained in the shank of the rivet. Figure 12·29 illustrates a Du Pont rivet before and after expansion. During installation, a heated rivet gun is placed against the head of the rivet to detonate the explosive and thus expand the rivet. As in the case of all other blind rivets, it is essential that the manufacturer's instructions be followed closely.

Rivnuts

A **rivnut** is a specialized type of blind rivet which also can be used as a nut because it is threaded inside to fit the threaded shank of a screw or a bolt, as illustrated in Fig. 12·30. Rivnuts are manufactured by the B. F.

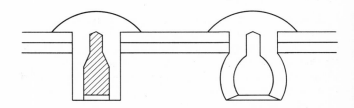

Figure **12·29** Explosive rivets.

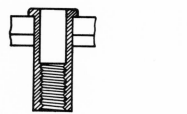 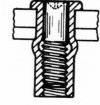

Figure 12·30   Rivnuts.

Goodrich Company and used both for aircraft and for general commercial purposes. The rivnut is installed with a rivet gun containing a mandrel which is screwed into the threads of the rivnut. The rivnut is expanded by tension on the mandrel which causes the shank to expand as shown in the figure.

Hi-Shear rivets

Hi-Shear rivets are a specialized type of rivet manufactured by the Hi-Shear Corporation, designed to provide exceptional resistance to shear loads in a riveted joint.

The Hi-Shear rivet is a two-piece rivet. The pin is generally made of alloy steel, although some are stainless steel and others are 7075T aluminum alloy. Most collars are made from 2117T or 2024T aluminum alloy, although some are of heat-resistant mild steel.

The hole into which the rivet is inserted must be drilled to extremely close tolerances as specified by the manufacturer. The rivet may be installed with a rivet gun and bucking bar, as illustrated in Fig. 12·31. The sequence of drawings in the illustration shows the action taking place during the installation process.

Hi-Shear rivets can be removed easily by cutting the aluminum collar off the shank of the rivet. This can be accomplished with the cape chisel. The point of the chisel is applied to the collar on one side of the shank and a bucking bar is held against the opposite side. The chisel is then struck with a medium-weight hammer. Care must be taken to see that the chisel is not touching the sheet metal in which the rivet is installed.

Cherry lockbolts

Cherry lockbolts serve a purpose similar to the Hi-Shear rivet and are manufactured in both the **pull type** and the **stump type.** The pull type is shown in Fig. 12·32. These fasteners are approved under National Aerospace Standard specifications and can be used for both aircraft and space vehicles.

The Cherry lockbolt consists of a steel or aluminum alloy pin with various head designs, and grooves around the pin into which is swaged a collar which may be made of aluminum-alloy (2024-T4), steel, or Monel metal.

The pull-type lockbolt is installed as indicated by the drawings of Fig. 12·33. The pin is inserted from one side of the work, the locking collar is placed over the projecting lockbolt pin tail, the gun is applied, and the chuck jaws automatically engage the pull grooves of the projecting pin tail. (See view 1.)

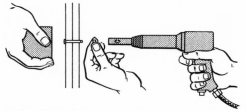

PREPARING TO INSTALL A HI-SHEAR RIVET
WITH A RIVET GUN AND BUCKING BAR

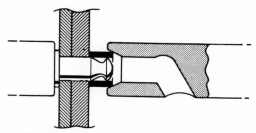

RIVET GUN AND COLLAR IN PLACE

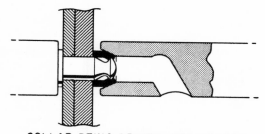

COLLAR BEING DRIVEN INTO GROOVE

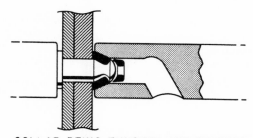

COLLAR BEING FINISHED AND TRIMMED

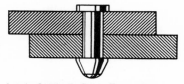

A HI-SHEAR RIVET INSTALLED

Figure 12·31   Installation of Hi-Shear rivets.

Depressing the gun trigger causes a pull to be exerted on the pin, as shown in view 2. The reaction of the pull is taken against the collar by the swaging anvil which draws the work tightly together as in a fitting-up operation, and the pin is pulled into the hole. As the pull on the pin increases, the anvil of the tool is drawn over the locking grooves of the pin to form a rigid, permanent lock. (See view 3.)

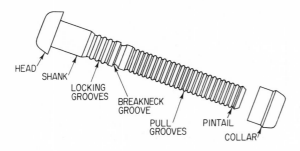

HEAD SHANK LOCKING GROOVES BREAKNECK GROOVE PULL GROOVES PINTAIL COLLAR

Figure 12·32 A pull-type Cherry lockbolt. (Cherry Rivet Div., Townsend Co.)

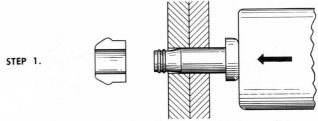

STEP 1.

Insert the stump in the prepared hole. If an interference fit is required drive the stump into the hole with a hammer or air hammer.

Continued buildup of force automatically breaks the lockbolt pin in tension at the breakneck groove, and the pin tail is automatically ejected. (See view 4.) View 5 shows the completed installation of the lockbolt.

The installation of the stump-type lockbolt is shown in Fig. 12·34. The stump bolt is inserted in the precision drilled hole and the collar is placed over the grooved end. The driving gun is fitted with a swaging set and a bucking bar is used against the head of the lockbolt. The air hammer can be applied to the swaging set or to the bucking bar, depending upon the rigidity of the work.

In view 3 of Fig. 12·34, the gun has swaged the collar over the locking grooves of the stump bolt to provide a positive lock. The swaging set is designed so it does not touch the stump because this would cause the installation to be loose.

Kaylock K-bolts

Another special fastener, used for either blind installation or in areas where its features are advantageous, is the **Kaylock K-bolt** (NAS 1669–1670), manufactured by the Kaylock Division of the Kaynar Manufacturing Company, Inc.

The K-bolt consists of a nut, sleeve, and core or screw, as shown in Fig. 12·35. These parts are preas-

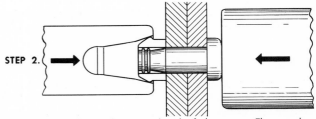

STEP 2.

Apply the collar to the grooved end of the stump. Then apply the swaging set to the collar. Use bucking bar against the head. The air hammer can be applied to the swaging set or to the bucking bar depending upon the rigidity of the work.

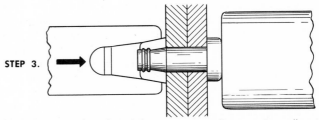

STEP 3.

The swaging set is forced down over the collar, swaging collar material into the locking grooves providing a positive lock. Note that the swaging set DOES NOT touch the stump which would cause looseness.

Figure 12·34   Installation of stump-type lockbolt.

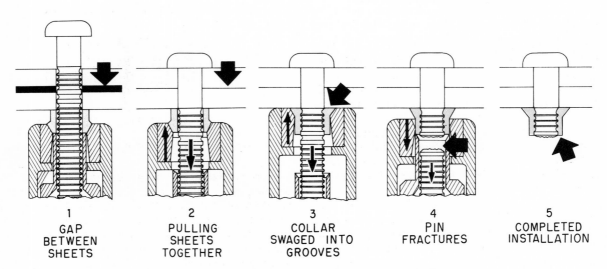

| 1 | 2 | 3 | 4 | 5 |
| GAP BETWEEN SHEETS | PULLING SHEETS TOGETHER | COLLAR SWAGED INTO GROOVES | PIN FRACTURES | COMPLETED INSTALLATION |

Figure 12·33   Installation of pull-type lockbolt.

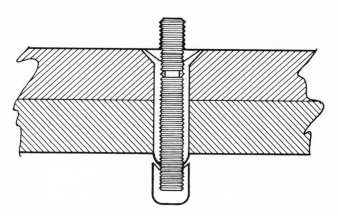

Figure 12·35 A Kaylock K-bolt. (Kaynar Manufacturing Co., Inc., Kaylock Div.)

sembled and ready for installation. A sectioned drawing of such an assembly is shown in Fig. 12·36.

To install the K-bolt, the proper type is selected, being careful to note diameter, grip length, and head style. The unit is inserted in the hole which is sized according to specifications. The drive tool is engaged with the head of the K-bolt at the same time the core screw engages with the wrenching bit of the drive tool. As the tool rotates the core screw, it causes the sleeve to be drawn over the tapered end of the nut member. The action of the sleeve expansion continues until the desired sheet take-up and tensile preload in the fastener has been accomplished. At this point the torsional shearing of the core screw takes place at the designated break-off point, and the installation is complete. Completed installations of the flushhead and hex-head K-bolts is shown in Fig. 12·37.

Another blind fastener similar to the K-bolt is called a **Jo Bolt.** The construction and principle of installation for the Jo Bolt is similar to those of the K-bolt.

TYPICAL REPAIRS

The number of different types of repairs for damaged sheet-metal structures is almost endless; hence we can provide only a few typical examples in this text and explain the requirements for repairs. The primary objective of a sheet-metal repair is to restore the original

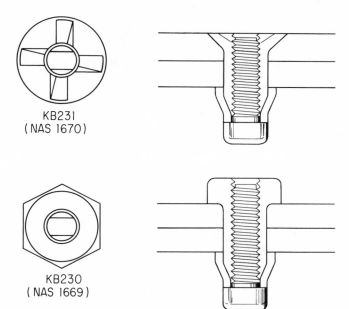

KB231
(NAS 1670)

KB230
(NAS 1669)

Figure 12·37 Installation of K-bolts. (Kaynar Manufacturing Co., Inc., Kaylock Div.)

strength of the structure without increasing the weight of the vehicle any more than necessary. The technician or his superior must usually decide whether to replace a damaged structure or make a repair. In any event, the repair must be made in accordance with the manufacturer's instructions or the methods set forth in FAA Advisory Circular 43.13. In some cases it may be necessary to design a special repair and have it analyzed by engineers to assure that it will accomplish its purpose.

Repairs for small holes

Small holes in sheet-metal skin may be repaired by means of a patch plate or a flush patch if the damage does not affect ribs or other structural members. The rough edges of the hole may be smoothed with a file or cut away with a **hole saw.** A hole saw is a small, circular saw, the shank of which can be inserted in the chuck of a drill motor or drill press. Several hole saws are shown in Fig. 12·38.

When using a hole saw with a drill motor, it is usually necessary to drill a pilot hole and use a hole-

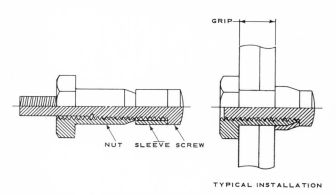

GRIP

NUT SLEEVE SCREW

TYPICAL INSTALLATION

Figure 12·36 Sectioned drawing of a K-bolt.

Figure 12·38 Hole saws.

saw pilot or a hole-saw guide with a pilot. This keeps the saw in place while cutting the metal.

Small holes may be punched in sheet metal with a **chassis punch.** The chassis punch includes a punch-and-die assembly with a screw device for pulling the punch through the metal. The punch has sharp edges which enable it to cut progressively as the screw is turned.

The patch for a small hole can be riveted to the outer surface of the skin or it may be made flush as shown in Fig. 12·39. In either type of patch the number of rivets should conform to the patterns shown in Fig. 12·39 which illustrates patches for 1-, 2-, and 3-in. round holes.

Where a flush patch is used, the patch is placed on the inner side of the skin. A plug is cut to fit the hole and is riveted to the patch. The rivets should be of the flush type as previously described in this chapter.

Replacement of skin panels

In cases where damage to stressed skin has occurred over an extensive area, it is often necessary to replace an entire panel. The original panel is removed by carefully drilling out the rivets at the seams. A new panel of the same material and thickness is cut to the same size as the original. The rivet pattern at the seams must conform to the original pattern. In cases where a portion of a panel is replaced and different patterns are used on the opposite edges of panels, it is best to copy the pattern of the stronger seam. Before a damaged wing panel is replaced, the interior of the wing structure must be inspected carefully. All damaged ribs or other damaged structures must be repaired before replacing the skin panel.

Repairs of sheet-metal ribs

Typical repairs for formed sheet metal and built-up ribs are shown in Fig. 12·40. In making repairs of the type shown, the technician must make sure he uses the correct number of rivets of the proper size and material. The replacement material and material used in making reinforcements must be of the same type as that used in the original structure. Furthermore, the material must have the same heat treatment as the original. The thickness of the repair material must be the same or greater than that of the original.

Repairs for formed sheet-metal rib cap strips are illustrated in Fig. 12·41. The repairs shown are indicative of the types of repairs required; however, many different types of repairs can be made as long as the strength and durability are adequately restored.

Splicing of sheets

Splicing of sheet metal should be accomplished as shown in Fig. 12·42. A double row of rivets in a splice, as shown in the upper part of the drawing, will give a seam strength which is 75 percent of the sheet strength without holes. The pattern shown in the lower part of the drawing will give a seam strength of 83 percent of the sheet without holes.

When splicing sheets, the splice should be designed as illustrated in the following examples:

Material   2024-T3 Alclad sheet, 0.032-in. thickness
Width of sheet (length of splice) $W = 12$ in.

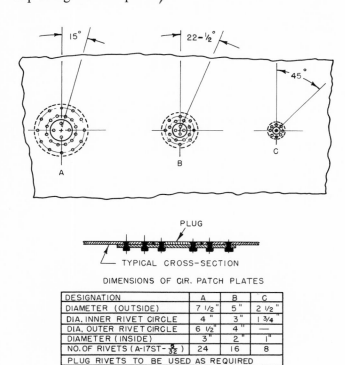

DIMENSIONS OF CIR. PATCH PLATES

DESIGNATION	A	B	C
DIAMETER (OUTSIDE)	7 1/2"	5"	2 1/2"
DIA. INNER RIVET CIRCLE	4"	3"	1 3/4"
DIA. OUTER RIVET CIRCLE	6 1/2"	4"	—
DIAMETER (INSIDE)	3"	2"	1"
NO. OF RIVETS (A-17ST-$\frac{3}{32}$)	24	16	8
PLUG RIVETS TO BE USED AS REQUIRED			

Figure **12·39** *Flush patch for a small hole.*

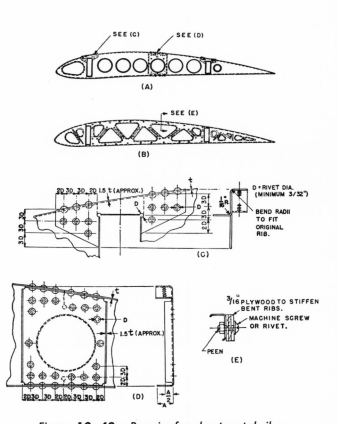

Figure **12·40** *Repairs for sheet-metal ribs.*

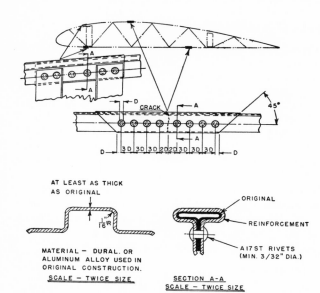

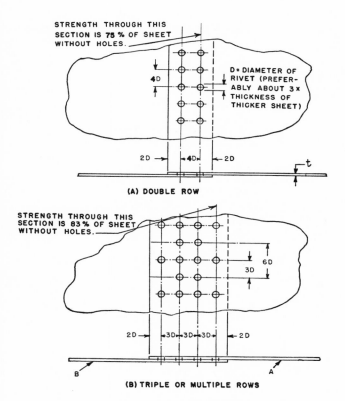

Figure **12·41** Repairs for cap strips.

Figure **12·42** A riveted sheet-metal splice.

1. Select the rivet diameter approximately three times the sheet thickness. Thus, $3 \times 0.32 = 0.096$ in. Use ⅛-in. 2117-T4 (AD) rivets.
2. Determine the number of rivets required per inch of

width W from Table 12·1. The number of rivets per inch equals 6.2, hence the total number of rivets required is $12 \times 6.2 = 74.4$, or 75 rivets.

3. Lay out the rivet pattern with spacings not less than those shown in Fig. 12·42. With the rivet pattern shown in B of Fig. 12·42, 75 rivets can be installed in the 12-in. width. This will make a satisfactory splice for the material used.

In the splice example above, if flush rivets are used, it is recommended that an edge distance of 2½D (rivet diameter) be used. For universal-head rivets an edge distance of not less than 2D is satisfactory.

Stringer and flange splices

Splices for stringers and flanges are shown in Fig. 12·43. The original material is shown unshaded, the reinforcing material shaded. Remember that **stringers** are the longitudinal supporting members to which the skin of the fuselage or wing is attached. The stringers are attached to the bulkheads or beltframes (formers) which are principal structural members of the assembly, and are designed to take both compression and tension loads. It is therefore necessary that certain general riveting principles be followed.

1. To avoid eccentric loading and buckling in compression, splicing or reinforcing parts are placed as symmetrically as possible about the center line of the member. Attachment is made to as many elements as necessary to prevent bending in any direction.
2. So that reduction of strength under tension of the original member is avoided, the rivet holes at the

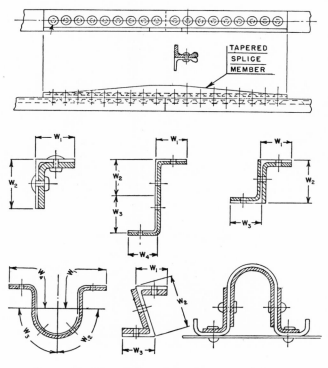

Figure **12·43** Splices for stringers and flanges.

end of the splice are made small, that is, not larger than the original skin-attaching rivets, and the second row of rivets is staggered back from the ends.

3. To prevent concentrating the loads on the end rivet and the consequent tendency toward progressive rivet failure, the splice member is tapered at the ends. This also has the effect of reducing the stress concentration at the ends of the splice.

4. When several adjacent stringers are spliced, the splices should be staggered if possible.

5. The diameter of rivets in stringers should be between two and three times the thickness of the leg but should not be more than one-quarter its width.

Repairing cracked structures

Methods for repairing cracked structures are shown in Fig. 12·44. This illustration shows repairs at the intersection of ribs and spars at both the leading edge and the trailing edge of a wing or other airfoil. Reinforcing plates must be of the same alloy and approximately 1½ times the thickness of the original material. In every case where cracks are repaired, the cracks should be stop-drilled before installing the reinforcements. **Stop drilling** can be defined as the process of drilling a small hole at the extreme end of a crack to prevent the crack from progressing farther into the material. The hole at the end of the crack removes the sharp stress-concentration area.

The condition causing cracks to develop at a particular point is stress concentration at the point combined with the repetition of the stress, as would occur with vibration. Stress concentrations are caused by nicks, scratches, or incorrect design factors. Complete failure of wing structures has been caused by stress concentrations where material has been cut to form a notch. In all repairs, the technician must make sure that material is not cut to form a sharp angle between two edges and that where two edges come together to form an angle, the material is rounded ("radiused") to a radius sufficient to prevent stress concentrations. The radius should be made as smooth as possible.

Members of aircraft structures which have developed cracks at fittings can be repaired as shown in Fig. 12·45. The treatment of cracks in these repairs is the same as described previously.

Special repairs

Where specific instructions for sheet-metal structural repairs are not available in publications such as Advisory Circular 43·13, published by the Federal Aviation Administration, they may sometimes be shown in manufacturer's manuals. For example, Fig. 12·46 is an illustration of a repair for a fuselage stringer repair provided in the service manual for the Cessna 310 airplane. Although a repair similar to this could be designed without the manual, it is still good practice to use the manufacturer's design when available.

Another repair illustrated in the manufacturer's manual is shown in Fig. 12·47. In this case the repair illustrated is for a cracked channel member. Note that the crack is stop-drilled as described previously.

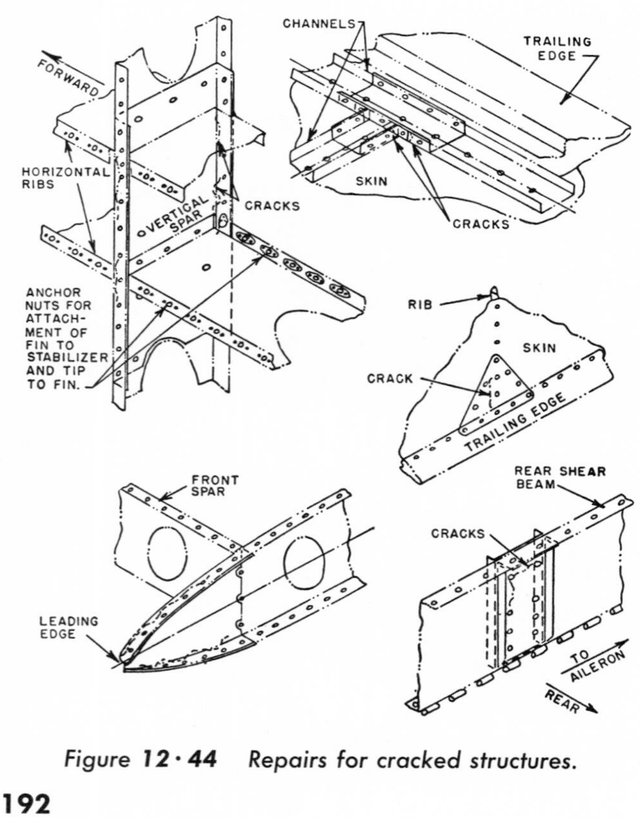

Figure **12·44** Repairs for cracked structures.

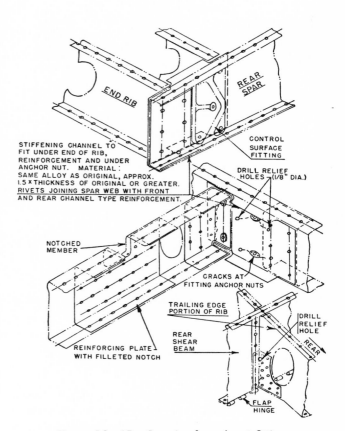

Figure **12·45** Repair of cracks at fittings.

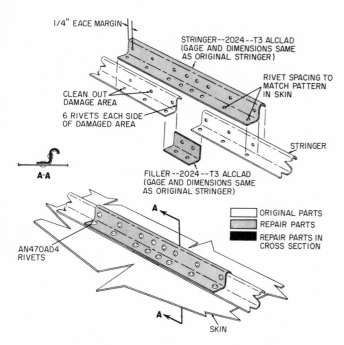

Figure 12·46 Repair of fuselage stringer. (Cessna Aircraft Co.)

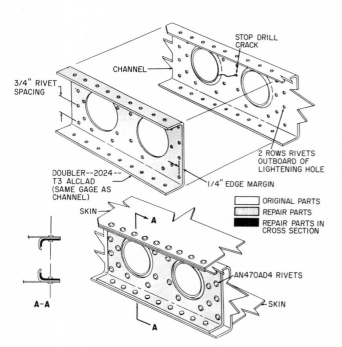

Figure 12·47 Repair of cracked channel member. (Cessna Aircraft Co.)

BONDED AND SANDWICH CONSTRUCTION

From World War II to the present, the plastics industry has developed many very powerful adhesives useful for aircraft construction. The technician will therefore encounter adhesive-bonded structures from time to time, and he must know how these should be handled. Usually the manufacturer's manual will give specific instructions for the inspection and repair of such structures. The principal points to be observed in the repair or rebonding of an assembly are cleanliness, correct bonding materials, correct adhesive-removing materials, correct metal-treating procedures, and correct bonding procedures. The age of adhesives is important, because many will deteriorate in a comparatively short time. The temperature at which an adhesive is stored may be critical and the temperature at which an adhesive is applied must be in accordance with the adhesive manufacturer's instructions.

Honeycomb sandwich material

Honeycomb structural sheets may be manufactured from many materials. Glass-fiber plastic materials are often used for the outer faces and also for the honeycomb core. For aircraft structures, the core material is sometimes made of glass fiber and the face sheets are of metal. Metal honeycomb core material is often used with metal faces and is bonded to the faces with chemical adhesives. An illustration of honeycomb construction is shown in Fig. 12·48.

For supersonic aircraft, stainless steel and titanium are used, and the metal honeycomb core is metal-bonded (brazed) to the face plates. In many cases, the sandwich construction must be custom-made for the particular airplane upon which it is used. This is because honeycomb material cannot be formed or shaped by bending. For this reason, if a part is of a complex shape, the core material and the outer face sheets must be shaped before assembly and bonding.

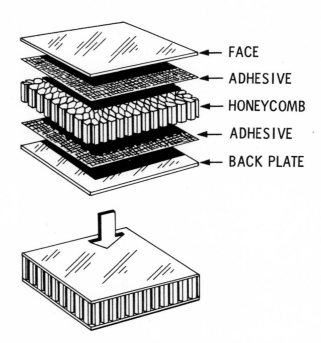

Figure 12·48 Honeycomb sandwich construction. (Federal Aviation Administration)

Repair of honeycomb structures

A variety of honeycomb structural repairs have been designed to meet the needs of various aircraft operators. The particular type of repair is usually determined by the extent of damage to the structure and the type of honeycomb material in the damaged part.

On the Boeing 720 airplane, aluminum, honeycomb sandwich construction is employed in control-surface panels, parts of the wing trailing edge, flap trailing edge, and floor panels. This type of structure is light and rigid and has good resistance to vibration. Because of the close prefit and careful fabrication methods required, honeycomb panels are expensive. They are easily damaged by impact or misapplied loads; hence considerable care must be exercised by crewmen working with the airplane. When punctured or dented, the cells of the honeycomb are crushed and torn, thus reducing the rigidity of the part, and the damage will likely cause progressive unbonding.

Potted repair. When the damage to a honeycomb structure is comparatively light and involves a small dent on only one side of the material, a potted repair may be used. This repair involves the removal of the damaged surface by cutting through the skin with a hole saw and then peeling the section of damaged skin away from the core material. Damaged core material is removed and bent cell walls are then straightened.

To use the hole saw, a hole-saw guide is framed over the damaged area and taped securely in place. The hole saw guide holds the saw in place for cutting.

After the damaged material is removed, the opening is filled with potting compound such as Epon 815. The potting compound is a semiliquid plastic which hardens when cured. If the damaged area is greater than 1 in. in diameter, a glass-fiber cloth overlay is installed as explained later. The cross section of a potted repair is shown in Fig. 12·49.

Replacement core repair. When the damage to a honeycomb structure is more extensive, it may be necessary to remove a section of the core and prepare a replacement. A repair of the type is illustrated in Fig. 12·50.

In this type of repair, the skin and core material are cut out with a hole saw; however, the opposite skin is not cut unless it is damaged. The core material is removed from the inside of the opposite skin but the original adhesive is not removed. A glass-fiber honeycomb replacement core is cut to the proper size to fit the opening.

The surface area around the repair must be cleaned

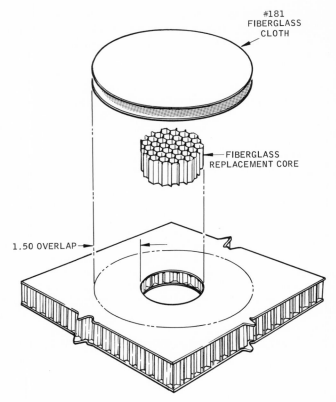

Figure 12·50 Replacement core repair. (United Air Lines)

and prepared for bonding the glass-fiber overlay. First any paint or other coating is removed with a stripping agent such as Delco 639 stripper. The stripper must not be allowed to run into the bonded joints or contact adjacent finished areas. After stripping, the surface is wiped with methyl ethyl ketone (MEK) solvent and then dried with a soft cloth. The surface is then sanded with 400-grit abrasive cloth and wiped again with MEK. The surface thus prepared is coated with a thin layer of adhesive primer, EC-776R. This is allowed to dry for 1 hr at 70°F or 30 min at 130°F. If a heat source is used, it must be explosionproof.

The glass-fiber, honeycomb core filler is made from NP ³⁄₁₆-112-6.0 material, or the equivalent. This is cut to fit the opening tightly and to be flush with the metal surface. Potting compound is then applied inside the cleaned-out area and around the contact edges of the core. The outside cells of the core are filled with the compound. The core is then pressed into place.

To prepare the glass-fiber overlay, two layers of No. 181 glass-fiber cloth are used. These are cut to a size which will permit at least a 1½-in. overlap around the edges of the cut-out area. Adhesive, BMS 5-29, is then prepared according to manufacturer's directions.

The glass-fiber patches are impregnated with adhesive by using plastic parting film and a squeegee. One piece of 0.008-in. parting film is taped securely to a smooth, flat surface. Adhesive is then spread near the center of the film and one piece of the glass fiber is placed over it. The glass-fiber cloth is covered with a

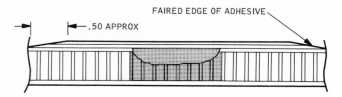

Figure 12·49 Potted repair for honeycomb structure. (United Air Lines)

second piece of parting film and pressed down with a squeegee. The squeegee is moved back and forth until the glass-fiber cloth is evenly impregnated with the adhesive.

To impregnate the second patch, the top-layer parting film is carefully peeled from the first patch, additional adhesive is applied, and the second patch is laid over the first. The parting film is placed over the two layers of glass fiber and the adhesive is worked through as before.

The glass-fiber overlay patch is now cut to finished size with both layers of parting film still adhering to the patch. The film is then removed carefully from one side of the patch and this side of the patch is centered over the core-filled hole and pressed smoothly into place. The 0.008 parting film is then peeled from the surface and a larger layer of 0.001 film is used as a cover with 1 in. extending beyond the edge of the patch. The patch is then swept with a squeegee in a manner to smooth out the wrinkles, remove the air bubbles, and fair the edges to a feathered edge. Excess adhesive is wiped away, but care must be taken to avoid squeezing out too much of the adhesive.

When the patch is smoothed and faired as desired, it is allowed to cure. The curing requires about 12 hr at 70°F or 1 hr at 130°F. After curing, the film is peeled from the surface.

The area around the patch is wiped with MEK to remove excess primer. A chemical- and solvent-resistant primer is then applied and this is followed with a chemical- and solvent-resistant enamel. The finished job should be very smooth to eliminate aerodynamic drag.

Tapered-panel trailing-edge repair. The trailing edge of a tapered honeycomb panel can be repaired as shown in Fig. 12·51. The damaged section is cut out cleanly as shown and a section of glass-fiber honeycomb is cut to fit the opening. The cut-out area and the honeycomb core are made with at least a 1-in. radius at the corners.

The bonding surface around the repair is prepared by cleaning, sanding, and priming, as explained in the foregoing section.

The repair core is cemented in using potting compound and is covered with double layers of glass-fiber cloth prepared with adhesive as previously explained. The patched area is faired, trimmed, cured, and finished to make a smooth surface.

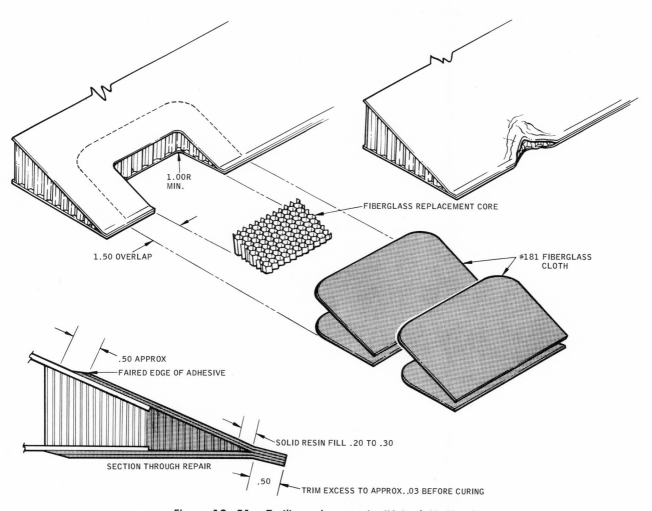

Figure 12·51   Trailing-edge repair. (United Air Lines)

Variety of repairs for honeycomb structures

In addition to the repairs described in this section for honeycomb structures, many other types have been designed and others will be forthcoming. The examples given provide examples of typical methods used.

Other types of repairs can include flush-riveted and cemented sheet-metal patches over the core material. In some cases, balsa wood is used as a core material for a repair.

In every case, the structural strength of the part must be restored with a minimum of weight increase. Furthermore, the repair must be such that it will not fail because of vibration or repeated operational stresses.

REVIEW QUESTIONS

1. List at least six causes of sheet-metal structure deterioration making frequent inspection and repair necessary.
2. To what information sources should an aircraft repairman refer in determining what type of repair to employ for a particular case of structural damage?
3. Describe a *rivet*.
4. How are rivets for aircraft use identified?
5. Explain the meaning of AN470AD-4-5.
6. What is an *icebox rivet*?
7. Explain how the *rivet gun*, *rivet set*, and *bucking bar* are used in installing rivets.
8. What preparation is necessary for installing flush rivets?
9. Describe the process known as *hot dimpling*.
10. Give the minimums for spacing between rivets and *edge distance*.
11. How is the number of rivets for a given repair determined?
12. Explain the significance of *shear strength* and *bearing strength* in determining the number of rivets for a repair.
13. Give the minimum dimensions for a driven rivet.
14. Explain the process of *burring*.
15. Discuss the size of rivet guns with respect to size of rivets.
16. Describe the care of a rivet gun.
17. What is the purpose of a *sheet fastener* and when is it used?
18. Explain how a rivet should be removed from an assembly.
19. Describe the process for the installation of *shaved* rivets.
20. What is meant by the term *blind rivet?*
21. Explain the use and installation of Cherry rivets.
22. What is the difference between a bulbed Cherrylock rivet and a standard Cherrylock rivet?
23. Explain the installation of an explosive rivet.
24. Discuss the value of fasteners such as the Hi-Shear rivet and the Cherry lockbolt.
25. What is the difference between a lockbolt and a stumpbolt?
26. Describe the installation of the Kaylock K-bolt.
27. Describe the flush patch for a hole in sheetmetal of less than 3 in. in diameter.
28. When replacing a panel in a sheetmetal structure, what determines the rivet pattern at the seams?
29. What determines the type of material to be used in the repair of a sheetmetal rib?
30. Give the general principles applicable to stringer splices.
31. What is the purpose of stop-drilling cracks?
32. Explain some of the causes for cracks in a sheetmetal structure.
33. Wherever a cut is made which forms a sharp angle between two edges of sheet metal, what must be done to prevent stress concentration?
34. Describe a typical sandwich (honeycomb) structure.
35. Describe a method for repairing a small hole in one side of a honeycomb panel.
36. Explain the steps necessary for repairing a honeycomb structure where extensive damage is done to the core material.

CHAPTER 13

Aircraft Hydraulic Systems

PRINCIPLES OF HYDRAULICS

Hydraulics is a division of the science of fluid mechanics which includes the study of liquids and their physical characteristics, both at rest and in motion. The type of hydraulics applied to aircraft and other aerospace-vehicle systems is called **power hydraulics** because it involves the application of power through the medium of hydraulics. Among the uses of hydraulic systems in aerospace vehicle systems are the operation of landing-gear and gear doors, flight controls, cowl flaps, and a wide variety of other devices requiring high power, quick action, and/or accurate control.

Development of power through hydraulics

Power is the product of force and distance divided by time. **Work** is force times distance; hence, power can be defined as work divided by time.

Force may be considered as a "push" or "pull" or any cause which tends to produce or change motion. In the English system, force is measured in pounds; in the metric system, it is measured in grams or kilograms. To measure the force of hydraulics, we must be able to determine **force per unit area.** This is called **pressure** and is measured in pounds per square inch, or **psi.**

Power can be measured in **horsepower** (hp). One horsepower is the power required when 550 pounds of force is exerted through a distance of one foot in one second. This power can also be expressed as 550 ft-lb per sec. To determine the amount of power required to do a given amount of work in a given time, we divide the work by the time. For example, if a hydraulic actuating cylinder lifts a weight of 11,000 lb a distance of 2 ft in 5 sec, we find the power as follows:

$$P \text{ (in ft-lb per sec)} = \frac{11,000 \times 2}{5}$$
$$= 4400 \text{ ft-lb per sec}$$

To convert this to horsepower we divide by 550 and obtain the value of 8 hp. To obtain horsepower directly from the first computation, we merely include the horsepower factor, 550, in the equation, thus:

$$P \text{ (in hp)} = \frac{11,000 \times 2}{5 \times 550} = 8 \text{ hp}$$

Characteristics of liquids

In general, and for practical purposes, liquids are regarded as being incompressible. This means that the volume of a given quantity of a liquid will remain constant even though it is subjected to high pressure. Because of this characteristic, it is easy to determine the volume of hydraulic fluid required to move a piston through its operating range. For example, if a piston is 4 in. in diameter and its stroke is 10 in., the volume of liquid necessary to move the piston through its full stroke is 125.67 cu in. This is determined as follows.

The volume of the cylinder through which the piston moves is equal to the area of the pistonhead multiplied by the length of the cylinder. The area of the pistonhead is determined by the formula $A = \pi r^2$; hence for the piston in the example, $A = 3.1416 \times 2^2 = 12.567$. Multiplying this value by 10, we obtain the volume 125.67 cu in. We know then that it will require 125.67 cu in. of hydraulic fluid to move the piston through its 10-in. stroke.

Because of the relative incompressibility of a liquid, we know that a given output volume from a hydraulic pump will provide an equal volume of fluid at the operating unit. For example, if a hydraulic pump discharges 100 cu in. of fluid through a filled connecting line between the pump and an actuating cylinder, the piston in the cylinder will have to move through sufficient distance to provide a volume of 100 cu in. to accommodate the fluid.

Hydraulic fluids and other liquids expand as temperature increases; hence, safeguards must be provided in hydraulic systems to allow for the expansion and contraction of fluid as temperature changes. Devices to provide the necessary protection are called **thermal relief valves.**

A liquid which is unconfined will seek its own level as shown in Fig. 13·1. Here the liquid is in a container

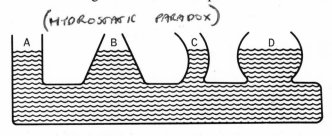

(HYDROSTATIC PARADOX)

Figure 13·1 Liquid seeks its own level.

open at the top and is subjected only to the force of gravity. Assuming that the container shown in the illustration is level, the pressure is the same at all points on the bottom of the container. The liquid surfaces at *A*, *B*, *C*, and *D* are all equidistant from the bottom of the container.

A basic principle of hydraulics is expressed in Pascal's law formulated by Blaise Pascal in the seventeenth century. This law states that a confined hydraulic fluid exerts equal pressure at every point and in every direction in the fluid. This is true under static conditions and when the force of gravity is not taken into consideration. In Fig. 13·2 if the piston *P* has a face area of 1 sq in. and a force of 10 lb is applied to it, the fluid in the container will exert 10 psi in all directions on all surfaces within the container. In actual practice the weight of the fluid would cause a small increase in the pressure on the bottom and lower sides of the container.

Liquids in motion

When liquids are in motion, certain *dynamic* characteristics must be taken into consideration. One of the principal factors in liquid motion is **friction**. Friction exists between the molecules of the liquid and between the liquid and the pipe through which it is flowing. The effects of friction increase as the velocity of liquid flow increases. The result of friction can be seen in the simple experiment illustrated in Fig. 13·3. As the liquid flows from the container through a pipe which is open at the end, the pressure of the liquid decreases progressively until it becomes 0 psi at the open end of the pipe. If the pressure at *A* is 4 psi, then it will be 3 psi, 2 psi, 1 psi, and 0 psi at *B*, *C*, *D*, and *E*, respectively. As liquid velocity increases through a given length of pipe, the pressure differential between the ends of the pipe will increase. The same is true when a liquid is flowing through a restriction in a pipe. For this reason, the rate of fluid flow can be determined by measuring the pressure differential on opposite sides of a given restrictor. This is illustrated in Fig. 13·4. The differential pressure reading on the gage will increase as liquid velocity through the restrictor increases and the reading of the

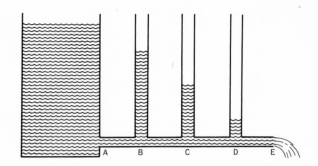

Figure 13·3   *Reduction of pressure because of friction.*

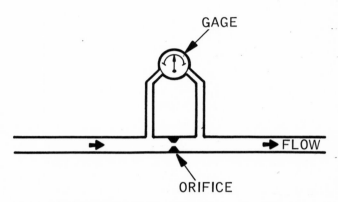

Figure 13·4   *Differential pressure across a restriction.*

gage can be converted to gallons per minute or some other rate measurement.

Friction in a moving liquid produces heat, and this heat represents a loss of energy in a hydraulic system. According to the **law of conservation of energy**, which states that energy can neither be created or destroyed, energy converted to heat must be subtracted from the total energy of the moving liquid. Hence, if a hydraulic pump is discharging hydraulic fluid at a rate and pressure equivalent to 3 hp, and in the system the equivalent of 0.2 hp is converted to heat, the power available for useful work is reduced to 2.8 hp.

Performing work with a liquid

One of the principal advantages of hydraulics is the fact that force can be multiplied to almost any degree by the proper application of hydraulic pressure. In the diagram of Fig. 13·5 a piston and cylinder with a diameter of 2 in. is used to develop a force of 2500 lb by acting through a cylinder with a diameter of 10 in. The area of the 2-in. piston is 3.1416 sq in. (The area of a circle is $r^2 \times \pi$.) The area of the 10-in. piston is then $5^2 \times 3.1416$, or 78.54. When a force of 100 lb is applied to the small piston, a pressure of 100/3.1416 is developed in the system. This pressure is 31.83 psi. The force exerted by the large piston is then 31.83 × 78.54, or approximately 2500 lb. It will be noted that the areas of circles are proportional to the squares of the diameters; hence the force developed by one piston driving another is also proportional to the squares of the

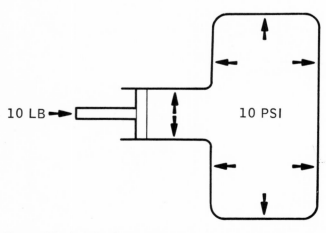

Figure 13·2   *Fluid pressure is the same in all directions.*

10 LB ➤

10 PSI

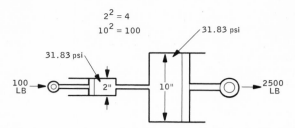

Figure 13·5 Multiplication of force by means of hydraulics.

diameters. In the foregoing problem, the square of the diameter of the smaller piston is 2×2 or 4, and the square of the larger piston is 10×10 or 100. The ratio is then $4:100$ or $1:25$. Since the force applied to the small piston is 100 psi, the force delivered by the large piston is 100×25, or 2500 lb.

Since energy cannot be created or destroyed, the multiplication of force is accomplished at the expense of distance. In the foregoing problem, the ratio of force multiplication is $25:1$. The distance through which the pistons move must then be in an inverse ratio, or $1:25$. That is, the large piston will move one twenty-fifth the distance the small piston moves. If the small piston is connected to a fluid input with check valves so it can act as a pump, it can be moved back and forth, and during each forward stroke it will move the large piston a short distance. This action can be observed in the hydraulic jacks which are used to raise automobiles or airplanes.

In some aircraft hydraulic systems, fluid pressures of as much as 5000 psi are employed. With a pressure of this level, a very small actuating cylinder can exert tremendous force. For example, a cylinder having a cross-section area of 2 sq in. can exert a force of 10,000 lb.

A simple hydraulic system

Basically, a hydraulic system requires a source of hydraulic power (the pump); pipes or hoses to carry the hydraulic fluid from one point to another; a valve mechanism to control the flow and direction of the hydraulic fluid; a device for converting the fluid power to movement (actuating cylinder or hydraulic motor); and a reservoir to store the hydraulic fluid.

A **simple hydraulic system** is shown in the diagram of Fig. 13 · 6. The pump (P) draws hydraulic fluid from the reservoir (R) and directs it under pressure to the four-way valve (V). When the valve is in the position shown, the fluid will flow into the left end of the actuating cylinder (A) and force the piston to the right. This moves the piston rod and any device to which it is connected.

As the piston moves to the right, the fluid to the right of the piston is displaced and flows out the port at the right end of the cylinder, through the tubing to the valve, and from the valve to the reservoir. When the valve is rotated one-quarter turn, the reverse action will take place.

It must be emphasized that the diagram shown is not

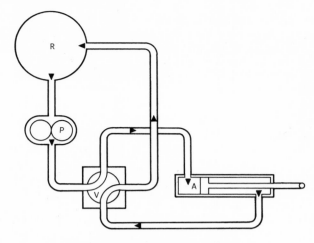

Figure 13·6 Simple hydraulic system.

intended to illustrate an actual system but only to illustrate the principle of a hydraulic system. In an actual system, a pressure regulator or relief valve is necessary between the pump and the valve in order to relieve the pressure when the cylinder reaches the end of its travel. Otherwise, the pump would be damaged or the tubing would burst.

Another simple system is illustrated in Fig. 13 · 7. This system is similar to a hydraulic brake system. Hydraulic fluid is stored in the cylinder and is directed through a valve into the master cylinder as it is needed. When the brake pedal is depressed, the fluid is directed to the brake cylinders; these cylinders push the shoes apart, thus causing them to bear against the brake drum and provide brake action. When the pedal is released, springs attached to the brake shoes cause the shoes to contract and push inward on the brake cylinders, thus causing some of the fluid to return to the master cylinder.

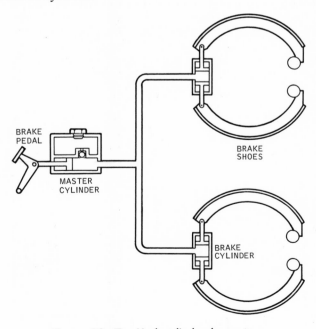

Figure 13·7 Hydraulic brake system.

HYDRAULIC PUMPS

Hydraulic pumps are designed to cause fluid flow and are made in hundreds of different designs from simple hand pumps to very complex, multiple-piston, variable-displacement pumps. We shall examine a few pumps which could be used for aircraft or space vehicles.

Hand pumps

A diagram of a **single-acting hand pump** is shown in Fig. 13·8. This diagram illustrates the basic principle of a piston pump. When the handle is moved toward the left, the piston movement creates a low-pressure condition and draws fluid from the reservoir through the check valve and into the cylinder. Then when the handle is moved toward the right, the piston forces the fluid out through the discharge check valve. The check valves allow the fluid to flow only in one direction, as shown by the arrows.

A **double-acting piston-displacement type** of hand pump is shown in the diagram of Fig. 13·9. The in port from the reservoir is connected to the center of the cylinder where there is a space between the two pistons and surrounding the shaft connecting the pistons. In each piston is a check valve (Nos. 1 and 2) and a passage which allows fluid to flow from the center chamber to the spaces at each end of the dual piston assembly. When the pump handle is moved to the right, the piston assembly moves to the left forcing fluid out through check valve 3 into the system. The

check valve in the left-hand piston is held closed by fluid and spring pressures. As the piston assembly moves to the left, a low-pressure area is created in the chamber in the right end of the cylinder, and this causes fluid to flow through check valve 1 into the chamber. Check valve 4 is held in the closed position by spring and fluid pressure. When the pump handle is moved to the left, the piston assembly moves to the right and the fluid is forced out of the right-hand chamber through check valve 4 into the system. Note that a fluid passage connects the outlet chambers at each end of the cylinder.

Gear-type pump

A **gear-type pump** is shown in the drawing of Fig. 13·10. This pump is classed as a **positive-displacement pump** because each revolution of the pump will deliver a given volume of fluid, provided the pump is not worn and no leakage occurs. One of the two gears is driven by the power source which could be an engine drive or an electric-motor drive. The other gear is meshed with and driven by the first gear. As the gears rotate in the direction shown, fluid enters the in port to the gears where it is trapped and carried around the pump case to the out port. The fluid cannot flow between the gears because of their closely meshed design; hence it is forced out through the out port.

Vane-type pump MAX. WORKING PRESS. 300 PSI

The **vane-type pump** is also classed as a positive-displacement pump because of its positive action in moving fluid. This pump is illustrated in the drawing of Fig. 13·11 and consists of a slotted rotor located off-center within the cylinder of the pump body with rectangular vanes free to move radially in each slot. As the rotor turns, the vanes are caused to move outward by centrifugal force and contact the smooth inner surface of the casing. Since the rotor is eccentric with respect to the casing, the vanes form chambers which increase and decrease in volume as the rotor turns. The inlet side of the pump is integral with the side of the casing in which the chambers are increasing in volume. Thus the fluid is caused to enter the chambers because of the low-pressure area created by the expanding chambers. The fluid is carried around the casing to the point where the chambers begin to

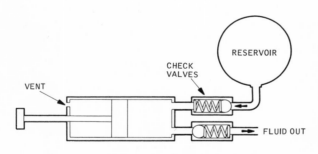

Figure *13·8*   Single-acting hand pump.

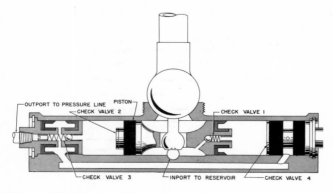

Figure *13·9*   Double-acting, piston-displacement hand pump.

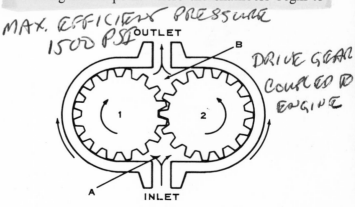

MAX. EFFICIENT PRESSURE 1500 PSI

DRIVE GEAR COUPLED TO ENGINE

Figure *13·10*   Gear-type pump.

MAX. PRESSURE 2000 PSI

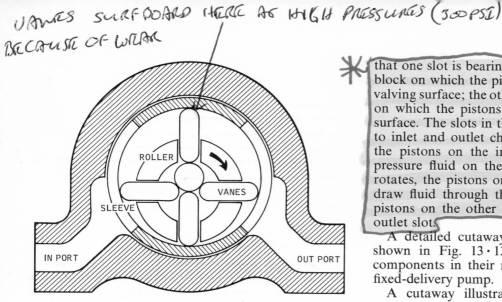

Handwritten annotation: VANES SURFBOARD HERE AT HIGH PRESSURES (300 PSI) BECAUSE OF WEAR

Figure 13·11   Vane-type pump.

contract, and this section of the casing is connected to the output port of the pump. The contraction of the chambers forces the fluid into the outlet port and into the system.

Multiple-piston pumps   *FIXED-DELIVERY*

One of the most widely used hydraulic pumps for modern aerospace vehicles is the **axial multiple-piston pump.** A simple drawing to illustrate this type of pump is shown in Fig. 13·12. The pump consists of a drive shaft to which the pistons are attached by means of ball sockets, a cylinder block into which the pistons are inserted, and a stationary valving surface which fits closely against one end of the cylinder block. The drive shaft is connected to the cylinder block by means of a universal link to rotate the cylinder block with the drive shaft. The axis of rotation for the cylinder block is at an angle to the axis of rotation of the drive shaft; hence the pistons are caused to move in and out of the cylinders as rotation occurs. The pistons on one side of the cylinder block are moving outward, thus increasing the volume of the cylinder spaces; on the other side of the cylinder block, the pistons are moving inward. The valve plate is made with two slots such

that one slot is bearing against the side of the cylinder block on which the pistons are moving away from the valving surface; the other slot is bearing against the side on which the pistons are moving toward the valving surface. The slots in the valving surface are connected to inlet and outlet chambers to provide fluid feed to the pistons on the inlet side and an outlet for the pressure fluid on the other side. As the drive shaft rotates, the pistons on one side of the cylinder block draw fluid through the valving surface slot, and the pistons on the other side force the fluid through the outlet slot.

A detailed cutaway drawing of an axial pump is shown in Fig. 13·13. This drawing shows all the components in their respective positions in a typical fixed-delivery pump.

A cutaway illustration of a **fixed-delivery pump** manufactured by Vickers, Inc., is shown in Fig. 13·14. **Fixed delivery** means that the pump will normally deliver a fixed amount of fluid at a given rpm. A **variable-delivery pump** is shown in Fig. 13·15. This pump is designed so the rotational axis of the cylinder block can be changed as desired to vary the volume of fluid being delivered at a given rpm. By changing the angle of the rotational axis, the stroke of the pistons is decreased or increased; hence the volume of fluid pumped during each stroke of the pistons is reduced or increased. If the axis of the cylinder block is parallel to the axis of the drive shaft, no fluid will be delivered because there will be no movement of the pistons within their respective cylinders.

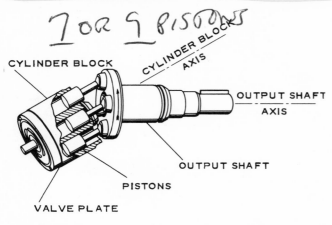

Handwritten annotation: 7 OR 9 PISTONS

Figure 13·12   An axial multiple-piston pump.

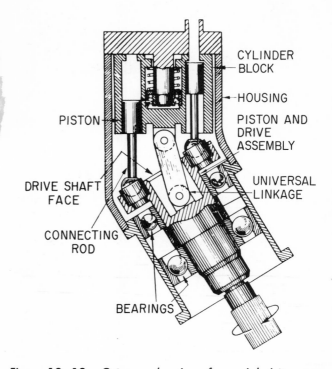

Figure 13·13   Cutaway drawing of an axial piston pump.

201

Figure 13·14   Fixed-delivery piston pump. (Vickers, Inc.)

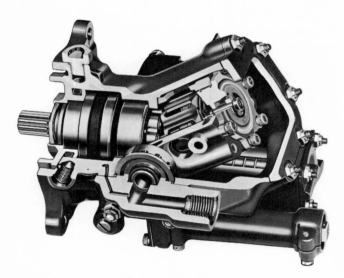

Figure 13·15   Variable-delivery piston pump. (Vickers, Inc.)

FLOW CONTROL VALVES

In almost any hydraulic system, one or more **control valves** or **selector valves** are needed to control fluid flow. The simplest type of valve is merely an on-off valve to open or close a passage to permit flow or to stop flow. Such a valve can be used where the fluid flow is always in the same direction (as in a hydraulic motor system in which the motor always turns in the same direction).

In the majority of hydraulic systems, the actuating cylinder or hydraulic motor is required to reverse operation; in such cases it is necessary to incorporate a four-way valve which permits fluid flow in either direction.

Rotary valve

A **rotary four-way valve** is shown in Fig. 13·16. When the valve is in the position shown in *A*, the fluid will be flowing from the valve at the top port and will cause the actuating cylinder to be extended. When the valve is rotated 90° as in *B*, the fluid to and from the actuating cylinder will be in the opposite direction, and the cylinder will retract.

Poppet valve

Another type of flow-control valve is shown in Fig. 13·17. In this valve assembly, individual **poppet valves** are used to open and close the ports to change

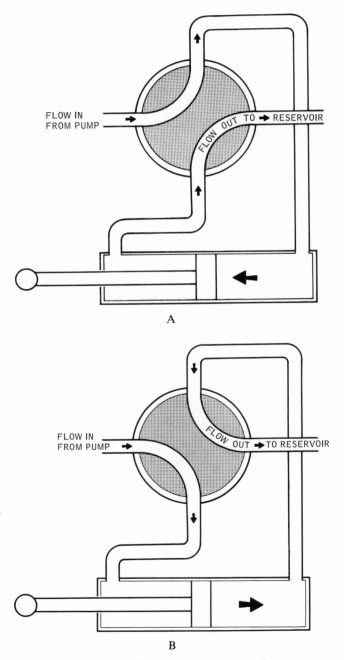

Figure 13·16   Rotary four-way valve.

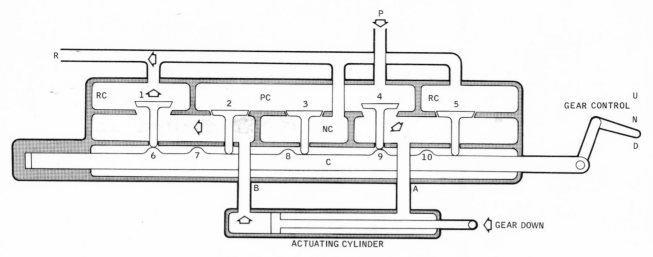

Figure 13·17   Poppet-type four-way valve.

the direction of fluid flow. The valves are operated by cams on cam rod *C*. Fluid enters the valve through line *P* from the pressure pump, and with the gear control in the DOWN position, it passes through open valve 4 and on to the actuating cylinder. As the piston moves to the left, fluid from the left end of the actuating cylinder flows through passage *B* and open valve 1 to the return chamber and back to the reservoir through the return line *R*.

If the gear-control handle is placed in the neutral position, cam lobe 8 will open poppet valve 3, and cam lobes 6 and 9 will close poppet valves 1 and 4; assuming, of course, that the poppets are equipped with springs which keep them closed unless they are lifted by a cam. When poppet valve 3 is open, fluid flow will pass from the pressure chamber *PC* to the neutral chamber *NC* and from thence to the return manifold, thus permitting the fluid to flow freely and thereby reducing the load on the pressure pump. In the neutral position, valves 2 and 5 are closed because the cams 7 and 10 are not yet in position to open them.

When the gear control handle is placed in the UP position, valves 2 and 5 will be open and the others will be closed. Fluid will therefore flow through poppet valve 2 and out the passage *B* to the left end of the actuating cylinder. The piston will move to the right and force fluid through passage *A* and poppet valve 5 to the return chamber and return line to the reservoir.

Some poppet valve assemblies are arranged with the valves in a radial position, and they are opened and closed by means of a rotary cam unit. The results are the same in any case. Poppet valves are also manufactured with electric controls and the individual valves are opened and closed by means of solenoids.

Spool or piston selector valves

A schematic drawing of a typical **spool-type selector valve** is shown in Fig. 13·18. The three positions of the valve are shown to illustrate the passages for fluid in the OFF, DOWN, and UP positions. It will be noted that

there is no fluid flow when the valve is in the OFF position; hence the valve must be used in a system where a pressure regulator or variable delivery pump is employed. Otherwise a high pressure would build up and cause excessive wear or other damage to the pressure pump.

A simple **piston-type selector valve** is illustrated in the drawing of Fig. 13·19. In the first drawing, the valve is in the OFF position and fluid flow is blocked because both port *A* and port *B* are blocked by the piston. In the second view, port *A* is open to allow fluid to flow out to an actuating cylinder; the return flow from the cylinder enters port *B* and flows out port *R* to the reservoir. The third view shows the reverse position where fluid flows out port *B* and back through port *A*. The center of the piston rod is provided with a drilled passage which allows the return fluid to flow to the right and out through the return port *R*.

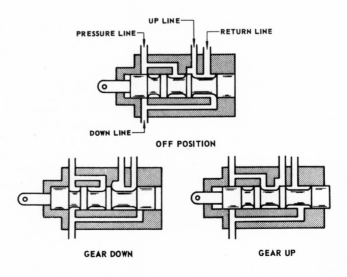

Figure 13·18   Spool-type selector valve.

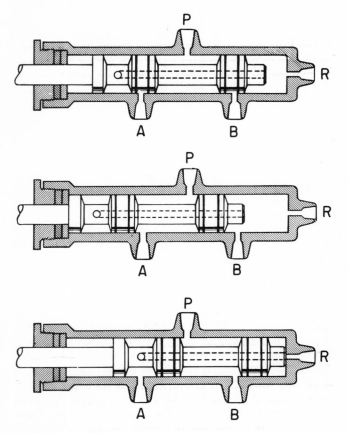

Figure 13·19   Piston-type selector valve.

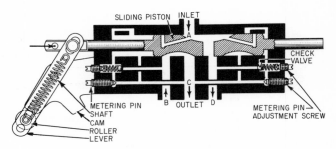

Figure 13·20   Selector valve for open-center system.

Open-center-system selector valve

The details of an open-center hydraulic system are given later in this chapter; however, it is important to understand that in this type of system all selector valves are connected in series to a common fluid supply and return line. The valve shown in Fig. 13·17 is suitable for an open-center system.

Like other forms of selector valves, the **open-center selector valve** provides a means of directing hydraulic fluid under pressure to one end of an actuating cylinder and of simultaneously directing fluid from the opposite end of the actuating cylinder to the return line. The advantage is that the valve automatically returns to neutral when the actuating cylinder reaches the end of its stroke. The fluid output of the power pump is directed through this valve to the reservoir when the valve is in neutral position.

The valve illustrated in Fig. 13·20 consists of a housing which has four ports, a piston, two metering pins, two relief valves, and a spring-loaded roller-and-cam-arrangement which is attached to the end of the piston. The roller and cam is designed to hold the piston in either the operating position after it has been engaged or the neutral position.

In the illustration the sliding piston is in one of the two operating positions. The sliding piston has been moved manually to the right and is held in position by the spring-loaded cam mechanism. Fluid under pres-

sure flows from the inlet port *A* through port *D* to one side of the hydraulic actuating piston, moving the actuating piston to its fully extended or retracted position. Fluid returning from the opposite side of the piston enters the selector valve at *B* and discharges through the return port *C* to the reservoir.

Figure 13·21 shows the same valve in the neutral position where it is held by the lever and cam arrangement. The position of the lever, which rotates about the shaft, is determined by the position of the roller which rolls on the cam. In the neutral position, the inlet port *A* is connected directly to the return port *C*, thus allowing the fluid to flow freely through the valve.

The valve is automatically returned to the neutral position by action of fluid pressure which opens the relief valve and admits fluid pressure to the end of the piston. This pressure forces the valve piston back to the neutral position. The action takes place for either position of the valve.

Orifice or restrictor valves

An **orifice** is merely an aperture, opening, perforation, passage, or hole. A **restrictor** can be described as an orifice or similar to an orifice. A **variable restrictor** is an orifice which can be changed in size so its effect can be altered. The size of a fixed orifice must remain constant, whereas a variable restrictor permits adjustment to meet changing requirements.

The purpose of an orifice, or a variable restrictor, is to limit the rate of flow of the fluid in a hydraulic line. In limiting the rate of flow, the orifice causes the mechanism being operated by the system to move more slowly.

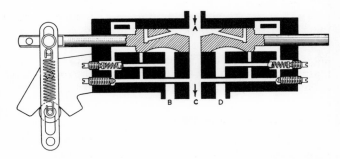

Figure 13·21   Open-center selector valve in the neutral position.

Figure 13·22 is a drawing of an orifice. This form of the device is merely a fitting which contains a small passage and which has threaded ends. When fluid enters the in port, which is the larger of the two ports, the fluid flows through the central passage and out through the out port, which is the smaller of the two ports, thus limiting the rate of flow. An orifice of this construction may be placed in a hydraulic line between a selector valve and an actuating cylinder to slow the rate of movement of the actuating cylinder.

Figure 13·23 is a drawing of a **variable restrictor.** In this drawing, there are two horizontal ports and a vertical, adjustable needle valve. The size of the passage through which the hydraulic fluid must flow may be adjusted by screwing the needle valve in or out. The fact that the passage can be varied in size is the feature that distinguishes the variable restrictor from the simple fixed orifice.

Orifice check valve

An **orifice check valve** is designed to provide free flow of hydraulic fluid in one direction and restricted flow in the opposite direction. One of the most common applications of this device is in the UP line of a landing-gear system. Since landing gear is usually quite heavy, it will tend to fall too rapidly upon lowering, unless some means of restricting its movement is utilized. Since the UP line of a landing-gear actuating cylinder is the return line for hydraulic fluid from the actuating cylinder to the reservoir, any restriction in this line will limit the movement of the gear. That is, the gear movement must await the flow of the return fluid as it moves toward the down position. An orifice check valve is also used for certain

flap control systems. Because of the air pressure on the flaps during flight, there is a continuous force tending to raise the flaps to a streamline position. It is therefore advisable in some systems to restrict the UP movement by placing an orifice check valve in the DOWN line of the flap system.

The construction of an orifice check valve is illustrated in Fig. 13·24. When the valve is on its seat, fluid flow can occur only through the orifice, but when the fluid flow is in the opposite direction, the valve moves off its seat and there is free flow of the hydraulic fluid.

The improper installation of an orifice check valve in a landing-gear system can cause serious problems. If the valve is installed in the reverse position, the movement of the landing gear will be restricted as the gear is raised, but there will be free flow as it is lowered. The hydraulic pressure in the system plus the force of gravity will cause the gear to lower with excessive speed; when it reaches the end of its travel, the inertial forces will be likely to damage the aircraft structure because of the sudden stop.

Check valves

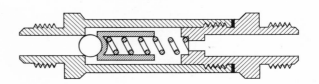

It is often necessary to prevent hydraulic-fluid flow in one direction while permitting free flow in the opposite direction. The **check valve** is designed to accomplish this purpose. The construction of a simple ball check valve is shown in Fig. 13·25. Fluid pressure at port A will tend to push the ball off its seat and allow the fluid to flow through the valve. When the pressure is applied at port B, the ball will hold firmly on its seat and prevent the flow of fluid. Check valves are used as individual units in hydraulic systems and they are also used as components of more complex valves and devices to control the flow of fluid in a given direction.

During the installation of a check valve, the technician must observe the direction of flow indicated on the body of the valve. Usually there is an arrow on the body or case of the valve to show the direction of free fluid flow.

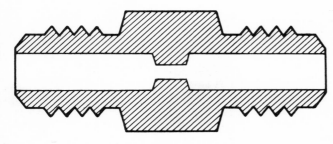

Figure **13·22**   Drawing of an orifice.

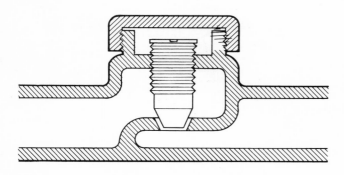

Figure **13·23**   Variable restrictor.

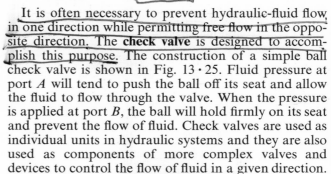

Figure **13·24**   Construction of an orifice check valve.

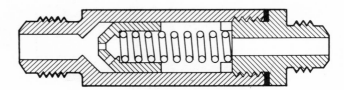

Figure **13·25**   Ball check valve.

Metering check valve

A **metering check valve,** sometimes called a **one-way restrictor,** serves the same purpose as an orifice check valve. However, the metering check valve is adjustable while an orifice check valve is not.

A drawing of a metering check valve is shown in Fig. 13·26. This unit has a housing, a metering pin, and a check-valve assembly. The pin is adjusted to hold the ball slightly off its seat. When fluid enters port *B*, it forces the ball away from its seat and then flows out through port *A* to the actuating cylinder. When the flow of fluid is reversed, the fluid entering from the actuating cylinder flows through the tiny opening between the ball and its seat, thus restricting the flow. By adjusting the metering pin in or out with a screwdriver, the rate at which the fluid can return from the actuating cylinder is controlled because the position of the metering pin changes the width of the opening between the ball and its seat.

Sequence valve

A **sequence valve** is sometimes called a **timing valve** because it times certain hydraulic operations in proper sequence. This unit has been called a "load-and-fire" check valve, although **sequence valve** is the correct term. A common example of the use of this valve is in a landing-gear system where the landing-gear doors must be opened before the gear is extended, and the gear must be retracted before the doors are closed.

Figure 13·27 is a drawing of a sequence valve. It is essentially a by-pass check valve that is automatically operated. There is a free flow of hydraulic fluid from port *A* to port *B*, but the flow from *B* to *A* is prevented unless the ball is unseated by depressing the plunger.

Figure 13·28 is a schematic diagram of a landing-gear system with sequence valves. During the retraction of the landing gear, the fluid flows under pump pressure from the selector valve to the landing-gear cylinder and to the sequence valve *A*. In this position, sequence valve *A* is closed, thus preventing the fluid from entering the door cylinder. As the landing-gear actuating-cylinder piston approaches the end of its travel, either the piston rod or some other part of the landing-gear mechanism depresses the plunger of the sequence valve, thereby permitting the fluid to flow to the door actuating cylinder and to close the doors. The fluid displaced at the other end of the landing-gear actuating cylinder by the motion of the piston passes to the down line through sequence valve *B*. The flow is not restricted, because it is flowing directly from port *A* to port *B* in the sequence valve illustrated in Fig. 13·27.

During the extension of the landing gear, the fluid under system pressure flows through the down line and enters the door actuating cylinder, but it is prevented from moving the landing-gear actuating-cylinder piston because sequence valve *B* is closed. However, when the door actuating-cylinder piston reaches the limit of its travel, the plunger on sequence valve *B* is depressed, and a passage is opened for the fluid to enter the landing-gear actuating cylinder and extend the gear. The fluid displaced by the motion of the door actuating-cylinder piston flows to the up line through sequence valve *A* without restriction.

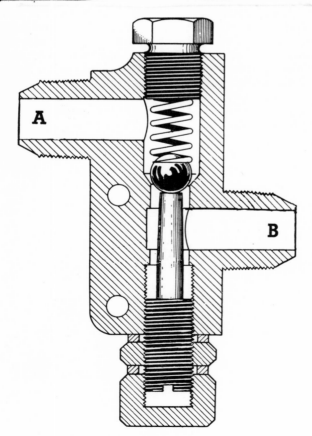

Figure **13·26** Metering check valve.

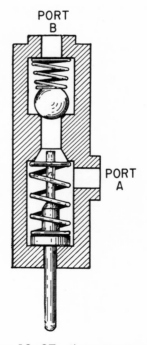

Figure **13·27** A sequence valve.

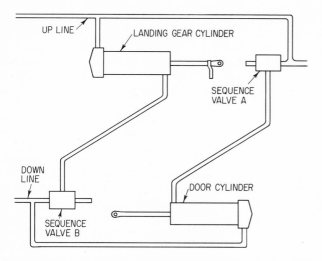

Figure 13·28 *Landing-gear system with sequence valves.*

Sequence valves are sometimes used in conjunction with hydraulically operated landing-gear up locks and down locks. In such instances, the sequence valve either blocks the fluid from the landing-gear actuating cylinder until the unlocking cylinder (sometimes called the **unlatching jack**) has released the lock or prevents the fluid from entering the locking jack until the landing gear has reached its fully retracted or extended position. Sometimes the sequence valve and the unlocking jack are manufactured as one unit.

To illustrate the operation of a sequence valve in a landing-gear system, the drawing of Fig. 13·29 is provided. This drawing shows a view of the sequence valve in the open position. If the valve is installed with port *A* connected to the landing-gear *up* line and port *B* connected to the gear door actuating cylinder, fluid entering at port *A* cannot pass through to the actuating

cylinder until the landing gear has been retracted and the valve plunger pressed in as shown in the drawing. Hence, the gear doors cannot be closed until the gear is retracted.

For the part of the system extending the landing gear, the sequence valve is installed with port *A* connected to the *down* line of the landing-gear actuating cylinder. The plunger of the valve is not depressed until the gear doors are open; hence the gear cannot be extended until the door operation is nearly complete.

If, in the installation and adjustment of the landing-gear system, the sequence valves are not set correctly, it is possible for the landing gear to strike the gear doors. If the landing-gear mechanism hits the doors on either the up or down operation, it is quite likely that the sequence valve in one or the other lines is not adjusted correctly.

Shuttle valves

Quite frequently in hydraulic systems it is necessary to provide alternate or emergency sources of power with which to operate critical parts of the system. This is particularly true of landing-gear systems in the case of hydraulic-pump failure. Sometimes the landing gear is operated by an emergency hand pump and sometimes by a volume of compressed air or gas stored in a high-pressure air bottle. In either case it is necessary to have a means of disconnecting the normal source of hydraulic power and connecting the emergency source of power. This is the function of the **shuttle valve.**

The operation of a shuttle valve is shown in the drawings of Fig. 13·30. Port 1 of the valve is the normal entrance for hydraulic fluid from the pressure system. Port 2 is the outlet leading to the down line of the landing-gear actuating cylinder. In view *A* the valve is in the normal position with free passage of fluid from port 1 to port 2. If main system pressure fails and it is desired to lower the landing gear, the landing-gear selector valve is placed in the DOWN position and emergency pressure is applied to port 3. As explained previously, this pressure can come from an emergency

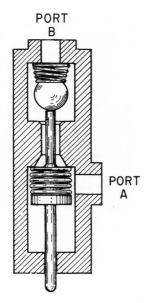

Figure 13·29 *Sequence valve in open position.*

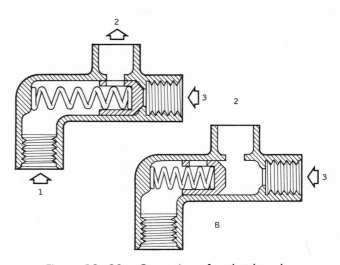

Figure 13·30 *Operation of a shuttle valve.*

207

pump or from a high-pressure air bottle. The emergency pressure forces the shuttle valve to the left and opens port 2 to port 3; thus fluid or air is permitted to flow through the valve to the down line of the actuating cylinder. Return fluid from the cylinder will flow through the normal up line, back through the main selector valve and to the reservoir.

The installation of a shuttle valve in the landing gear system is shown in the schematic drawing of Fig. 13·31. The down line is blocked when emergency pressure is applied, and emergency fluid or air enters the cylinder, flowing from port 3 to port 2 and into the actuating cylinder.

PRESSURE-CONTROL DEVICES

Numerous devices have been designed to control pressure in hydraulic systems; however, we shall attempt to describe but a few of the most important. Among these are **relief valves, pressure regulators,** and **deboosters.**

Relief valve SYSTEM RELIEF VALVE

A **relief valve** is comparatively simple in construction, and its function is to limit the maximum pressure which can be developed in a hydraulic system. Thus it acts as a safety valve similar in function to one which would be found in an air- or steam-pressure system. During operation, the relief valve remains closed unless the system pressure exceeds that for which the valve is adjusted. At this time the valve opens and allows the fluid to flow through a return line to the reservoir.

A drawing to illustrate the construction of a relief valve is shown in Fig. 13·32. During normal operation, the valve is on its seat and fluid flows from the in port to the out port without restriction. As the pressure on the line increases to a level above that for which the valve spring is adjusted, the valve lifts off its seat and the fluid then flows through the valve and out the return line. The design of the valve must be such that it will not rapidly open and close and cause chattering, since this would damage the system. Relief valves are used to control maximum system pressure and to control pres-

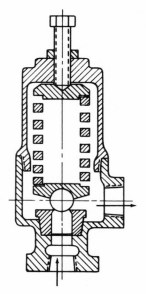

Figure 13·32   *Construction of a relief valve.*

sure in various parts of the subsystems. For example, a flap relief valve is often placed in the down line of the wing-flap subsystem to prevent lowering of the flaps at too high an air speed. The pressure in the down line will rise above a specified level because of air pressure against the wing flaps if the air speed is too great. The flap relief valve will then open and allow excess pressure to be relieved, thus causing the down movement of the flaps to stop.

When several relief valves are incorporated in a hydraulic system, they should be adjusted in a sequence which will permit each valve to reach its operating pressure. Thus, the highest-pressure valves should be adjusted first, the others in the order of descending pressure values.

Pressure regulators

A **pressure regulator** is designed to maintain a certain range of pressures within a hydraulic system. Usually the pressure regulator is designed to relieve

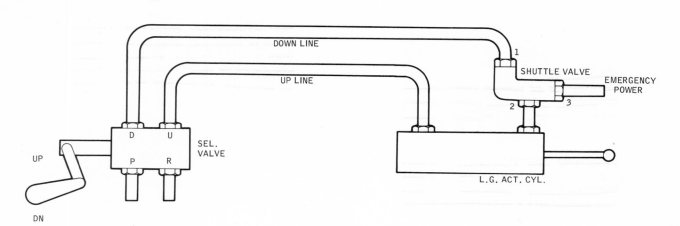

Figure 13·31   *Location of a shuttle valve in a landing-gear system.*

the pressure on the pressure pump when it is not needed for operating a unit in the system. Some pressure regulators are also called **unloading valves,** because they _unload_ the pump when hydraulic pressure is not required for operation of landing gear, flaps, or other subsystems. Continuous pressure on the pump increases wear and the possibility of failure.

A pressure regulator which is also an unloading valve is illustrated in Fig. 13·33. In this view, the unit is operating to supply fluid for charging an accumulator (hydraulic-pressure storage chamber) and to supply fluid pressure for operating units in the system. Fluid flows into port B and out of port A to the system. The check valve is off its seat because of the fluid pressure being exerted by the pressure pump. When the pressure in the accumulator builds up to the maximum level for the system, the same pressure is exerted in chamber F, Fig. 13·34. This pressure moves the plunger (piston) (3) upward to raise the **pilot valve** (2) against the pressure of the spring (1). In Fig. 13·33, observe that fluid pressure is applied to one of the pilot-valve chambers through a passage from the inlet line, around an annular groove surrounding the unloading valve [(4) in Fig. 13·34], and to the pilot valve. As the pilot valve is raised, this pressure is ported and directed through a passage to the left end of the **directional spool** (5). This spool moves to the right and causes hydraulic pressure to be directed against the right end of the unloading spool, thus moving it to the left. This permits the main flow of fluid to go from port B, through passage E, and out the return port C. Under this condition the power pump is unloaded because the fluid has free flow back to the reservoir. The regulator is said to be "kicked out" in this position. The check valve has seated because of spring pressure and holds the pressure locked in the system. In the drawings, port D is the "bleed-off" port which permits fluid from the chambers at the ends of the directional spool and unloading spool escape and allow movement of the spools as required.

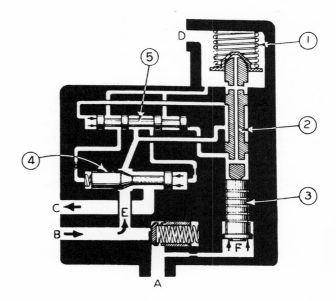

Figure 13·34 Unloading valve in the kicked-out position.

When a subsystem is operated and fluid pressure in the pressurized part of the system drops to a predetermined level, the pilot valve and plunger will move back to the lower position, directing pressure against the right end of the directional spool as shown in Fig. 13·35. The directional spool moves to the left and causes fluid pressure to be directed to the left end of the unloading spool, moving it to the right and blocking the return line. Pump pressure then builds up and opens the check valve (bullet valve) to allow fluid flow to the operating system through port A as shown in Fig. 13·33. This position is often referred to as "kicked in."

Another type of pressure regulator which serves a purpose similar to the one just described is the Bendix balanced type. A drawing of this regulator in the

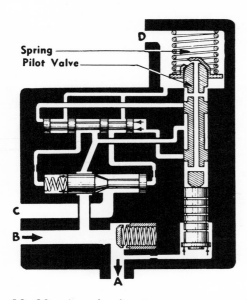

Figure 13·33 An unloading-type pressure regulator.

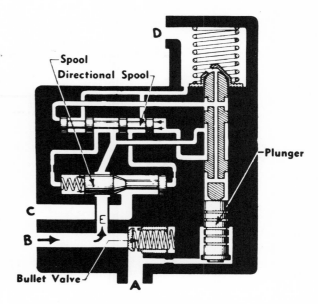

Figure 13·35 Moving to the kicked-in position.

"kicked-in" position is shown in Fig. 13·36. In this drawing, the bypass valve E is held closed by spring pressure and system pressure. Fluid from the power pump enters at port F and the pressure forces the check valve G off its seat and allows the fluid to flow out port H to the accumulator and the system. When the system operating requirements are met, the pressure continues to build up from the pump and throughout the area in operation. This pressure bears against the poppet valve I and also increases above the piston N because of the sensing line O. The piston N has greater area than the poppet valve I; hence the force downward increases faster than the force upward. At a certain point the force downward becomes equal to the force upward and the valve is then said to be in the **balanced** condition. As pressure continues to increase, the downward force becomes greater than the upward force and the rod M moves downward against the force of the spring L. The hollow piston rod M moves downward and contacts the poppet valve, thus forcing it off its seat. Pressure fluid then can flow through the passage K to act against the directional valve C which pushes the bypass valve E off its seat. When this occurs, pressure fluid entering port F can flow out through port D to the reservoir and the pressure entering the port F drops to the free-flow level. Check valve G is then immediately seated by spring pressure to trap the high pressure in the system. This is the "kicked-out" position, and it is illustrated in Fig. 13·37.

For proper operation, the regulator should remain in the kicked-out position until the pressure in the system has dropped to the lower operating level. This it will do, because the pressure for the initial kick-out was great enough to overcome the force of the spring L and the pressure against the poppet I. Since the poppet has been lifted from its seat, the only force necessary to keep the valve in the kicked-out position is that on the

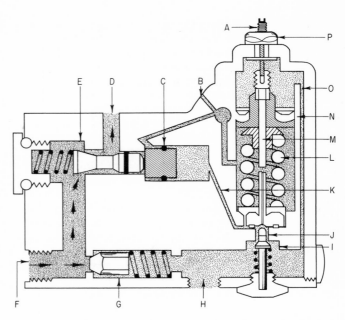

Figure **13·37** Bendix pressure regulator in the kicked-out position.

piston N acting against the spring L. Therefore, the pressure will drop substantially before the valve kicks in again.

The kick-out pressure of the valve is adjusted by turning the adjusting screw A. This changes the effect length of the rod below the piston and changes the amount of force necessary to bring about the kicked-out condition.

Thermal relief valves   30-50% above

A **thermal relief valve** is similar to a regular system relief valve; however, such valves are installed in parts of the hydraulic system where fluid pressure is trapped and may need to be relieved because of the increase caused by higher temperatures. During the flight of an airplane, it is quite likely that fluid in many of the hydraulic lines will be at a low temperature. When the airplane lands, this cold fluid will be trapped in the landing-gear system, the flap system, and other systems, because selector valves are in the neutral or *off* position. The fluid-temperature increase owing to warm air on the ground results in fluid expansion and could cause damage unless thermal relief valves are incorporated in the systems. Thermal relief valves are adjusted to pressures which are above those required for the operation of the systems; hence they do not interfere with normal operation.

Debooster valve

In some hydraulic systems, it is desired to reduce system pressure to some lower pressure for operation of a particular unit. Typical of such pressure-reduction devices is the **debooster** employed in some brake systems. Such a valve operates by the differential area of two pistons. If a small-area piston is connected by a rod to a large-area piston, the two pistons will be capa-

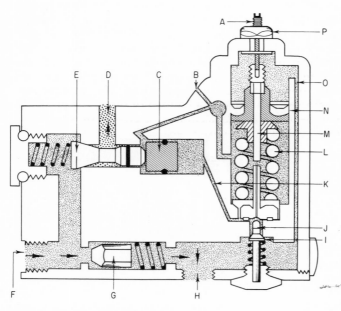

Figure **13·36** Bendix balanced-type pressure regulator.

ble of developing pressure in inverse proportion to their areas. Figure 13·38 illustrates the debooster principle. If the area of the small piston is 1 sq in. and the area of the large piston is 4 sq in., the large piston can transmit a pressure of only one-quarter that of the small piston. When 1000 psi is applied to the small piston, a force of 1000 lb will be exerted through the rod to the large piston. Since the large piston has a 4 sq in. area, a force of 1000 lb will develop a pressure of only 250 psi in the large cylinder. In actual practice the construction of the debooster valve is more complex than that shown in the drawing; however, the principle of operation is as explained.

Other types of pressure reducers employ springs and pistons to cause a reduction in pressure. Such pressure-reducing valves utilize springs to create the pressure differential required. For example, if a spring controlled valve is adjusted to open and relieve all pressure above a given level, the pressure transmitted to an actuating cylinder will be effectively reduced.

ACCUMULATORS

An **accumulator** is basically a chamber for storing hydraulic fluid under pressure. It also serves as a surge dampener to reduce shock in a system when sudden pressure changes or changes of flow occur. In this section we shall discuss three types of accumulators.

Diaphragm-type accumulator

Since hydraulic fluid is incompressible, practically speaking, some means is necessary to provide sustained pressure on the fluid if effective energy storage is to be attained. For this purpose compressed air or an inert gas is used. The usual construction of the accumulator is such that a volume of compressed air is applied to a volume of fluid so the fluid will continue to be under pressure. The fluid and air are separated by a diaphragm so air cannot enter the hydraulic system.

The **diaphragm-type accumulator** consists of a sphere separated by a synthetic-rubber diaphragm as shown in Fig. 13·39. The sphere is constructed in two parts which are joined by means of screw threads. At the bottom of the sphere is an air valve, such as a Schrader valve, and at the top is a fitting for the hydraulic line. A screen is placed at the fluid outlet inside the sphere to prevent the diaphragm from being pressed into the fluid outlet.

During operation of the accumulator, the air chamber is **preloaded** or **charged** with air pressure approxi-

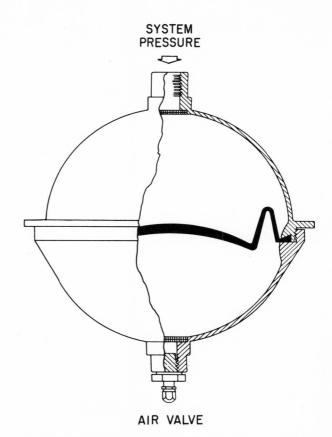

SYSTEM PRESSURE

AIR VALVE

Figure 13·39   Diaphragm-type accumulator.

mately one-third maximum system pressure. As soon as a very small amount of fluid is forced into the fluid side of the accumulator, the system pressure gage will show the pressure in the air chamber. This provides a means for checking the air charge in the accumulator. If the system is inactive and the main pressure gage shows zero pressure, a few strokes of the hand pump directed to the accumulator will cause the pressure gage to rise suddenly to the charge pressure in the accumulator. The accumulator charge can also be checked by the reverse method. For example, if the system gage shows a pressure of 1500 psi when the system pump is not operating and the brakes are depressed and released a number of times, the pressure will decrease to the accumulator charge pressure and then will suddenly fall to zero.

Bladder-type accumulator

The **bladder-type accumulator** usually consists of a metal sphere in which a bladder is installed to separate the air and the hydraulic fluid. The bladder serves as the air chamber, and the space outside the bladder contains the hydraulic fluid. The construction of a bladder-type accumulator is shown in Fig. 13·40. The air valve is at the bottom of the sphere, the fluid port is at the top. Initially, the bladder is charged with air pressure as specified in the aircraft manual. When fluid is forced into the accumulator, the bladder collapses to the extent necessary to make space for the fluid, depending

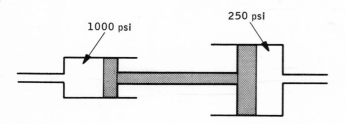

1000 psi   250 psi

Figure 13·38   Principle of the debooster.

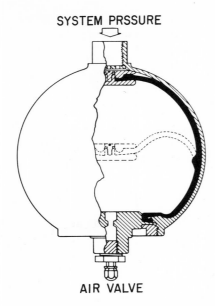

SYSTEM PRSSURE

AIR VALVE

Figure 13·40   Bladder-type accumulator.

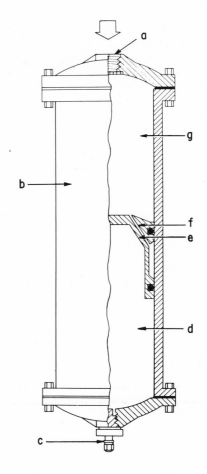

a

b

g

f

e

d

c

a.	Fluid port	d.	Air chamber
b.	Cylinder	e.	Piston assembly
c.	High-pressure air	f.	Drilled passage
	valve	g.	Fluid chamber

Figure 13·41   Piston-type accumulator.

upon the fluid pressure. As long as fluid is in the accumulator, the air pressure is at the same level as the fluid pressure.

Piston-type accumulator

Many modern hydraulic systems employ **piston-type accumulators** because they require less space than an equivalent spherical accumulator. A piston-type accumulator is shown in Fig. 13·41. Note that this unit consists of a cylinder with a free piston inside to separate the air from the hydraulic fluid. The piston is equipped with seals which effectively prevent the air from leaking into the fluid chamber and vice versa.

Removal and installation of accumulators

Great care must be exercised in the servicing and repair of hydraulic systems. This is particularly true of the high-pressure systems which operate at pressures in excess of 3000 psi. Before an accumulator or any other unit is removed, the technician must make certain that all the pressure in the system has been relieved. This is accomplished by operating one of the subsystems until all pressure is gone, and the main pressure gage reads zero pressure. The air pressure in the accumulator is reduced to zero by opening the air valve in accordance with the manufacturer's instructions. The accumulator can then be disconnected; however, provision should be made for fluid drainage. If the system contains a synthetic, fire-resistant fluid, such as Skydrol 500, the fluid must not be permitted to drain onto painted areas or other parts where the fluid can cause damage.

The installation of an accumulator is usually the reverse of removal. Sometimes the air charge is placed in the accumulator before installation. In any event, the manufacturer's instructions should be followed. Particular care must be taken to see that all seals,

valves, and fittings are of the proper type for the fluid being used in the system.

If hydraulic fluid is found in the air chamber of an accumulator, there is a leak between the two chambers. In such cases, the accumulator must be removed and repaired.

Seal couplings

Where it is necessary to disconnect hydraulic lines frequently, such as at the firewall of an engine nacelle, **seal couplings** or "quick-disconnect" fittings are often employed. A simplified drawing to illustrate the construction of such a coupling is shown in Fig. 13·42. As shown in the drawing, each end of the coupling contains a check valve. When the coupling is loosened, the check valves close and prevent the escape of fluid. When the coupling is assembled, the valves are opened by a pin or other mechanism to provide free flow for the fluid. If a seal coupling is found to be leaking, the coupling should be replaced.

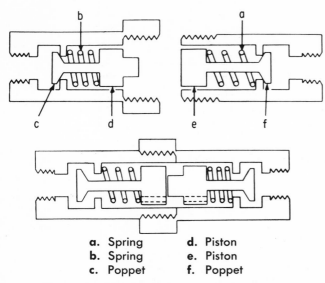

a. Spring	**d.** Piston	
b. Spring	**e.** Piston	
c. Poppet	**f.** Poppet	

Figure 13·42   Quick-disconnect seal coupling.

HYDRAULIC FLUIDS

Purposes of hydraulic fluids

Hydraulic fluids make possible the transmission of pressure and energy. They also act as a lubricating medium, thereby reducing the friction between moving parts and carrying away some of the heat.

Hydraulic-fluid types

There are three principal types of hydraulic fluids: **vegetable-base fluids, mineral-base fluids,** and **fire-resistant fluids.** CHEMICAL BASE

Vegetable-base fluids are usually mixtures containing castor oil and alcohol and are colored blue, blue-green, or almost clear. They are still used in some brake systems but are not generally found in hydraulic-power systems.

Mineral-base fluids consist of a high-quality petroleum oil and are usually colored red. They are still used in many systems, especially where the fire hazard is comparatively low. Small aircraft which have hydraulic power systems for operating flaps and landing gear will usually use mineral-base fluids conforming to MIL-O-5606. Mineral-base fluids are less corrosive and less damaging to certain parts than other types of fluid.

Because of the fire hazard associated with petroleum-base fluids, synthetic, **fire-resistant fluids** were developed for large aircraft. Typical of fire-resistant fluids is Skydrol 500 which is employed in modern jet-transport aircraft. This fluid is purple and all units designed for use with the fluid are identified by purple nameplates or are dyed purple. Seals, gaskets, and hoses used with the fluid are made of butyl synthetic rubber. Great care must be taken to see that the units installed in the hydraulic system are of the type designed for fire-resistant fluid. When replacing gaskets, seals, and hoses, positive identification must be made to assure that they are made of butyl rubber.

Fire-resistant hydraulic fluid will soften or dissolve many types of paints, lacquers, and enamels. For this reason, areas which may be contaminated with this type of fluid must be finished with special coatings. When any of the fluid is spilled it should immediately be removed and the area washed.

Rules for use of hydraulic fluid

In addition to any other instructions given in the airplane manufacturer's manual, the following should be observed in the use of hydraulic fluids:

1. Mark each airplane hydraulic system to show the type of fluid to be used in the system. The filler cap or filler valve should be marked so that it is immediately apparent to the technician what type of fluid should be added to the system.
2. Never under any circumstances service an airplane system with a type of fluid different from that shown on the instruction plate.
3. Make certain that hydraulic fluids and fluid containers are protected from contamination of any kind. Dirt particles will quickly cause many hydraulic units to become inoperative and may cause severe damage. If there is any question regarding the cleanliness of the fluid, it should be filtered through a filter paper into a dustfree container. Containers for hydraulic fluid should never be left open to the air for longer than necessary.
4. Never allow hydraulic fluids of different types to become mixed. Mixed fluid will render a hydraulic system useless.

HYDRAULIC PACKING RINGS AND SEALS

Purpose

The purpose of hydraulic packing rings and seals is to prevent leakage of the hydraulic fluid and thereby preserve the pressure in the aircraft hydraulic system. Seals are installed in most of the units that contain moving parts, such as actuating cylinders, valves, pumps, etc. Packing rings, seals, or gaskets are made in a variety of shapes and sizes.

The handling, installation, and inspection of rings, seals, and gaskets in an aircraft hydraulic system are extremely important because a scratched or nicked packing ring may cause the failure of a unit in the system at a critical time.

Seals and packings

Typical shapes for hydraulic packing rings, seals, and gaskets are shown in Fig. 13 · 43. These drawings show the standard O-ring seal, chevron seal, universal gasket, and crush washer.

The **O-ring** seal is probably the most common type used for sealing pistons and rods because it is effective in both directions. The O ring is easy to install and does not need to be adjusted. Care must be taken to see that the ring is the correct size; it should be examined to be sure that there are no cuts, nicks, or scratches on the

AN 6227 O-RING

AN 6225 V-RING

AN 902 UNIVERSAL GASKET

AN 901 CRUSH WASHER

Figure 13·43 Shapes for packing rings, seals, and gaskets.

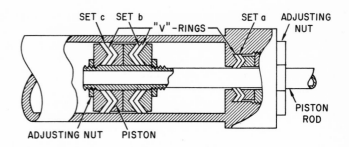

Figure 13·45 Installation of a dual set of chevron seals.

surface which could permit leakage of fluid. The ring must be the correct size, both in ring diameter and cross-section diameter. When the ring is installed it should be lubricated with hydraulic fluid of the type with which it is to be used. It should not be twisted or distorted after installation, or it will not seal effectively.

The O-ring seal should not be used alone in a system where the pressure is greater than 1500 psi. If the hydraulic pressure is too great, the ring can become pinched between the moving part and stationary part of the unit, thus damaging the ring and destroying the seal. When the O ring is used in higher-pressure systems, backup rings are installed. Where the pressure is exerted alternately in each direction, these backup rings are installed on both sides of the O ring. Backup rings are usually made of chrome-tanned leather with a grease content of about 5 percent. The side of the leather ring from which the hair has been removed is called the **grain side**; the opposite side is called the **flesh side**. When the backup rings are installed with O rings, the grain side is always placed next to the O ring. A typical installation of backup rings with O rings is illustrated in Fig. 13·44.

The V-shaped (chevron) seal and the U-shaped seal must be installed with the same care as that used for the other types of seals. The size of the seal must be correct and there must be no nicks, scratches, or other damage on the seals. When high pressure is exerted in only one direction, one set of seals is sufficient, but when the pressure is alternately applied, first in one direction and then in the other, two sets of seals are required because this type of seal works effectively in only one direction. The installation of a dual set of chevron seals is shown in Fig. 13·45.

The general procedure to follow in installing V-shaped or U-shaped seals is as follows:

1. Install one ring at a time, being sure that it is seated properly. Never install such rings in sets.
2. Use shim stock (very thin metal sheet) to protect the packing rings if the packing crosses sharp edges or threads. The shim stock should be from 0.003 to 0.010 in. thick. It is rolled and then placed over the threads or sharp edges. After installing the packing, the shim stock is removed.
3. If the unit in which the packing is being installed does not have an adjustable packing gland nut, insert metal shims of graduated thickness behind the adapters to hold the packing securely in place.
4. If the unit in which the packing is being installed has an adjustable packing gland, adjust the gland nut until the V-ring stack is held together firmly but not squeezed. The gland nut is then loosened to the first lock point.
5. Whenever possible, the technician should check the unit by hand for free operation after installation before the hydraulic pressure is applied.
6. In all cases possible, the technician should consult the manufacturer's instructions regarding the installation of seals.

Hydraulic tubing

The metal tubing used in hydraulic systems is identical with that used for other fluid-carrying systems; however, the specific tubing used in hydraulic systems must be of sufficient strength to withstand the pressures to which it may be subjected. For hydraulic systems in which a pressure of 1500 psi will be exceeded, corrosion-resistant (stainless-steel) tubing is used for the high-pressure sections of the system. In other parts of the system, such as the return lines and the pump suction lines, aluminum-alloy tubing is satisfactory. A generally suitable alloy is 5052, hardened in accordance with manufacturer's requirements.

Metal tubing installed in aircraft hydraulic systems should be free from scratches, dents, nicks, wrinkles, or any other defect which will either limit the flow of fluid or lead eventually to tube failure. It must be remembered that hydraulic fluid under high pressure contains great energy and can cause considerable injury or damage if suddenly released through the failure of a tube or fitting. This is particularly true of high-pressure systems where the pressure may be higher than 3000 psi.

Certain tolerances are permitted to allow for very

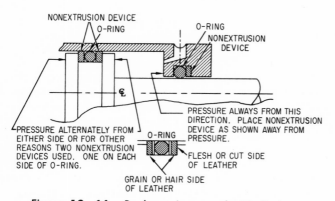

Figure 13·44 Back-up rings used with O rings.

minor defects. For example, a small amount of flattening in bends is acceptable, provided the smaller diameter of the tube is not less than 75 percent of the original outside diameter. A smooth dent is allowable if it is not in the heel of a bend and if it is not deeper than 20 percent of the diameter of the tube.

Aluminum-alloy tubing which has nicks or scratches no deeper than 10 percent of the wall thickness of the tube and not in the heel of a bend, may be repaired by burnishing out the nick or scratch with hand tools. If tubing has severe die marks, seams, or splits, it should be replaced. Cracks or other defects in the flared end of tubing is also cause for rejection.

Where the damage to a section of tubing is severe and it is not economical to replace the entire section of tubing, a repair may be effected by cutting out the damaged section of tubing and replacing it with a new section made up to fit the space where the damaged tubing was removed. The new section is installed by means of standard tubing fittings of the type approved for the system. Where the section removed is very short, the space may be filled by means of the fittings only. In any case where a section of tube is cut out and a new section is inserted, care must be taken to see that no metal chips or particles get into the system. The cut ends of the tube should be smooth and clean before flaring or before installing flareless fittings. The inside of the tubing should be cleaned by drawing a piece of soft cloth through the tube with soft safety wire or a strong piece of string.

Except for very small diameter tubing, it is necessary to use a suitable bending tool for making bends in the tubing. This is particularly true of stainless-steel tubing. Otherwise the tubing will flatten or wrinkle at the bend.

Tube fittings

Tube fittings are assemblies for joining sections of tubing in a system and to hydraulic accessories. The most commonly used fittings are the standard **AN-type fittings,** examples of which are shown in Fig. 13·46 and **flareless fittings,** illustrated in Fig. 13·47.

The AN fitting is used for flared tubing and must include a body, sleeve, and nut for the complete assembly. The fitting itself is designed in a number of different shapes to provide for a variety of installations. For example, we may find straight fittings, T fittings, elbow fittings, and cross fittings, all in the same system. The hydraulic seal for a flared-tube fitting is formed between the flare cone on or within the fitting and the flare at the end of the tubing. The tube flare is pressed tightly against the flare cone by means of the sleeve and the nut.

When flare fittings are to be used, the tubing should be flared with a tool designed for the purpose. The standard angle for the flare is 37° as shown in Fig. 13·48. To make a double flare, which is required for some installations, a special double-flaring tool is required.

Flareless fittings are installed as shown in Fig. 13·49. The installation of this type of fitting is very critical

Figure 13·46 Flare-type fittings.

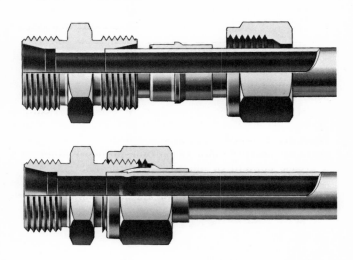

Figure 13·47 Flareless fittings.

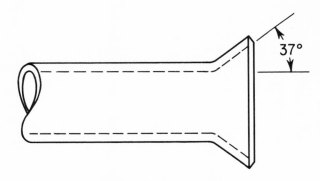

Figure 13·48 Tubing properly flared.

because too much torque will cut the tubing and cause it to fail, and too little torque will permit the fitting to slip or leak. If specific instructions for the installation of a particular flareless fitting are not available, a general rule for the installation may be used. The fitting is installed with the sleeve and the end of the tubing is seated firmly against the counterbored shoulder in the body of the fitting. The nut is turned to pull the sleeve into the body until strong resistance to turning is encountered. At this time, the sleeve should be in solid

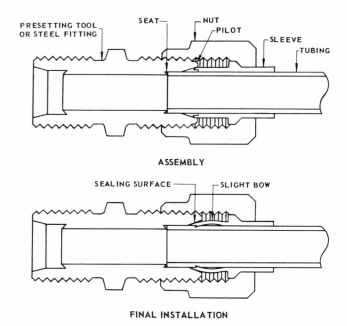

ASSEMBLY

SEALING SURFACE — SLIGHT BOW

FINAL INSTALLATION

Figure 13·49   Installation of flareless fittings.

contact with the taper inside the body. The nut is then turned one-sixth to one-third turn so that the inner edge of the sleeve will indent the tube and form a seat. Flareless tube fittings are assigned standard specification numbers from MS 21900 upward to MS 21918.

Installation of hydraulic tubing

When a section of hydraulic tubing is installed, the fittings at each end should come together in good alignment and without the application of any force. The fitting nuts should be easily tightened, usually by hand, before applying the final torque with a suitable torque wrench.

Before the tubing is installed, the fittings at the ends of the tubing sections should be examined closely to make sure that there is no dirt, lint, or other substance in the fittings or threads. Extreme cleanliness must be practiced at all times.

A straight section of tubing should never be installed between two fixed points on the structure of the airplane. Changes in temperature will cause contraction and expansion, which is likely to cause failure of the connections. Wherever tubing must be installed between rigid or fixed points, a bend is made in the tubing to allow for contraction and expansion.

Flexible hydraulic hose

For portions of a hydraulic system between parts of the airplane where there is relative movement and possible vibration, flexible hose is required. In the replacement of hose sections, the technician must observe several precautions. The hose replacement must be of the same type and material as the original part. The replaced section must not be twisted or stretched. Twisting can be detected by the painted or woven line which should be straight along the axis of the hose and

not spiraling around it. The hose should have a small amount of slack to allow for movement and vibration. It is particularly important that high-pressure hose be installed in high-pressure sections of the system and that the material of the hose be correct for the type of fluid in the system.

Hydraulic hoses are often made with reusable end fittings so that a hose can be replaced without the need for a complete assembly. When a new hose section is cut and the original fittings are installed, the technician must be sure that he follows the manufacturer's instructions regarding the installation of the fittings, and he must make certain that he is using the proper type and size of hose for the installation. A hose with reusable fittings is shown in Fig. 13 · 50. Used fittings should be very carefully inspected before installation on a new section of hose. The inner sleeve, threads, nut, etc., must be checked for cracks, nicks, or scratches which could cause failure. This is particularly important for the high-pressure section of a system.

HYDRAULIC SYSTEMS FOR AIRCRAFT

Aircraft hydraulic systems have been designed in many configurations for a wide variety of aircraft. Some very simple systems are used for light aircraft while extremely complex systems have been designed for operating modern jet aircraft, both military and commercial. On a light airplane, a power hydraulic system may be used only for landing gear and flaps. On a large transport aircraft the system is used for landing gear, flaps, spoilers, control-surface boost, retractable-stair operation, brakes, leading-edge slats, and possibly other devices. In this section we shall examine a few sample systems and a few specific systems used on modern aircraft.

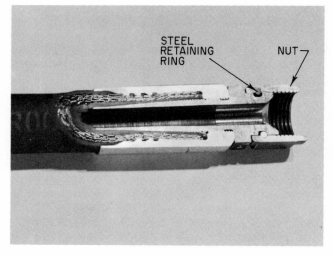

STEEL
RETAINING
RING

NUT

Figure 13 · 50   Hose with reusable fittings. (Aeroquip Corp.)

216

System with pressure regulator or unloading valve

Figure 13·51 is a schematic drawing of a direct pressure system that has its pressure regulated by an unloading valve (pressure regulator) operating in conjunction with an accumulator.

When the actuating equipment is not in use, pressure is relieved from the continuously operating engine-driven pump by means of the unloading valve after the accumulator is charged to the correct level. As soon as a subsystem is operated, pressure will first come from the accumulator for operation; when accumulator pressure has dropped to a predetermined level, the unloading valve will "cut in" and direct pump flow to the operating system. A study of the diagram will make it clear that the pump output flows directly through the unloading valve and back to the reservoir when no pressure is required. When a subsystem (brakes, landing gear, or flaps) is operated, pump pressure will then flow through the subsystem and back to the reservoir through the subsystem return line.

The main relief valve in the system is located between the unloading valve and the return line. If the unloading valve should become stuck in the kicked-in position, the excess pressure would be bypassed through the relief valve to the reservoir. The pressure gage would show higher than normal pressure, and the system would probably be making noise because of the operation of the relief valve. The relief valve is usually set at least 100 psi above the normal operating pressure.

The open-center system

An **open-center hydraulic system** consists basically of a fluid reservoir, filter, check valve, pump, relief valve, selector valves, actuating units, and tubing to connect the units. As shown in the diagram of Fig. 13·52, the system consists of a single circuit for fluid

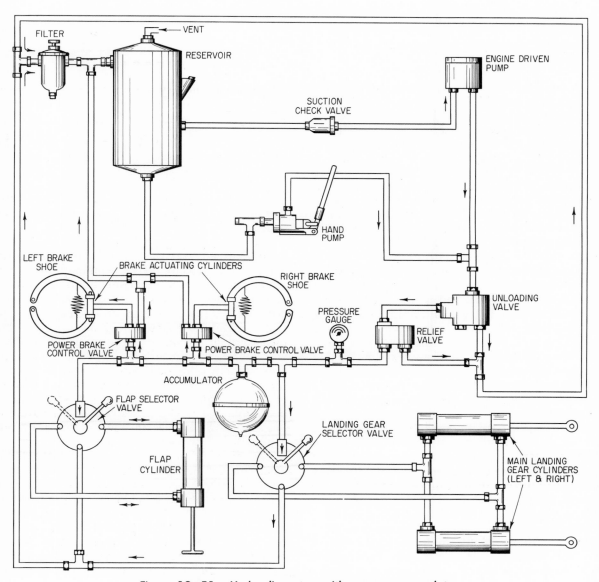

Figure **13·51** *Hydraulic system with a pressure regulator.*

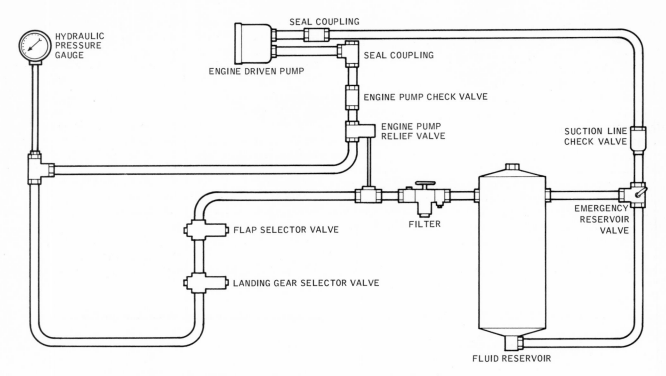

Figure **13·52** *Open-center hydraulic system.*

flow with selector valves in series. The fluid flows continuously through the system under low pressure except when a subsystem is operated. For example, if the landing gear is to be raised, the gear selector valve is moved to the UP position and the main flow of fluid is rerouted to the gear selector valve. The return fluid from the actuator flows back through the selector-valve passage and then continues on to the next selector valve in the system. As soon as the actuator reaches the end of its operation, the valve automatically "kicks out" and allows free flow of fluid through the system. One of the advantages of the open-center system is that it does not require expensive and complicated pressure regulators; the power pump can be a simple gear pump, although a fixed-displacement piston pump is likely to be used.

A disadvantage of the open-center system is that the operation of only one subsystem at a time is possible without interference from other systems. For example, if the flap subsystem precedes the landing-gear subsystem, and the two systems are operated at the same time, the speed of gear operation will be limited by the amount of fluid returning from the flap actuating cylinder. As soon as the flap operation is complete and the flap selector valve kicks out, the landing-gear operation will proceed at its normal rate.

Light-plane hydraulic system

A schematic diagram of a hydraulic system for a modern light airplane is shown in Fig. 13·53. This system is installed in the Piper Apache PA-23 airplane to operate the wing flaps and landing gear.

From the diagram it is seen that the engine-driven hydraulic pump 10 draws hydraulic fluid from the reservoir 15 and pumps it through the pressure port of the "Powerpak" assembly into the landing-gear-selector pressure chamber. When the two selector valves are in the neutral position, the fluid travels from the landing-gear selector valve 1 through the flap selector valve 2 and back to the reservoir.

The Powerpak assembly is a modular unit which includes the reservoir, relief valve, hand pump, landing-gear selector valve, wing-flap selector valve, filters, and numerous other small parts essential to the operation. When both selector valves are in the neutral position, the system acts as an open-center system in that the fluid flows first through one selector valve and then through the other before returning to the reservoir. During this time the fluid flows freely at a reduced pressure. Since the fluid supply line runs first through the landing-gear selector valve, the flaps cannot be operated while the landing-gear subsystem is in operation. Each selector valve has a separate return line to allow fluid from the actuating cylinder or cylinders to flow back to the reservoir.

The diagram of Fig. 13·54 shows the fluid flow when the landing-gear selector is placed in the UP position. When the selector valve is placed in either operating position, it is held in the position by a detent which consists of a ball, O ring, plunger, and spring. The ball snaps into a groove in the spool which operates the poppet valves and prevents the spool from moving linearly until the operation is complete. When the actuating cylinder reaches the end of its movement, pressure builds up to approximately 1150 psi. This

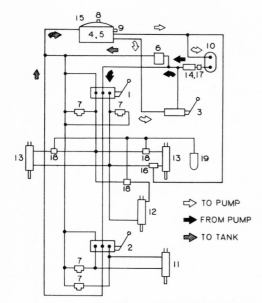

1. Landing-gear selector
2. Flap selector
3. Hand pump
4. Emergency fluid-trap stand pipe
5. Emergency hand-pump check filter
6. Main relief valve
7. Thermal relief valve
8. Atmospheric vent
9. Filter and filtering port
10. Pump
11. Flap-actuating cylinder
12. Nose-gear actuating cylinder
13. Main-gear actuating cylinder
14. System check
15. Reservoir
16. Antiretraction valve
17. Hydraulic filter
18. Shuttle valves
19. CO_2 bottle

⇨ TO PUMP
➡ FROM PUMP
▨ TO TANK

Figure 13·53   Schematic diagram for Piper Apache hydraulic system. (Piper Aircraft Corp.)

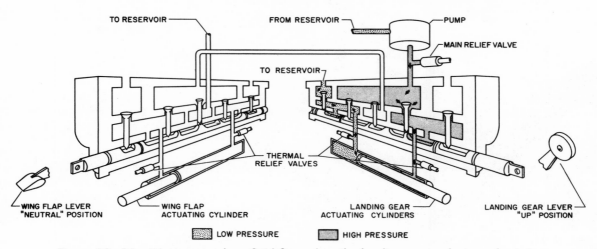

Figure 13·54   Diagram to show fluid flow when the landing-gear selector valve is in the UP position. (Piper Aircraft Corp.)

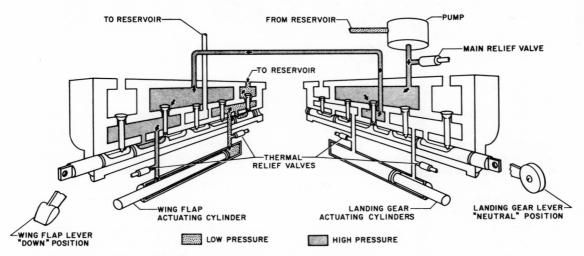

Figure 13·55   Fluid flow when the wing-flap selector valve is in the DOWN position. (Piper Aircraft Corp.)

pressure acts against the plunger of the detent mechanism and relieves the pressure of the spring, thus allowing the ball to pop out of the groove. A spring then causes the spool and selector lever to return to the neutral position.

Figure 13·55 shows the fluid flow in the system when the wing-flap selector valve is placed in the DOWN position. The action is generally the same as that described in the foregoing paragraph. It should be noted that the fluid to the flap selector valve has passed through the landing-gear selector valve first, and that the landing-gear valve is in the neutral position.

The arrangement of the hydraulic system components in the Piper PA-23 Apache airplane is shown in the drawing of Fig. 13·56. The Powerpak 23 is mounted in the center of the airplane in the pedestal

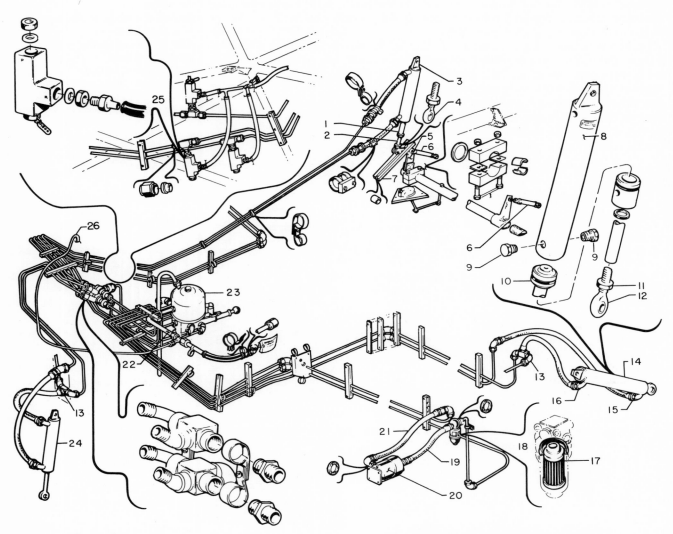

1. Bushing	14. Main gear actuating cylinder
2. Tube	15. Lower elbow
3. Flap actuating cylinder	16. Upper elbow
4. End bearing	17. Filter element
5. Flap bellcrank assembly	18. Oil filter assembly
6. Flap control rod assembly	19. Flexible hose assembly
7. Flap actuating arm guide block	20. Hydraulic pump
8. Gear cylinder body and bushing assembly.	21. Flexible hose assembly
9. ⅛-inch pipe plug	22. Powerpak filler tube
10. O-ring packing	23. Powerpak
11. Check nut	24. Nose gear actuating cylinder
12. End bearing	25. Thermol relief valve
13. Shuttle valve	26. Thermol relief valve return line

Figure 13·56   Arrangement of hydraulic components in the Piper Apache airplane.

forward of the pilot's position. The landing-gear and wing-flap control handles and the hand-pump handle extend from the rear of the pedestal within easy reach of either the pilot or copilot.

The fluid used in the above-described system is petroleum-type, MIL-O-5606. The operating pressure is 1150 psi and the main relief valve "cracking" pressure is 1250 to 1300 psi. Thermal relief valves are set to open at 2000 to 2050 psi or 1850 to 1900 psi, depending upon the particular model of Powerpak. The main reservoir capacity is approximately 4.5 pints with an emergency supply of 0.95 pint.

Troubleshooting and servicing of the hydraulic system should be accomplished in accordance with the instructions given in the *Piper Apache Service Manual*. General inspection can be performed as with any other system and includes checking for leaks, loose tubing or fittings, loose attachments, damaged tubing, and other common discrepancies. Operational checks can be made only with the airplane jacked up.

REVIEW QUESTIONS

1. What principle is expressed in Pascal's law?
2. Discuss the effects of friction in moving liquids.
3. Explain the multiplication of force by means of hydraulics.
4. Describe the operation of a single-acting hand pump.
5. Why is a gear-type pump described as a *positive displacement* pump?
6. In an axial multiple-piston pump, what causes the reciprocating motion of the pistons?
7. Explain the principle by which a *variable-delivery* axial piston pump can have its fluid output changed.
8. Describe a poppet-type valve.
9. Explain the operation of a spool-type valve.
10. How are the selector valves connected in relation to one another in an *open-center* system?
11. Describe an orifice check valve.
12. Explain the purpose of a *sequence valve*.
13. What can occur if a sequence valve is not properly adjusted?
14. Under what conditions is a shuttle valve needed?
15. Describe the operation of a relief valve.
16. Define a pressure regulator.
17. What is an *unloading valve*?
18. Explain the value of an unloading valve in a hydraulic system.
19. Why are *thermal relief valves* necessary in parts of a hydraulic system?
20. Explain the *debooster* principle.
21. What are the two principal functions of an *accumulator*?
22. Describe a piston-type accumulator.
23. What precaution should be taken before removing an accumulator from a hydraulic system?
24. Describe a quick-disconnect seal coupling.
25. Name three types of hydraulic fluid and describe their basic characteristics.
26. What precautions must be taken with Skydrol, a fire-resistant hydraulic fluid?
27. If the wrong type of fluid is placed in a system, what should be done?
28. Compare an *O-ring seal* with a *chevron seal*.
29. When O-ring seals are used in high-pressure systems, what devices are often necessary?
30. What material is used for tubing when pressures exceed 1500 psi?
31. What materials are used for fittings in high-pressure systems?
32. To what percentage of outside diameter may tubing be flattened at a bend before it must be rejected?
33. How deep may a scratch or nick in aluminum tubing be before the tubing must be rejected?
34. How can a nick or scratch be removed from aluminum tubing?
35. Describe two types of tube fittings.
36. Describe the installation of flareless fittings.
37. What will occur if a flareless fitting is overtorqued?
38. At what points in a hydraulic system is flexible hose used?
39. Describe an open-center system.
40. Describe the Powerpak in the hydraulic system for the Piper Apache airplane.
41. Why cannot the landing gear and flaps be operated at the same time in a Piper Apache hydraulic system?

CHAPTER 14

Hydraulic and Pneumatic Systems for Large Aircraft

Hydraulic systems for large aircraft operate according to the same laws and principles described for those of smaller aircraft; however, the systems are more complex and include many more components. Not only is hydraulic power used to operate landing gear, flaps, and similar devices, but it also supplies power to operate the airplane controls.

In this section we shall examine a few typical systems to gain an understanding of their design, operation, and special features. In any servicing or repair of such systems, the technician must be thoroughly familiar with the system and must follow the instructions given in the manufacturer's maintenance manual.

HYDRAULIC SYSTEM FOR BOEING 727 AIRPLANE

The hydraulic power system for the Boeing 727 airliner is typical of those employed for modern jet-transport-type aircraft. These systems are of the high-pressure type, utilizing pressures up to 3000 psi. The advantage of high-pressure systems is that they can deliver more power for a given weight of fluid and system components than can the lower pressure systems.

The Boeing 727 incorporates three separate and independent hydraulic power systems. These are designated "hydraulic system A," "hydraulic system B," and "standby hydraulic system." Hydraulic fluid is supplied from two pressurized reservoirs and one unpressurized reservoir, each system being supplied

by one of the reservoirs. System A receives fluid under pressure from two engine-driven pumps installed on engines No. 1 and 2. System B receives fluid under pressure from two electric, motor-driven pumps installed in the left fairing adjacent to the rear of the left-wing root.

The standby system receives fluid pressure from one electric-motor-driven pump installed in the left side-wall of the aft stairwell. This system operates only on demand and supplies hydraulic power for the leading-edge devices and the lower-rudder operation.

Figure 14·1 is a schematic diagram to show the interconnections between units in each system and between the systems. It will be noted that system A supplies hydraulic power for the outboard flight spoilers, ground spoilers, ailerons, leading-edge flaps, landing gear, nose-wheel steering and brakes, elevators, lower rudder, and main-wheel brakes, when the brake interconnect valve is open.

System B supplies power to the ailerons, elevators, inboard flight spoilers, aft airstairs, upper rudder, and main-wheel brakes. The interconnections between system B and system A are shown in the schematic drawing of Fig. 14·1. Note that certain operating components are provided with power by both systems.

A **modular unit** is used in each of the systems combining a number of the smaller system components in one case to simplify maintenance. The modular units serve as manifolds directing hydraulic fluid to the various easily replaceable cartridge-type components. This allows component removal without disrupting tube connections. As an example of the function of a modular unit, the one installed in system A contains a pressure filter, two check valves, two

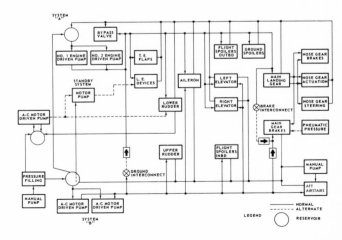

Figure 14·1 Schematic of hydraulic power system. (Boeing Co.)

pressure warning switches, a pressure relief valve, and a bypass valve.

The **hydraulic fluid** used for the Boeing 727 systems is Skydrol 500, a fire-resistant, phosphate ester-base, synthetic fluid. This purple fluid has an operating temperature range of -65 to $+225°F$, with a pour point below $-90°F$. With this fluid, the seals, gaskets, and hoses must be made of either butyl rubber or Teflon. Other materials will soften, swell, or deteriorate. As previously explained, Skydrol fluid will cause damage to ordinary paints and enamels; therefore, precautions must be taken to prevent spillage. Where spillage is likely, special protective materials are used. The technician servicing a system using Skydrol should take every precaution to prevent the fluid from coming in contact with his skin or getting it in his eyes. Protective clothing and goggles or a face shield are recommended.

Since the hydraulic power system employs pressure up to and more than 3000 psi, the tubing carrying the high pressures must be of a material which will withstand all pressure to which they may be subjected. All pressure lines in the systems subject to more than 1500 psi are made of seamless, corrosion-resistant (stainless-) steel tubing. This tubing is used in class I fire zones and on the landing-gear structure, regardless of pressure. All other lines are made of seamless aluminum-alloy tubing. Tubing of ¾-in. outside diameter or less requires flareless-type fittings. For pressures under 1500 psi, aluminum-alloy fittings are used; for greater pressures, titanium and steel fittings are used. Tubing of 1-in. outside diameter and larger requires flared-type fittings. On this tubing size, aluminum fittings are used, except in class I fire zones and on the landing-gear structure where titanium or steel fittings are used. The technician who repairs or services the systems must make sure that all replacement tubes and fittings are of the correct type and material for the section of the system in which they are located.

When it is necessary to replace a tubing assembly, the technician should obtain a new tube assembly having the same part number as the existing assembly. However, tube assemblies whose dash numbers have an "X" suffix are not stocked as spares; they can only be replaced by bending another tube assembly to the same contour from the same material as the existing tube assembly.

Flexible hose used in the hydraulic systems is made of Teflon and designed for high pressure or medium pressure. High-pressure hoses are used in the pressure lines and medium-pressure hoses are used in supply lines, return lines, and brake lines.

Servicing of any particular airplane hydraulic system must be accomplished according to the specific instructions issued by the manufacturer for the particular airplane. On the Boeing 727, the servicing station is located in the aft left-wing fairing area and is accessible through an access door. The filling equipment consists of a manually operated hand pump, reservoir selector valve, system A and standby-system fluid-quantity indicators, service connection for external fluid servicing, and the necessary tubing and hydraulic lines. The arrangement of the equipment in the filling area is shown in Fig. 14·2.

Hydraulic power system A

Hydraulic system A, illustrated in the schematic drawing of Fig. 14·3, is powered by engine-driven hydraulic pumps mounted on engines No. 1 and No. 2. Engine No. 1 is mounted in the pod on the left rear portion of the fuselage; engine No. 2 is in the center of the fuselage near the tail of the airplane. As previously mentioned, system A supplies a fluid pressure of 3000 psi to operate the outboard flight spoilers, ground spoilers, ailerons, leading-edge flaps, landing gear, nose-wheel steering and brakes, elevators, lower rudder, and main-wheel brakes when the brake interconnect valve is open.

System A includes the equipment necessary to store, pressurize, deliver, control, monitor, and filter the hydraulic fluid to operate the systems previously noted. Hydraulic fluid for the system is stored in a reservoir which is pressurized by engine bleed air routed through a filter and a pressure regulator to insure a positive supply of hydraulic fluid to the pumps. Two supply shutoff valves controlled by either separate engine fire switches or separate hydraulic shutoff switches are installed downstream of the reservoir to stop the flow of hydraulic fluid to the engine area in case of an engine failure or fire.

Two **variable-displacement** engine-driven pumps supply fluid to the various systems upon demand. Each pump is equipped with an electrically controlled depressurizing valve to depressurize the pump when output is not required. As explained previously, a variable-displacement pump is provided with an automatic control such that it will deliver fluid under pressure as needed for operation but will not be pumping fluid when there is no need for it.

A filter in the pressure line from each pump filters the fluid before it enters the various subsystems. A pressure switch in the pressure line from each pump is connected to a pump low-pressure warning light on the third crewman's panel to provide an indication of

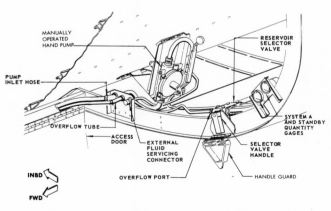

Figure 14·2 Hydraulic equipment in filling area.

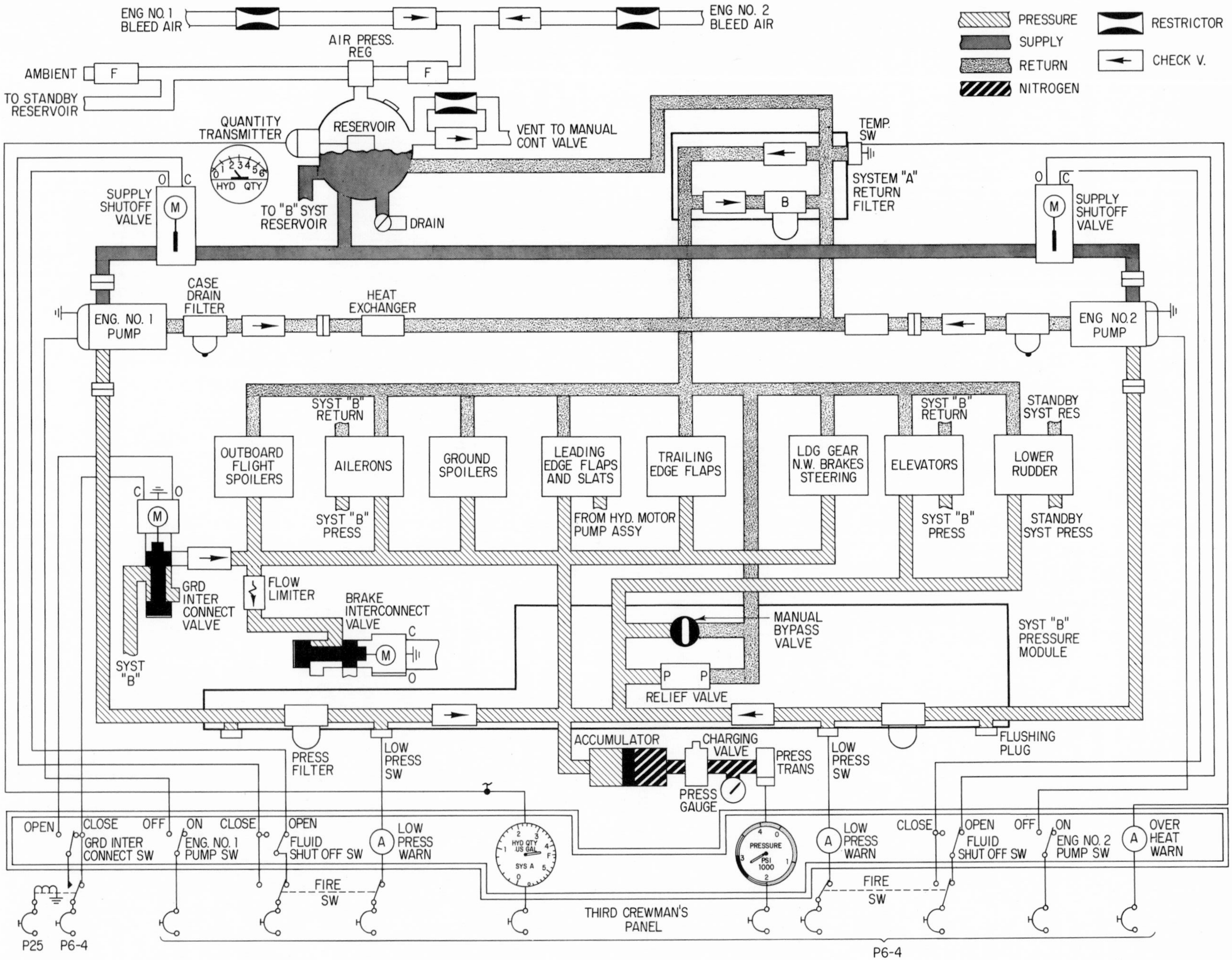

Figure 14·3 Schematic diagram of system A.

224

low hydraulic pressure. A piston-type accumulator is provided in the system to absorb sudden pressure surges. Pressure gages in the control cabin and accumulator servicing station are connected to the gas side of the accumulator to monitor hydraulic pressure when the system is pressurized and accumulator preload when the system is not pressurized. The accumulator preload consists of nitrogen gas under pressure (approximately 2000 psi when the system is depressurized).

A pressure relief valve protects the system against damage in case a malfunction permits the pressure to rise to an abnormally high level. A pump-case drain filter in each pump return line is provided to detect incipient pump failures and to filter return-line fluid before it enters the reservoir. A hydraulic-fluid heat exchanger in the pump return line is provided to cool the hydraulic fluid by transferring heat from the fluid to a cooling airflow. A system return filter just ahead of the reservoir filters returns fluid from the subsystems supplied by system A. Hydraulic-fluid overheat is sensed by a switch installed in the system return filter assembly and indicated by a warning light in the control cabin.

A brake interconnect valve is installed to supply hydraulic power to the brakes from system A whenever system B is inoperative and the brake system is intact.

When the airplane is on the ground, system A can be depressurized through a manual bypass valve. Placing the bypass valve handle in the OPEN position connects the pressure and return lines, thus permitting pressurized fluid to return to the reservoir. For ground operation, system A can be pressurized to supply normal pressure without engine operation by attaching an external hydraulic pressure source to the airplane at the engine hydraulic self-sealing disconnect fittings. System A can also be pressurized without engine operation by attaching an external electrical ground power supply to the airplane electrical system, opening the ground interconnect valve and operating system B pumps. System B pumps are then feeding pressure into system A.

Hydraulic reservoir

System A on the Boeing 727 airplane is supplied with fluid from a 5.4-gal reservoir which is pressurized to approximately 45 psi by bleed air from engines No. 1 and 2. Pressurization of the reservoir assures a positive supply of fluid to the engine-driven pumps.

Air from the engine bleed is fed through check valves, a filter, and a pressure regulator. The regulator is designed to admit air to the reservoir if the pressure is below the required amount, and it will relieve air from the reservoir if pressure rises above the correct level. It also acts as a vacuum relief valve when the reservoir pressure drops below 0.50 psi under ambient pressure. In this case, air entering the reservoir is filtered by the vent filter. A schematic drawing of the reservoir pressurization system is shown in Fig. 14·4.

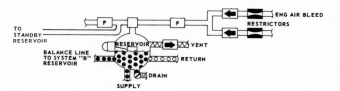

Figure 14·4   Reservoir pressurization system.

Engine-driven pumps

As explained previously, the engine-driven hydraulic pumps are of the variable-displacement (VD) type. Each pump has a maximum displacement of 1.77 cu in. per revolution and at 3000 rpm delivers approximately 22½ gpm at 2850 psi. Pump discharge pressure is limited by a **pressure compensator** and each pump may be depressurized by an electrically controlled **depressurizing valve**.

The control mechanism for the variable-displacement pump is shown in Fig. 14·5. It will be remembered that the output of a VD pump is determined by the angle of a **cam plate** which rotates to produce a reciprocating action of the pump pistons. The cam-plate angle is changed by varying the position of the **hanger** upon which it is mounted. Figure 14·5 shows schematically how the hanger position is changed as required by the output pressure of the pump.

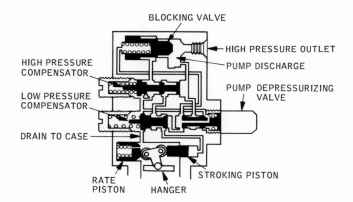

FULL PRESSURE, NO FLOW CONDITION

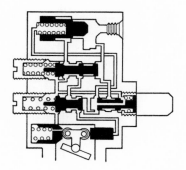

FULL PRESSURE, FULL FLOW CONDITION

Figure 14·5   Control system for variable-displacement pump.

In the top drawing, the pump pressure is high (3000 psi) and the cam plate is level; hence there is no reciprocating motion of the pump pistons and no fluid output. Observe that the high pressure is acting against the **high-pressure compensator spool valve,** thus moving the valve against a spring and allowing fluid to be directed around the **low-pressure compensator spool** and on to the end of the **stroking piston.** The stroking piston forces the hanger to the left against the rate piston spring, thus bringing the cam plate to the NO-FLOW position.

The lower drawing shows the position of controlling elements when the system is using fluid and the cam is in the FULL-FLOW position. Since system pressure has dropped, the spring has pushed the high-pressure compensator spool to the right, thus opening passages so the fluid pressure against the stroking piston is released. The rate piston spring has moved the hanger to the right against the stroking piston and changed the angle of the cam. The cam can be seen clearly in the drawing of the pump in Fig. 14·6.

Modular unit

The modular unit for system A is shown in the drawing of Fig. 14·7. As shown in the drawing, this unit contains filters, check valves, a relief valve, a bypass valve, and pressure-warning switches. By bringing these units together in one case, the maintenance of the system is simplified. A schematic flow diagram of the modular unit is shown in Fig. 14·8.

Heat exchanger

Because of the high pressures involved in the system and the high rates of fluid flow, the hydraulic fluid becomes heated as the subsystems are operated. For this reason it is necessary to provide cooling for the fluid. The **heat exchanger,** shown in Fig. 14·9, is a heat radiator similar in design and construction to an oil cooler for an engine. Note that the heat exchanger is equipped with a temperature-operated bypass valve to increase the fluid flow through the cooling element as temperature rises.

One heat exchanger is installed in each engine-driven pump-case drain return line. Each heat-exchanger unit consists of an inlet scoop, oil cooler, ejector duct, exhaust outlet, engine bleed-air ejector nozzle, and an air-ejector shutoff valve. The heat exchanger for the No. 1 engine pump is in the No. 1 engine strut, and the heat exchanger for the No. 2 engine pump is in the tail section of the airplane on the right side. Cooling is provided by ram air in flight and by engine bleed-air ejection when the airplane is on the ground.

The temperature-operated bypass valve in the oil-cooler fluid inlet controls the volume of return fluid circulating through the oil cooler. At fluid temperatures above 100°F the bypass valve starts to close, porting return fluid through the oil cooler. At a fluid temperature of 155°F ($\pm$5°F) the bypass valve will be fully closed, porting all return fluid through the oil cooler.

Accumulator

The **accumulator** for system A is a cylindrical, free-floating piston-type unit, precharged with nitrogen gas. As explained previously, the purpose of the unit is to store fluid under pressure and to protect the system against sudden pressure surges. A fluid line is connected to the fluid end of the accumulator and a nitrogen line is connected to the opposite end. The accumulator is mounted vertically in the airplane with the fluid end at the top. On the nitrogen end is connected a direct-pressure gage, a pressure transmitter, and a nitrogen charging valve. The pressure

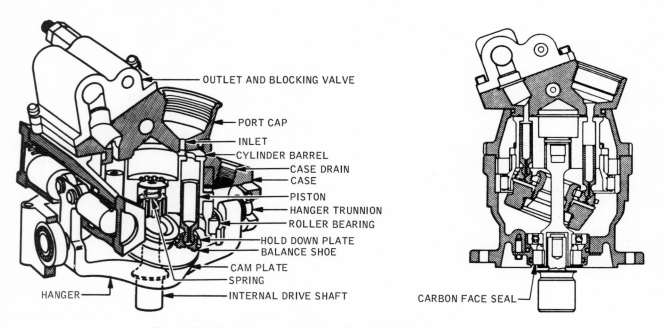

Figure 14·6 Cutaway drawing of variable-displacement pump.

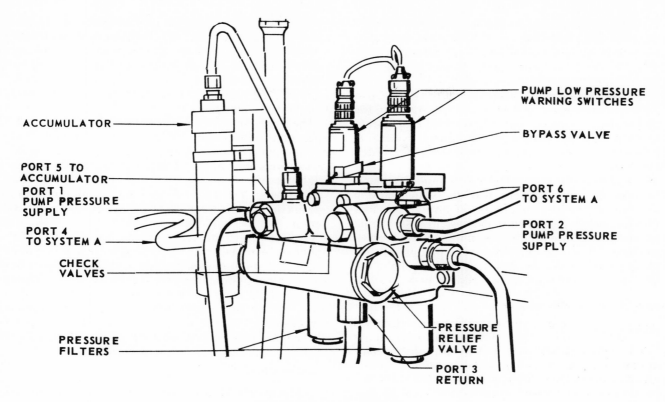

ACCUMULATOR

PORT 5 TO ACCUMULATOR

PORT 1 PUMP PRESSURE SUPPLY

PORT 4 TO SYSTEM A

CHECK VALVES

PRESSURE FILTERS

PUMP LOW PRESSURE WARNING SWITCHES

BYPASS VALVE

PORT 6 TO SYSTEM A

PORT 2 PUMP PRESSURE SUPPLY

PRESSURE RELIEF VALVE

PORT 3 RETURN

Figure 14·7   Modular unit.

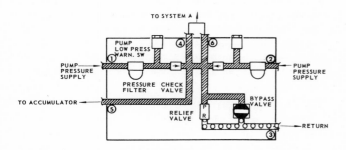

Figure 14·8   Schematic flow diagram of modular unit.

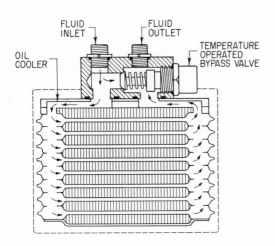

Figure 14·9   Heat-exchanger cooling unit.

transmitter is connected electrically to the pressure gage on the third crewman's panel in the cabin.

The preload gas pressure placed in the accumulator is approximately 2000 psi when the ambient temperature is 65 to 70°F; hence the pressure gages will indicate 2000 psi when the system is not in operation and is depressurized. When hydraulic pressure is applied above 2000 psi, the accumulator will begin to charge, and the nitrogen will be compressed to a pressure equal to the hydraulic pressure. The pressure gages will then show system pressure.

The accumulator is installed in the aft-stairwell left sidewall. The accumulator charging valve and direct-reading gage are located aft of the left-wing fairing area and are accessible through an access door.

Valves

The valves incorporated in system A are the **relief valve, hydraulic supply shutoff valve, ground interconnect valve, brake interconnect valve,** and **bypass valve.**

The purpose of the relief valve, discussed previously, is to protect the system against excessive pressure. It is set to relieve at 3500 (±50) psi and reset at 3100 psi minimum.

The **hydraulic supply shutoff valves** are provided to stop the flow of hydraulic fluid to the engine area. These valves are electrically operated and are automatically shut off when the engine fire switch is operated. They are also operated from switches on the third crewman's panel.

227

The **ground interconnect valve** is provided so system A can be pressurized for ground operation and testing through system B. System B is pressurized by electrically driven pumps; hence it can be operated without running the engines.

The **brake interconnect valve** connects system A to the brake system when system B is inoperative and the brake system is intact. This allows brake operation and brake-accumulator charging using system A pressure. The valve is electrically operated by a switch on the third crewman's panel.

The **bypass valve** is installed in the modulator unit to provide for depressurization of the system during ground maintenance operations. The valve provides a flow of only 5 gpm; hence the system will operate when the engines are running, even if the valve is open. Remember that the engine-driven pumps furnish 22½ gpm each at full-flow position. During flight, the bypass valve is lockwired in the CLOSED position.

System B and standby system

The system B and standby systems were discussed earlier in this chapter; since their operation is similar to that explained for system A (except for specific function and source of hydraulic power), it is not deemed essential that their details be described further. Servicing and repair of any of the systems must be done in accordance with the maintenance practices given in the manufacturer's manual or in the maintenance orders provided by the air carrier; hence further discussion here is not necessary.

HYDRAULIC SYSTEM FOR THE DOUGLAS DC-9 AIRLINER

Hydraulic power for the Douglas DC-9 airliner is supplied by two separate and completely independent closed-circuit systems identified as the left system and the right system. The two systems are almost identical, except for component location and the subsystems served by each. The systems are shown schematically in Fig. 14·10.

The **left hydraulic system** provides hydraulic power for left and right outboard actuating cylinders for the flight spoilers, the left and right outboard actuating cylinders for the wing flaps, one-half the dual brake system, one-half the dual nosewheel steering system, ground spoilers, and left-engine thrust reverser. The **right hydraulic system** provides hydraulic power for the left and right inboard actuating cylinders for the flight spoilers, the left and right inboard actuating cylinders for the wing flaps, one-half the dual brake system, one-half the dual nosewheel steering system, landing-gear retraction and main-gear wheel-well doors, rudder power control, and right engine thrust reverser. It will be noted that the systems operate together for all the subsystems except the rudder power and landing-gear retraction system which are operated by the right system, and the ground spoiler subsystem which is operated by the left hydraulic system.

Each hydraulic system is equipped with a hydraulic-fluid supply reservoir, an engine-driven hydraulic pump, and an electrically driven auxiliary hydraulic pump to provide system power. Accumulators are installed to absorb fluid shock and to provide reserve high-pressure fluid to assist the pumps in supplying high-volume demands.

The hydraulic systems are of the high-pressure type, operating at pressures up to 3000 psi. Skydrol fire-resistant fluid is utilized in the systems; hence the usual precautions must be taken in service and maintenance. High-pressure lines are seamless, corrosion-resistant steel tubing; flexible hoses in both the high-pressure and medium-pressure parts of the system are made of Teflon.

Ground power suction and pressure connections for applying external hydraulic power and filling the reservoirs are provided for each system. A ground service hand pump is located in each main-gear wheel well. Quick-disconnect fittings, connected to the inlet ports of the hand pumps, can be connected to a ground source of hydraulic fluid to fill the reservoirs by means of the hand pumps. The hand pumps can also be used to pressurize the systems for actuation of the various subsystems for ground maintenance.

Most of the components of the left and right hydraulic systems are located in their respective main-gear wheel wells. The engine-driven hydraulic pumps are mounted on the accessory drive pads of their respective engines. Pressure-line and case drain-line filters and engine-driven pump pressure relief valves are located on the left- and right-hand sides of the fuselage in the aft accessory compartment, aft of the fuselage pressure dome.

System reservoirs

The hydraulic-system reservoirs are of a rather complex design and are located in the inboard aft corners of the main-gear wheel wells. They are attached to the aircraft structure by two support legs at the bottom of each reservoir and a bracket for vertical, lateral, and fore-and-aft support. The bracket is attached to the edge of the reservoir cover and to the fuselage bulkhead. The reservoirs are identical and interchangeable from left to right locations, except for the location of external components. Left and right mounting locations for the external components are provided on each reservoir so the reservoirs can be interchanged or replaced with other reservoirs of the same type. Each reservoir supplies hydraulic fluid to its respective system exclusively.

A reservoir for the DC-9 systems is shown in Fig. 14·11. It is cylindrical in shape with a corrugated, perforated shield around the shell and has a fluid capacity of 2.5 U.S. gal. A **manifold,** equipped with four main ports, a small pressure-line port, and a thermoswitch probe port, is welded to the bottom of the reservoir shell. The four main ports are internally connected in tandem pairs with both pairs opening into the supply fluid section of the reservoir. This configuration of ports makes possible either left or right installa-

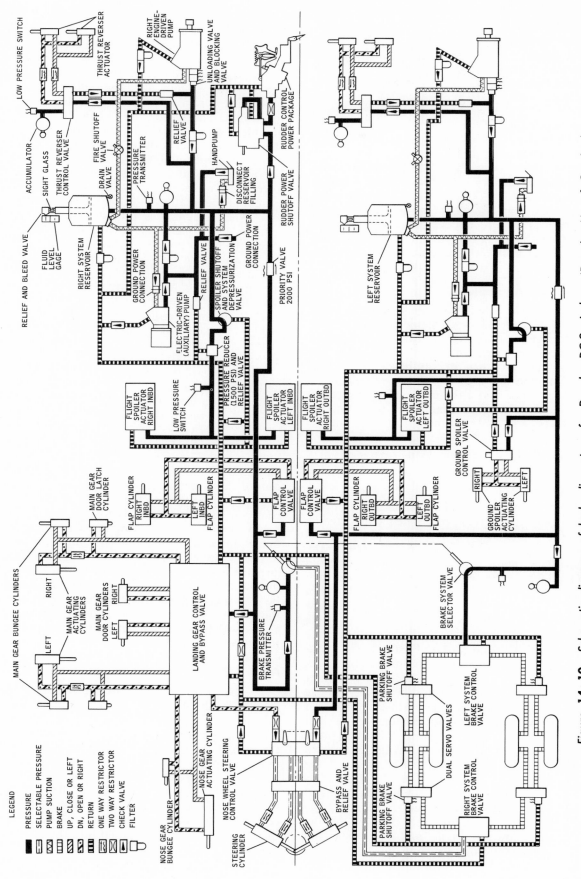

Figure 14·10 Schematic diagram of hydraulic systems for Douglas DC-9 airplane. (Douglas Aircraft Co., Inc.)

LEGEND

PRESSURE
SELECTABLE PRESSURE
PUMP SUCTION
BRAKE
UP, CLOSE OR LEFT
DN, OPEN OR RIGHT
RETURN
ONE WAY RESTRICTOR
TWO WAY RESTRICTOR
CHECK VALVE
FILTER

229

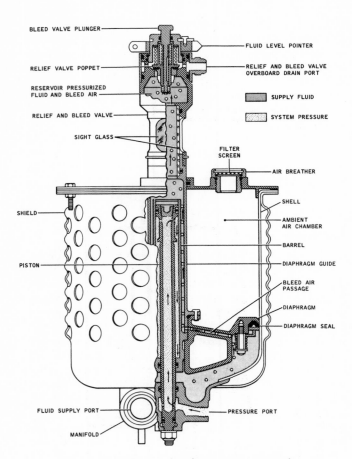

BLEED VALVE PLUNGER

RELIEF VALVE POPPET

RESERVOIR PRESSURIZED
FLUID AND BLEED AIR

RELIEF AND BLEED VALVE

SIGHT GLASS

SHIELD

PISTON

FLUID SUPPLY PORT

MANIFOLD

FLUID LEVEL POINTER

RELIEF AND BLEED VALVE
OVERBOARD DRAIN PORT

SUPPLY FLUID

SYSTEM PRESSURE

FILTER
SCREEN

AIR BREATHER

SHELL

AMBIENT
AIR CHAMBER

BARREL

DIAPHRAGM GUIDE

BLEED AIR
PASSAGE

DIAPHRAGM

DIAPHRAGM SEAL

PRESSURE PORT

Figure 14·11   Hydraulic system reservoir.

tion of the reservoir by reversing the location of port connector unions and reducers. When connected in the system, one pair of ports delivers fluid to the suction ports of the engine-driven pump, the electrically driven auxiliary pump, and the ground service hand pump. One of the other pair of ports receives system return fluid, and the fourth port is equipped with a valve to drain the reservoir. A **sight glass,** located below the **relief-and-bleed valve** in the upper portion of the **diaphragm-guide cylinder** above the main portion of the reservoir, provides an indication of excessive accumulation of air in the reservoir. An instruction plate, mounted adjacent to the sight glass, and a pointer attached to the top of the relief-and-bleed valve above the sight glass, provide fluid-level instructions and direct fluid-level indications for system pressurized and system depressurized conditions. A fluid-quantity transmitter, bracket, and actuating linkage, not shown in the illustration, is mounted on the inboard side of the reservoir cover. The lower end of the linkage is attached to the transmitter rotor, while the upper end is attached to the **fluid-level pointer** at the top of the relief-and-bleed valve. Fluid-level changes in the reservoir raise or lower the relief-and-bleed valve and pointer, thus extending or retracting the linkage and changing the position of the rotor in the fluid-quantity transmitter. The transmitter delivers a fluid-quantity

signal to the fluid-quantity indicator in the flight compartment.

The relief-and-bleed valve, located at the top of the diaphragm guide and above the sight glass, is provided to relieve excessive reservoir pressure and to bleed off accumulated system air. The relief valve is set to relieve pressure above 47 psi. A drain line is attached to the relief-and-bleed valve to conduct excess pressure and bleed air overboard. An **air breather** is provided in the reservoir cover forward of the diaphragm guide. It allows the upper, ambient air section of the reservoir to breathe air in and out as the reservoir diaphragm lowers and raises with pressurization of the hydraulic system and operation of the various subsystem actuators. A filter screen is provided in the breather to remove atmospheric impurities from the air which enters the upper portion of the reservoir.

Internally, the reservoir is equipped with a piston and diaphragm assembly which utilizes system pressure from the small pressure-line port to maintain a pressure head on the supply fluid. This pressure is from 28 to 30 psi and is reduced from the system pressure of 3000 psi by means of the difference in area between the piston and the diaphragm. This difference ratio is approximately 100:1.

The application of force to the diaphragm can be understood by a study of the drawing of Fig. 14·11. Observe the arrows which indicate fluid pressure to the inside of the piston shaft and out through holes at the top. The pressure is then exerted downward between the barrel and the piston to the surface at the lower end of the barrel. The 3000 psi pressure on this small area is balanced by the 28 to 30 psi pressure against the bottom of the diaphragm, which has about 100 times the area at the bottom of the barrel. As fluid enters the reservoir, the diaphragm is forced upward inside the reservoir shell, thus carrying the diaphragm guide and barrel upward.

The position of the reservoirs when installed in the airplane is shown in Fig. 14·12. In this illustration the fluid-quantity transmitter and linkage are shown. It can be seen that as the diaphragm guide raises and lowers, the linkage will be moved, and this will provide the signal which is sent electrically to the fluid-quantity indicator in the cabin.

Filters

The two hydraulic systems are each equipped with four hydraulic fluid filters: (1) a filter for the engine-driven pump pressure lines, (2) a case drain-line filter for the engine-driven pumps, (3) a pressure-line filter for each of the electrically driven pumps, and (4) a system return-line filter. All the filters are identical line-type, 15-μ filters. The construction of these units is shown in the drawing of Fig. 14·13. The inlet and outlet ports are internally threaded and are marked IN and OUT. The filter bowl is cylindrical with wrench flats at the lower end and is threaded into the filter head immediately below the ports.

Internally the filters are of the nonbypassing type; however, a differential pressure indicator is provided to

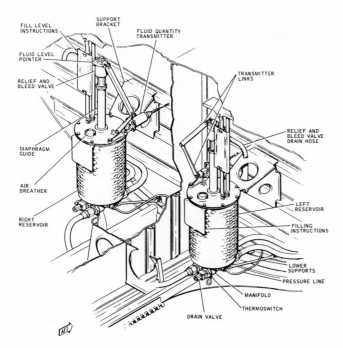

Figure 14·12   Installation of reservoirs.

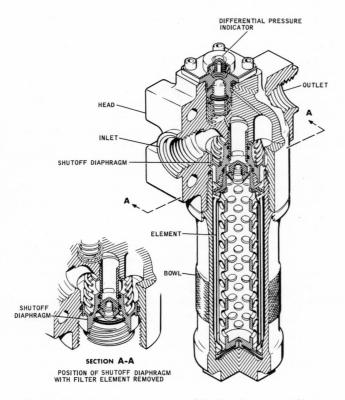

SECTION A-A
POSITION OF SHUTOFF DIAPHRAGM
WITH FILTER ELEMENT REMOVED

Figure 14·13   Construction of hydraulic system filters.

indicate an overloaded condition of the filter element. The indicator consists of a red button which protrudes 3/16 in. from the top of the filter head when the filter element becomes overloaded causing a differential pressure of 70 (±10) psi or more across the filter. The

indicator can be reset by manually depressing the button only after the overloaded condition has been corrected. A low-temperature cutoff device consisting of a bimetallic spring is provided to prevent a false indication of an overloaded element, which would be caused by high viscosity of the fluid at low temperatures. Below 32°F the spring contracts inward above a shoulder on the indicator button preventing movement of the button. Above 80°F the spring is expanded and the indicator button operated normally. The filter elements are of the disposable type and the filter head incorporates a spring-loaded shutoff diaphragm to prevent loss of hydraulic fluid when the filter bowl is removed for element replacement.

Fire-shutoff valve

The **fire-shutoff valves,** one for each of the systems, are manually operated, two-position, ball-type valves. These valves are mounted on brackets attached to the aft bulkhead of each main-gear wheel well. Mechanical control from the flight compartment is provided by a cable system operated by two fire-shutoff push-pull handles. The two handles, left and right, are located directly above the engine instrument panel and are easily accessible to either the pilot or first officer. They operate both the hydraulic-fluid and fuel-shutoff valves. A cable drum, located on the wheel-well bulkhead above each hydraulic fire-shutoff valve, has a pushrod attached near its outer circumference. The lower end of the rod is attached to the fire-shutoff valve crank. A drawing of the valve is shown in Fig. 14·14.

The operation of the fire-shutoff push-pull handles will, as indicated above, shut off both hydraulic fluid and fuel to the engine pod. If a fire warning is received in the flight compartment, the pilot or copilot will pull the handle for the engine compartment indicated. The engine will stop because the fuel is shut off and the hydraulic fluid will be cut off from the engine-driven pump.

Engine-driven hydraulic pump

As previously mentioned, the engine-driven hydraulic pumps for the two hydraulic power systems are of the variable-displacement (VD) type. The operation of these pumps has been described in previous sections of the text; however, since there are some differences in their control and operation, these will be explained.

The pumps operate at approximately 3000 psi and incorporate solenoid-operated **unloading valves** for reducing output pressure to 1500 psi for cruise flight. **Depressurization valves,** which are also solenoid-operated, shut off all output from the pumps. The unloading valve and depressurization-valve solenoids are controlled by two engine-driven-pump control switches located in the flight compartment. The switch for control of the left pump is marked LEFT-HIGH, LOW, and OFF. The switch for control of the right pump is marked RIGHT-HIGH, LOW, and OFF. When either pump is placed in the LOW position, the unloading valve for that pump is actuated and the pump pressure is reduced to 1500 psi. When the switch is placed in the

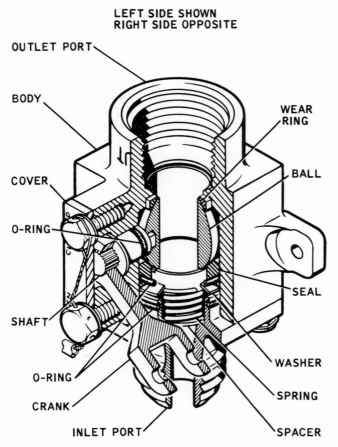

OUTLET PORT

BODY

WEAR RING

COVER

BALL

O-RING

SHAFT

SEAL

O-RING

WASHER

CRANK

SPRING

INLET PORT

SPACER

Figure **14·14** *Fire-shutoff valve.*

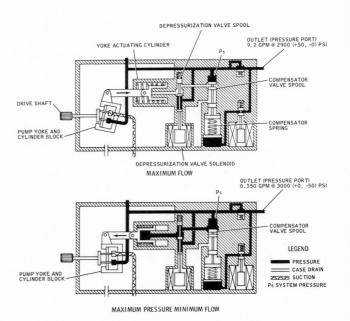

DEPRESSURIZATION VALVE SPOOL

YOKE ACTUATING CYLINDER

OUTLET (PRESSURE PORT) 9.2 GPM @ 2900 (+50, -0) PSI

Ps

COMPENSATOR VALVE SPOOL

DRIVE SHAFT

PUMP YOKE AND CYLINDER BLOCK

COMPENSATOR SPRING

DEPRESSURIZATION VALVE SOLENOID

MAXIMUM FLOW

OUTLET (PRESSURE PORT) 0.350 GPM @ 3000 (+0, -50) PSI

Ps

COMPENSATOR VALVE SPOOL

PUMP YOKE AND CYLINDER BLOCK

LEGEND

PRESSURE
CASE DRAIN
SUCTION
Ps SYSTEM PRESSURE

MAXIMUM PRESSURE MINIMUM FLOW

Figure **14·15** *Schematic flow diagrams of pump regulating system.*

HIGH position, the unloading valve is deactuated and the pump returns to its normal operating pressure of 3000 psi. When the switch is placed in the OFF position, the depressurization valve is actuated and the spring-loaded blocking valve closes, shutting off all flow from the pressure side of the pump and returning pump leakage and lubrication fluid to the reservoir through the case drain return line. The solenoids are operated on 28-volt d-c at 0.55 amp and are rated for continuous-duty operation. They are provided with electrical connectors of different sizes to prevent reversing the connections. Two case drain connections are provided on each pump, located 180° apart on the pump case. Only the top connection is used. This ensures that the pump case is always maintained full of fluid to provide lubrication during the starting period. Each pump is mounted with a quick-disconnect clamp on the accessory drive pad located on the right side of each engine. The pumps are accessible through the lower engine-access doors.

The operation of the regulating system for the engine-driven hydraulic pumps is similar to that described previously for VD pumps. The principle of the regulating system can be understood by a study of the schematic diagrams of Fig. 14·15.

The heart of the VD pump is the **rotating group** which consists of a **drive shaft, bearing, pistons, piston rods,** a **cylinder block,** and a **universal link.** (Refer to Fig. 13·15 in the previous chapter for a cutaway illustration of a variable-delivery pump.) The drive shaft and the cylinder block rotate at the same speed. The cylinder-block angular relation to the drive shaft is variable, hence the greater the angle, the greater will be the pump displacement. The angular relationship between the cylinder block and drive shaft is controlled by the **cylinder-block yoke.** The yoke position is regulated by the **yoke actuating cylinder, compensator valve,** and **pump output pressure.** Fluid enters the variable pump through the inlet port, passes through the **inlet pintle seal,** through the yoke and **valve plate,** and into the cylinder block. The kidney-shaped inlet port in the valve plate is located so that the pistons are moving away from the valve plate when their respective cylinder-block ports rotate past the valve-plate inlet port. This allows fluid to pass into the cylinder bores. As rotation continues, the cylinder-block ports rotate toward the valve-plate outlet port. The pistons are moving toward the valve plate in their bores during this half of the cycle and this forces the fluid out of the cylinder bores, through the valve plate, yoke outlet pintle seal, and the outlet port. It is apparent, then, that a change of the angle of the pump yoke will change the stroke of the pistons, and, therefore, the amount of fluid that will be pumped for each stroke of a piston.

Yoke position is regulated as a function of outlet pressure. With no initial resistance to fluid flow, the system pressure is 0 psi and the pump is delivering maximum flow which is approximately 9 gpm. As the load is increased, the pump outlet pressure increases but the flow remains maximum until the system pressure P_s reaches the pressure setting of the **compensator valve spring.** This pressure is 2900 (+50, 0) psi, and is just sufficient to center the **compensator valve spool.** Any additional load increase causes the system pressure to temporarily exceed 2900 psi, thus causing the compensator spool to be displaced downward to a position where it will meter fluid from the outlet pressure line to the yoke actuating cylinder. This fluid flow is proportional to the system pressure in excess of 2900 psi.

The yoke actuating cylinder integrates the control flow so that the angle of the cylinder and yoke is proportional to the position of the compensator valve. Consequently, the rate of system flow reduction varies with the magnitude of excess pressure. The yoke angle is thereby reduced until the flow is again just sufficient to maintain the 2900-psi system pressure. At this point, the compensator valve spool is centered, locking the yoke in its new position. As system load and pressure continue to rise, the yoke angle and flow are further reduced until pressure reaches 3000 (0, −50) psi and flow is reduced to approximately 0.350 gpm.

If the load on the pump is subsequently decreased, the system pressure is temporarily reduced; this causes the compensator valve spool to move upward, thus opening the yoke actuating cylinder to the pump case. The yoke actuating spring then causes the yoke angle to increase until the flow is again just sufficient to develop the 2900-psi system pressure. The compensator valve spool subsequently centers and locks the yoke in the new position. If the discharge circuit is completely blocked (zero flow), the yoke shifts to a near center position with a minimum displacement sufficient to compensate for the pump internal-leakage flow. Meanwhile, the 3000-psi system pressure is maintained, and the pump is ready to provide flow instantly when required.

The preload on the pressure compensator spring determines the system pressure at which the pump begins to regulate. Compressing the spring causes the pump to regulate at a higher pressure and relaxing the spring causes regulation at a lower pressure. As shown in Fig. 14·16, the compensator spring will be in the extended position when there is no pressure at point E. This means that a relatively low pressure (1500 psi in this case) is required to overcome the spring preload force, and the pump will regulate at the lower range. During high-range operation, pressure is introduced at point E and the lower end of the spring is forced upward until the stop is reached. The position of this stop determines the amount of high-range preload and therefore determines the system pressure at which regulation in the high-range occurs. In the low range, the unit regulates in the same manner as described for the high range but at the lower system pressure. In the high range the pressure at point E must be sufficient to hold the lower seat firmly against the stop. This pressure is supplied from hydraulic system pressure through the unloading valve which is in the de-energized or open position. When the unloading valve is closed, the pressure at point E is removed, thus allowing the compensator spring to extend and permitting regulation in the lower range.

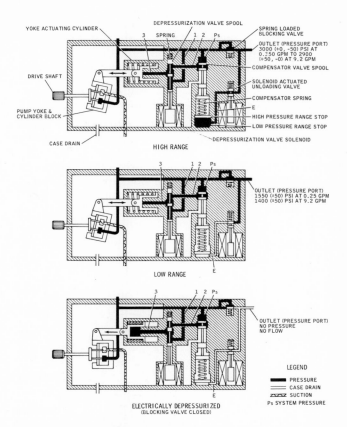

Figure 14·16 Flow diagrams for high-range, low-range, and depressurized operation of the main pumps.

Electrical depressurization of the pump is accomplished by means of the solenoid-actuated depressurization valve. Energizing the solenoid causes the depressurization valve spool to port outlet pressure to the yoke actuating piston and at the same time blocks the line from the compensator valve. As shown in Fig. 14·16, when the depressurization-valve solenoid is not energized, the depressurization-valve spool is held down by a spring so that the yoke actuating cylinder line (3) is connected to the compensator line (2) but is closed to the outlet-pressure line (1). In this condition the pump acts as a basic pressure-compensated unit.

When the depressurization valve solenoid is energized, the valve spool is forced upward thus connecting the yoke actuating cylinder line (3) to the outlet-pressure line (1) but blocking the compensator line (2). With pressure on the actuating cylinder, the yoke is forced to a position very near center. Actually, there is still a small displacement to provide sufficient outlet pressure (450 psi maximum) to hold the yoke in the depressurization position and to supply enough leakage for pump lubrication. The spring-loaded blocking valve located in the outlet port closes when the depressurization valve is energized to depressurize the pump, thereby blocking all outlet flow to the hydraulic system. Leakage flow at 450 psi is returned to the system reservoir through the case drain line.

Since the driving speed of the pump is continuous and unaffected by depressurization, the outlet pressure builds up very rapidly when the depressurization solenoid circuit is opened. The valve spool moves downward, the rising pressure opens the spring-loaded blocking valve, and pressure-regulated operation resumes.

Hydraulic-pump pressure relief valve

The **hydraulic-pump pressure relief valves,** one for each of the engine-driven hydraulic pumps, are spring-loaded, poppet-type valves which serve to relieve excess pressure that may build up on the pressure side of the pump. A relief valve of this type is illustrated in Fig. 14 · 17. The valves are located, one on each side of the fuselage, aft of the pressure bulkhead in the aft accessory compartment.

Externally, the valve body is cylindrical, 6 in. in length and 1⅜ in. in diameter. Both ends of the valve body are provided with wrench flats to facilitate installation and removal of union connections.

When an overpressure condition occurs, the poppet starts to relieve at 3400 (±50) psi. If pressure continues to build up, the poppet continues to open until a pressure of 3600 psi and a maximum flow of 9 gpm are reached. When pressure is relieved, the poppet reseats at 3150 psi and relief-valve flow ceases.

Accumulators

The hydraulic system **accumulators** for the Douglas DC-9 systems are spherical, welded-steel, bladder-type units installed in the pressure lines of each system. They serve the normal purposes of supplying a reserve of hydraulic fluid under pressure and acting as shock absorbers to reduce the effects of pressure surges. A cutaway drawing of one of the accumulators is shown in Fig. 14 · 18. The accumulators are located in the aft inboard corner of each main-gear wheel well and are mounted on brackets located on opposite sides of the airplane centerline shear web below the brake-system accumulators.

The accumulators are initially charged with nitrogen or air to a pressure of 1000 psi. As the system pressure builds up above 1000 psi, the air or gas in the accumulator increases in pressure at the level of the fluid pressure in the system. The fluid flows into the accumulator,

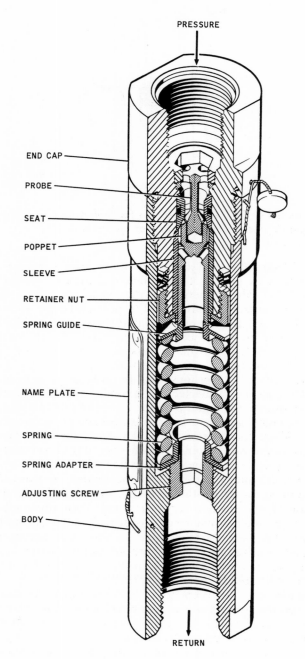

Figure 14 · 17 Pressure relief valve.

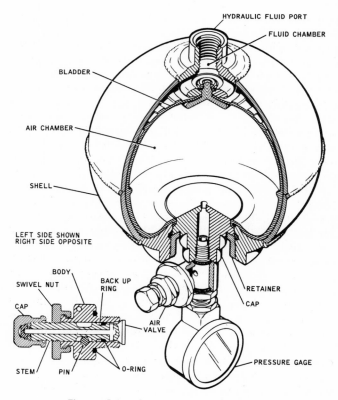

Figure 14 · 18 System accumulator.

increasing the volume of the fluid space and decreasing the volume of the air or gas space. When the system pressure reaches its maximum, the air or gas pressure will be the same as the system pressure. The accumulator permits a gradual rise in system pressure, thereby absorbing the shock of pump surges and relieving the piping and system operating units of high-impact loads. When the hydraulic pumps are not operating, the accumulator provides system pressure at a diminishing rate until a quantity equal to the stored volume in the accumulator has been used by the systems.

Priority valve

The purpose of the **priority valve** in each system is to divide the system into two sections such that one section will have priority over the other. In the system under discussion, the priority valve gives priority to the flight spoiler, rudder control, and thrust-reverser subsystems, all of which are upstream of the priority valve. The valve consists of a cylindrical body with threaded ports in both ends. The ports are identified as PRESSURE and RETURN, and the ends of the valve are provided with wrench flats to facilitate installation of the valve. Internally, the valve contains a poppet seat, a poppet, a poppet guide, a poppet spring, a poppet-guide spring, a return spring, shims for adjustment of the valve, and O rings and backup rings. A cutaway drawing of the priority valve is shown in Fig. 14·19.

The priority valve is a balanced-type relief valve which operates automatically to provide priority to the subsystems upstream of the valve whenever system pressure drops below 2000 psi. When system pressure rises above 2000 psi, regardless of downstream pressure, the valve opens to allow full flow and pressure downstream of the valve. Hydraulic pressure from the pressure manifold enters the priority valve through the pressure port, shown at the bottom of the illustration, and applies pressure against the poppet and the poppet seat. The force of this pressure is resisted by the force of the return spring against the poppet and the poppet seat, and by any back pressure from the return port against the poppet. When sufficient pressure is applied to overcome the return-spring preload, it starts to compress and the poppet and poppet seat move away from the pressure until the poppet is restrained from following the seat by the **poppet guide.** At approximately 1800 psi, the force on the poppet seat, without the poppet, is sufficient to overcome the return-spring restraining force; the return spring again starts to compress, moving the poppet seat away from the poppet. As the valve starts to open, hydraulic fluid flows through the valve from the pressure port to the return port. The valve is completely open at and above 2000 psi.

When the system pressure decreases to less than the opposing force of the return spring, as when the pump unloading valve is set for the cruise flight pressure of 1500 psi, the spring forces the poppet seat against the poppet and shuts off fluid flow through the valve from the pressure port. As the system pressure decreases below the closing pressure of the valve, and the pressure downstream of the valve exceeds the upstream

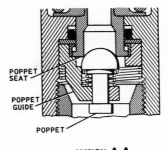

SECTION A-A

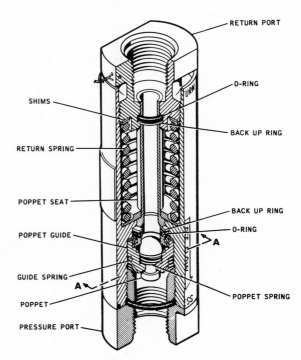

RETURN PORT

O-RING

BACK UP RING

SHIMS

RETURN SPRING

POPPET SEAT

POPPET GUIDE

GUIDE SPRING

POPPET

PRESSURE PORT

BACK UP RING

O-RING

POPPET SPRING

Figure 14·19   System priority valve.

pressure, the higher return port pressure is applied against the round face of the poppet, compressing the small poppet and poppet-guide springs and allowing free flow back through the valve until the pressure and return port pressures are equalized. At this time the return flow through the valve ceases. As the pressure downstream of the priority valve continues to decrease due to the normal leakage rates of the various components, the valve will remain closed and the downstream pressure will finally reach return system pressure. Resumption of high-pressure operation will again open the priority valve to port high-pressure fluid to the subsystems downstream of the valve.

Spoiler shutoff and system depressurization valve

Each of the two hydraulic systems is provided with a **spoiler shutoff** and **system depressurization valve.** These are separately operated, three-way hydraulic valves which are operable only on the ground for ground servicing and maintenance operations. They are located on opposite sides of the airplane centerline shear web above the priority valves and below the brake-system selector valves in each main-gear wheel well.

The three-way characteristic permits the inlet port to be connected to either of two outlet ports or to both outlet ports simultaneously. The three ports are designated **port 1, port 2,** and **port 3,** as shown in Fig. 14 · 20. Port 1 is connected to the pressure side of the spoiler subsystem, port 2 is connected to the hydraulic system pressure, and port 3 is connected to the main fluid-return system. A nameplate is attached to the face of the valve to indicate the valve operating position and to indicate the SPOILER ON, SPOILER OFF, and SYSTEM BYPASS positions. An operating handle with a pointer at one end to register with the markings on the name-plate is used to rotate the valve through its various positions. The handle is equipped with a latch mechanism and a safety pin to secure the valve in the SPOILER ON or SPOILER OFF position. With the handle in the SPOILER ON position, hydraulic pressure is supplied to the spoiler subsystem and the return port (3) is blocked. With the handle in the SPOILER OFF position, hydraulic

pressure to the spoiler subsystem is shut off and the spoiler subsystem pressure is directed through the valve and port 3 to the hydraulic-fluid-return system. When the handle is placed in the SYSTEM BY-PASS position, both system hydraulic pressure from port 2 and spoiler subsystem pressure from port 1 are directed through the valve and port 3 to the hydraulic fluid-return system. With both valves in the SYSTEM BYPASS position, both hydraulic power systems, left and right, are depressurized. A low-pressure warning light for each system is provided in the flight compartment to indicate a low-pressure or bypass condition in the spoiler subsystem.

Ground service hand pump

The **ground service hand pumps,** one for each of the two hydraulic systems, are single-cylinder, single-action, piston-type, hand-operated hydraulic pumps capable of delivering 0.750 cu in. of hydraulic fluid per cycle. Each pump is located in the forward outboard corner of its respective main-gear wheel well, with

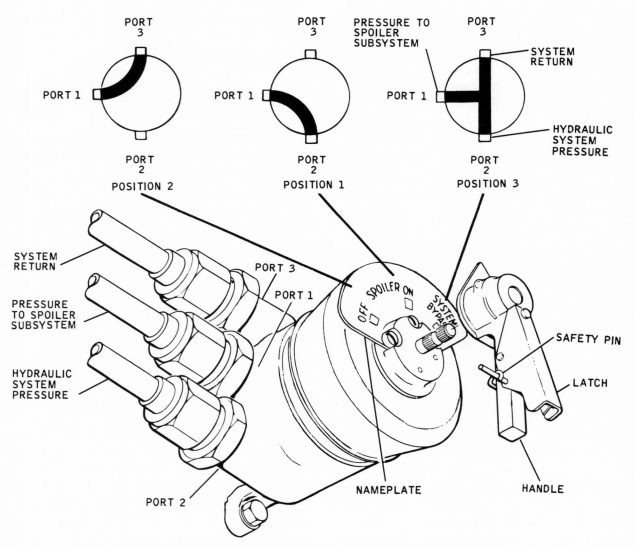

Figure 14 · 20 Spoiler shutoff and depressurization valve.

access through the wheel-well door. The pumps are connected between the reservoir supply lines and the system pressure lines so that operation of the hand pump will pressurize its respective hydraulic system for ground maintenance operations.

A quick-disconnect fitting in the hand-pump suction line is provided for filling the hydraulic reservoir by means of the hand pump. This operation is accomplished by separating the quick-disconnect fitting, placing the female half of the fitting, which is on the hand-pump suction hose, in a container of hydraulic fluid, and placing the spoiler shutoff and system depressurization valve in the BYPASS position. Operation of the hand pump will then pump fluid from the external container through the depressurization valve, into the return system lines, through the return-line filter, and into the reservoir. A check valve is incorporated in the outlet port of the hand pump to prevent system pressure from backing up through the hand pump and into the suction side of the system.

Electrically driven hydraulic pumps

As mentioned previously and shown in Fig. 14·10, each of the two hydraulic systems for the Douglas DC-9 airplane is provided with an auxiliary, electrically driven, variable-displacement hydraulic pump. The pumps are explosion-resistant, hydraulic-fluid-cooled and lubricated, self-supercharged, and pressure- and horsepower-controlled. They are capable of supplying a nonpulsating flow of hydraulic fluid in varying volume, depending upon system pressure, with a maximum flow of approximately 8 gpm at 2200 psi, 6 gpm at 2750 psi, and a minimum flow of 0 gpm at 3000 to 3150 psi. Control of the pumps is accomplished by means of switches in the flight compartment. If one engine should stop or if the hydraulic pump on that engine should fail, it is merely necessary to turn on the electric pump switch to place the system back in full operation. Each pump is connected to its respective system by means of flexible hoses with a ground power suction disconnect fitting installed in the suction line. The left pump can be quickly removed and installed in the right system in the event of failure of the right pump.

The pump electric motor is a three-phase, induction-type motor operating on 115/200-volt 400-cycle a-c power. It delivers 10 hp at 11,400 rpm with the electric power being supplied by the opposite engine-driven generator. Thus if one engine fails, the electric power supplied from the opposite engine will be available to operate the hydraulic system for the failed engine. The electric motor is cooled by hydraulic fluid supplied by an integral centrifugal pump. The cooling fluid flows through an internally finned cooling jacket around the case.

An overtemperature switch set to open at 220°F coolant fluid temperature is provided for thermal protection of the motor. After overtemperature switch actuation, which results from excessive motor temperature, the switch automatically resets at approximately 150°F. An override function of the control switch in the flight compartment is provided to bypass the overtemperature switch for emergency operation.

The centifugal pump provides a flow of hydraulic fluid to supercharge the variable pump and to cool the electric motor. The motor-cooling fluid also passes through the variable pump case. The centrifugal and variable pumps are driven at a speed reduction of 3.56:1 by the electric motor. This speed reduction is provided by a 16-tooth pinion, driving a 57-tooth gear. The gear and pinion, the motor drive end bearing, and the motor shaft are lubricated by a flow of hydraulic fluid from an orifice in the centrifugal pump which is directed into the gearbox and is then returned through an external line to the suction line port.

The pump flow control system is similar to that described for the engine-driven pump. That is, as system pressure increases above the lower operating level, the yoke angle of the VD pump is changed to reduce the displacement of the pistons, thus reducing pump output.

Hydraulic indicating systems

The hydraulic systems are provided with indicators in the cockpit to show fluid quantity, fluid pressure, and fluid temperature. Indications are transmitted electrically from the source of the measurement to the flight compartment.

PNEUMATIC SYSTEM FOR AN AIRLINER

The principle of operation for a pneumatic power system is the same, with one important exception, as that of a hydraulic power system. The air in a pneumatic system is compressible; hence the pressure in the system can reduce gradually from the maximum system pressure to zero pressure. In the hydraulic system, as soon as the accumulator fluid has been used and the pump is not operating, the fluid pressure immediately drops from accumulator pressure to zero pressure. The entire pneumatic system, including the air-storage bottles, can act to store air pressure. In the hydraulic system, the only pressure-fluid storage is in the accumulators and the pressure is supplied by compressed air or gas in the air chamber of the accumulator.

The air in a pneumatic system must not only be kept clean by means of filters, but it must also be kept free from moisture and oil droplets or vapor. For this reason, liquid separators and chemical air driers are incorporated in the systems.

Another important feature of a pneumatic system is that there is no need for return lines. After the compressed air has served its purpose, it can be dumped overboard. This provides a saving of tubing, fittings, and valves.

Pneumatic-system description

The pneumatic system described in this section is utilized in the Fairchild F-27 Friendship airliner. It provides power for operation of the landing-gear retraction and extension, nose-wheel centering, propeller brakes, main-wheel brakes, and passenger-entrance-door retraction. The system description includes only the development and delivery of compressed air to each component or subsystem, not to the actual *operation* of the component or subsystem. The pneumatic power in the airplane is delivered by one of two systems: the primary system and the emergency system.

The power section of the primary pneumatic system is that portion which is located in each engine nacelle, shown in Fig. 14·21. It consists of a gearbox-driven **compressor, bleed valve, unloading valve, moisture separator, chemical drier, back-pressure valve** (right nacelle only), and a **filter.** In addition, each nacelle contains a **shuttle valve, disk-type relief valve,** and a **ground charging connection** to aid in ground maintenance or initial filling. Each power section independently supplies compressed air to the primary and emergency systems. The air in the primary system is stored in two storage bottles, and the system delivers the air for normal operation of components as required by directional valves. A schematic diagram of the pneumatic power system is shown in Fig. 14·22.

A 100 cu in. bottle is used for the main-wheel brakes, and a 750 cu in. bottle is used for gear operation, nose-wheel centering, propeller brakes, and passenger-door retraction. A pressure relief valve is installed to protect the system from excessive pressure buildup. In the air-supply tube from the large primary bottle, an air filter is installed to filter the air for the primary system. An **isolation valve,** which is in the tube between the large primary bottle and the smaller brake bottle, permits maintenance to be performed downstream of the valve without discharging the large bottle. On the downstream side of the isolation valve, a pressure reducing valve is used to reduce system pressure from 3300 psi to 1000 psi. All components except the pressure gages and the power-section components are located in the fuselage pneumatic compartment.

Compressor

Two views of the **compressor** for the pneumatic system are shown in Fig. 14·23. One compressor is located in each engine nacelle. The compressors are of four-stage, radial design, providing a delivery pressure of 3300 psi and 2 cu ft per min at sea-level intake

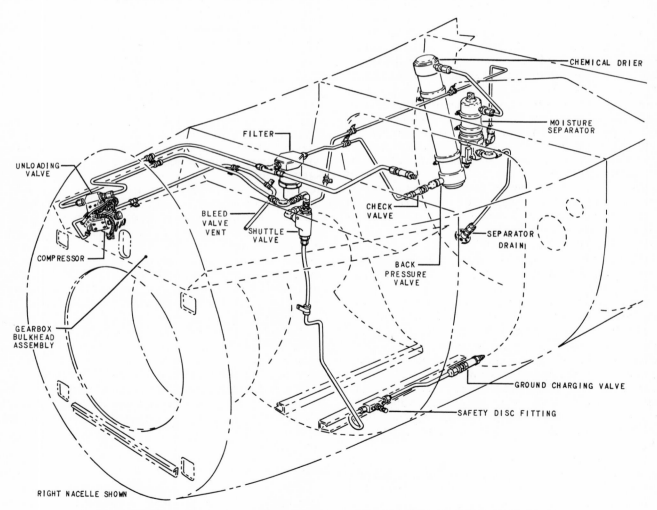

Figure 14·21   Pneumatic system in engine nacelle. (Fairchild Aircraft and Missiles Div., Fairchild Engine and Airplane Corp.)

238

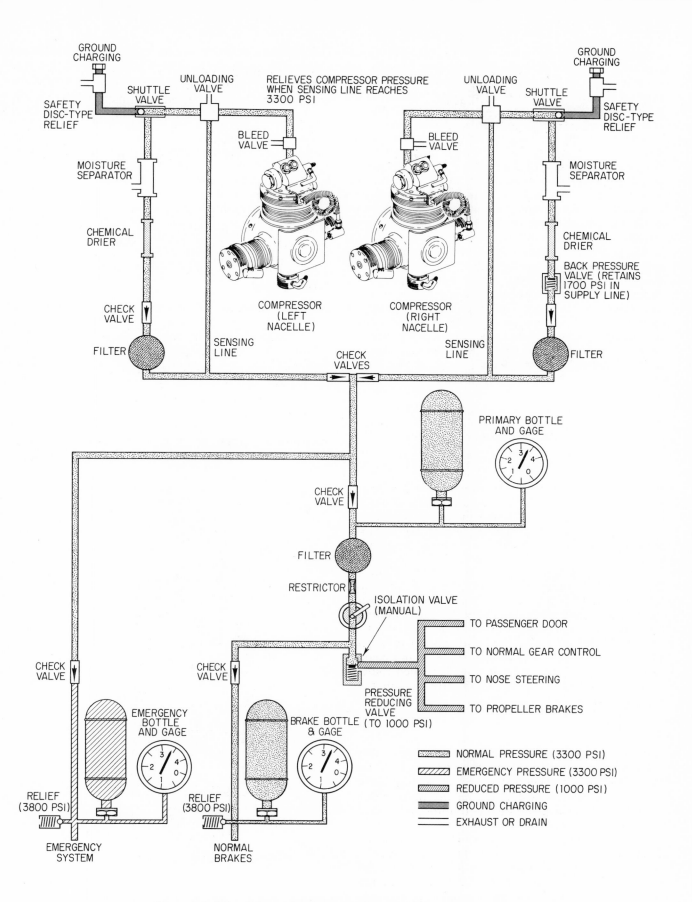

Figure 14·22   Schematic diagram of pneumatic power system.

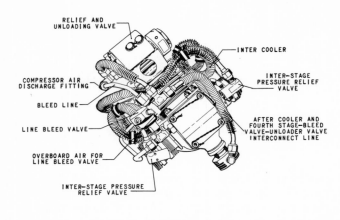

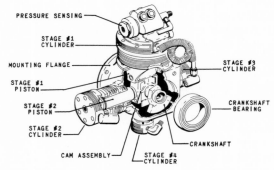

Figure 14·23   Pneumatic compressor.

Unloading valve

The **unloading valve** contains a sensing valve and a directional control valve, and it directs compressor output through dehydration equipment to the system or vents the output overboard. The directional control valve, controlled by the sensing valve, opens and vents overboard when system pressure reaches 3300 psi and closes when system pressure is less than 2900 psi.

Shuttle valve

Installed in both the right and left nacelles is a two-position, three-port **shuttle valve.** The valve functions to direct air to the primary system from the compressor or the ground charging valve while preventing air flow from escaping through the lines not being used for supplying air.

Moisture separator

In a pneumatic system it is of the utmost importance that the air in the system be completely dry. Moisture in the system can cause freezing of operating units; interfere with the normal operation of valves, pumps, etc.; and cause corrosion. It is for this reason that moisture separators and chemical driers are used in pneumatic systems.

In each compressor pressure line, a mechanical **moisture separator,** shown in the drawing of Fig. 14·24, is installed to remove approximately 98 per-

pressure on a standard day. As shown in the drawings, the cylinders and pistons of the compressor diminish in size from No. 1 to No. 4. The cylinders are caused to reciprocate in the proper sequence by a cam-assembly mechanism which rotates with the crankshaft.

Ducted ram air is provided for cooling of the finned cylinders and the finned interstage lines. Oil pressure from the gearbox provides lubrication for the compressor through a drilled passage in the mounting flange. Air is compressed by stages 1 through 4 of the compressor, while overpressure protection is provided by means of relief valves between stages 1 and 2, and 2 and 3. Compressed air from stage 4 is then routed by an intercooler line to the bleed valve mounted on the compressor.

Bleed valve

The **bleed valve,** controlled by compressor lubricating oil pressure, directs the compressed air to the compressor circuit relief valve and unloading valve. In the event the compressor oil pressure drops below 40 psi, the bleed valve will direct compressed air from the fourth stage overboard.

Pressure output from the bleed valve is routed to a **relief valve** in the unloading valve. The relief valve protects all components of the compressor circuit from excessive pressure buildup in the event any component downstream of the compressor malfunctions. The relief valve is set to open at 3800 psi.

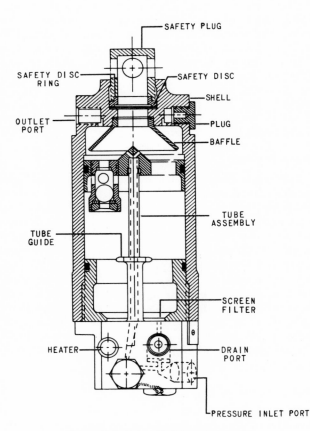

Figure 14·24   Moisture separator.

cent of any moisture and/or oil that may pass from the compressor. The separator is an aluminum tubular chamber, mounted vertically on the outboard side of the right nacelle and on the inboard side of the left nacelle.

Two valves are installed in the bottom of the separator. An inlet air pressure of 750 psi maximum closes the drain valve, while the inlet valve remains closed, thus preventing air from entering the separator. When pressure reaches 900 ± 150 psi, the inlet valve opens and allows air to flow. The inlet valve stays open as long as inlet pressure is above 1050 psi. The air entering the inlet port flows through the inlet valve seat, guide, and tube assembly, and through the orifices in the retainer assembly onto the baffle. The moisture droplets are deflected by the baffle, separated from the air stream, and caused to settle at the bottom of the air chamber against the closed drain valve.

As long as the inlet air pressure remains above 400 ± 150 psi, the flow of air is through the inlet port, guide, tube assembly, and outlet port. When inlet air is reduced to 0 psi, the residual air flows through the ball check of the retainer assembly and out the open drain valve, pushing the collected moisture ahead of it. The separator is equipped with a safety disk which will burst at 5800 to 6200 psi as a safety measure against overpressurization.

In the unit base is a small thermostatically controlled heater which prevents freezing of any accumulated moisture in the bottom of the air chamber. The heater is automatically operated by a hermetically sealed thermostat, located in the moisture separator body. The thermostat closes the electrical circuit at 35°F to provide heating and opens the contacts at 85°F maximum. With the primary bus switch ON and either the master or external power switch ON, 28-volt d-c power is available to the separator from the d-c primary bus. To function properly, the moisture separator must be mounted vertically with the overboard drain at the bottom.

Chemical drier

A tubular, **chemical-drier** housing is installed in each nacelle downstream of the mechanical moisture separator. The driers are mounted on brackets; one is located in the upper, inboard side of the left nacelle, the other on the upper, outboard side of the right nacelle. Each drier has an inlet and outlet port and contains a desiccant cartridge. Air is directed through this replaceable cartridge, and any moisture which the mechanical moisture separator has failed to remove will be absorbed by the dehydrating agent in the cartridge. The cartridge with dehydrating agent specification MIL-D-3716 incorporates two bronze filters, one at each end, which allows a 0.001-in. maximum-size particle to pass through.

Back-pressure valve

A **back-pressure valve,** illustrated in Fig. 14·25, is installed in the pressure tube of the right nacelle only, to ensure that the engine-driven air compressor out-

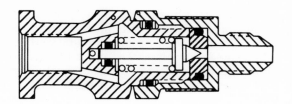

Figure 14·25   Back pressure valve.

put is kept at a predetermined value of 1700 ± 150 psi. This is to provide and maintain a fixed back pressure of approximately 1700 psi upstream of the air-drying equipment. The back-pressure valve is similar in construction and operation to a check valve and consists of a valve seat, piston, and spring. It is installed in the outlet port of the chemical drier and is directly connected to the inlet port of a check valve. The right engine compressor, or a ground charging unit, should always be used for normal charging of the pneumatic system.

Poppet-type, spring-loaded, line check valves are installed in the primary system, and each is identified by part number according to tube size. The construction of such a valve is shown in Fig. 14·26. One valve is located in the inlet tube just before the point where the tube enters the primary bottle inlet port. This is a No. 3 check valve and is used with ³⁄₁₆-in. tubing. Note that the No. 3 designation for the check valve is an indication that the valve is to be used with ³⁄₁₆-in. tubing.

Another check valve is installed in the supply tube leading to the brake storage bottle and is located on the left center edge of the fuselage pneumatic panel. This valve is a No. 6 valve and is used with ³⁄₈-in. tubing. Two spring-loaded, poppet-type, line-check valves are installed in each pneumatic power system in each nacelle. One No. 4 valve is installed in the outlet end of the back pressure valve; the other valve, a No. 3 size, is installed in the upper outlet port of the "T" fitting at approximate nacelle station 98.

Sintered filters

Three sintered pneumatic filters are used, one in each compressor circuit and one in the primary circuit. The **filter** is a vertically mounted unit, containing a replaceable filter element of stainless steel which removes foreign matter of 10 μ or larger from the compressor output air. Two of the filters are mounted, one on the inboard side of the left nacelle on the forward side of the station 101 bulkhead and

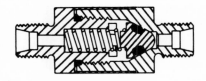

Figure 14·26   Check valve.

the other on the outboard side of the right nacelle on the aft side of the station 101 bulkhead. The filters are accessible for inspection when the main landing gear is in the extended position. The other filter is located on the top of the fuselage pneumatic panel and filters air as it comes from the primary storage bottle.

Primary storage bottle

The primary air-storage bottle is constructed of steel with a plastic coating on the inner surface to provide a longer service life. The bottle is mounted above the fuselage pneumatic panel and is fitted with three ports. It has a volume of 750 cu in. and stores air at 3300 psi for operating landing-gear, propeller-brake, nose-steering, and rear-door-retracting subsystems. The air pressure is reduced to 1000 psi before being routed to subsystems other than brakes. The bottle is provided with a standpipe which permits the withdrawal of air without the danger of allowing any accumulated moisture to enter the operating systems. Accumulated air can be drained from the bottle by means of a drain valve located on the bottom. Access is gained to the air bottle through the fuselage pneumatic power panel door.

Primary pressure gage

A direct-reading pressure gage is connected to the primary air-storage bottle and is mounted in the pneumatic instrument panel on the right side of the crew compartment to provide a visual indication of the pressure in the primary bottle. The gage is mounted adjacent to the emergency pressure gage and is illuminated with two post lights. The dial of the gage is calibrated from 0 to 4×1000 psi and should read 3300 when the system is fully charged.

Relief valve

A spring-loaded, piston **relief valve** is installed in the primary system and is located halfway up the fuselage pneumatic panel on the left side. The valve is preset, safetied, and tagged by the manufacturer for a cracking pressure of 3800 ± 50 psi. It protects the primary system from excessive pressure buildup in the event of thermal expansion or compressor power system malfunction.

This relief valve is designed to relieve pressure as a metering device instead of an instantaneous on-off valve. Its rate of relief automatically increases in direct proportion to the amount of overpressure. It reseats when the pressure decreases to approximately 3400 psi.

Isolation valve

The pneumatic power system is provided with an **isolation valve** so that the air-pressure storage section of the system can be isolated from the subsystems; thus work on the subsystems may be performed without discharging the entire system. The isolation valve is a two-position (open-close) type installed on the top right side of the pneumatic panel. The valve contains a spring-loaded, poppet-type plunger which is cam- and lever-operated. The location of the valve in the system is shown in Fig. 14 · 22. Connected to the valve lever is a push-pull rod-and-latch assembly which prevents closing the pneumatic panel door while the valve is in the closed position. This arrangement eliminates the possibility of operating the airplane while the air pressure is shut off.

Pressure-reducing valve

As mentioned previously, the air pressure employed for the operation of the landing-gear, propeller-braking, nose-wheel-steering, and passenger-door-retraction subsystems is reduced from 3300 to 1000 psi. This is accomplished by means of the **pressure reducing valve** installed in the primary pressure supply line. This valve is mounted on the pneumatic power panel just below the isolation valve as shown in the drawing of Fig. 14 · 27. The pressure reducing valve contains dual springs and poppets which not only reduce pressure but also provide for pressure relief of the reduced pressure should the valve fail. A cross section of the valve is shown in Fig. 14 · 28.

Additional protection is afforded the reducer relief valve by a restrictor elbow upstream of the isolation valve. The restrictor prevents excessive flow to the reducer and reducer relief valve.

Pneumatic manifold

An aluminum manifold having seven ports is mounted just below and to the left of the pressure reducing valve on the pneumatic panel. As shown in the drawing of Fig. 14 · 27, the manifold is connected directly to the pressure-reducing valve. The manifold receives 1000 psi air pressure and passes this air to the nose-steering, propeller-brake, landing-gear, and passenger-door subsystems through a network of aluminum tubing. The lower end port of the manifold is sealed by a threaded plug.

Ground charging valve

A **ground charging valve** is installed in both the left and right nacelles to provide a means of initial filling or ground charging the entire pneumatic system during the period when the engines are not operating. Normal ground charging is accomplished by using the right nacelle charging valve. If the system pressure is below 1000 psi, the isolation valve should be closed before charging. The left nacelle charging valve should be used only during maintenance pressure checking of nacelle components or servicing the system with a dry-air source of supply.

The charging valve also acts as a protective device against an excessive rate of inlet airflow. The valve serves as a restrictor by providing a fixed orifice through which all ground-supplied compressed air must pass.

Safety-disk fitting

Just upstream of the ground-charging valve in each nacelle is a two-port safety-disk fitting incorporating a disk-type pressure relief assembly. The disk will

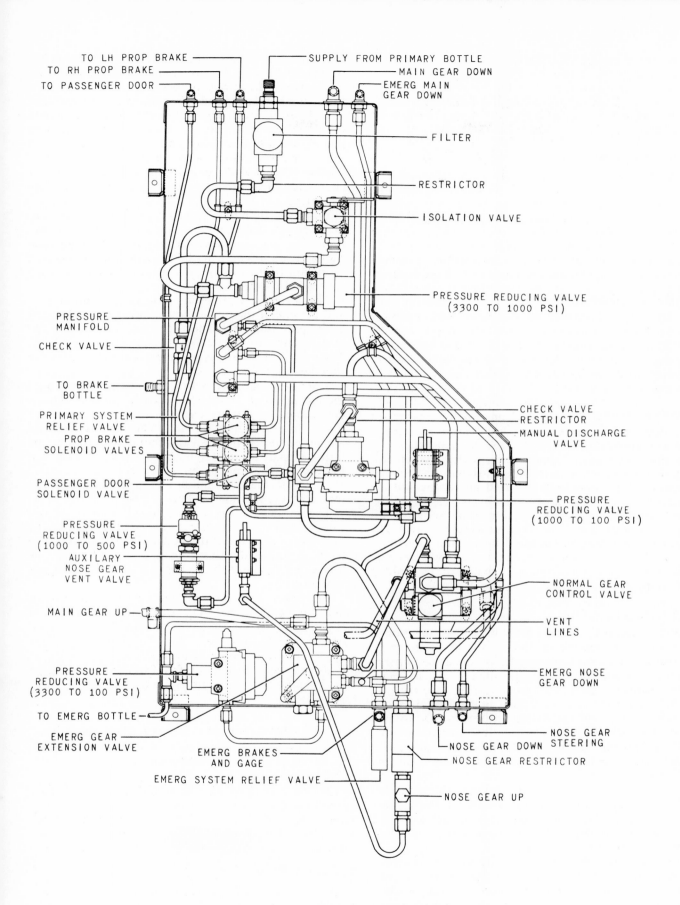

TO LH PROP BRAKE
TO RH PROP BRAKE
TO PASSENGER DOOR

SUPPLY FROM PRIMARY BOTTLE
MAIN GEAR DOWN
EMERG MAIN GEAR DOWN

FILTER

RESTRICTOR

ISOLATION VALVE

PRESSURE REDUCING VALVE (3300 TO 1000 PSI)

PRESSURE MANIFOLD

CHECK VALVE

TO BRAKE BOTTLE

PRIMARY SYSTEM RELIEF VALVE

PROP BRAKE SOLENOID VALVES

PASSENGER DOOR SOLENOID VALVE

PRESSURE REDUCING VALVE (1000 TO 500 PSI)

AUXILARY NOSE GEAR VENT VALVE

MAIN GEAR UP

PRESSURE REDUCING VALVE (3300 TO 100 PSI)

TO EMERG BOTTLE

EMERG GEAR EXTENSION VALVE

EMERG BRAKES AND GAGE

EMERG SYSTEM RELIEF VALVE

CHECK VALVE
RESTRICTOR
MANUAL DISCHARGE VALVE

PRESSURE REDUCING VALVE (1000 TO 100 PSI)

NORMAL GEAR CONTROL VALVE

VENT LINES

EMERG NOSE GEAR DOWN

NOSE GEAR STEERING

NOSE GEAR DOWN

NOSE GEAR RESTRICTOR

NOSE GEAR UP

Figure 14·27 Pneumatic power panel.

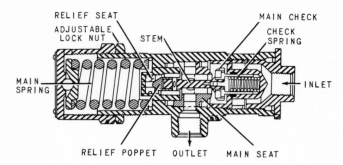

RELIEF SEAT
ADJUSTABLE LOCK NUT
STEM
MAIN CHECK
CHECK SPRING
MAIN SPRING
INLET
RELIEF POPPET   OUTLET   MAIN SEAT

Figure 14·28   Pressure reducing valve.

rupture at approximately 4300 to 4950 psi allowing air to escape through drilled passages in the retainer.

Pneumatic tubing

The tubing used for the pneumatic system follows the pattern described for hydraulic systems. For the high-pressure sections of the system, stainless-steel tubing is employed. This type of tubing is used where the pressures reach or exceed 3000 psi. The steel tubing conforms to specification MIL-T-8504 and varies in size from 3/16 to 3/8 in. outside diameter (OD). Steel tubing is used to carry pressurized air from the compressor to the three storage bottles, pressure gages, emergency brakes, and brake valve, and to the emergency landing-gear selector valve. Each end of the tubing is connected by the use of MS flareless fittings. Aluminum tubing is used to carry reduced pressurized air throughout the remainder of the system and conforms to specification MIL-T-7081. The aluminum tubing also uses MS flareless fittings and varies in size from 3/16 to 3/8 in. OD. The network of tubing is stabilized by the use of clamps, clamp blocks, T fittings, unions, and elbows. Bonding strips are used as necessary to reduce static buildup and interference.

MS flareless tube fittings

The use of MS flareless fittings has been mentioned previously in this section and in the associated text, *Basic Science for Aerospace Vehicles.* Since these fittings are commonly used in the pneumatic system under consideration and in high-pressure hydraulic systems, it is appropriate to discuss them in detail at this time.

The assembly of MS flareless fittings consists of two separate and distinct operations. The initial assembly of the sleeve and nut to the tubing, an operation called **presetting,** and the installation of the tube assembly into the seat of the fitting are both of great importance. A major advantage of the MS fitting is that assembly can be made in the field without special tools; however, with the limitation of one preset operation for aluminum and five for steel it is recommended that hand presetting tools be used.

MS fittings are illustrated in Fig. 14·29. The term **presetting** is used to describe the operation of setting the sleeve onto the tube before final installation in a flareless seat. It is recommended that the presetting operation be performed on a workbench and be in-

spected before final installation. In emergencies an MS fitting can be preset directly in place on the equipment.

To install MS fittings properly, a number of conditions should be observed. The tube must be round and straight in the area contacted by the sleeve. The end of the tubing must be cut square and be free from burrs and chips on both exterior and interior edges. Only a very small amount of metal should be removed with the burr, because the edges must not be rounded or chamfered. The tubing must not be scratched when deburring.

When the tubing is inspected and found to be suitable, the MS sleeve and nut are slid over the end of the tube. The threads and seat of the hand setting tool and shoulder of the sleeve are lubricated with the specified lubricant. In the case of pneumatic systems, the lubricant is MIL-L-4343.

The correct size presetting tool is clamped in a vise, and the end of the tube is bottomed firmly on the seat of the presetting tool. The sleeve and nut are then slid into position for tightening as shown in Fig. 14·29. The pilot of the sleeve is pointed toward the end of the tube being preset.

The nut is tightened with a proper-size wrench until the cutting edge of the sleeve grips the tube. This is determined by turning the tube slowly but firmly by hand while tightening the nut. When the tube can no longer be turned between the thumb and fingers, the fitting is ready for final tightening. The correct amount for turning the nut for presetting is shown in Table 14·1. Note that the amount of tightening is determined by the size and thickness of the tube.

The nut must not be overtightened because this will cause the sleeve to shear-cut the tube thus ruining the tight line seal of the cutting edge. Overtightening also tends to flatten the sleeve against the 24° cut in the fitting and eliminate the rocking action which dampens vibration.

After presetting, the nut is backed off so the assembly can be inspected. The sleeve should be bowed slightly and should not have a longitudinal movement on the tube of more than 1/64 in. The sealing surface of the sleeve which contacts the 24° angle of the fitting body seat must be smooth, free from scores, and have no longitudinal or circumferential cracks. The maxi-

Table 14·1   Turn values with and without mandrels

Tube size	Wall thickness, in.							
	0.020	0.025	0.028	0.035	0.042	0.049	0.058	0.065
2	1⅙	1⅙	1⅙	1⅙				
3	1⅙	1⅙	1⅙	1	1	1	1	1
4	1*	1⅙*	1⅙	1⅙	1	1	1	1
5	1*	1*	1⅙	1⅙	1	1	1	1
6	⅚*	⅚*	1⅙	1⅙	1⅙	1	⅚	⅚
8		⅚*	⅚*	1⅙	1⅙	1	1	⅚
10		⅔*	⅔*	1⅙	1⅙	1	1

*Mandrels are to be used to prevent damage to tube.

244

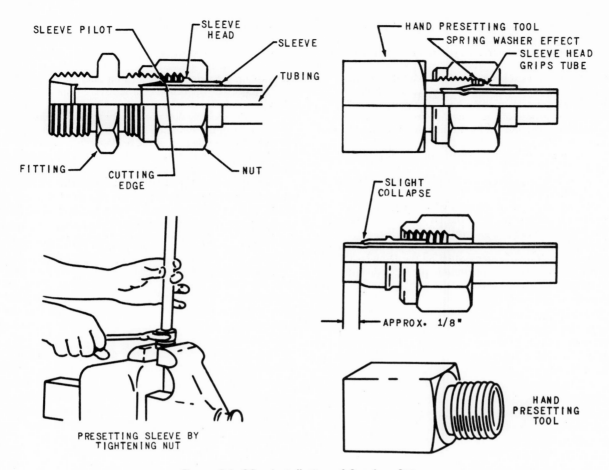

Figure 14·29   Installation of flareless fittings.

mum inside-diameter (ID) reduction at the sleeve cut must not exceed 0.015 of the nominal ID of the tube prior to presetting. The sleeve, nut, and tube must be free from foreign material and burrs. The end of the tube and the sealing surface of the sleeve must seat satisfactorily on installation when it is inserted into the quarter-sectioned presetting tool used as an inspection gage. If the tube projection is too long, the sealing surface of the sleeve will not contact the 24° bevel of the inspection gage. If the tube projection is too short, the tube will not rest on the bottom seat of the gage.

SUMMARY OF IMPORTANT NOTES ON HIGH-PRESSURE SYSTEMS

High-pressure systems, either hydraulic or pneumatic, can be very dangerous unless the technician observes all appropriate precautions. It is therefore essential that pressure be relieved from any system upon which work is to be performed.

Stainless-steel tubing and fittings are used in all parts of a system where pressures exceed 1500 psi. Titanium fittings can be used in place of steel fittings. Where vibration is to be encountered, high-pressure hose is used.

When Skydrol fluid is used in a hydraulic system, precautions must be taken to avoid damage or injury from the fluid action. The correct materials must be used in the seals, gaskets, etc., to avoid swelling or other deterioration. No other fluid must ever be mixed with Skydrol.

MS flareless fittings are commonly used in modern hydraulic and pneumatic systems. The installation of these fittings is critical and must be done according to exact specifications. The technician must make sure that he has the correct information for the fittings being installed.

Under all conditions, the technician must make sure that he is using the data furnished by the manufacturer for repair and maintenance of the system upon which he is working.

REVIEW QUESTIONS

1. What is the principal advantage of a high-pressure hydraulic system?
2. Name the three principal hydraulic power systems for the Boeing 727 airplane.
3. What types of pumps are employed in the hydraulic power systems for the Boeing 727 airplane?
4. What is the function of a *modular unit?*
5. Discuss the use of Skydrol 500 hydraulic fluid and explain precautions required.
6. What material is used for the tubing in the high-pressure portions of the hydraulic systems?

7. What materials are used for tubing, gaskets, and seals in a system using Skydrol fluid?
8. What subsystems are served by system A in the Boeing 727?
9. Describe the heat exchanger and tell why it is needed.
10. What type of accumulator is used in the Boeing 727 hydraulic power system and what is the gas preload?
11. What is the purpose of the *ground interconnect valve?*
12. Compare the right and left hydraulic power systems for the Douglas DC-9 airplane.
13. Describe the hydraulic reservoir for one of the DC-9 systems.
14. How is the fluid quantity transmitter for the DC-9 hydraulic reservoir actuated?
15. By what means is the fire-shutoff valve operated?
16. Describe the accumulator for the DC-9 hydraulic system.
17. What is the function of a *priority valve?*
18. Describe how a ground-service hand pump is used to add fluid to the hydraulic power system on the Douglas DC-9.
19. For what functions is the pneumatic power system on the Fairchild F-27 airplane used?
20. How is the high-pressure air stored in the Fairchild F-27 pneumatic system?
21. What is the purpose of the *isolation valve* in the F-27 pneumatic system?
22. Explain the need for dry air in a pneumatic system.
23. Describe the operation of a moisture separator.
24. What is a *desiccant?*
25. Give the specification number for the desiccant used in the air drier in the Fairchild F-27 pneumatic system.
26. What is the function of the *back-pressure valve?*
27. Why is an *isolation valve* used in the pneumatic system?
28. What air pressure is actually used for the operation of the landing-gear, propeller-braking, nosewheel-steering, and passenger-door subsystems?
29. How is the lower pressure obtained from the high-pressure air of the pneumatic power system?
30. Explain the use of the *ground charging valve.*
31. What type of tubing is used in the F-27 pneumatic system?
32. What precautions must be taken in the installation of MS flareless fittings?

CHAPTER 15

Aircraft Landing Gear

CLASSIFICATION OF LANDING GEAR

The **landing gear** of an airplane serves a number of very important functions. It supports the airplane during ground operations, dampens vibrations when the airplane is being taxied or towed, and cushions the landing impact. The landing of an airplane often involves stresses far in excess of what may be considered normal; hence the landing gear must be constructed and maintained in a manner which provides the strength and reliability to meet all probable landing conditions.

The landing gear of an airplane consists of main and auxiliary units, either of which may be fixed (nonretractable) or retractable. The **main landing gear** provides the main support of the airplane on land or water. It may include a combination of wheels, floats, skis, shock-absorbing equipment, brakes, retracting mechanism, controls, warning devices, cowling, fairing, and structural members needed for attachment to the primary structure of the airplane.

The **auxiliary landing gear** consists of tail or nose landing-wheel installations, skids, outboard pontoons, etc., with the necessary cowling and reinforcements.

Main landing-gear types and operation

Nonretractable (fixed) landing gear is generally attached to structural members of the airplane with bolts, but it is not actually "fixed" because it must absorb stresses; hence the wheels must move up and down while landing or taxiing in order to absorb shocks. The landing gear is often equipped with cowling or fairing to reduce the drag (air resistance), and such cowling or fairing may be assembled in sections. Chafing strips are used to prevent excessive wear between the sections of such cowling or fairing because there is usually some motion between these sections. Nonretractable landing gear may have bracing, or it may be of the cantilever type without bracing.

Retractable landing gear was developed to eliminate as much as possible the drag caused by the exposure of the landing gear to air flow during flight. Usually the landing gear is completely retractable (that is, it can be drawn entirely into the wing or fuselage); however, there are aircraft in which a portion of the gear wheels is still exposed after the gear is retracted. The direction of retraction varies. On some airplanes, the retraction is toward the rear; on others the landing gear folds inward toward the fuselage; and on still others it folds outward toward the wing tips. The method of retraction also varies, although modern aircraft usually have gear which is power operated. The retraction is normally accomplished with hydraulic, electric, or pneumatic power. In addition to the normal operating system, emergency systems are usually provided to ensure that the landing gear can be lowered in case of main system failure. Emergency systems consist of stored air or gas which can be directed into actuating cylinders or mechanical systems which can be operated manually.

There are various types of landing-gear **position indicators**. These show whether the landing gear is up or down and whether it is locked. One type of indicator has a needle or a miniature wheel for each unit. The indicator is built into a single instrument on the instrument panel and arranged so that the needle or wheel moves along with the actual movement of the landing gear from the DOWN to the UP position (and in the same direction), thus simplifying its reading by the pilot. Many airplanes have indicator lights, such as a green light that glows when the gear is down and locked.

Mechanical locks engage the landing gear automatically in the DOWN and UP positions to assure that the gear will hold its position. When the pilot or copilot operates the gear lever to raise or lower the gear, the locks are automatically unlatched. Landing-gear systems are usually provided with safety switches or locks which make it impossible to raise the gear when the airplane is on the ground.

Warning signals are used with retracting mechanisms to reduce the possibility of the pilot landing when the landing gear is retracted. These are usually electric horns or lights installed in the cockpit. A warning horn will blow whenever the throttle is pulled back to a low-power position if the gear is still retracted.

Skis are used for taking off and landing on snow or ice. The usual type is made of metal and is designed so that the wheels need not be removed from the axles for the installation of the skis. The ski on this type of installation has an opening through which the wheel protrudes for a short distance and an attaching device for mounting the ski on the landing gear at each side of the wheel.

If an airplane is to be operated entirely from ice or snow, the wheels are removed and a different type of ski is installed. Ski installations can be made retractable for some airplanes.

Airplanes operated from water may be provided with either a **single float** or a **double float,** depending upon the design and construction; however, if an airplane is actually a flying boat, it has a **hull** for flotation and then may need only wing-tip floats. **Amphibious** airplanes have a floatable hull for operating on water and retractable wheels for land operation.

Some airplanes have the **conventional** two-wheel landing gear with two wheels in front and a wheel at the rear of the fuselage. The **tricycle-type landing gear,** common to most modern airplanes, utilizes a nosewheel and the main wheels are to the rear of the aircraft center of gravity.

Auxiliary landing gear

Auxiliary landing gear include nosewheels, tail wheels, tail skids, wing-tip floats, and other devices used in connection with the main gear to stabilize the airplane. The **tail wheel** on an airplane with "conventional" gear may be retractable or nonretractable. The nonretractable type is usually found on small, relatively slow airplanes while the retractable tail wheel is used on faster airplanes.

The tail wheel is usually free to swivel, and at the same time is connected to the rudder controlling system to aid in steering. When sufficient force is applied to swivel the tail wheel, an automatic device disengages it from the rudder system. This is to aid in turning the airplane on the ground during ground handling. Another reason for the disengaging mechanism is to protect the fuselage structure from the stresses which would occur whe taxiing over rough ground or when strong side loads are applied to the fuselage.

An **antishimmy device** is normally provided to reduce the tendency of the tail wheel to oscillate badly during taxiing and landing. It consists of two friction disks, usually made of different materials, held in contact with each other by a spring. One disk is fixed to the spindle-bearing housing and the other is integral with the upper plate of the disengaging device. When the tail wheel is in any controllable position, the friction between the disks dampens the oscillations of the tail wheel.

A **coil-spring shock unit** is often built into the tail-gear control cables to (1) absorb shocks caused by the oscillation of the tail gear; (2) prevent transmission of the shocks through the rudder control cables to the rudder pedals; and (3) permit the full movement of the rudder, regardless of any binding of the tail wheel.

The **nose gear** of a tricycle-gear airplane is often just a smaller version of the main gear, and in some cases it is almost as large as the main gear. It consists of a shock strut; axle; mounting trunnion; retracting mechanism (if it is of the retractable type); torque links (scissors), to keep the inner cylinder and wheel from turning

independently; a shimmy damper or steering mechanism; tire or tires; etc.

Modern aircraft of the tricycle type often are equipped with tail skids (bumpers) to protect the fuselage in case the tail drops too near the gear. These skids are not properly a part of the landing-gear system, although they are retracted and extended at the same time.

Shimmy dampers and shock struts

The nose gear usually consists of a single, cantilever **shock strut** to which a **fork-and-wheel** or an **axle-and-wheel assembly** is attached, and some type of retracting mechanism for retractable landing-gear systems. A **shimmy damper** restrains the motion of the nosewheel and prevents oscillation.

Shock struts reduce the shock that would otherwise be received by the airplane structure during taxiing and landing. Both shimmy dampers and shock struts are discussed in detail later in this chapter.

FIXED LANDING GEAR

Fixed, or nonretractable, landing-gear designs are usually one of three types. Each type requires a shock-absorbing mechanism which may be rubber shock (bungee) cord, spring steel struts, or air-oleo shock struts.

Shock cord

When rubber **shock cord** is used, the landing-gear struts are usually made of steel tubing mounted in such a manner that a lever action is applied to tightly wound rubber cord. When landing shock occurs, the cord is stretched, thus absorbing the shock. Shock cord must be replaced periodically because of rubber deterioration. The cord is color-coded to indicate when it was manufactured, thus giving the technician the information he needs to determine the life of the cord. According to MIL-C-5651A, the color code for the year of manufacture is repeated in cycles of five years. Table 15·1 shows the colors of the code threads for each year and quarter of year.

The color coding is composed of threads interwoven in the cotton sheath which binds the strands of rubber cord together. Two spiral threads are used for the year coding and one thread for the quarter of the year. If the technician inspected a shock-cord installation in 1968 and he found that the cord had two yellow threads and one blue thread spiraling around the sheath, he would

Table 15·1   Cord color codes

Year	Color	Quarter	Color
1960 and 1965	Black	1st	Red
1961 and 1966	Green	2d	Blue
1962 and 1967	Red	3d	Green
1963 and 1968	Blue	4th	Yellow
1964 and 1969	Yellow		
1965 and 1970	Black		

know that the cord was manufactured in 1964 during April, May, or June.

Shock cord should be replaced when it shows any sign of deterioration, especially if it is over five years in age. Deterioration is indicated by "necking" (narrowing) of the cord and by breaks or worn spots in the sheath. The necking of the cord is caused by individual strands in the cord being broken.

Spring gear

The landing-gear struts for some models of Cessna aircraft consist of single, tapered strips of strong, spring steel. The wide end of the steel strut is bolted to the heavy structure of the aircraft under the cabin area, and the axles are bolted to the narrow ends. A landing gear of this type is shown in Fig. 15·1.

Spring-oleo struts

Spring-oleo struts, not usually found in modern aircraft, consist of a piston-type structure and a heavy, coiled spring. The piston-and-cylinder arrangement provides an oil chamber and an orifice through which oil is forced during landing. When the airplane is airborne, the strut is extended, and the oil flows by gravity to the lower chamber. When the plane lands, the piston with the orifice is forced downward into the cylinder and the oil is forced through the orifice into the upper chamber. This action provides a cushioning effect to absorb the primary shock of landing. As the strut collapses, the coil spring is compressed, thus providing additional shock absorption. Thus the spring supports the aircraft weight on the ground and during taxiing, and the oleo strut absorbs the shock of landing.

Air-oil shock strut

The **air-oil,** or **air-oleo, shock strut** can be used for either nonretractable or retractable landing gear. This type of gear is generally constructed as shown in

Figure 15·1   Spring-type landing gear.

Fig. 15·2, although there are many variations of the design.

In the strut shown, the ring-seal nut (1), the compressing-ring seal (2), and the ring seal (3) form the group which seals the air pressure in the upper part of the strut. The upper bearing (4) keeps the inner cylinder (11) aligned with the outer cylinder (10). The snubber valve (5) releases when the weight is off the landing-gear strut to allow the strut to extend. The outer torque collar is (6). The lower bearing (7) helps keep the inner cylinder aligned inside the outer cylinder. The filler plug (8) is used to plug the hole through which the cylinder is filled with hydraulic fluid. The bearing lock screw (9) is used to maintain the position of the upper bearing on the inner cylinder.

The metering pin (13), extending into the piston tube (12), restricts the flow of fluid from the lower part of the cylinder to the upper part when the cylinder is being compressed during landing or taxiing.

The bearing spacer ring (14) is located between the lower part of the outer cylinder and the inner cylinder. The bearing (packing) nut (15), at the bottom of the cylinder, holds the lower bearing and the packing ring seals in position. The wiper ring (16) prevents dirt or other foreign matter from being drawn into the cylinder when the cylinder is being compressed.

View A of the illustration is an enlarged drawing of the seals and bearing at the lower end of the shock strut, marked A in the first drawing. The upper packing spacer (17), the neoprene packing (18), and the lower packing spacer (19) are compressed together to form a tight seal between the inner and outer cylinders.

View B is an enlarged drawing of the seal nut (20), compressing ring seal (21), and the ring seal (22), which are shown within the circular arrow marked B in the first drawing.

View C is an enlarged drawing of the piston bearing (23), piston-bearing lock nuts (24), the stop nut (25), and the nut lock screw (26), shown within the circular arrow marked C in the first drawing.

As mentioned previously, the shock struts absorb the shocks of landing and taxiing. The initial shock of landing is cushioned by the hydraulic fluid being forced through the small aperture at the metering pin. As the strut is further compressed by the weight of the airplane, the pressure on the air in the upper part of the strut is increased until the air pressure is capable of sustaining the weight of the entire airplane. As the airplane rolls along the ground, the compressed air in the strut acts as a spring to reduce shocks. Additional information regarding shock struts is given later in this chapter.

RETRACTABLE LANDING GEAR

The majority of modern aircraft are equipped with retractable landing gear which may be operated either by a hydraulic system, electrical motor system, or a pneumatic system. Retractable landing-gear systems are so designed that they retract either into the wings or into the fuselage. The direction of retraction may be fore-and-aft, sideways, or a combination of the two.

249

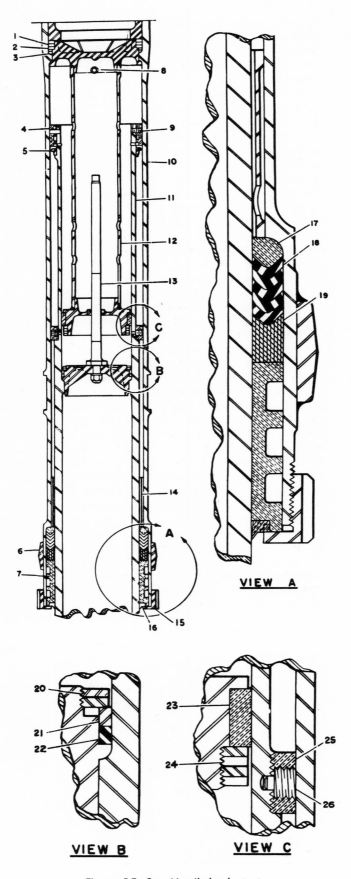

VIEW A

VIEW B

VIEW C

Figure 15·2 Air-oil shock strut.

It must be emphasized that the landing gear of an airplane is of primary importance in the safe operation of the aircraft and because of this, the technician must be especially careful in the inspection and maintenance of landing-gear systems. Since retractable-type landing gear is much more complex than fixed gear, it is essential that each operating component of the gear be carefully examined at frequent intervals to assure that there will be no chance of failure.

During the operation of an airplane with retractable landing gear, the system which raises and lowers the gear must operate without fail, and the gear must remain in the down-and-locked position after it is lowered. Periodically the airplane should be jacked up and the gear operated to assure that the operating system and the **down** and **up locks** function effectively.

Another important feature of retractable landing gear is the safety mechanism which prevents gear retraction while the airplane is on the ground. This safety system often consists of an electric circuit which includes switches operated by the extension and compression of the landing-gear struts. As long as the gear struts are compressed, the switches are open and an electrically operated lock prevents the raising of the gear. When the airplane leaves the ground, the gear struts extend and the switches are closed. This permits operation of the landing-gear control lever to raise the gear.

Another safety feature included with retractable landing-gear systems is the warning horn which has been mentioned previously. If the gear is in the retracted position and the throttle is retarded to a below-normal power setting, the warning horn sounds and warns the pilot that his landing gear is not in the down position.

Retractable landing-gear systems are usually provided with warning lights to give a visual indication of the safe operation of the gear. When the landing gear is lowered and the down lock has moved into the locked position, a green light will come on and indicate to the pilot that the landing gear is in a safe position to land.

During the inspection of landing-gear systems, the following items should be checked by the technician:

1. The gear should raise and lower easily and without any binding or strain.
2. The warning horn should sound if the gear is retracted and the throttle is retarded.
3. The down and up locks should hold the gear firmly in position and should not unlock without actuation of the system.
4. The warning lights on the instrument panel should light as required to show the safe operation of the landing gear.
5. The compressed air pressure in the air-oil-type struts should be at a level which provides the correct extension of the strut. The amount of strut extension is given in the manufacturer's maintenance manual.
6. The ground safety-lock system should be checked to assure that the gear cannot be retracted while the airplane is on the ground.

7. The emergency system should be inspected to see that it will function satisfactorily. In the case of a manual emergency system, the system can be checked by operation with the airplane jacked up.

In all cases, the technician must be thoroughly familiar with the landing-gear system which he is inspecting or repairing. If he does not know all the details of a system, he should consult the manufacturer's manual. It must be remembered that there are many variations in the design of landing-gear systems, and it is up to the technician to be sure he understands the particular system upon which he is working.

Main landing gear

One type of retractable main landing gear is illustrated in Fig. 15·3. The assembly consists principally of the shock strut; the wheel; the brake assembly; the trunnion and side brace; the torque link, or "scissors;" the actuating cylinder; the down and up locks; and the bungee system.

To retract the gear, the actuating cylinder is extended by hydraulic pressure. Since the actuating cylinder can provide greater force during extension of the cylinder than it can during retraction because of the greater piston area exposed to fluid pressure, the extension movement of the actuating cylinder is used to retract the gear. Retraction of the gear requires the greater force because of gravity. Extension of the actuating cylinder causes the gear to rotate on the trunnion pin until the gear is approximately in a horizontal position. When the gear reaches the full up position, a pin on the strut engages the up latch and locks the gear in the up position.

When the gear is extended, the first movement of the actuating cylinder releases the up lock. This permits the gear to fall of its own weight, and the actuating cylinder acts to snub the rate of fall. Usually there is an orifice check valve in the up line of the landing-gear hydraulic system; this restricts the fluid flow from the actuating cylinder to the return line, thus slowing the rate of gear descent. As the gear approaches the down position, the actuating cylinder moves it to the full down position. In the down position, a blade engages the down-lock track and slides into the down-lock latch as shown in Fig. 15·4. The down lock prevents the gear from retracting after it has been lowered.

When the operation of a retractable gear system includes the opening and closing of gear doors, an associated system controlled by **sequence valves** is often used to operate the doors. The sequence of operation is (1) opening of doors and (2) lowering of gear. During retraction, the gear retracts and then the doors close. The doors can be operated through the hydraulic system or by a mechanical linkage in connection with the movement of the landing-gear mechanism. In some designs, the landing-gear doors are closed when the gear is extended or retracted. In such cases, the doors must operate twice for either retraction or extension of the gear.

The landing gear shown in Fig. 15·3 is equipped with a pneumatic **bungee** system for emergency operation. The purpose of the system is to provide air or gas pressure to lower the gear in the event of hydraulic power failure. The bungee tank is charged with air or gas at a high pressure and when it becomes necessary to lower the gear in an emergency, the air or gas is released from the tank by means of a valve and is carried through tubing to a special bungee cylinder. This cylinder provides enough force to lock the gear in the down position. In many systems, the air or gas is

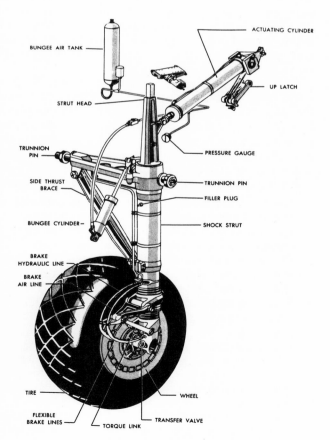

Figure 15·3 Retractable landing gear.

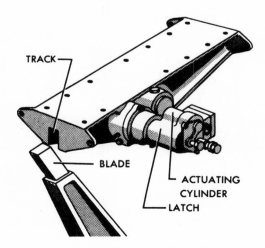

Figure 15·4 A down-lock mechanism.

251

directed to a **shuttle valve** which blocks off the hydraulic system and opens the down line to the main landing-gear actuating cylinder which then lowers and locks the gear. In any case, the landing-gear control handle must be placed in the DOWN position.

Nose landing gear

One type of retractable nose gear is illustrated in Fig. 15 · 5. The operation of this gear is similar to that of the main gear and the movement of the gear is in a straight fore-and-aft direction.

Especially important to the operation of the nose gear are the torque links and the shimmy damper. The torque links hold the nose wheel in alignment and must be kept in such condition that there is a minimum of side play or end play in the connecting rods and bolts. The allowable play is usually specified in the manufacturer's repair manual. The shimmy damper is a hydraulic snubbing unit which reduces the tendency of the wheel to oscillate from side to side.

Retractable nose-gear systems are equipped with up and down locks which operate in the same manner as those on the main gear. Figure 15 · 6 is an enlarged drawing of the up-lock mechanism shown in Fig. 15 · 5.

Landing gear for light twin airplane

Drawings of the main- and nose-gear assemblies for the Piper PA-23 airplane are shown in Fig. 15 · 7. These drawings show the principal components of the gear assemblies together with associated structural parts and landing-gear doors. The gear assemblies are of the air-oil type and include the features discussed previously. The nose gear is steerable and this requires the

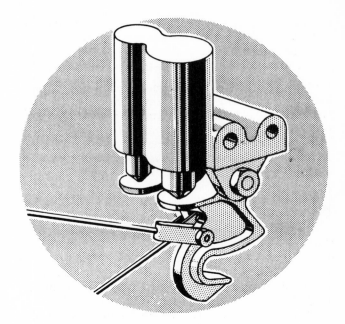

Figure 15 · 6 *Up-lock mechanism.*

addition of the steering mechanism shown in the drawing.

Servicing instructions for the landing gear are given in the manufacturer's overhaul manual and all service and repair operations must be accomplished accordingly.

The fluid used in the struts is MIL-O-5606, petroleum-base, and the struts are inflated to give approximately 3 in. extension. The struts are filled with fluid by attaching one end of a clear plastic tube to the air-valve stem after the core is removed and by placing the other end of the tube in a container of clean fluid. With the airplane jacked up, the strut can be extended and compressed to pump fluid through the tube into the strut. The strut is full when air bubbles no longer enter the tube from the strut. The strut is then compressed to within ¼ in. of full compression, and excess fluid is permitted to drain out through the valve stem. The valve core is replaced before the strut is inflated by means of a strut pump. Inflation of the main struts to an extension of 3 in. with the airplane weight on the strut is required.

As mentioned earlier in this text and illustrated in the schematic diagram of Fig. 13 · 52, the hydraulic system for the Piper PA-23 aircraft includes an emergency CO_2 bottle for operation of the landing gear in case of main-system failure.

LANDING GEAR FOR THE DOUGLAS DC-9 AIRLINER

The Douglas DC-9 airplane has a tricycle, fully retractable landing gear. The nose gear is a dual-wheel, steerable type with the oleo strut mounted in the forward, lower section of the fuselage. The main gear consists of two pairs of wheels and brakes on oleo (air-

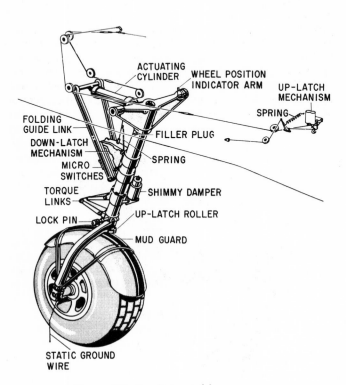

ACTUATING CYLINDER
WHEEL POSITION INDICATOR ARM
UP-LATCH MECHANISM
SPRING
FOLDING GUIDE LINK
FILLER PLUG
DOWN-LATCH MECHANISM
MICRO SWITCHES
SPRING
TORQUE LINKS
SHIMMY DAMPER
LOCK PIN
UP-LATCH ROLLER
MUD GUARD
STATIC GROUND WIRE

Figure 15 · 5 *Retractable nose gear.*

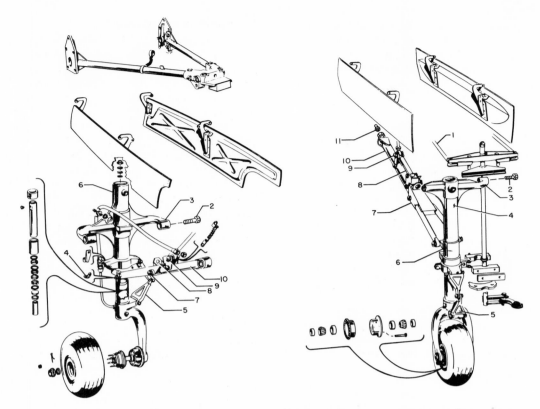

1. Nose-gear steering arm assembly
2. Bolt
3. Bushing
4. Wire support lug
5. Scissor and bushing assembly
6. Oleo strut assembly
7. Lower drag link assembly
8. Down-lock link assembly
9. Hydraulic actuating piston rod end bearing
10. Upper drag-link assembly
11. Lubricator fitting

Figure 15·7   Landing gear for Piper PA-23 airplane. (Piper Aircraft Corp.)

oil) struts mounted in the wing-root area aft of the right- and left-wing rear spar.

The main-gear inboard doors and the nose-gear forward doors are connected to their respective gear assemblies through linkages which sequence the doors to the open position during gear travel and to the closed position at the end of each cycle. The nose-gear aft doors and the main-gear outboard doors move with the gear. Each wheel well is completely enclosed by doors when the gear is retracted, and the major portion of each wheel well is enclosed after the gear is extended.

Gear retraction and extension and the mechanical release of the door latches are controlled by the landing-gear control lever. The hydraulic power system actuates the gear, door latches, bungee cylinders, brakes, and the nose-wheel steering system. Without hydraulic power, the gear can be mechanically released to free-fall and lock in the down position through the use of an alternate extension control lever.

The nose-wheel steering system is hydraulically controlled through its full range of 164°, (82° to either side of center), by a steering wheel located on the captain's left console. The rudder pedals can be used for 17° or less steering control to either side of the neutral position. When the steering cylinders are in the neutral position, they act as shimmy dampers.

Each main-gear wheel is fitted with a hydraulic power disk brake. The brakes are controlled by the brake control valves which are operated by a cable system connected to the brake pedals. An electrically controlled **antiskid system** provides a locked-wheel protection feature and affords maximum efficiency to the brake system. The antiskid-system dual-servo valves meter applied pressure to the brakes as required to provide maximum braking effect without skidding.

An electrically monitored indicating-and-warning system provides the flight crew with all the necessary gear- and gear-door position indications. These indications are visible in the cockpit.

Main-gear assemblies

Each main gear consists of two wheels and brakes attached to an oleo (air-oil) strut which is mounted on a support fitting on the rear spar in each wing-root area. One of the main-gear assemblies is shown in Fig. 15·8.

A main-gear assembly can be used as either a right gear or left gear by installing the bungee cylinder and bracket on the outboard side of the strut and by attaching the torque links (scissors) to the forward axle lugs with apex bolt heads facing inboard. Provisions are made for attaching the door-sequence drive

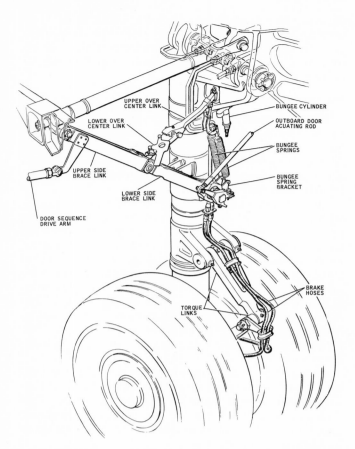

Main-gear swivel glands

The **main-gear swivel glands** are flexible joints with internal passages which route hydraulic fluid to the wheel brakes and the bungee cylinder on each gear. Swivel glands are used where the bend radius is too small or space limitations prevent the use of coiled, hydraulic lines.

The three swivel glands, one of which is illustrated in Fig. 15·9, are mounted on a bracket secured to the main-gear trunnion fitting between, and in line with, the forward and aft trunnion bolts. Each gland remains stationary and is the terminus of the stationary hydraulic lines. The movable portion of each swivel gland is connected to the hydraulic lines that are routed down the strut to the bungee cylinder and the wheel brakes. The location of the swivel glands with respect to the main-gear assembly is shown in Fig. 15·8.

A clamp-and-bracket assembly is attached to each pair of hydraulic lines and to the fittings in the movable gland ports and acts as the swivel driver.

In Fig. 15·9, it can be seen that the gland consists of annular grooves separated from one another by means of slipper rings and packings to isolate the pressure fluid from the return fluid. Thus the gear can be raised and lowered without disturbing the fluid passage to and from the brakes and bungee cylinder.

Figure 15·8 Main landing-gear assembly for Douglas DC-9. (Douglas Aircraft Co., Inc.)

arm to the upper side of the upper side brace link.

Each main gear is supported laterally by the **side brace links.** These are locked in the down position by **over-center links** which are driven hydraulically by a **bungee cylinder** and mechanically by the **bungee springs.** The side brace links and the over-center links fold up along the rear strut during gear retraction. Each main gear is hydraulically raised to the up position by a main-gear actuating cylinder and is held in the up position by the main-gear doors and latches during flight. At this time the hydraulic pressure is reduced to 1500 psi.

A segmented rotor- and disk-type power brake is installed on each main-gear wheel. The brake carrier is bolted to a flanged portion of the fixed axle, which is an integral part of the oleo piston.

The main-gear wheels are split-type, machined aluminum, and rotate on tapered roller bearings. There are two wheels on each main-gear assembly, as shown in Fig. 15·8.

One large inboard and one small outboard door enclose each gear well. The inboard doors are moved to the open position during gear travel by means of a hydraulic cylinder sequenced by the **door-sequence drive arm** attached to the upper side-brace link. The outboard doors are linked directly to the gear strut and follow the gear at all times.

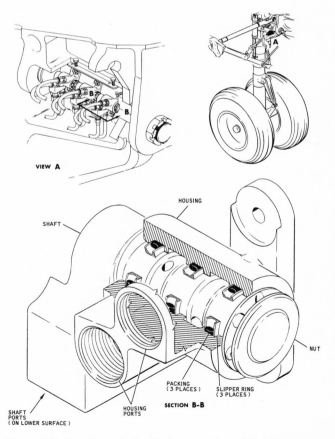

Figure 15·9 Swivel glands for transfer of fluid pressure. (Douglas Aircraft Co., Inc.)

Main-gear torque links

The **main-gear torque links** are two A-frame-type members, as shown in Fig. 15 · 10, used to connect the main-gear strut cylinder to the piston and axle. The torque links, also called "scissors," restrict the extension of the piston during gear retraction and hold the wheels and axle in a correctly aligned position.

The upper torque link is connected to a clevis fitting on the lower forward side of the shock strut by a hollow pin which is secured by a lock bolt. The strut clevis fittings are the torque link and are fitted with flanged bushings. When the bushings are properly pressed into the fittings, a nominal clearance gap remains to allow free movement of the link. A bumper bushing is pressed into the open ends of the pin with the bushing flange riding the clevis fitting.

The lower torque link is connected to a clevis fitting on the axle. There are two clevis fittings on the axle, each facing 180° apart and each canted several degrees outboard to permit interchangeability. The clevis fittings and torque links are assembled with bushings as explained above.

The upper and lower torque links are joined together, as shown in the drawing, by a bolt and nut and are spaced with washers. Each link is fitted with flanged bushings. The gap between the flanged ends of the bushings is taken up by a washer.

The correct adjustment of the torque links and the clearances permitted are specified in the manufacturer's maintenance manual. The satisfactory operation of the gear units and the alignment of the wheels depend upon the adjustment of the torque links. It is therefore important that the units be inspected periodically according to the manufacturer's directions to assure that any deviation from requirements is corrected.

Main-gear doors

The **main-gear doors** and their position in relation to the landing gear are shown in Fig. 15 · 11. The doors enclose the main-gear wheel wells and a section of the wing-root area when the gear is retracted. There are two doors for each gear, designated as the **inboard door** and the **outboard door.**

The inboard door, the larger of the two, is square, with the outboard portion curved upward to conform to the shape of the adjoining fuselage structure. The core of the door is honeycomb construction strengthened by heavy frames. The door is exceptionally sturdy because it must support the weight of the main-gear assembly in the retracted position. A single hook-and-roller-type latch assembly holds the door in the closed position. The door is actuated by a single hydraulic cylinder that attaches to a clevis on the forward frame and to the bracket attached to the shear web.

The outboard door is a smaller, irregular-shaped, honeycomb-core-type assembly attached to the lower wing section by a standard piano-type hinge. The door is linked directly to the gear strut by a pushrod and follows the gear strut during the gear extension and retraction operations.

Nose gear

The **nose gear** of the Douglas DC-9 airplane is a dual-wheel, steerable, oleo shock-strut unit which retracts forward and up into the fuselage during flight and is completely enclosed by doors when retracted. A drawing of the unit and its associated parts is shown in Fig. 15 · 12.

The nose-gear strut is supported by the side braces

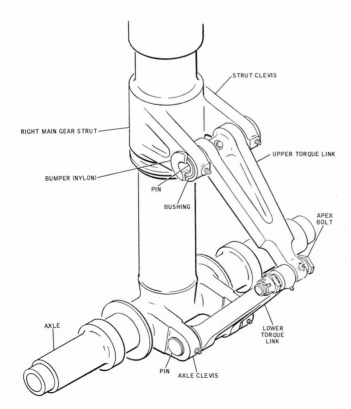

Figure **15 · 10**   Torque links.

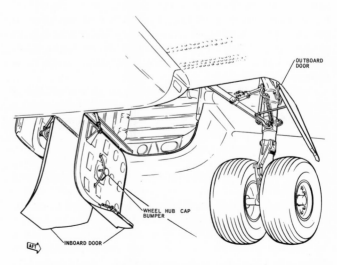

Figure **15 · 11**   Main-gear doors for Douglas DC-9. (Douglas Aircraft Co., Inc.)

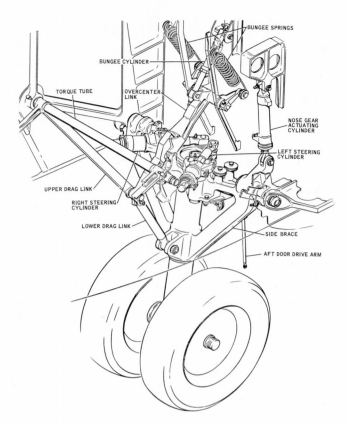

Labels on figure:
BUNGEE SPRINGS
BUNGEE CYLINDER
TORQUE TUBE
OVERCENTER LINK
NOSE GEAR ACTUATING CYLINDER
LEFT STEERING CYLINDER
UPPER DRAG LINK
RIGHT STEERING CYLINDER
LOWER DRAG LINK
SIDE BRACE
AFT DOOR DRIVE ARM

Figure **15·12** *Nose-gear assembly for Douglas DC-9.*

and the crossarm, which comprise an integral part of the strut casting, and by the drag links. The wheels are mounted on an axle that is attached to the lower end of the strut piston. Over-center linkage, which is attached between the drag links and the fuselage structure, locks the drag links and strut in the down position. The nose-gear actuating cylinder is attached to a cross-arm crank and to the fuselage structure on the left side of the assembly. The cylinder is compressed when the gear is extended.

The nosewheel steering cylinders are mounted on the upper forward side of the strut cylinder body, and the pistons are attached to the piston and axle by the torque links. When the gear is retracted, the nosewheel well is completely enclosed by four doors. The two forward doors are driven by a linkage connected to the upper drag links and sequence with gear travel. The aft doors are linked directly to the gear strut and move with the gear.

Nose-gear strut

The nose-gear strut is a steerable, dual-wheel, fully retractable oleo strut. It supports the forward portion of the airplane, absorbs landing shock, and steers the airplane through ground maneuvers.

The strut is supported by the side braces and crossarm, which are part of the strut casting, and by the drag links. The major components of the strut are the **cylinder body,** the **steering cylinder,** and the **piston.** The cylinder body is the major support for the strut

with the side braces and crossarm as an integral part of the body. The steering cylinder is installed inside the body between the body and the piston and mounts the steering bosses on the top side. The piston is inside the steering cylinder and is the shock absorber and support for the axle and wheels. Torque links are attached to the steering cylinder and to the axle boss. They transfer steering motion from the steering cylinder to the wheels and limit the extension length of the piston during gear retraction. The *main* steering described here must not be confused with the two cylinders called the **right steering cylinder** and the **left steering cylinder** shown in Fig. 15·12. These two units are *actuating cylinders.*

The side braces and crossarm support the nose-gear strut vertically and laterally. A torque arm extension on the left side brace is the attach point for the nose-gear-actuating cylinder. The drag link is attached to the forward side of the strut body and supports the strut longitudinally. The gear is locked in the DOWN or UP position by the over-center linkage. Internally, the nose-gear strut contains a metering-pin and strap assembly, a metering-plate and plate support, a piston seal adapter with static and dynamic O rings and D rings, and a piston guide. The internal construction of the strut is illustrated in Fig. 15·13. It will be observed that the strut resembles others which have been described previously.

As shown in the drawing, the metering-pin, plate, and centering assemblies are installed inside the piston assembly. The piston assembly is installed inside the steering-cylinder assembly, and the steering assembly is installed inside the cylinder body. The cylinder body is the main support for all nose-gear-strut components. The steering cylinder is free to rotate within the body and rides on a pair of bushings on the body. It is secured within the body by a jam nut at the top of the cylinder. The piston is free to rotate, compress, or extend within the steering cylinder. It is retained by a gland nut at the bottom of the steering cylinder and by the nose-gear torque links. The metering-plate support assembly is held in position by the same jam nut that retains the steering cylinder. The metering pin is attached directly to the piston assembly and moves with the piston.

Nose-gear linkage

The **nose-gear linkage** consists of the **drag links, over center linkage,** and **torque-tube assembly.** These are illustrated in Fig. 15·14. The drag links are the longitudinal-axis support members for the nose-gear strut in the down position. They consist of three tubular links. The upper two links are connected to the nose-gear support structure by a torque tube that acts as a pivot point. The lower drag link attaches to the upper two links at the midway point and connects to the nose-gear-strut clevis on the lower forward side of the cylinder body. The junction point of the three drag-link members is also the connecting point for the lower **over-center link.** The over-center links hold the drag links and the nose-gear strut in the downlocked posi-

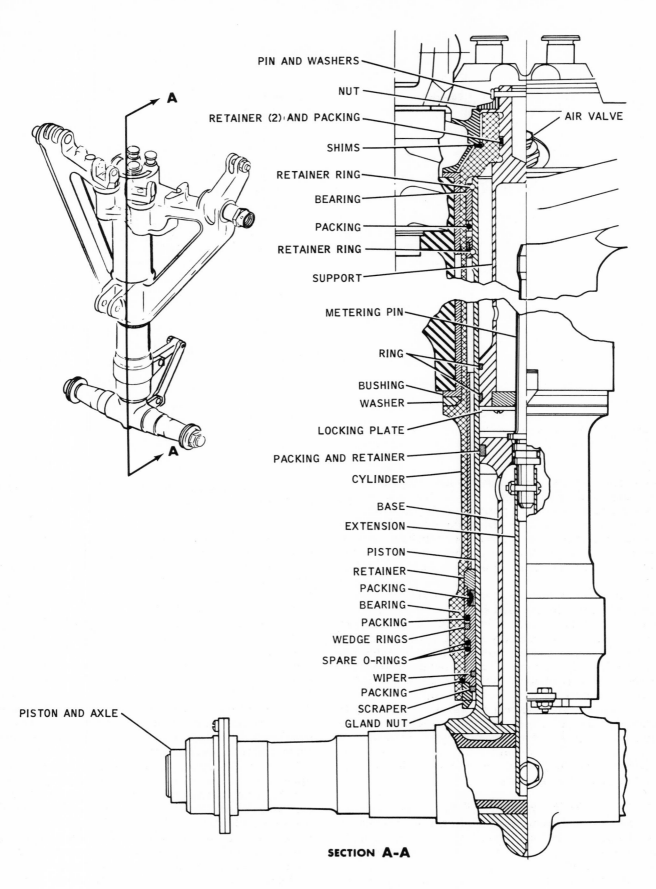

PIN AND WASHERS

NUT

RETAINER (2) AND PACKING

SHIMS

RETAINER RING

BEARING

PACKING

RETAINER RING

SUPPORT

AIR VALVE

METERING PIN

RING

BUSHING

WASHER

LOCKING PLATE

PACKING AND RETAINER

CYLINDER

BASE

EXTENSION

PISTON

RETAINER

PACKING

BEARING

PACKING

WEDGE RINGS

SPARE O-RINGS

WIPER

PACKING

SCRAPER

GLAND NUT

PISTON AND AXLE

A

A

SECTION A-A

Figure 15·13   Cross-section drawing of Douglas DC-9 nose-gear strut.

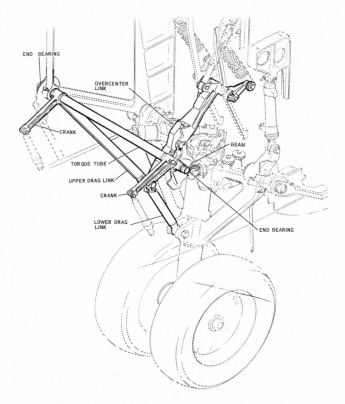

Figure **15·14** *Nose-gear actuating linkage for Douglas DC-9.*

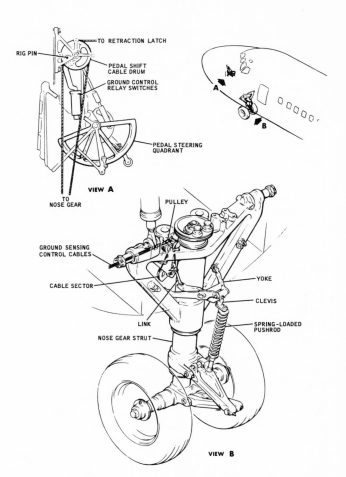

Figure **15·15** *Ground-sensing mechanism on Douglas DC-9 airplane. (Douglas Aircraft Co., Inc.)*

tion. The links lock over center when the gear is fully extended and when the gear is fully retracted. When in the down-and-locked position and it is desired to retract the gear, the over-center links are released by the hydraulically actuated **bungee cylinder** to permit gear retraction. The bungee cylinder, which is attached to the upper over-center link, can be seen in Fig. 15·12.

When the gear is in the UP position, the over-center links are normally released by the same bungee cylinder but, in the absence of hydraulic power, they can be released by a manually operated trip lever and roller that is connected to the alternate extension control lever mechanism. The two bungee springs are a mechanical backup for the hydraulically operated bungee cylinder.

The upper two nose-gear drag links are fitted with cranks at the pivot axis points. These cranks are the connecting points for the nose-gear forward-door drive linkage. The forward doors are cycled to the open position during gear travel and are closed at the end of each cycle of gear travel.

Ground-sensing control mechanism

The **ground-sensing control mechanism** provides a mechanical means of establishing a ground or flight mode with the functions of various systems differing as the mode differs.

The mechanism, shown in the drawings of Fig. 15·15, consists of a few simple linkages and a two-way, closed cable circuit actuated by the nose-gear links during gear-strut extension and compression. When the airplane takes off, the strut extends and establishes the flight mode. When the airplane is on the ground, the strut is compressed and the ground-operation mode is established.

The linkage for the ground-sensing control mechanism on the nose gear consists of a lever, a spring-loaded rod, and a cable sector. The linkages in the flight compartment consist of a cable drum and shaft that drives the pedal steering override mechanism, and a striker that actuates the ground control relays. The two-way, closed-circuit cable system runs from the sector on the nose gear to the cable drum on the rudder pedal-over-ride mechanism. The **antiretraction latch cable** takes off from the same cable drum.

When the nose-gear strut extends, the nose-gear upper torque link draws the linkage downward pulling the spring-loaded rod assembly down and rotates the cable sector clockwise. The cable drives the pedal-override cable drum and shaft, which disengages the pedal steering mechanism. At the same time, the ground-control relays are actuated causing various electrical circuits to assume the flight mode.

When the nose-gear strut is compressed, a ground mode is established. The pedal steering system is actuated to permit rudder-pedal steering, the antire-traction latch is engaged to prevent inadvertent operation of the landing-gear control lever, and the ground-control relays assume the ground operations mode. The feature which prevents retraction of the gear while the airplane is on the ground is required on all aircraft having retractable landing gear. The design of these systems varies widely although they all serve the same function.

Landing-gear extension-and-retraction system

The landing-gear extension-and-retraction system is composed of two major systems designated as the **mechanical control system** and the **hydraulic control system.** These are illustrated in Fig. 15 · 16.

The mechanical control system is divided into four sections. These are (1) the landing-gear control valve cable system; (2) the main-gear inboard door-sequence follow-up valve system; (3) the alternate, or bypass, valve system; and (4) the subsystems.

The landing-gear control valve cable system is a dual-cable system that runs from the landing-gear control-lever cable drums in the flight compartment to the landing-gear control valve cable drums in the right wheel well. This cable system operates the landing-gear control valve during normal operation.

The **main-gear door-sequence valve follow-up system** is made up of two push-pull cables and associated linkages on the main-gear side braces to drive the main-gear inboard doors open and closed. The sequence valves are also linked to the landing-gear control-valve cable drums for initial motivation.

The **alternate,** or **bypass valve, system** is a dual-cable system. One cable drives the bypass valve cable drum, which actuates the bypass valve, the door-latch releases, and the door skids. The other cable actuates the nose-gear over-center release mechanism. The alternate system (bypass valve) is used as a backup system to free-fall the gear in case of hydraulic power failure.

The hydraulic control system is divided into two sections. The landing-gear control valve and the door-sequence valves comprise the basic system. The second section is the alternate, or bypass, system mentioned above. The bypass valve is used on the ground to relieve door-cylinder pressure and permit the doors to be opened manually for ground-maintenance access.

The landing-gear control valve ports hydraulic pressure to the main- and nose-gear actuating cylinders, the bungee cylinders, and the main-gear door-latch cylinders. The door-sequence valves port pressure to the door actuating cylinders.

When the landing-gear control lever is placed in the GEAR UP position, the cable system positions the landing-gear control valve to port *up* pressure to the main- and nose-gear actuating cylinders, *unlock* pressure to the bungee cylinders, and *unlock* pressure to the door-latch cylinders. At the same time the cable-drum linkages position the door-sequence valves in the door-open position. As the gear travels toward the up position, the side braces fold up, driving the door follow-up mechanism toward the door-closed position.

As the gear nears the end of its upward travel, the follow-up mechanism positions the door-sequence valves to the door-closed position, and the doors close. The door-latch cylinders lock the latches to secure the doors which, in turn, support the gear.

The nose-gear linkage will move to the over-center position when the gear is up and the bungee springs will hold the over-center locked condition. To extend the gear, the landing-gear control lever is placed in the GEAR DOWN position. The cable system positions the landing-gear control valve and the door-sequence valves to port (direct) hydraulic fluid to the door actuating cylinders and the gear actuating cylinders. The fluid pressure moves the gear actuating cylinders in the *down* direction and causes the door-latch cylinders and the bungee cylinders to unlock. As the gear moves down, the door follow-up mechanism begins to drive the door-sequence valves toward the *up* position. By the time the gear is down and locked, the door-sequence valves have reached the closed position and the inboard doors close. The nose-gear doors are actuated mechanically through linkage with the gear; they are sequenced to the open position during gear travel and to the closed position at the end of each travel cycle.

In the event of hydraulic power failure or a jammed control valve, the gear can be extended by free-fall. When the alternate landing-gear control lever (located in a floor well to the right of the center pedestal) is pulled up, two backup systems are actuated. One cable system operates the nose-gear mechanical release to free the nose gear, and the other system operates the bypass valve, the door latches, and the door skids. The gear will then free-fall and lock in the down position. The bungee springs assure the locked condition of the gear in the down position.

LANDING GEAR FOR THE BOEING 720 AIRLINER

Because of the complexity of the landing-gear systems for a large jet airliner, no attempt will be made in this text to describe such gear in detail. The principles of operation are similar to those previously discussed; however, the technician desiring detailed design, construction, and assembly information should consult the manufacturer's maintenance manual. It is our purpose here to give a brief description of the landing gear for the Boeing 720 airplane, primarily so comparisons can be made with those previously discussed and so the student will have an appreciation of the magnitude of the engineering involved and the great skill and precision necessary to produce systems and mechanisms which perform their functions so effectively.

Description and operation of the main landing gear

Figure 15 · 17 illustrates the arrangement of the main landing gear on the Boeing 720 airplane. Observe that the main gear has many of the same components and features of the gear mechanisms described previously

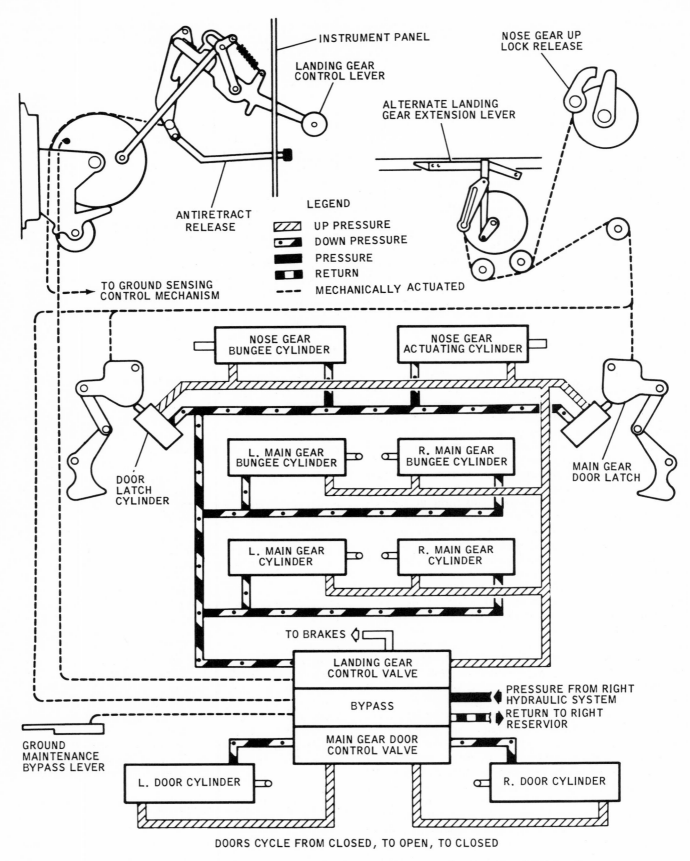

INSTRUMENT PANEL

LANDING GEAR CONTROL LEVER

NOSE GEAR UP LOCK RELEASE

ALTERNATE LANDING GEAR EXTENSION LEVER

ANTIRETRACT RELEASE

LEGEND

▨	UP PRESSURE
▨	DOWN PRESSURE
▮	PRESSURE
▬	RETURN
– – –	MECHANICALLY ACTUATED

TO GROUND SENSING CONTROL MECHANISM

NOSE GEAR BUNGEE CYLINDER

NOSE GEAR ACTUATING CYLINDER

DOOR LATCH CYLINDER

L. MAIN GEAR BUNGEE CYLINDER

R. MAIN GEAR BUNGEE CYLINDER

MAIN GEAR DOOR LATCH

L. MAIN GEAR CYLINDER

R. MAIN GEAR CYLINDER

TO BRAKES

LANDING GEAR CONTROL VALVE

BYPASS

PRESSURE FROM RIGHT HYDRAULIC SYSTEM

RETURN TO RIGHT RESERVOIR

MAIN GEAR DOOR CONTROL VALVE

GROUND MAINTENANCE BYPASS LEVER

L. DOOR CYLINDER

R. DOOR CYLINDER

DOORS CYCLE FROM CLOSED, TO OPEN, TO CLOSED

Figure 15·16 Mechanical and hydraulic control systems for Douglas DC-9 landing gear. (Douglas Aircraft Co., Inc.)

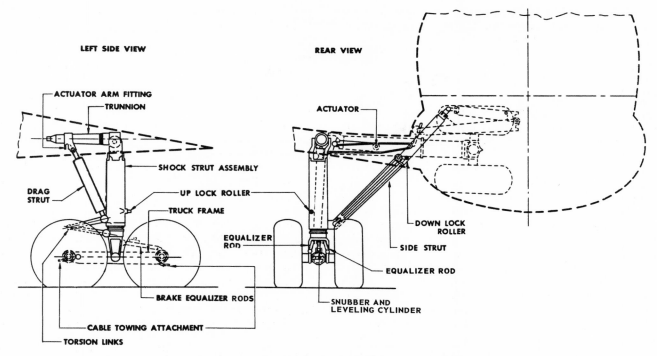

LEFT SIDE VIEW

ACTUATOR ARM FITTING
TRUNNION
SHOCK STRUT ASSEMBLY
DRAG STRUT
UP LOCK ROLLER
TRUCK FRAME
EQUALIZER ROD
BRAKE EQUALIZER RODS
CABLE TOWING ATTACHMENT
TORSION LINKS

REAR VIEW

ACTUATOR
DOWN LOCK ROLLER
SIDE STRUT
EQUALIZER ROD
SNUBBER AND LEVELING CYLINDER

Figure 15·17 Schematic drawing of main landing gear for the Boeing 720 airplane. (Boeing Co.)

in this chapter. One of the principal differences is that this particular gear has four wheels mounted on a truck assembly at the bottom of the oleo shock strut.

Each main-gear unit retracts into a wheel well in the fuselage, and gear doors close over the gear to provide a completely smooth wing-root and fuselage surface. As with other systems for large aircraft, the gear actuation for retraction and extention is accomplished by means of hydraulic power. Because of the four wheels on each main gear, a smaller wheel can be used than would otherwise be required. An emergency extension system is provided for the gear in case of hydraulic power failure.

A **trunnion,** pivoting on an axis parallel to the airplane center line, provides the main attachment for each main landing gear. Trunnion support bearings are carried in a **torsion box** attached to the wing rear spar. Drag and side loads are transmitted from the oleo strut to the structure through brace struts as shown in Fig. 15·18.

Moving the landing-gear control handle to the UP or DOWN position directs hydraulic-fluid pressure for landing-gear actuation. To retract an extended landing gear, the control handle is moved to the UP position. The wheel-well doors open, down locks release, and the landing-gear retracts. The up locks engage and the wheel-well doors close. When the control lever is placed in the DOWN position, the wheel-well doors open, the up locks release, the gear extends and locks in the down position, and the wheel-well doors close again.

Figure 15·18 illustrates the principal components of the main-gear structure. The drawing should be

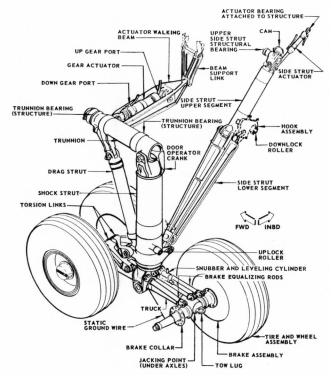

ACTUATOR BEARING ATTACHED TO STRUCTURE
ACTUATOR WALKING BEAM
CAM
UPPER SIDE STRUT STRUCTURAL BEARING
UP GEAR PORT
GEAR ACTUATOR
DOWN GEAR PORT
BEAM SUPPORT LINK
SIDE STRUT ACTUATOR
TRUNNION BEARING (STRUCTURE)
SIDE STRUT UPPER SEGMENT
TRUNNION BEARING (STRUCTURE)
HOOK ASSEMBLY
TRUNNION
DOWNLOCK ROLLER
DOOR OPERATOR CRANK
DRAG STRUT
SIDE STRUT LOWER SEGMENT
SHOCK STRUT
TORSION LINKS
FWD INBD
UPLOCK ROLLER
SNUBBER AND LEVELING CYLINDER
BRAKE EQUALIZING RODS
TRUCK
TIRE AND WHEEL ASSEMBLY
STATIC GROUND WIRE
BRAKE COLLAR
BRAKE ASSEMBLY
JACKING POINT (UNDER AXLES)
TOW LUG

Figure 15·18 Main landing-gear components for Boeing 720 airplane. (Boeing Co.)

studied carefully to note the similarities and differences when comparing the gear with those previously described. Observe particularly the **snubber-and-leveling cylinder** necessary to afford smooth operation of the

261

truck-type wheel-and-axle supporting structure. Note also the **side-strut actuator** and the main-gear actuator with the **actuator walking beam.**

Main-gear shock strut

The main-gear shock strut for the Boeing 720 airplane, illustrated in Fig. 15·19, is made of steel and consists of an **outer and inner cylinder,** a **piston** attached to the upper inner side of the outer cylinder, and an **orifice rod** attached to the inner cylinder. This construction varies from others we have described; however, the functional principle is the same as that for other air-oil-type shock struts.

The shock strut is filled with hydraulic fluid (MIL-H-5606) and charged with dry compressed air to absorb landing and taxi shock loads. Landing shock absorption is accomplished by the flow of hydraulic fluid through a variable orifice formed by the tapered orifice rod through an opening in the piston and by the flow of hydraulic fluid through openings in the **piston rod.** As the shock strut is compressed, the tapered orifice rod permits a diminishing rate of hydraulic-fluid flow from the inner-cylinder chamber to the upper side of the piston. Landing and taxi shocks are also cushioned by the increasing volume of hydraulic fluid above the piston which further compresses a volume of air in the upper end of the outer cylinder. The shock strut is serviced with hydraulic fluid through an air valve in the upper inboard side of the outer cylinder. The shock strut is serviced with dry, clean air through the air valve to the specified shock-strut extension given on a servicing chart on the keel beam of the fuselage in the left wheel well.

Upper and lower bearings in the shock strut provide sliding surfaces and an air-oil seal between the inner and outer cylinders. Between the lower bearing and the spacer, a **seal adapter** with annular grooves is installed. A D-ring and an O-ring seal with backup rings are inserted in the grooves to provide the air-oil seal between the cylinders. The shock struts have annular grooves in the lower bearing for storage of spare D and O rings. The spare seals can be used to replace the working seals without complete disassembly of the shock strut.

Lugs are provided on the forward side of the outer and inner cylinders for attachment of the **torsion links** to keep the inner cylinder, which is attached to the main-gear wheel truck, from turning within the outer cylinder. The lugs on the forward side of the outer cylinder are also used for drag-strut attachment. Three lugs on the lower terminal of the inner cylinder provide attachment points for the brake equalizer rods and the snubber and leveling cylinder. Lugs on the lower inboard side of the outer cylinder furnish an attachment for the lower side-strut segment universal fitting. Shock-strut doors are attached to the outer cylinder.

A **lock roller** on the lower aft side of the shock-strut outer cylinder contacts a **rabbit-ear crank** on main-gear retraction. Movement of the crank actuates the main-gear position switch and the door-control valve. The lock roller simultaneously engages a power-operated lock hook. This holds the landing gear securely in the up-and-locked position. Rotation of the lock crank to the GEAR-LOCKED position also actuates a lock switch in the circuit with the position switch to illuminate green, down-and-locked indicating lights or a red, gear-unlocked, warning light.

Main-gear wheel truck

The majority of fuselage and wing loads, with the airplane on the ground, are transmitted through the main-gear support trunnion, drag strut, and side strut into the main-gear shock strut. In turn, the loads in the main-gear shock strut are transmitted through the main-gear trucks into the four wheels of each main gear. The main-gear truck is a T-shaped, tubular steel beam to which the forward and aft axles are attached. These are shown in Fig. 15·18. A jacking pad and a towing eye are formed on the front and aft ends of the truck beam. The forward horizontal arms of the truck beam carry the two-piece forward axle. One axle stub is secured in each horizontal arm by a single bolt. Integral flanges on the truck-beam arms carry the forward brake assemblies. The one-piece aft axle is installed through the aft end of the truck beam and locked in position by two bolts through the truck beam and axle. The aft axle is machined on each side of the truck beam to support movable collars. Each movable collar carries an aft-brake assembly and provides an attachment lug for a brake equalizer rod. The **brake**

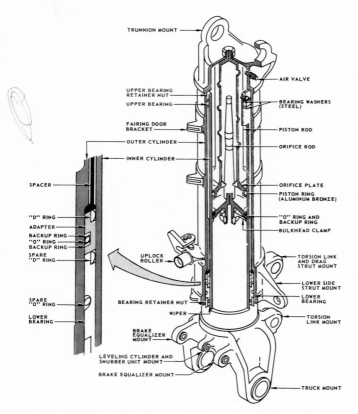

Figure 15·19 Cutaway drawing of the main landing-gear shock strut for Boeing 720 airplane.

equalizer rods link the movable collars with the lugs on the lower terminal shock-strut inner cylinder above the truck beams. The brake equalizer rods prevent "porpoising" (raising of rear-gear wheels) when the brakes are applied on landing or during the taxi roll. The center portion of the truck beam is machined and drilled to mate with the yoke at the lower end of the shock-strut inner cylinder. A lug is formed on the truck beam directly above the rear axle for the attachment of the snubber-and-leveling cylinder. One large bolt attaches the truck to the shock strut. Hydraulic and pneumatic tubing, electric wiring, and a truck leveling switch are attached or bracketed to the truck. A static ground wire is attached to a lug on the underside of the truck between the forward wheels and the shock strut. This wire discharges the static electrical charge which often builds up on the aircraft fuselage during flight.

AIRCRAFT BRAKE SYSTEMS

The brake systems for aircraft all serve the same purpose even though there are a variety of designs. The majority of brake systems fall into one of four categories: (1) shoe brakes, (2) expander-tube brakes, (3) single-disk brakes, and (4) multiple-disk brakes.

The shoe-type brakes have been used for many years on some of the older aircraft and are still used extensively for automobiles. A typical shoe brake is illustrated in Fig. 15·20. This brake system consists of two master cylinders with a single reservoir for storing reserve hydraulic fluid. The master cylinder contains a piston operated by foot pressure to force hydraulic fluid through tubing to the wheel cylinders, which ex-

pand the brake shoes and press them against the inner surface of the brake drums. The brake shoes are lined with tough, heat-resistant material to withstand the wear and heat developed by the friction of the shoe against the drum.

Expander-tube brakes consist of a flat, synthetic-rubber tube mounted on a drum-shaped member attached to the inner end of the axle. Brake blocks (linings), shaped to the contour of the brake drum, are mounted over the expander tube and are held in place by leaf springs which pass through slots in the ends of the lining blocks and lock in slots in the flanges on each side of the expander tube. The inside of the tube is connected to the hydraulic-fluid line by means of suitable fittings. When hydraulic-fluid pressure from the brake master cylinder or brake valve enters the expander tube, the tube is expanded and presses outward against the brake blocks. The blocks, in turn, press against the inner surface of the brake drum on the wheel, thus tending to stop the wheel rotation. When the pressure of the fluid is released, the leaf springs pull the brake linings away from the brake drum and release the braking action.

A single-disk brake consists of a steel disk which is keyed to the wheel and brake linings arranged so they can apply pressure to both sides of the disk when hydraulic pressure is applied to the brake pistons. Figure 15·21 illustrates the principle of the single-disk brake. It will be noted that stationary and movable brake linings are placed on opposite sides of the disk so the disk will be gripped between the linings when force is applied to the movable lining. The movable lining is

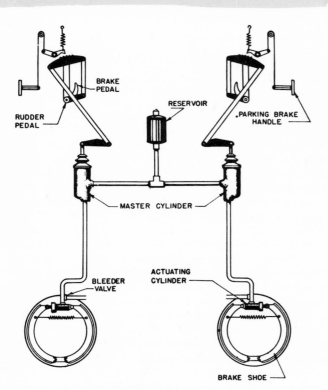

Figure 15·20   A shoe-type brake system.

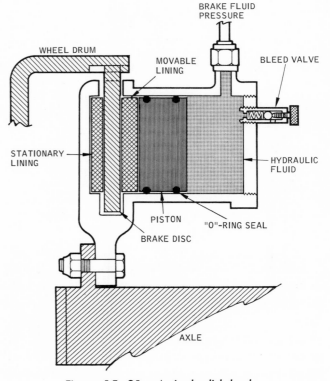

Figure 15·21   A single-disk brake.

actuated by means of the cylinder and piston which receives hydraulic-fluid pressure from the brake master cylinder or brake valve.

The **multiple-disk brake** is constructed somewhat like a disk clutch. Brake disks, alternately stationary and moving, are arranged to provide a maximum of braking surface when the disks are compressed by means of the annular piston or by means of a number of individual pistons arranged in a circle such that their radial distances from the axle are equal. The movable disks (rotor disks) are keyed to the wheel, and the stationary disks (stator disks) are keyed to the axle. When the wheel is turning, each movable disk is turning between two stationary disks. When the brake piston or pistons receive fluid pressure, all the disks are pressed together, thus tending to stop the movement of the movable disks. Since the movable disks are keyed to the wheels at the outer edges, the wheel stops turning when the disks stop.

Brake actuating systems

Brake actuating systems for aircraft can be classified as mechanically operated, hydraulically operated, or pneumatically operated. All brake actuating systems provide for applying either one or both brakes by operating foot pedals.

Mechanical brakes are found on only a few of the older, small airplanes. A mechanical brake actuating system includes pulleys, cables, and bell cranks for connecting the foot pedals to the brake-shoe operating mechanism.

In some airplanes, the hydraulic brake system is a subsystem of the main hydraulic system. In other airplanes, there is an entirely independent brake system. Many of the large airplanes have a power-brake system which is a subsystem of the main system. The smaller airplanes usually have an independent, master brake-cylinder system.

Pneumatic brake systems utilize air pressure instead of fluid pressure to operate the brakes. Some hydraulic brake systems are arranged with a pneumatic backup system for operation in case of hydraulic-fluid loss or failure of hydraulic pressure.

Basic brake system using master cylinders

In Fig. 15·20, a comparatively simple brake system utilizing master cylinders and shoe-type brakes is illustrated. As shown, the system includes brake pedals, a fluid reservoir, two master cylinders, fluid lines, actuating cylinders at the wheels, brake shoes, and bleeder valves.

The **master cylinder** is the energizing unit. There is one for each main landing-gear wheel. The master cylinder is actually a foot-operated, single-action reciprocating pump, the purpose of which is to build up hydraulic-fluid pressure in the brake system.

The **reservoir** is a storage tank that supplies the fluid to compensate for small leaks in the connecting lines or cylinders. The reservoir may be a part of the master cylinder or it may be a separate unit as shown in the drawing. It is vented to the atmosphere to provide for feeding the fluid to the master cylinders under the force of gravity; hence the fluid must be kept at the correct level, or air will enter the system and reduce its effectiveness.

The **fluid lines** may consist of flexible or rigid tubing or a combination of both. Usually flexible tubing is employed with retractable gear systems and between the movable parts of the shock strut.

Mechanical linkages are required to transmit the energy of the foot to the master cylinder. Some airplanes have the master cylinders mounted on the rudder pedals and others have the master cylinders mounted at a distance from the pedals. A system of rods, levers, bell cranks, and cables is often employed to carry the mechanical energy to the master cylinders. In Fig. 15·20, the **brake pedals** are toe brakes mounted on the rudder pedals. When the brake pedals are pressed, the linkage causes the master cylinder piston to move into the cylinder and force fluid into the brake lines. When brakes of this type are pressed, it is necessary for the pilot to balance the force on one pedal with equal force on the other pedal unless he wishes to turn the airplane. The brakes and rudder control are operated independently; however, since the brake pedals are on the rudder pedals, the pilot should be practiced in their use.

The **brake actuating cylinders** are units of the brake assembly that cause the brake shoes to press against the inner surface of the brake drum when pressure from the master cylinders is transmitted to them. If expander-tube brakes or disk-type brakes are employed, the effect is the same even though the braking force is applied in a different manner.

The **parking-brake mechanism** is a subassembly of the usual hydraulic brake system. The control for the mechanism is in the pilot's compartment and usually consists of a pull handle or lever. When the brake pedals are depressed and the parking-brake lever is pulled back by hand, the brakes are locked in the ON position. Depressing the brake pedals again releases the brakes. Various types of master cylinders can be used, but the action of depressing the pedals the second time must cause the master-cylinder piston to return to the OFF position. Depending upon the type of master cylinder used, depressing the pedals will either build up enough pressure to unseat the parking valve, or it will unload a ratchet-type parking lock.

Goodyear master cylinders

One type of master cylinder for light aircraft is illustrated in Fig. 15·22. This master cylinder is a type designed and built by the Goodyear Tire and Rubber Company and is used in some models of older aircraft. It is a simple but effective unit, normally connected by a linkage to the brake pedal mounted on the rudder pedal. The hydraulic fluid enters the master cylinder through the **inlet port** and **compensating port** from the external reservoir which supplies the master cylinders for both the right and left brake systems. The application of the brake forces the **piston** into the cylinder and causes hydraulic fluid to flow toward the brake actu-

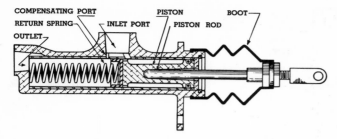

Figure 15·22   A master cylinder.

ating cylinder in the wheel. The illustration shows the cylinder in the horizontal position, but when it is installed in the aircraft it is in a vertical position with the eye of the piston rod downward. When the piston moves against the **return spring** in an upward direction, the compensating port is closed and the fluid in the cylinder is trapped under pressure. Continued pressure applied through the brake pedal forces the fluid pressure to the brake actuating cylinder and applies the brake. When the force is removed from the brake pedal, the piston is returned to the OFF position by means of the return spring and the compensating port is again open to the reservoir. The compensating port permits the fluid to flow toward or away from the reservoir as temperature changes, thus preventing a buildup of pressure when the brake is off.

With this type of master cylinder, the brakes are locked in the ON position for parking by means of a ratchet-type lock that is constructed as part of the mechanical linkage between the foot pedal and the master cylinder. If an increase of temperature occurs, expansion increases the volume of the fluid. This is compensated for by means of a spring built into the linkage. To unlock the brakes, the pilot applies enough force to the brake pedals to unload the ratchet-type lock.

A more recently designed Goodyear master cylinder is used on a number of modern, light aircraft. This cylinder is illustrated in Fig. 15·23. On the Cessna 310 airplane, these cylinders are mounted on the rudder pedals as shown in the drawing of Fig. 15·24. In the illustration of Fig. 15·23, this type of master cylinder incorporates a fluid reservoir (8) on the top of the cylinder (11) within the same body (7). A plastic filler plug (18) is used to close the opening in the cover (4), which is threaded into the body. The filler plug is not vented because sufficient ventilation is provided by clearance between the piston rod (3) and the piston-rod opening through the cover boss (6).

With the exception of the piston return spring (12), all internal operating parts are assembled onto the piston rod. These parts are the piston (15), piston spring (14), "lock-o-seal" (16), and compensating sleeve (17). A seal between the piston and the cylinder walls is provided by the O ring (9) installed in a groove around the piston. As pressure is applied to advance the piston rod into the cylinder, the piston remains stationary until the lock-o-seal is seated on the piston which requires a 0.040-in. movement of the piston rod.

Proper operation of the master cylinder depends upon this seating action. When the lock-o-seal is seated, fluid cannot pass the piston and with continued movement of the piston rod forcing the piston into the cylinder, pressure in the cylinder is increased. At any time during the stroke that force on the piston is eased, the piston return spring will tend to keep the piston seated against the lock-o-seal, maintaining pressure in the cylinder. As the force is further eased, allowing the piston return spring to force the piston to retreat, the upper end of the compensating sleeve will contact the cover boss; thus the piston is forced to unseat itself from the lock-o-seal. This will allow additional fluid from the reservoir to enter the cylinder. This positive unseating also allows unrestricted passage of fluid from the cylinder to the reservoir while the piston is in the static position. This is to compensate for any excess fluid which may be present in the system due to pumping or from thermal expansion.

Power brake control valves

On large aircraft with hydraulic power-brake actuating systems, the control of fluid pressure to the brake mechanism is accomplished by means of **brake control valves,** or **brake metering valves.** These valves are merely special types of flow control valves designed to meet the requirements of brake operation.

The brake control valve for the Douglas DC-9 airplane is illustrated in Fig. 15·25. The upper drawing is the external view, and the lower drawing shows the internal arrangement. As shown in the drawing, the brake control valve has one pressure port, one return port and two brake ports.

It is seen from Fig. 15·25 that during operation the **brake valve crank** is moved toward the ON position, and this forces the plunger toward the right. This action moves the spool inside the **sleeve-and-shuttle** assembly to direct fluid from the pressure inlet to the outlet and thence to the **brake servo valve.** When the system is in the automatic position, the servo valves (not shown in the drawing) automatically control the fluid pressure from the brake control valves to the brakes in response to signals from the antiskid system. When the system is in the nonautomatic, or "manual," condition, the brake control valves control pressure directly to the brakes. During automatic operation, the pilot holds the brake pedals in the FULL ON position.

The power brake control valve for the Boeing 720 airplane is illustrated in Fig. 15·26. These are called **brake metering valves** and are actuated by a mechanical cable linkage connected to the pilot's and copilot's brake pedals. One metering-valve assembly is used for each main landing-gear brake.

Four hydraulic lines are attached to each valve. These are for pressure, return, brakes, and automatic braking. Valve ports are opened or closed by operating a circular, grooved, sliding **valve rod** (spool). The linkage end of the valve rod projects beyond the valve body while the opposite end is supported in a sealed **compensating chamber.**

When the brake pedals are depressed, an inward

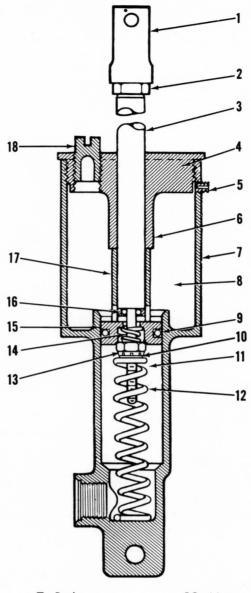

1. Clevis	7. Body	13. Nut
2. Jamb nut	8. Reservoir	14. Piston spring
3. Piston rod	9. O-ring	15. Piston
4. Cover	10. Washer	16. Lock-o-seal
5. Setscrew	11. Cylinder	17. Compensating sleeve
6. Cover boss	12. Piston return spring	18. Filler plug

Figure 15·23 *A Goodyear master cylinder. (Cessna Aircraft Co.)*

movement is imparted to the metering valve rod through the mechanical linkage and cables. As the rod moves in, the return port is closed, and the pressure port is opened to direct hydraulic fluid pressure to the brakes. A passage through the valve rod permits the hydraulic fluid under pressure to enter a compensating chamber enclosing the inner end of the valve rod. Pressure acting on the end of the rod creates a return force tending to close the valve. This return force varies with the intensity of braking force and provides *feel* at the

pedals. The desired braking effort is obtained by depressing the pedals a greater or lesser distance. Cable stretch and adjustment of pedal position permits the valve rod to move back until both pressure and return ports are closed. At this point the braking effort remains constant. This condition is shown schematically in Fig. 15·26. Releasing the brake pedals allows the pressure in the compensating chamber to move the valve rod out and open the brake line to the return line. As pressure in the brake line falls, the brakes are

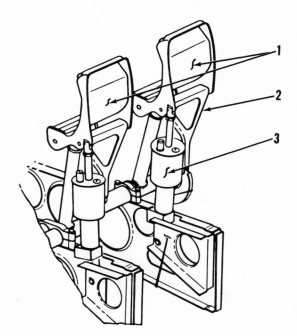

1. Brake pedal
2. Brake link
3. Master cylinder

Figure 15·24   Master cylinders mounted on brake pedals in the Cessna 310 airplane. (Cessna Aircraft Co.)

Figure 15·25   Brake control valve for the Douglas DC-9 airplane (Douglas Aircraft Co., Inc.)

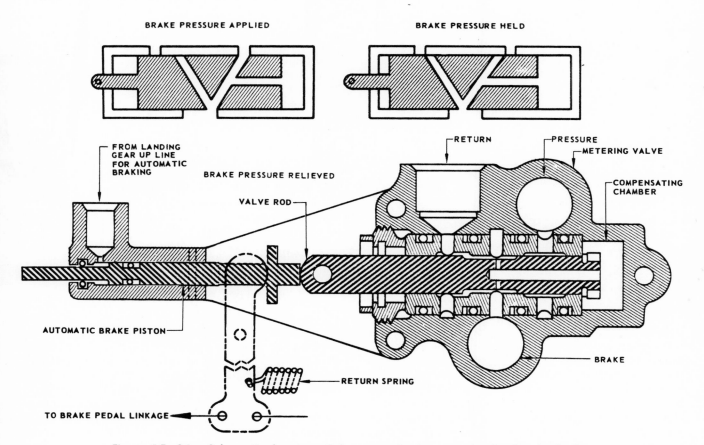

Figure 15·26   Schematic drawing of the power brake control valve for the Boeing 720 airplane. (Boeing Co.)

released, and return force on the valve rod is relieved.

Automatic braking to stop the rotation of the wheels before retraction is provided by a small-diameter piston actuating cylinder attached to the metering valve. The cylinder is connected to the landing-gear retract hydraulic line. When the landing-gear control handle is placed to UP, hydraulic pressure is directed to the automatic cylinder and the piston extends. One end of the piston rod rests on the valve rod; hence extension of the piston opens the metering valve and applies the brakes.

Brake lockout-deboost valve

As explained previously in this text, **deboost valves** or **deboosters** are incorporated in some hydraulic power-brake systems to reduce the hydraulic pressure before it is applied to the brake actuating cylinders. In the brake systems for the Boeing 720 airplane, two brake **lockout-deboost valves** are incorporated in the systems and are mounted in each wing fillet area, immediately outside the main wheel wells. A drawing to illustrate these valves is shown in Fig. 15·27. The lockout-deboost valve is so named because it locks out the brake actuating portion of the system from the main system, thus preventing loss of fluid in case of leakage or damage to the system in the wheel areas. The debooster function is performed by means of a stepped cylinder, housing a double-diameter piston. The piston separates fluid in the brakes from the rest of the hydraulic system as explained previously. When the brake pedals are depressed, pressure released through the **metering valves** acts on the small diameter of the piston and the resulting force causes a pressure buildup in the fluid between the large diameter of the piston and the brake. A reduction in fluid pressure downstream of

the valve is proportional to the diameter ratio of the pistons. This ratio is 2.9:1 for the valve described. The lockout-deboost valve is inoperative when the piston bottoms on the large diameter. This is the *lockout* position.

A manually operated bypass valve permits fluid to pass through the piston when it is required to charge the brake side and raise the piston of the deboost valve. When the **reset handle** is raised, the **slug** is lifted from its seat and hydraulic fluid can pass through the deboost piston to the **ball-check valve.** If the deboost piston is bottomed, the ball check will be raised from its seat by the **pintle.** Hydraulic fluid then flows past the ball check to the underside of the piston. The fluid lifts the piston until the ball check is clear of the pintle. At this point the ball check seats, cuts off the fluid flow, and the piston stops in the correct position. A color plate on the indicator over the reset handle shows piston position at any time. When the brakes are off, the reset handle must be within the green band.

Internal expanding-shoe brakes

The types of internal expanding-shoe brakes are (1) the **one-way,** or **single-servo,** and (2) the **two-way,** or **dual-servo type. Servo action** in a brake of this type means that the rotation of the brake drum adds braking energy to the brake shoes and makes them operate more effectively and with less effort by the pilot.

In single-servo brakes, the servo action is effective for one direction of the wheel only, as contrasted with a **dual-servo** or **reversible type,** which operates, and may be adjusted, to give servo action in either direction. Both types are supplied with either single-shoe or two-shoe construction. Brakes are attached to the strut flange by means of bolts through the torque plate, which has as many as 12 equally spaced holes, with bolts in only one-half of the holes. The alternate holes are used to permit a variation of the position of the brake assembly to assure that the brake cylinder is at the top or highest position on the assembly.

A dual-servo brake assembly is shown in the drawing of Fig. 15·28. As explained previously, dual-servo

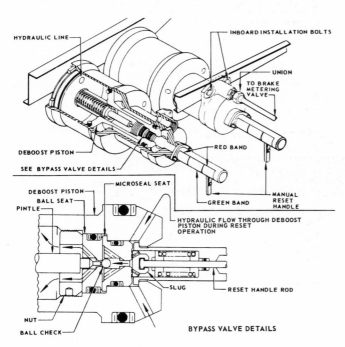

Figure **15·27** Brake lockout deboost valve for the Boeing 720 airplane.

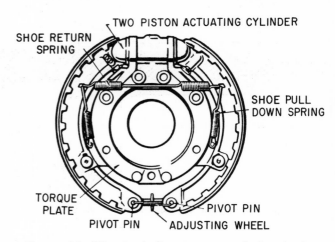

Figure **15·28** A dual-servo type of shoe-brake assembly.

brakes are effective for either direction of wheel rotation; hence they are interchangeable between the left and right wheels of the airplane and are effective for both forward and backward motion of the airplane.

Expander-tube brakes

Side and end views of an **expander-tube type of brake** are shown in Fig. 15·29, and Fig. 15·30 illustrates the principle of operation. Each expander-tube brake consists of four main parts: (1) **brake frame,** (2) **expander tube,** (3) **return springs,** and (4) the **brake blocks.** The single-type brake has one row of blocks around the circumference and is used on small aircraft. The duplex-type, expander-tube brake has two rows of brake blocks and is designed for larger aircraft. An inner fairing, or shield, fits between the **torque flange** on the axle and the brake frame to protect the frame against water.

The brake expander tube is a flat tube made of synthetic-rubber compound and fabric. It is stretched over the circular brake frame between the side flanges, and it has a nozzle that is connected with the hydraulic-fluid line by means of suitable fittings.

The brake blocks are made of a material which is similar to the material used for molded brake linings. The blocks have notches at each corner to engage with lugs on the brake frame and to prevent movement with the brake drum as it rotates. There are grooves across the ends of each block, and flat springs are inserted in these grooves. The ends of the springs fit into slots in the side flanges of the brake frame, holding the blocks firmly against the expander tube and keeping them from dragging when the brake is released.

The expander-tube brake is hydraulically operated and can be used with any conventional hydraulic brake system. When the brake pedal is pressed, the fluid is

Figure **15·30** *Principle of operation of the expander-tube brake.*

forced into the expander tube. The frame prevents any expansion either inward or to the sides. The pressure of the fluid in the tube forces the blocks radially outward against the brake drum. When the pressure is released, the springs in the ends of the blocks tend to force the fluid out of the expander tube and to pull the blocks away from contact with the brake drum. This action is increased by the tube itself, since it is molded slightly smaller in diameter than the brake frame and tends to contract without the help of the springs. Each block is independent in its action; hence there is no build-up of servo action and no tendency to grab.

Single-disk brakes

One of the most popular types of brakes, especially for smaller aircraft, is the **single-disk brake.** An exploded view of such a brake is shown in Fig. 15·31. This brake is manufactured by the Goodyear Tire and Rubber Company.

The main disk (1) of the brake shown in Fig. 15·31, is locked into the wheel by means of teeth or keys around the outer rim of the disk, causing it to turn with the wheel. On each side of the disk are located the lin-

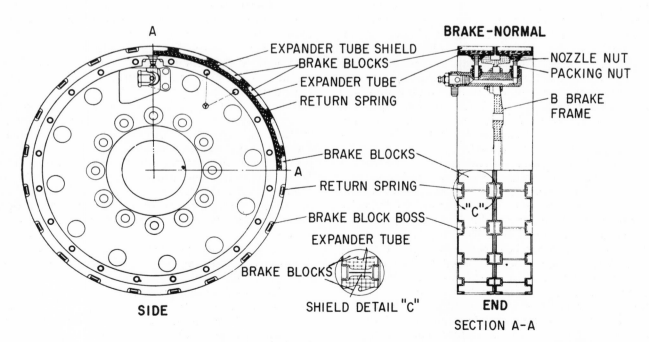

Figure **15·29** *Views of the expander-tube-type brake.*

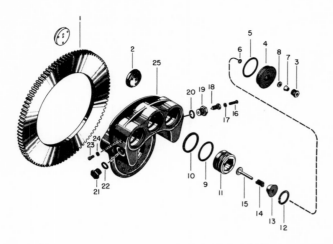

1. Disk
2. Brake lining
3. Adjusting-pin nut
4. Cylinder head
5. Cylinder-head O ring
6. Adjusting-pin O ring
7. Adjusting-pin grip
8. Adjusting-pin washer
9. Piston O ring
10. Felt wiper
11. Piston
12. Retaining ring
13. Spring-retaining plate
14. Brake-release spring
15. Adjusting pin
16. Bleeder-valve screw
17. Bleeder-valve washer
18. Bleeder valve
19. Bleeder adapter
20. Bleeder gasket
21. Inlet bushing
22. Inlet gasket
23. Bleeder screw
24. Bleeder washer
25. Brake housing

Figure 15·31 Exploded view of a single-disk-type brake.

ings (2) which bear against the disk when the brakes are applied, causing the wheel to slow down or stop.

One lining of the brake is mounted in a recess in the plate attached to the main axle structure. The other lining (2) is mounted against the piston (11) and moves according to the amount of hydraulic pressure applied to the piston. In Fig. 15·31, three pistons are incorporated in the brake housing (25), hence three linings must be mounted on the opposite side of the disk to back up the movable linings. Single-disk brakes may be constructed with as many separate pistons and linings as deemed advisable for the airplane for which they are designed. Each piston is equipped with separate sets of linings which bear against the brake disk (1) when the brakes are applied.

Most hydraulic brake systems require a method for the removal of air from the system. In Fig. 15·31, items 16 to 20 comprise the **brake bleeder valve** assembly. In order to bleed the air from the brakes, the valve is opened slightly and hydraulic fluid under pressure is applied to the piston. This causes hydraulic fluid and any air in the system to be expelled through the bleeder valve. When all air has been expelled, the bleeder valve is closed. Usually a clear plastic tube is connected to the bleeder valve with one end of the tube in a container of hydraulic fluid. As the fluid and air flows from the brake system, it is easy to see when air bubbles stop coming from the system; it is then known that the system is cleared of air.

Service and inspection of the brake system should be accomplished strictly in accordance with the manufacturer's instructions.

Multiple-disk brakes

The construction of a typical **multiple-disk brake** assembly is shown in Fig. 15·32. This brake assembly is designed for, and used on, the Douglas DC-9 airplane.

The brake assembly in Fig. 15·32 is described as a **dual-system, five-rotor, disk-type power brake.** Each brake contains two independent cylinder and passageway systems; each system contains seven brake pistons, two **bleed valves,** one **hydraulic pressure port,** and its associated passageways. Each brake contains one **carrier,** four **stator plates,** one **pressure plate,** one **back plate,** five **rotor plates,** and one **torque tube.**

The carrier houses the two independent, internally drilled, hydraulic passageway systems; fourteen hydraulic pistons, seven for each system; the **brake return assemblies;** four bleed valves; and two pressure ports, one for each system.

The four stator plates and the pressure plate are keyed to the torque tube of the brake. The stator plates consist of a steel heat-sink-type core with 14 stainless-steel pads riveted onto both outer surfaces. The pads are comparable to brake linings on conventional disk-type brakes but resist wear more effectively. The heat-sink feature helps to absorb and carry the heat away from the stainless-steel brake pads.

The five rotor plates are keyed to the wheel and rotate with the wheel. Each rotor plate consists of a steel heat-sink-type core with each outer surface faced with a bronze sheet. The bronze sheet takes the wear, while the stainless-steel **wear pads** on the stator plates remain comparatively stable.

The **torque tube** is the structural drum-type member that links the carrier with the back plate. It provides the keys for the stator plates and ties the brake assembly to the axle flange. The torque tube is the structural backbone of the brake assembly and transfers brake moment to the axle and gear strut.

Braking action is produced by hydraulic pressure forcing the pistons against the pressure plate which, in turn, forces the disk stack together and creates friction between the rotating and stationary disks. Each piston is fitted with an organic insulator to prevent brake heat transfer to the pistons and carrier. When hydraulic-fluid pressure is released from the brake pistons, the return springs and pins pull the pressure plate and the pistons to the full off position, thus allowing the disks to release and the wheel to rotate.

A self-adjusting mechanism on the return pins maintains a constant running clearance throughout the life of the brake. No adjustment is necessary.

A simplified drawing of the main brakes of the Boeing 720 airplane is shown in Fig. 15·33. These brakes are of the multiple-disk type, similar to others for large aircraft. Each brake assembly is bolted to a flange on the axle. Five **carrier disks** with full-circle,

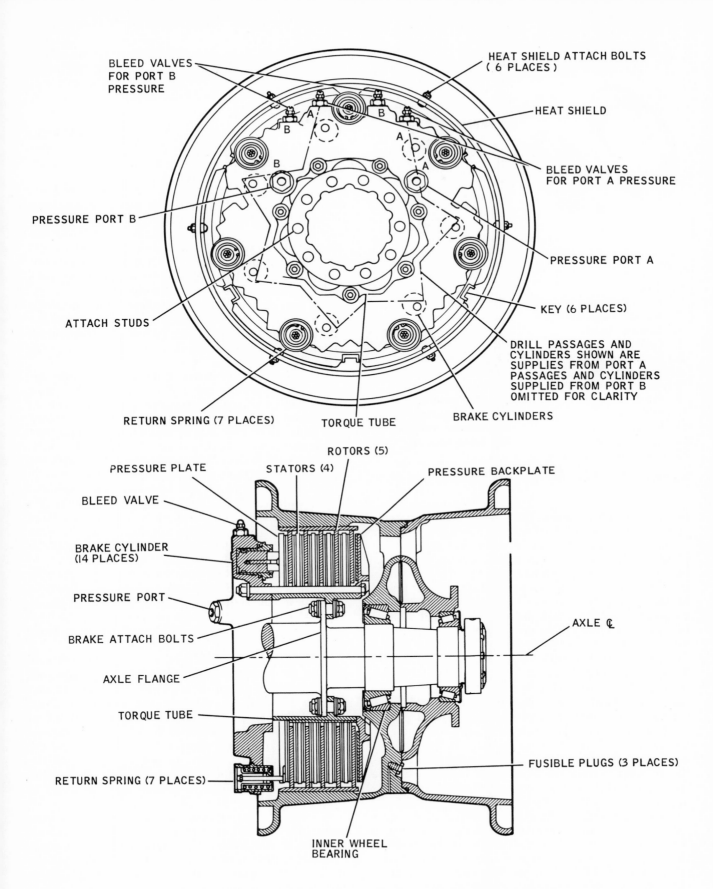

BLEED VALVES
FOR PORT B
PRESSURE

HEAT SHIELD ATTACH BOLTS
(6 PLACES)

HEAT SHIELD

BLEED VALVES
FOR PORT A PRESSURE

PRESSURE PORT B

PRESSURE PORT A

KEY (6 PLACES)

ATTACH STUDS

DRILL PASSAGES AND
CYLINDERS SHOWN ARE
SUPPLIES FROM PORT A
PASSAGES AND CYLINDERS
SUPPLIED FROM PORT B
OMITTED FOR CLARITY

RETURN SPRING (7 PLACES)

TORQUE TUBE

BRAKE CYLINDERS

ROTORS (5)

PRESSURE PLATE

STATORS (4)

PRESSURE BACKPLATE

BLEED VALVE

BRAKE CYLINDER
(14 PLACES)

PRESSURE PORT

AXLE ℄

BRAKE ATTACH BOLTS

AXLE FLANGE

TORQUE TUBE

FUSIBLE PLUGS (3 PLACES)

RETURN SPRING (7 PLACES)

INNER WHEEL
BEARING

Figure 15·32   Multiple-disk-type brake for the Douglas DC-9 airplane. (Douglas Air-craft Co., Inc.)

271

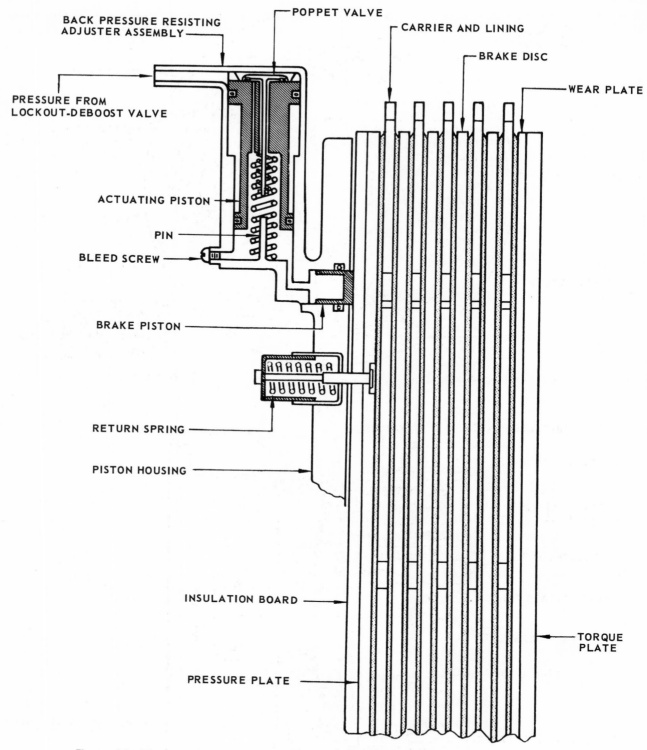

BACK PRESSURE RESISTING
ADJUSTER ASSEMBLY

POPPET VALVE

CARRIER AND LINING

BRAKE DISC

WEAR PLATE

PRESSURE FROM
LOCKOUT-DEBOOST VALVE

ACTUATING PISTON

PIN

BLEED SCREW

BRAKE PISTON

RETURN SPRING

PISTON HOUSING

INSULATION BOARD

TORQUE PLATE

PRESSURE PLATE

Figure 15·33   Simplified drawing of the multiple-disk brake for the Boeing 720 airplane. (Boeing Co.)

sintered bronze linings on both sides are keyed into and turn with the wheel. Four brake disks are keyed to the **torque plate** and do not rotate. A replaceable **wear plate** provides a friction surface on the inner face of the torque plate. When brakes are applied, 12 pistons act on a **pressure plate** to press all disks together and against the **wear plate.** Friction between the rotating carrier and lining disks, and the stationary brake disks, provides the required braking. When the brakes are released, the pressure plate is moved back by 12 return springs equally spaced around the periphery of the piston housing. As the pressure plate moves back, the carrier and lining disks separate from the brake disks and run free. An automatic adjuster compensates for brake-lining wear.

The **automatic brake adjuster** separates fluid in the brake assembly from the rest of the hydraulic system. When brakes are applied, hydraulic fluid exerts a force to depress the adjuster piston. Fluid under the adjuster piston is forced into the eight brake cylinders through drilled passages in the **brake carrier**. This operates the brake. The piston in the brake adjuster incorporates a poppet valve in the head. If wear on linings necessitates increased travel of the pistons in the brake cylinders, the piston in the automatic brake adjuster must travel further and expel extra fluid. When lining wear reaches a predetermined amount, the extra travel of the adjuster piston will bring its poppet in contact with a screw projecting from the bottom of the cylinder. This opens the poppet valve, and fluid from the brake

system passes through the adjuster piston into the brake carrier. When the brakes are released, the adjuster piston returns and closes the poppet valve. The additional fluid is trapped in the brake carrier and cylinders. This reduces return travel of the brake pistons sufficiently to compensate for lining wear. Under heavy braking, the brake unit may become very hot. Expansion of the hot brake components will reduce the clearance between the rotors and stators, and the brakes may drag when released. The automatic brake adjuster will act to restore clearances to normal if the brakes are applied and then quickly released.

The brake hydraulic system for the Boeing 720 airplane is shown schematically in Fig. 15·34. In this diagram are shown the emergency air supply for brake operation and the **shuttle valves** which block off the hydraulic part of the system when the emergency

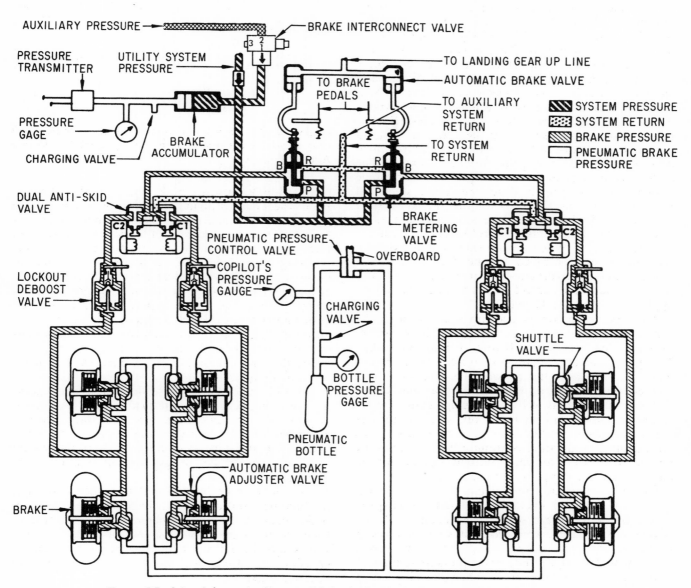

Figure **15·34** *Schematic diagram of the hydraulic brake system for the Boeing 720 airplane.*

system is placed in operation. Also shown is the location of the **lockout-deboost valves,** the **automatic brake valves,** and the **brake accumulator.** The brake accumulator stores energy for brake operation, dampens pressure fluctuations, and assures instantaneous flow of fluid to the brakes. When fully charged, the accumulator holds a reserve of fluid sufficient for approximately five full brake applications. The air precharge for the accumulator is approximately 1500 psi.

Antiskid systems

Modern jet-transport aircraft are usually equipped with **antiskid systems** to prevent loss of airplane control on the ground which would be caused by skidding of the wheels. The system installed on the Douglas DC-9 airplane provides a good example of the operation of an antiskid system.

The system for the DC-9 airplane is a completely automatic, electrically controlled means of preventing each individual main-gear wheel from skidding during brake operation. The system consists of a solid-state (**Note:** "Solid-state" refers to electronic systems which utilize transistors, crystal diodes, and similar devices in place of electronic vacuum tubes.) circuitry **control box,** four **wheel-speed sensor transducers,** four **dual servo valves,** four **failure-indicating lights,** and one **system arming switch.** The antiskid system has a locked-wheel protection feature which prevents braking action prior to wheel rotation. The system is controlled by a two-position, three-pole switch that will arm or deactivate the system and reset the indicating lights. When the antiskid system is deactivated, the wheel-brake system is controlled directly through the brake control valves by means of the brake pedals. When the antiskid system is armed, the brakes are controlled by the dual-servo valves which meter the hydraulic-fluid pressure that is supplied by the brake-control valves through the pilot's application of the brake pedals.

Antiskid protection is accomplished through the control of wheel torque at the point of maximum braking effectiveness, just before an impending skid. This point, however, changes continuously as the airplane travels down the runway, because there is a greater weight down on the landing-gear and larger-tire-footprint area, as well as changing environmental conditions on the runway itself. Yet, whatever the airplane or runway conditions are, the antiskid system's self-adaptive modulation continuously determines the maximum pressure at which braking can be utilized and automatically applies that pressure.

Basically, there are three elements to the antiskid system: (1) the frequency-modulated wheel-speed sensor transducers that sense speed change; (2) the control-box circuitry, which computes on the basis of speed change information; and (3) the servo valves which meter the appropriate brake pressure to prevent stoppage of wheel rotation. A schematic diagram of the antiskid control circuit is shown in Fig. 15·35.

The control box contains a solid-state printed cir-

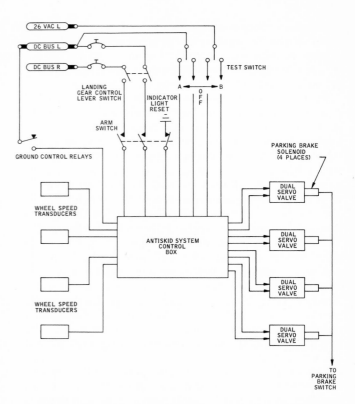

Figure 15·35 Schematic diagram to show components of antiskid control system on the Douglas DC-9. (Douglas Aircraft Co., Inc.)

cuit card for each wheel brake and two self-test cards. Each wheel card is divided into two basic circuits: (1) a control circuit and (2) a memory circuit. The control circuit senses the rate of wheel departure from free-rolling wheel speed, while at the same time rejecting false skid signals generated by mechanical noise or normal wheel deceleration of the slowing airplane. The sensing of rate-of-change of wheel speed, rather than wheel speed itself, creates an anticipatory feature which provides the high response necessary for wheel torque control. The memory circuit provides the delineation or reference curve to which the sensor information is compared to produce this anticipation.

The two self-test cards provide a means for checking the components of the antiskid system. If any component is inoperative, the failure indicating light will come on. The test card does not single out the component but does indicate the section of the system involved. The brake in that section will revert to nonautomatic operation.

The dual servo valves are two-stage, pressure-modulating, control valves which provide a ratio of brake pressure to pilot's metered pressure, proportional to the signal from the control unit. The servo valves modulate the brake pressure in both an increasing and decreasing direction to produce more effective braking.

The wheel-speed transducers are the detecting elements of the antiskid system. They are variable-reluctance, frequency-modulating, sine-wave generators driven by each main-gear wheel. These transducers provide a sinusoidal (sine-wave-shaped) signal whose frequency is proportional to wheel speed; they are unaffected by changes in signal amplitude.

In flight, during letdown procedure, the antiskid system is armed by placing the arming control switch in the ARMED position. At this time a small voltage is applied to the memory circuit in the control box, and the locked-wheel protection becomes effective. The wheel brakes will be released; that is, no hydraulic pressure will be allowed beyond the dual servo valves with the brake pedals depressed. While it is not advisable to do so as a general policy, a pilot could land the airplane with both feet solidly on the brake pedals. The airplane would land with brakes off, and then the pilot would automatically and rapidly apply brake pressure compatible with airplane and runway conditions. The pilot's function is to select and hold a steady brake pressure high enough to skid a tire under normal conditions. The antiskid system's function is to adjust the pressure selected by the pilot to give the best stopping performance under existing airplane and runway conditions.

During ground roll, with the brakes fully applied, the pressure bias modulation provides the mean pressure level usable by each wheel brake and permits wheel skid control to operate about this mean. This results in fast, efficient control of brake torque since only small pressure changes are necessary. The pressure bias-modulation circuit achieves its mean level by integrating the amplitude and duration of the control signal. Thus, as a wheel recovers from a skid and the rate control signal ends, a bias voltage remains on the valve proportional to the time integral of the amplitude and duration of the last signal added to the bias generated by the preceding skids. The bias results in a pressure from the servo valve such that as bias voltage increases, pressure decreases. This bias will decrease in the absence of a skid signal according to a time characteristic determined for the airplane. Thus, at recovery of a wheel to normal speed, brake pressure will come on at a slightly lower level than that at which the skid occurred. This sampling of skid pressure and corresponding correction of bias level occurs constantly throughout the ground roll because skid pressure levels are constantly changing.

For operation of the locked-wheel control circuit, the wheel-speed transducer frequency pulses are converted into a d-c voltage constant over the airplane speed range from maximum to 10 knots. A comparator amplifier measures a voltage for all other wheels. Should this voltage drop while any other wheel is rolling and delivering a voltage, an overdriving signal is sent to the servo valve driver effecting full pressure release at the locked wheel. On wet runways with the very small coefficient of friction, a skidding or stopped wheel would take longer to recover to synchronous speed. Normal reapplication of pressure would be too fast. The control-box memory circuits remember what the wheel speed was before

skidding and allow the wheel to recover to very near that speed before reapplication of pressure. However, as the pressure returns, it does not return to the former level, but to a lower level, and it is slowly allowed to increase as the pressure bias-modulation circuit discharges.

The antiskid-system wheel-speed transducers are variable-reluctance, sine-wave generators used to detect a skid condition in each of the four main-gear wheels. The transducers are installed in the axle of each main-gear wheel and are coupled to the wheel hubcap. A transducer is bidirectional; that is, its output is the same in either direction of rotation. A fixed, wound coil provides the magnetic field for the transducers, and wheel rotation produces variations in the magnetic air gap at 50 cycles per revolution. This is accomplished by rotation of a toothed rotor inside a mating toothed-stator segment. The flux changes thus produced induce an a-c component on the d-c input line. The frequency of this a-c component is sensed as wheel speed by the control-unit circuits.

The transducer envelope contains two independent sensor units. One unit serves the antiskid system, and the other unit serves the spoiler automatic control system. Although both sensor units are housed in a common body, their functions in their respective systems differ. Throughout this discussion relative to the antiskid system, reference to the transducers deals only with that part of the transducer that affects the antiskid system. Figure 15·36 shows both sections of the transducer because the parts affecting the antiskid system and the spoiler system are inseparable.

During the landing approach, with the arming switch in the ARMED position, the antiskid system is activated when the landing-gear safety switches open. At this time, the control circuit will have a small voltage imposed on the memory portion of the circuit. Prior to landing, the wheel-speed transducers have no direct effect on the system because the wheels are not turning and the system is under locked-wheel protection. Immediately upon touchdown, the wheels begin to spin and the transducers supply a voltage to the control circuit. From this point to the cutoff point, which is approximately 15 mph, the wheel-speed transducers sense any variation in wheel rotation speed. Since each wheel transducer controls an individual wheel brake, a variation at the individual level will cause a brake-pressure release for a brief time at the wheel involved. If an individual wheel-speed transducer should fail, the corresponding brake servo valve reverts that brake to nonautomatic operation.

When wheel speed decreases to approximately 15 mph, the voltage produced by the transducers will be at a level to deactivate the antiskid system and revert the braking system to nonautomatic operation.

A schematic diagram of one of the antiskid system dual servo valves is shown in Fig. 15·37. These valves are electrically operated, slave-metering, hydraulic valves used in the antiskid system to prevent skidding of the wheels during brake application. Each dual

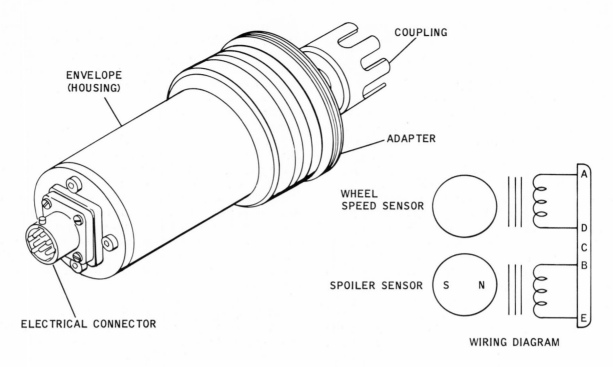

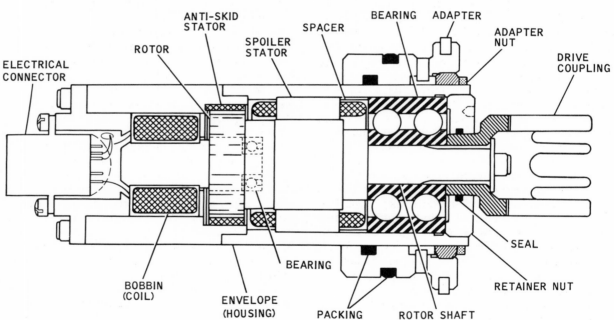

Figure **15·36** *Drawing to illustrate the wheel-speed transducer. (Douglas Aircraft Co., Inc.)*

servo valve has a single inlet pressure port and a single return port. There are two pressure outlet ports that direct hydraulic fluid to the inboard and outboard brake of the corresponding gear served by the valve. A small, normally-closed, solenoid-operated shutoff valve is incorporated into each dual servo valve to shut off the flow of hydraulic fluid through the servo pilot section of the valve whenever the parking brakes are required.

During normal brake operation, with the antiskid system deactivated, the dual servo valves are ported to permit the brake-control valves to meter pressure directly to the brakes. When the antiskid system is armed and brake pressure is applied to the dual servo valves, the servo valves act to reduce braking-fluid pressure whenever a wheel starts to skid. A force balance is set up between the inlet pressure and the outlet pressure by means of **feedback pistons** in the ends of the valve slide (spool). As long as no differential pressure is applied by the flapper-nozzle valve (first-stage valve), the slide forces are balanced and the slide is held open by a spring. When a skid signal is

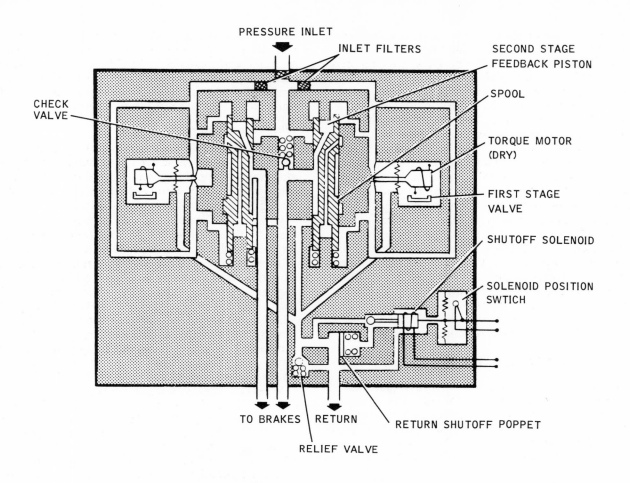

PRESSURE INLET

INLET FILTERS

SECOND STAGE
FEEDBACK PISTON

SPOOL

CHECK
VALVE

TORQUE MOTOR
(DRY)

FIRST STAGE
VALVE

SHUTOFF SOLENOID

SOLENOID POSITION
SWTICH

TO BRAKES   RETURN

RETURN SHUTOFF POPPET

RELIEF VALVE

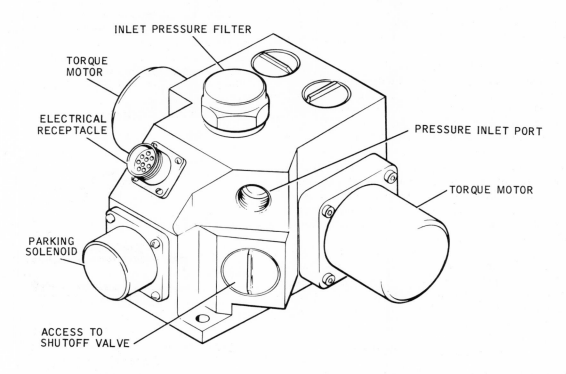

INLET PRESSURE FILTER

TORQUE
MOTOR

ELECTRICAL
RECEPTACLE

PRESSURE INLET PORT

TORQUE MOTOR

PARKING
SOLENOID

ACCESS TO
SHUTOFF VALVE

Figure 15·37 Schematic drawing of antiskid-system dual servo valve. (Douglas Aircraft Co., Inc.)

applied, the servo pilot stage applies a differential pressure to the slide ends and unbalances the slide toward the return port. Brake pressure is then metered down until the differential force between the feedback pistons equals the differential force created across the spool. At this point, the spool is again balanced and centered with both inlet and return closed to the brake. When the skid signal is removed or reduced, the reverse action occurs.

The spool spring force adds about 50 psi bias in the open direction. The pilot's metered brake pressure is fed directly to the brakes as long as no electrical skid signal is applied. When a skid control signal is applied, the ratio of brake pressure to pilot's metered pressure is reduced in proportion to the signal strength.

An electrical switch is coupled to the shutoff solenoid valve plunger and is actuated when the plunger is moved from the OPEN position to the BYPASS position. The switch completes a circuit to the antiskid indicating light to notify the pilot that one or more dual-servo valves are inoperative and the corresponding brakes have reverted to nonautomatic operation.

BLEEDING OF BRAKES

Whenever a brake line has been disconnected for any reason, it is necessary to "bleed" the brakes, that is, remove any air that has entered the line or system. Air in the hydraulic brake line will cause the brake action to be "spongy." This is because the air compresses and expands, and the brake action is not positive.

Brakes are bled by passing hydraulic fluid through the lines to carry the air out of the lines. On many aircraft, a special bleeder fitting is installed at the main-gear brakes to permit the flow of fluid through the lines.

To bleed the brakes, a clear plastic hose is connected to the brake bleeder fitting, and the free end of the hose is placed in a container of fluid. The reservoir for the brake system is filled with the correct type of fluid, and the brakes are operated to pump fluid through the lines. Air bubbles are seen through the clear plastic bleeder line as the fluid passes into the container. When the fluid flows with no air bubbles passing through the line, the bleeder valve is closed and the reservoir is refilled to the specified level. For any particular type of brake system, the manufacturer's instructions should be followed to insure that the bleeding procedure is correct.

For some aircraft a pressure bleeding system is employed. For this type of bleeding, brake fluid is forced through the brake lines by means of a pressurized reservoir connected to the brake system. Fluid is forced through the system until air bubbles no longer appear in the fluid outflow.

WHEELS AND TIRES

The wheels and tires of an airplane are subject to severe stresses during landing and in taxiing over rough ground. Failure of a tire or wheel can lead to ex-

tremely serious accidents, often resulting in the complete destruction of the aircraft and injury or death to the crew and passengers. For these reasons, the technician must make certain that the wheels and tires of the aircraft are in good condition for all conditions under which the aircraft may operate.

Wheel construction

Airplane wheels are constructed by a number of methods. Among these are (1) forming of heavy-sheet aluminum alloy, (2) casting of aluminum alloy or other type of alloy, and (3) forging. For large aircraft, forged aluminum alloy is commonly used.

One type of wheel-and-axle assembly is shown in Fig. 15·38. As shown in the illustration, the bearings for the wheel are of the tapered roller type and consist of the **bearing cone; rollers** with a **retaining cage;** and a **bearing cup,** or **outer race.** Each wheel has the bearing cup, or outer race, pressed into place and is supplied with a hubcap to keep dirt out of the outside bearing. Suitable retainers are supplied inboard of the inner bearings to prevent grease from reaching the brake surfaces. Felt seals are provided to prevent dirt from fouling the brakes. Seals are also provided on amphibian airplanes to keep water out.

Wheels for many modern airplanes are made in two sections. Typical of such a wheel is that illustrated in the drawing of Fig. 15·39. This is a cutaway drawing of the main landing-gear wheel for the Douglas DC-9 airplane and is described as a Goodyear 40 × 14, type VII, forged-aluminum, split-type wheel. The wheel halves are joined by 12 high-tensile steel bolts with self-locking nuts. An air seal is provided by an O ring installed in a groove in the outer wheel half to prevent loss of air from the tubeless tire. Standard, tapered roller bearings are installed in each wheel half. The inner bearings are protected against loss of lubricant and the entrance of dirt by moisture-resistant seals. The tires are protected against blowouts resulting from excessive pressure created by heat by three fuse plugs equally spaced around the wheel. The fuses are in-

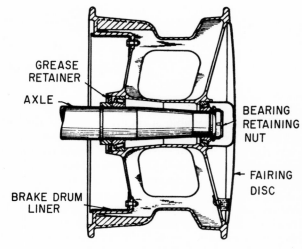

Figure 15·38 A wheel-and-axle assembly.

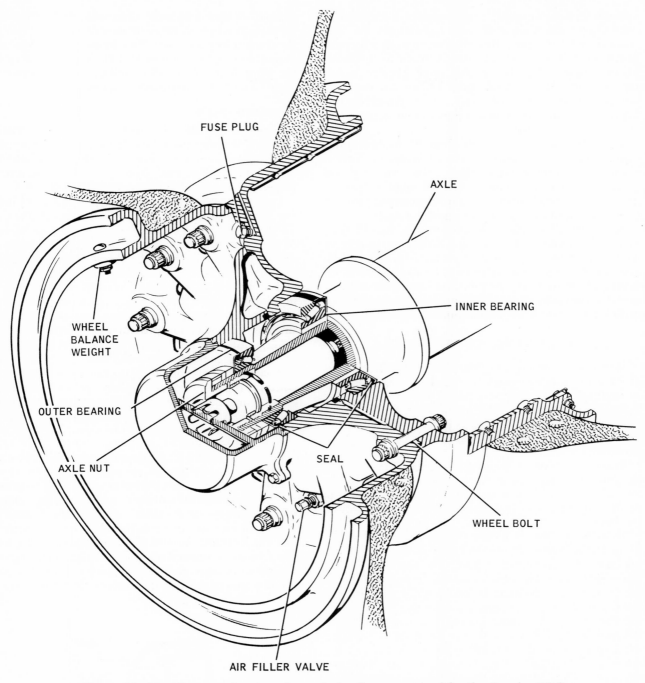

FUSE PLUG

AXLE

INNER BEARING

WHEEL BALANCE WEIGHT

OUTER BEARING

AXLE NUT

SEAL

WHEEL BOLT

AIR FILLER VALVE

Figure 15·39   Cutaway drawing of a main landing-gear wheel for the Douglas DC-9 airplane.

stalled in an accessible location to allow fuse plug replacement without removing the tire.

On the inside half of the wheel are installed the steel keys which hold the brake rotor disks. These are secured to the wheel forging by means of screws.

Figure 15·40 shows the construction of the main landing-gear wheel for the Fairchild F-27 airplane. This drawing shows only the upper half of the wheel cut away to reveal the position of the seal ring, air-valve stem, bearings, and brake disk lugs. This wheel is designed for use with tubeless tires although tube-type tires can be installed.

Tires for aircraft

Tires are manufactured in a wide variety of sizes and strengths, and the manufacturer of the aircraft specifies the proper type and size for use on a particular airplane. Usually the tubeless tire, or the tire, tube, and wheel of the mounted assembly have been individually balanced at the time of manufacture. When replacing

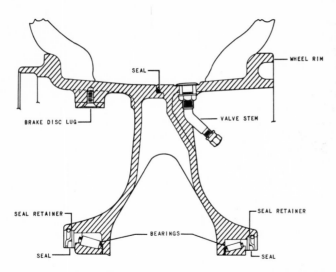

Figure 15·40 *Cutaway drawing to illustrate the construction of a main-gear wheel for the Fairchild F-27 airplane. (Fairchild Aircraft and Missiles Div., Fairchild Engine and Airplane Corp.)*

a tire, tube, or tire and tube, the original balance must be matched. For the Goodyear tire and tube, the balance mark on the tire consists of a branded dot which is painted red, and the balance mark on the inner tube is a painted yellow stripe on the base of the tube.

Demountable flange-type wheels are balanced with the flange assembled on the wheel. Divided-type wheels have each half balanced individually and do not have to be matched at the time of assembly.

Installing tubes and tires

After the wheel parts have been carefully inspected for cracks, dents, scratches and other damage and it is determined that the wheel is airworthy, the tire and tube can be installed. Before placing the tube in the tire, the tube should be lightly dusted with tire talc. This is to prevent the tube from sticking to the inside of the tire. An excessive amount of talc should not be applied.

To obtain the proper balance of the tire and tube, the inner tube should be placed in the tire so that the yellow stripe is located at the red dot in the tire. Mating of the tire and tube in this manner will bring the unit into the balance tolerance required. Before placing the tube in the tire, the tube should be inflated sufficiently to give it shape but not so much that the rubber will be stretched.

After mounting the tire and tube on the wheel, divided-type wheels should have the wheel-half bolts drawn up evenly and torqued to the value marked on the wheel. Bolts 90° apart should first be drawn snug, but not tight, to assure that the wheel halves are joined evenly. Then the other bolts should be tightened to a snug fit. Progressive tightening should then be done, first on one side of center and then on the other, until all bolts are brought up to the torque value marked on the wheels. Demountable flange wheels should have the flange locked in place as specified before the tire is inflated.

When mounting tires having inner tubes, the dual method of inflation should be used. This consists of inflating the tube just enough to set the tire beads on the wheel flanges, then removing the valve core and permitting the tube to deflate completely. This operation permits the tube to equalize itself inside the tire and eliminate excessive stretching and thinning of the tube in the rim base section. The valve core should then be reinstalled and the tube inflated to approximately one-half the operating pressure. The inflation should not be brought up to full pressure until the wheel and tire are mounted on the aircraft.

During the installation of tires on automobile wheels, a soap solution is sometimes used to make the bead of the tire slip more easily over the rim. This should not be done with airplane tires because it may cause slippage of the tire on the rim, particularly upon landing. If the tire slips on the rim, the valve stem will be pulled out of the tube and the tire will deflate. If tubeless tires slip on the rim, the air seal will be broken and the tire will deflate.

Dismounting and mounting tubeless tires

Modern aircraft are usually equipped with tubeless tires, and these require the exercise of certain precautions to make sure that the tire will continue to hold air. The general procedures are not difficult, and it is only necessary that the technician use good judgment and follow the instructions provided by both the manufacturer of the airplane and the manufacturer of the tires.

Before removing a wheel from the airplane, the tire should be deflated. This is accomplished by removing the core from the air valve. The wheel is then removed according to instructions, the technician being careful to see that the bearings are protected from damage and dirt.

With the wheel lying flat, the tire beads are broken away from the rims by applying pressure in even increments around the entire sidewall as close to the tire beads as possible. Sharp tools should not be used to pry the tire loose because the tire air seal will likely be damaged and the wheel can be nicked or scratched.

The nuts and bolts holding the wheel halves together should then be removed and the wheel halves separated from the tire. The O-ring air seal should be carefully removed and placed in a protected area where it will not be damaged or contaminated with dirt.

Before reinstalling a tubeless tire, the wheel should be examined carefully to make sure there are no nicks, scratches or cracks in the wheel or rims which will cause air leaks or weaken the structural strength of the wheel. Small rough spots can be removed by filing, fine sanding, or burnishing.

The tire should be examined to make sure the word "tubeless" is molded on the sidewall. The beads of the tire must be inspected to see that there are no nicks, cuts, or other conditions which can cause air leaks between the tire and the wheel rim.

The air-seal mating surface of the wheel should be cleaned with denatured alcohol. Small particles of sand or dirt in this area can cause leakage of air. The air valve in the rim should be examined to make sure that the seal between the valve stem and the wheel rim is intact.

The wheel air seal (O ring) should be lubricated with a light coat of grease, preferably of the type conforming to MIL-L-7711. This permits the seal to slide easily into the seal seat when the two halves of the wheel are joined. The seal should be equalized on the wheel and not twisted. If the seal is reused it should be installed as nearly as possible in the position originally placed.

The wheel section containing the seal should then be placed on a flat surface and the tire installed with the red dot placed at the valve stem. The other half of the wheel is then placed in the tire and the bolt holes are mated with the holes in the first wheel half. In some cases it is recommended that the bolts, nuts, washers, and bearing surfaces be lubricated with an antiseize compound conforming to MIL-T-5544.

Four bolts are installed 90° apart and drawn up evenly until the wheel halves seat; then the remaining bolts, washers, and nuts are installed. Where the washers are of the countersunk type to accommodate the radius under the bolt head, care must be taken to assure that the countersunk side faces the bolt head. All bolts are tightened in increments of 20 percent of the working torque value until the working torque is obtained. It is recommended that the bolts be tightened in a crisscross order to prevent dislocating of the wheel seal. On wheels which utilize external wrenching bolts and locking clips, each bolt may be tightened an additional amount up to 30° maximum, if necessary, for proper alignment of the locking clip.

For mounting tubeless tires on demountable flange-type wheels, the specific instructions for the wheels should be followed. The tire is installed on the rim with the red dot located at the valve stem. As in the case of the split wheel, tne wheel seal is lubricated with grease, MIL-L-7711 or equivalent, and installed on the flange sealing surface. The demountable flange is then installed on the wheel and secured in accordance with instructions.

The tire is inflated just enough to seat the tire beads. The wheel is then installed on the aircraft, and the tire is inflated to operating pressure. The valve cap is installed to prevent dirt or other material from entering the valve stem. The tire pressure should be adjusted after 24 hr to compensate for normal tire stretch.

Tubeless tires with sidewall inflation valves

A recent development in the design of tubeless tires is the inclusion of a **sidewall inflation valve.** Tires equipped with these valves are now standard equipment on many aircraft, both large and small.

The tubeless sidewall-valve tire for aircraft offers several advantages for the user and the aircraft designers. It eliminates the necessity of a valve hole in the wheel thereby permitting the design of a stronger, more equally stressed wheel. It eliminates the inner tube, which saves weight for the aircraft and simplifies the mounting of tires. Storage and stocking of inner tubes is no longer required.

Instructions issued to aircraft owners by the Goodyear Tire and Rubber Company when the airplanes are equipped with tubeless sidewall valve tires are given as follows:

Your airplane is equipped with the latest type Goodyear Tubeless Tires which contain sidewall inflation valves.

To obtain maximum service from this equipment the following inflation procedures should be used:

1. Open Zip-Lip bag according to printed instructions in bag.

NOTE

Retain bag for needle storage.

2. Lubricate end of inflating needle by pressing against the pads in the case.
3. Place end of needle and work glycerine lubricant around guide hole in the blue valve located in the sidewall of the tire.

CAUTION

Opening in valve should be well-lubricated before inserting needle. Needle should never be inserted dry.

4. Insert inflating needle into valve hole with a rotating motion.

CAUTION

Do not force needle. If needle does not enter easily, relubricate.

5. Inflate the same as conventional valve.
6. Check air pressure.
7. Remove inflating needle from valve as soon as possible. Replace needle in case, and store in Zip-Lip bag for protection.

Aviation Products Division

The Goodyear Tire and Rubber Company

INSPECTION AND MAINTENANCE FOR LANDING GEAR

A thorough inspection of landing gear involves the careful examination of the entire structure of the gear including the attachments to the fuselage or wings, struts, wheels, brakes, actuating mechanisms for retractable gear, gear hydraulic system and valves, gear doors, and all associated parts. It is recommended that the technician follow the instructions given in the manufacturer's manual for the aircraft being inspected. This is particularly important for the more complex types installed on modern aircraft with retractable gear.

Fixed-gear inspection

Fixed, or **nonretractable, landing gear** does not involve hydraulic, electrical, or mechanical systems for retraction of the gear; however, it is important that such gear be examined regularly for wear, deterioration, corrosion, alignment, and other factors which may cause failure or unsatisfactory operation.

During a periodical or annual inspection of fixed gear, the airplane should be jacked up so the gear does not bear the weight of the aircraft. The technician should then attempt to move the gear struts and wheels to test for play in the mounting. If any looseness is found, the cause should be determined and corrected.

When inspecting landing gear which employs rubber shock (bungee) cord for shock absorption, the shock cord should be inspected for age, fraying of the braided sheath, narrowing (necking) of the cord, and wear at points of contact with the structure. If the age of the shock cord is near five years or more, it is advisable to replace it with new cord, regardless of other factors. Cord which shows other defects should be replaced, regardless of age.

Shock struts of the spring-oleo type should be examined for leakage, smoothness of operation, looseness between the moving parts, and play at the attaching points. The extension of the struts should be checked to make sure that the springs are not worn or broken.

Air-oil struts should undergo an inspection similar to that recommended for spring-oleo struts. In addition, the extension of the strut should be checked to see that it conforms to the distance specified by the manufacturer. Before an air-oil strut is removed or disassembled, the air valve should be opened to make sure that all air pressure is removed. Severe injury and/or damage can occur as the result of disassembling a strut when even a small amount of air pressure is still in the air chamber.

The method for checking the fluid level of an air-oil strut is given in the manufacturer's maintenance manual. Usually the fluid level is checked with the strut collapsed and all air removed from the strut. With the strut collapsed, the fluid level should be even with the filler opening unless other instructions are given by the manufacturer. In all cases, the technician must make sure that he is using the correct fluid when refilling or replenishing the fluid in a strut. Modern airplanes usually use MIL-O-5606 fluid.

The entire structure of the landing gear should be closely examined for cracks, nicks, cuts, corrosion damage, or any other condition which can cause stress concentrations and eventual failure. Small nicks or cuts can be filed and burnished to a smooth contour, thus eliminating the point of stress concentration. If any crack is found in a landing-gear member, the member should be replaced.

Inspection of retractable landing gear

Inspection of retractable landing gear should include all applicable items mentioned in the foregoing discussion of inspection for fixed gear. In addition, the actuating mechanisms must be inspected for wear; looseness in any joint, trunnion, or bearing; leakage of fluid from any hydraulic line or unit; and smoothness of operation. The operational check is performed by jacking the airplane according to manufacturer's instructions and then operating the gear retracting-and-extending system. During this test, the smoothness of the operation, effectiveness of up and down locks, operation of the warning horn, operation of indicating systems, clearance of tires in wheel wells,

and operation of landing-gear doors should be checked. Improper adjustment of sequence valves may cause doors to rub against gear structure or wheels. The manufacturer's check list should be followed to assure that critical items are checked. While the airplane is still jacked up, the gear can be tested for looseness of mounting points, play in torque links, condition of the inner strut cylinder, play in wheel bearings, and play in actuating linkages.

The proper operation of the antiretraction system should be checked in accordance with manufacturer's instructions. Where safety switches are actuated by the torque links, the actual time of switch closing or opening can be checked by removing all air from the strut and then collapsing the strut. In every case, the adjustment should be such that the gear control cannot be placed in the UP position until the shock strut is very near the fully extended position.

Inspection of wheels

Airplane wheels receive very severe stresses at times; hence it is of the utmost importance that they be kept in airworthy condition. Unsatisfactory conditions for aircraft wheels include cracks, dents, abrasion, corrosion, distortion, looseness of assembly bolts, and worn or loose bearings. The degree of any such condition should be checked to determine whether the wheel should be repaired or replaced.

Cracks in wheels usually require replacement of the wheel; however, if it is believed that a crack can be repaired, the repair should be approved by an inspector of the Federal Aviation Administration.

Small dents in formed sheet-metal wheels do not necessarily impair the strength of the wheel. However, if the wheel is dented or distorted to the extent that it wobbles, it should be repaired or replaced.

Abrasion and corrosion can weaken a wheel until it is no longer safe for operation. In such cases the wheel should be replaced. Where the damage is slight, the area can be smoothed and recoated with zinc chromate or other corrosion inhibiting material. The wheel should then be painted with lacquer or enamel of the color desired.

Split-type wheels must be examined to determine the amount of wear in the assembly bolt holes. If the bolts have loosened during operation, they can very quickly enlarge the holes in the wheels. Sometimes enlarged or elongated holes can be repaired with inserts; however, the repair must have the approval of the manufacturer or a Federal Aviation Administration representative. During the assembly of a split-type wheel, the bolts should be torqued in the sequence and amount specified by the manufacturer. In the absence of specific instructions, bolts should be installed in holes 90° apart and tightened finger tight. The halves of the wheel and the air seal should be checked for position and then the bolts tightened slightly with a wrench. The other wheel bolts should then be installed in pairs across from each other and tightened to the same amount as the first bolts. Finally, the bolts are tightened in a crosswise pattern in increments of about 20 percent of specified operating torque until the full torque is obtained.

Wheel bearings are inspected by removing the wheels and examining the bearings and bearing cups (races). The bearings should be washed in a suitable petroleum solvent and then dried. The rollers should show no signs of wear or roughness and should rotate freely in their cages. The bearing cups should be smooth with no signs of ripple, cracks, scoring, galling, corrosion, or any other damage. If the bearings are in good condition, they can be reinstalled in accordance with the manufacturer's instructions. Great care must be exercised to see that the wheel retaining nuts are not overtightened. In the absence of specific instructions, the properly lubricated bearings are installed on the axle with the wheel and required washers and spacers, and then the wheel retaining nut is tightened snug but not tight. The nut is then backed off about one serration (castellation) or one-sixth turn before bending up the tab on the tab-lock washer or installing the cotter pin.

During inspection of the wheel bearings, the felt grease retainers should be examined for effectiveness. If they are hardened or glazed, they should be reconditioned or replaced with new ones.

Inspection of brakes

Brake inspection is accomplished at the same time that wheels are removed for other inspections. Shoe-type brakes are inspected for wear of the lining and security of the shoes on the axle mounting. The brake drum in the wheel is inspected for smoothness and freedom from cracks. Small, circumferential marks or grooves are not cause for rejection; however, they can be smoothed by the use of proper grinding equipment if desired.

The amount of wear permissible for the lining is usually specified in the manufacturer's manual. In case of doubt, the brake shoes should be relined.

Some aircraft employ the expander-tube-type brake and this type should be examined for lining wear, condition of expander tube, condition of lining blocks (linings) with respect to cracked or broken grooves, condition of the leaf springs which hold the linings in place, and condition of the brake drum. *During the inspection procedure while the wheel is removed, the brake pedals must not be depressed.* When the wheel is removed there is nothing to restrain the outward movement of the linings except the small leaf springs which pass through the grooves in the ends of the linings and engage the slots in the mounting flanges. Pressure applied to the expander tube at this time will break the linings at the grooved ends and render them useless.

The linings for single-disk-type brakes consist of flat cylinders or thick disks made of a tough abrasion-resistant material similar to that used for the linings of brake shoes. The manufacturer specifies the amount of wear which may be permitted for these linings before it is necessary to replace them. It is usually possible to inspect these linings without removing the wheel.

As explained previously, the brake linings for a single-disk brake are located on opposite sides of the brake disk. When the movable lining is pressed against the disk on one side, the disk is pressed against the stationary lining on the opposite side.

During inspection of single-disk-type brakes, the technician should check the retaining clips which hold the brake disk in the wheel. If the disk is distorted or the clips are broken, the brake disk will not stay in the correct position and brake failure will result.

Multiple-disk brakes are manufactured in a number of configurations, generally for use on large aircraft. It is therefore necessary that the technician follow the specifications given in the manufacturer's maintenance manual when inspecting and servicing such brakes. During major inspections the brakes are disassembled and the disks examined for wear as well as for damage resulting from heat. The lugs or keys which hold the rotor disks in the wheels are examined for wear and security in the wheel.

The actuating parts such as the pistons, pressure plates, and similar parts must also be examined for condition. Leaking pistons must be repaired as directed.

The hydraulic systems which actuate brakes should be inspected for the same defects which may be found in any other hydraulic system. Aluminum-alloy and steel tubing should be examined for wear at contact points and for security of the mounting attachments. Fittings should be checked for leakage of fluid. If it is necessary to replace a fitting or a section of tubing, the technician must make certain that he is installing the correct part. He should check the part number and then compare the part with the one which he removed. It must be remembered that fittings are made of steel or aluminum alloy, that they may be flare-type or flareless fittings, and that the threads may be for pipe fittings, flare-type fittings or flareless fittings. Proper identification is therefore extremely important.

Brake systems may be serviced with different types of fluid and the technician must be sure that he is using the correct type. Large aircraft often have power brakes supplied with the same fluid in the main hydraulic system. It is therefore likely that the brake hydraulic system will employ Skydrol fluid. On the same airplane, it will be found that the landing-gear struts are serviced with MIL-H-5606 petroleum-base fluid.

Flexible hoses used in the brake system must be examined for swelling, sponginess, leakage, and wear of the outer covering. A brake hose which has become soft or swollen is likely to cause "spongy" brakes because the hose will expand and take up some of the fluid volume. The effect is similar to the presence of air in the system.

Inspection of tires

Tire inspection includes examination for cuts, worn spots, bulges, cracks, foreign particles imbedded in the tread, and general wear. If a tire is in good condition, even though the tread is worn, it can be reconditioned by recapping or retreading. This operation should be performed by an experienced and reliable operator to assure good-quality work.

The military specification, MIL-C-7726, pertaining to the repair and recapping of used aircraft tires, states that tires should not be repaired if any of the following conditions are found during inspection:

1. Flex breaks or evidence thereof.
2. Bead injuries which extend into more than 3 plies of a tire having 16 or more plies or into 25 percent of the plies on all other tires.
3. Evidence of separation between plies or around bead wires.
4. Injuries requiring inside reinforcement. This includes casings needing section repairs.
5. Kinked or broken beads.

In actual practice, tires are often retreaded or recapped more than five times although three repairs of this type are considered a maximum for some tires. In any case, the basis for approval of retreading or recapping is the condition of the casing. Tires on an airplane which flies frequently and makes many landings can be retreaded or recapped more times than a tire on an airplane which operates less frequently. This is because the tire on a frequently flown airplane will usually be newer, and the rubber will be more flexible and in better condition than the tire on an airplane flown less frequently.

Inner tubes can usually be repaired in the same manner as those used for automobiles. It is recommended that the repair patches be vulcanized, and that an excessive number of patches be avoided. This is because the weight of the patching material can affect the balance of the wheel-and-tire assembly.

Inspection and repair of floats and skis

Inspection of floats and skis involves examination for damage due to corrosion, collision with other objects, hard landings, and other conditions which may lead to failure. Tubular structures for such gear may be repaired as described in the section covering welded repairs of tubular structures.

Sheet-metal floats should be repaired using approved practices described elsewhere in this text; however, the seams between sections of sheet metal should be waterproofed with suitable fabric and sealing compound. A float which has undergone repairs should be tested by filling it with water and allowing it to stand for at least 24 hr to see if any leaks develop.

Floats should be carefully inspected for corrosion damage at periodic intervals, especially if the airplane is flown from salt water. If small blisters are noticed on the paint, either inside or outside the float, the paint should be removed and the area examined. If corrosion is found to exist, the area should be cleaned thoroughly, and a coat of corrosion-inhibiting material applied. If the corrosion penetrates the metal to an appreciable depth, it is advisable that a patch be applied in accordance with approved practice.

For repair of either floats or skis, the manufacturers furnish approved repair instructions. These should be followed if it becomes necessary to make extensive repairs.

REVIEW QUESTIONS

1. What power sources are employed for the operation of retractable landing gear?
2. What locks are incorporated in retractable landing-gear systems and what are their functions?
3. What device is used to warn a pilot that the landing gear has not been extended prior to landing?
4. Describe the antishimmy device used with tail wheels.
5. What is the function of a shimmy damper installed with a nose gear?
6. How can the age of rubber shock cord be determined?
7. Under what conditions should rubber shock cord be replaced?
8. Describe an air-oil shock strut.
9. What prevents the retraction of landing gear when the airplane is on the ground?
10. What method is used for extension of the landing gear on a Piper PA-23 airplane in case of hydraulic power failure?
11. Explain how the nose wheel of a DC-9 airplane is steered.
12. After retraction of the gear on a Douglas DC-9 airplane, what holds the main gear in the UP position?
13. What controls the inboard landing-gear doors on the DC-9 during retraction and extension of the gear?
14. What is the function of the main-gear swivel glands?
15. Give two important purposes for torque links, or "Scissors."
16. Explain the purpose of the *over-center linkage* in the nose-gear mechanism on the DC-9 airplane.
17. Describe the nose-gear shock strut for the DC-9.
18. What is the purpose of the *ground-sensing control mechanism?*
19. How is the landing-gear control valve actuated on the DC-9?
20. If the nose gear of the DC-9 airplane would not stay in the up position, what might be wrong?
21. How is the landing gear of the DC-9 lowered in the case of hydraulic power failure?
22. Briefly describe the main-gear structure for the Boeing 720 airplane.
23. What is the advantage of four wheels on each of the main-gear units?
24. What type of fluid is used in the main-gear strut for the Boeing 720 airplane?
25. What cushions the shock of landing when an air-oil strut is installed in the landing gear?
26. Describe the operation of the up-lock mechanism for the main landing gear of the Boeing 720 airplane.
27. What device on the landing-gear truck of the Boeing 720 prevents the truck from rocking up and down?
28. Name four types of brakes used on aircraft.
29. Describe the principle of operation for the expander-tube brake.
30. How is braking action developed with the single-disk-type brake?
31. Describe a multiple-disk brake.
32. Name three methods for supplying brake actuating power.
33. Under what condition is a pneumatic system used with a hydraulic system?
34. Describe a master cylinder.
35. In what part of a brake system is flexible tubing used?
36. Describe the operation of a parking brake.
37. Describe the power brake control valve for the Boeing 720 airplane.

38. What device is used to stop the rotation of the landing-gear wheels on the Boeing 720 airplane before the gear is retracted?
39. Describe the operation of the brake lockout-deboost valves for the Boeing 720 airplane. What are their two principal functions?
40. How is air removed from brake lines and what is this process called?
41. What is the effect of air in the brake lines?
42. Describe the construction of the multiple-disk brakes used on the Douglas DC-9 airplane.
43. Describe the operation of the automatic brake adjuster for the Boeing 720 airplane.
44. Briefly describe the operation of an antiskid system.
45. Why is it not possible to land the DC-9 airplane with wheels locked when the antiskid system is armed?
46. Describe a wheel-speed transducer.
47. What material is generally used for the construction of airplane wheels?
48. What type of bearing is used for aircraft wheels?
49. What is the function of the fuse plugs in airplane wheels?
50. How is proper wheel balance attained when installing new airplane tires?
51. Describe the installation of tires and tubes on a split-type airplane wheel.
52. Describe the mounting of tubeless tires on split-type wheels.
53. Describe the removal of a tubeless tire.
54. What precautions should be observed to make sure that a tubeless tire will hold air after it is installed?
55. Discuss the installation and torquing of the wheel bolts for a split-type airplane wheel.
56. What is meant by the *dual-inflation* process during the installation of tires with inner tubes?
57. Describe the inflation of a tire with a *sidewall inflation valve*.
58. List the items which should be examined during the inspection of landing gear.
59. What precaution must be taken with respect to addition or replacement of shock-strut fluid?
60. How is the correct inflation of a landing-gear shock strut determined?
61. What should be done with respect to a cracked landing-gear structure?
62. Describe an operational test for retractable landing gear.
63. What precaution must be taken with respect to tightening of wheel-retaining nuts?
64. How can a technician determine when a brake lining must be replaced because of wear?
65. Describe the inspection of single-disk brakes.
66. What precautions must be taken when installing new tubing or hose?
67. What does the technician look for when inspecting tires?
68. What defects make a tire nonrepairable?
69. Discuss the inspection of floats and skis.

CHAPTER 16

Auxiliary Systems

UPA CO DETECTOR: YELLOW-BROWN (handwritten)

The majority of modern aircraft, primarily the large transport type, are equipped with certain systems which are not necessary for the actual operation and flight of the airplane but which are needed for the comfort and convenience of the crew and passengers. Some of these systems are important for the safe operation of the aircraft under a variety of conditions, and some are designed to provide for emergencies.

Systems not essential to the actual operation of the aircraft are commonly called **auxiliary systems.** Among such systems are air-conditioning, deicing and anti-icing, fire-warning and -extinguishing, oxygen, and water and waste systems. All these systems are needed for the safety and comfort of crew and passengers on high-altitude, long-range airplanes; hence it is important the technician have a good understanding of their operation and maintenance.

AIR CONDITIONING

The **air conditioning** of an airplane includes heating, cooling, ventilation, and pressurization. The components of the air-conditioning system must be interconnected and controlled in a system which will provide the correct pressure and temperature for the cabin air at all times and under all conditions of flight. Such a system must therefore include heaters, coolers, pressure control valves, and automatic controlling devices.

Heating systems

The simplest type of **heating system,** often employed on light aircraft, consists of a heater muff around the engine exhaust stacks, an air scoop to draw air into the heater muff, ducting to carry the heated air into the cabin, and a valve to control the flow of heated air. Such a system is shown schematically in Fig. 16·1.

During the inspection and maintenance of an

exhaust-type heating system, it is important to observe the condition of the exhaust manifold inside the heater muff. It may be necessary to remove the muff in order to inspect the exhaust manifold to make sure there are no cracks which could permit exhaust gases to enter the heater duct. The entire system should be examined for wear, cracks, security of mounting, and operation.

In larger and more expensive airplanes, combustion heaters are often employed to generate the heat needed for the cabin. This type of heater burns airplane fuel in a combustion chamber or tube to develop the required heat. Air flowing around the tube is heated and carried through ducting to the cabin. A Model 8240-A South Wind combustion heater system installed in the Cessna 310 airplane is shown in Fig. 16·2. The heater is mounted in the right side of the nose section. Fuel is routed from a tee in the fuel cross-feed line through a filter and a solenoid supply valve to the diaphragm-type heater fuel pump. The fuel pump is operated by the combustion air-blower motor which is mounted above the heater assembly. This pump provides the heater with sufficient fuel pressure, and no auxiliary boost pump assistance is necessary for proper operation of the heater.

The heater fuel pump and all external fittings on the heater are enclosed in metal housings which are vented and drained as a precaution against fire in the event of leaky fittings. Fuel passes from the heater fuel pump through a solenoid valve to the combustion-chamber spray nozzle. When the cabin heater switch is placed in the HEAT position, current is supplied to the combustion air blower and to the ventilating fan. The fan actuates the cam-operated breaker points which start the spark plug firing. As the combustion air-blower air increases, the vane-type valve at the inlet of the combustion chamber opens. This actuates a microswitch, which in turn operates the solenoid valve, thus allowing fuel to spray into the heater where the spark plug ignites the fuel. The heated air flowing from the heater to the cabin exceeds the temperature for which

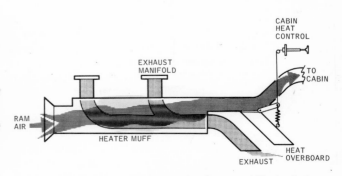

Figure 16·1   Heating system for a small airplane.

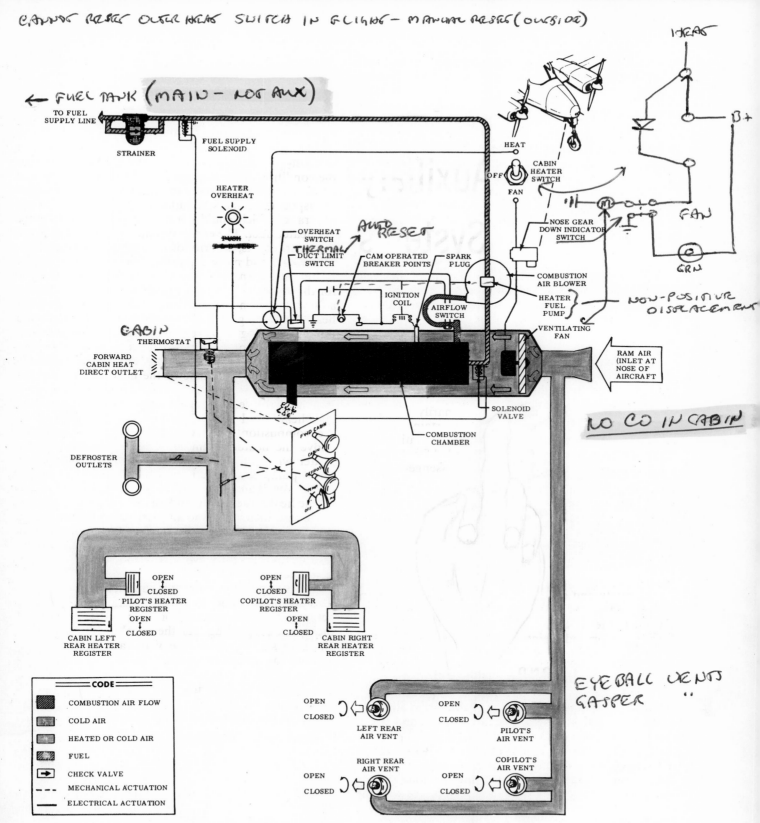

Figure 16·2 *Heater system for a Cessna 310 airplane. (Cessna Aircraft Co.)*

the thermostat is set. This causes the thermostat to close the solenoid valve and stop fuel flow to the heater. The heater thermostat cools and the solenoid valve opens again to allow fuel to flow to the heater. Heated air flows from the heater and the thermostat again causes the solenoid valve to close. This cycling on and off continues and the heater thereby maintains an even temperature in the cabin.

The heater combustion chamber is completely separate from the ventilating system to prevent any exhaust

287

gases from contaminating the cabin air. All exhaust gases are vented overboard through an exhaust tube directly beneath the heater.

Heating of large aircraft

Heated air required for large aircraft is obtained either from combustion heaters or from the compressors of gas-turbine engines. Jet transports often utilize the air from the engine compressors because this air is heated by compression, often to more than 600°F. The heated air is partially cooled by means of heat exchangers before it is actually delivered to the air-conditioning system.

Cooling

Air cooling is accomplished by means of air-cycle machines or evaporation refrigerating systems. The cooled air is then mixed with heated air to provide the desired temperature for the cabin.

Ventilation

Ventilation is automatic as the conditioned air is circulated through the cabin and discharged through the outflow valves. In flight, the cabin air is completely changed every few minutes to assure fresh air at all times for the passengers and crew.

Pressurization

Pressurization of the cabin, crew compartment, and cargo areas is accomplished by admitting pressurized air to the cabin and regulating the discharge rate by means of the outflow valves. The outflow valves are controlled by means of the cabin-pressure control unit and a cabin-pressure rate controller. The pressurized air is obtained from either a cabin supercharger (blower) or the engine compressors.

Air-conditioning system for a jet airliner

A typical air-conditioning system for a modern jet airliner is represented by the system employed for the Boeing 727 airplane. This system provides conditioned, pressurized air to the control cabin, passenger cabin, lower nose compartment, forward cargo compartment, air-conditioning distribution bay, and aft cargo compartment.

The air supply is furnished by engine bleed air when in flight and from engine bleed air, a ground pneumatic supply cart, or a ground conditioned-air supply cart during ground operation. Part of the warm-air supply from the engines (or pneumatic cart, if on the ground) is passed through the air-conditioning packs to be cooled. The cold air is then mixed with the remainder of the warm air as required to obtain the temperature of air called for by the temperature control system. This conditioned air then passes into the control and passenger cabins through the distribution system. After the air has passed through the cabins, it is exhausted through a number of outlets. The combined air from all outlets other than the pressurization outflow valves, however, is limited to a value less than that which enters the cabin from the air-conditioning

system. The outflow valves are regulated to exhaust only that additional quantity of air required to maintain the desired pressure in the cabin.

Other air outlets include the galley vent, lavatory vents, equipment-cooling outlets, the ground conditioned-air condensate drain, water-separator drains, the pressurization controllers cabin-to-ambient venturis, and the cargo-heat outflow valves. The cargo-heat outflow valves normally remain open to provide warmth around the cargo compartments, but they may be closed by a switch on the third crewman's panel.

Engines No. 1 and 3 furnish eighth- or thirteenth-stage air, depending upon engine power setting and air-conditioning demand, for air conditioning during normal operation. Eighth-stage bleed air from engine No. 2 is also available as an alternate source. Bleed air from engines No. 1 and 3 passes through a heat exchanger (precooler) to reduce the air temperature to approximately 370°F. A precooler controller and modulating valve combine to maintain the correct temperature. If difficulties occur in the controller, a thermoswitch prevents excessively hot air from entering the air-conditioning system by closing the bleed-air shutoff valve. Air flow to each air-conditioning system is regulated by a flow-regulating servo and modulating valve.

The air-conditioning system for the Boeing 727 airplane consists, by function, of four subsystems. These are for cooling, temperature control, distribution, and pressurization control. These subsystems are shown schematically in Fig. 16·3. Another schematic-type drawing which provides a more realistic illustration of the system is shown in Fig. 16·4. This drawing gives the relative position of the various components of the system and can be studied in connection with further descriptions given in this section.

Cooling packs

The cooling of air for the Boeing 727 airplane is provided by means of two cooling packs. These packs also remove excess moisture from the air. With the exception of the water separator, which is located in the distribution bay, all cooling-pack equipment is contained inside the center fuselage fairing.

The cooling devices used in the cooling packs consist of a primary heat exchanger, a secondary heat exchanger, and an air-cycle machine. The heat exchangers are of the air-to-air type with heat being transferred from the air going through the packs to air going through the ram air system. The air-cycle machine consists of a turbine and a compressor. Air expanding through the turbine drops in temperature as the energy is extracted for the major cooling in the pack. An air-cooling pack is shown in Fig. 16·5. In the drawing it can be seen that engine bleed air passes through the primary heat exchanger for initial cooling, then through the air-cycle-machine compressor, through the secondary heat exchanger, and then through the expansion turbine of the air-cycle machine. At this point the air is at its lowest tempera-

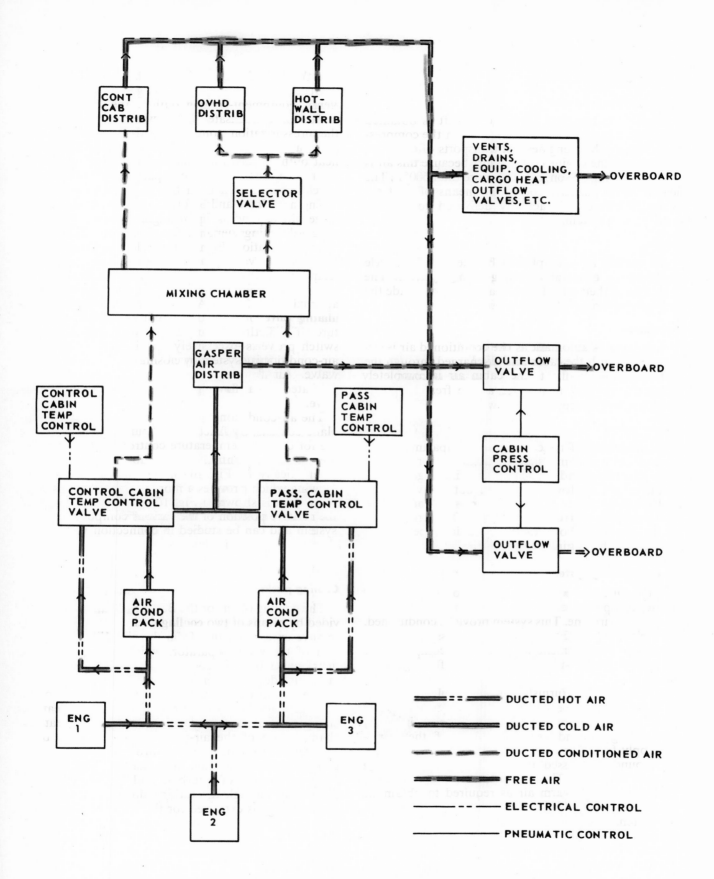

CONT CAB DISTRIB

OVHD DISTRIB

HOT-WALL DISTRIB

VENTS, DRAINS, EQUIP. COOLING, CARGO HEAT OUTFLOW VALVES, ETC. ⟹ OVERBOARD

SELECTOR VALVE

MIXING CHAMBER

GASPER AIR DISTRIB

CONTROL CABIN TEMP CONTROL

PASS CABIN TEMP CONTROL

OUTFLOW VALVE ⟹ OVERBOARD

CONTROL CABIN TEMP CONTROL VALVE

PASS. CABIN TEMP CONTROL VALVE

CABIN PRESS CONTROL

AIR COND PACK

AIR COND PACK

OUTFLOW VALVE ⟹ OVERBOARD

ENG 1

ENG 3

ENG 2

═══ ══ DUCTED HOT AIR

─────── DUCTED COLD AIR

── ── DUCTED CONDITIONED AIR

═══════ FREE AIR

─── ─── ELECTRICAL CONTROL

─────── PNEUMATIC CONTROL

Figure 16·3   Block diagram of air-conditioning system for the Boeing 727 airplane. (Boeing Co.)

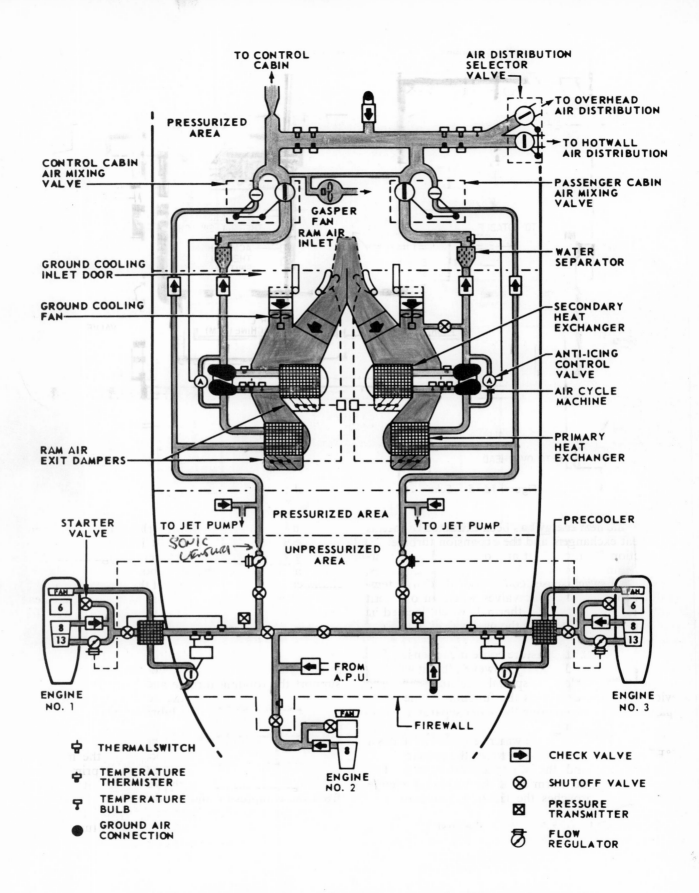

Figure 16·4   Arrangement of air-conditioning components for the Boeing 727 airplane.
(Boeing Co.)

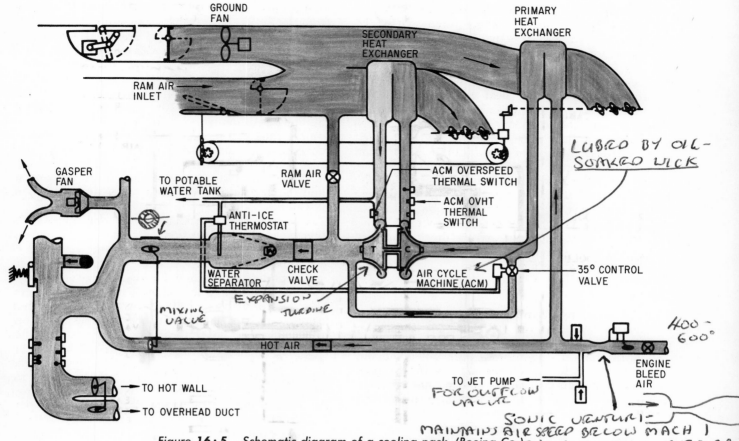

Figure 16·5   Schematic diagram of a cooling pack. (Boeing Co.)

Handwritten annotations on figure:
COLD AIR LINE LARGER THAN HOT AIR LINE BECAUSE MORE COLD AIR NEEDED
LUBED BY OIL-SOAKED WICK
EXPANSION TURBINE
MIXING VALVE
TO JET PUMP FOR OUTFLOW VALVE
400-600°
SONIC VENTURI- MAINTAINS AIR SPEED BELOW MACH 1 BY USING SHOCK WAVES AS VALVE.

ture since the heat energy has been extracted by means of the heat exchangers and the expansion turbine.

Protection from overheat and overspeed of the air-cycle machine is provided by two thermal switches. One thermal switch senses compressor discharge temperature to close the pack valves when an overheat condition exists. The other thermal switch, located in the turbine inlet duct, closes the pack valves to prevent overspeed.

As the air cools, its moisture content condenses. The moisture is atomized so finely, however, that it will stay in suspension unless a special moisture-removing device is employed. This is the function of the **water separator.** Moisture entering the water separator is prevented from freezing by an anti-icing system. An anti-icing thermostat in the water separator actuates a 35°F control valve in a duct between the primary heat-exchanger exit and the water-separator inlet. The valve opens to add warm air if the turbine discharge temperature approaches the freezing temperature of water.

The **primary heat exchanger** is the first unit of the cooling packs through which engine bleed air passes to be cooled. The unit is rectangular and is located between two sections of the ram air duct. Two plenum chambers in the heat exchanger are connected by a bank of tubes so as to allow maximum surface exposure of each tube to ram air passing across the outside

of the tubes. Hot air enters one plenum chamber from the pneumatic duct at the aft inboard side of the exchanger. It is cooled as it passes through the tubes to a header and returns through tubes to the other plenum chamber, then leaves by way of the air-cycle-machine duct connected to the forward inboard side of the heat exchanger. There is one primary heat exchanger for each cooling pack.

The **air-cycle machine** is a cooling unit consisting of an expansion turbine on a common shaft with a compressor. The shaft is bearing-mounted in a housing to support the rotating turbine and compressor. A wick extends from the shaft to the bottom of the oil sump formed by the housing for lubrication of the moving parts. A filler neck and filler cap with a dipstick is provided on each side of the housing.

The air-cycle machine is located in the midbody fairing between the duct leading from the primary heat exchanger and the duct to the water separator. A duct from the compressor and another to the turbine connect to the secondary heat exchanger. The turbine mounts are connected to the airplane structure through serrated plates to provide location adjustment. There is one air-cycle machine for each cooling pack.

As explained previously, the air-cycle machine cools compressed air by expansion. When the air is originally compressed by the engine compressor, its temperature rises in approximate proportion to the rise in

291

air pressure. The heated compressed air is passed through the primary heat exchanger, where some of the heat energy is removed. It is then directed to the compressor section of the air-cycle machine.

In the compressor section the air is recompressed and heated to some extent. This additional heat is reduced in the **secondary heat exchanger,** which is located between the compressor and turbine of the air-cycle machine. The secondary heat exchanger is identical to the primary heat exchanger and is located between two sections of the inboard branch of the ram air duct. Air from the air-cycle-machine compressor outlet enters the forward inboard connection to the secondary heat exchanger, passes through the cooling tubes, then returns to the turbine section of the air-cycle machine. As the air expands across the turbine, heat energy is expended in driving the turbine and through the expansion process. Thus the air leaving the turbine is at its lowest temperature.

Distribution

Air-conditioning **distribution** utilizes two entirely independent systems. The **individual air distribution system,** also called the **gasper** system, routes only the cold air from the air-conditioning packs to individually regulated outlets in the control and passenger cabins. The **conditioned-air distribution system** routes the mixture of hot and cold air to the passenger and control cabins.

The gasper system provides each crew member and each passenger with a method for cooling his local area to a value different from that provided by the normal air-conditioning automatic control. Air is received from the cold side of the **temperature control valve** and is ducted to each individual station. An adjustable nozzle at each station allows the individual a choice anywhere between no supplementary cold air and full-system-capacity cold air.

The conditioned-air distribution system distributes temperature-controlled air evenly throughout the passenger and control cabins. One duct system supplies the control cabin, and another entirely separate system supplies the passenger cabin. The passenger-cabin air is divided into two systems. The **overhead system** releases air into the cabin from holes in a duct running fore and aft in the passenger cabin ceiling. The **hot-wall duct system** takes air through ducts between the sidewall and interior lining and releases it through the cove light grills. A selector valve at the main distribution manifold controlled from the control cabin permits using all overhead, all hot-wall, or any combination of the two distribution methods.

All the distribution systems originate in the **air-conditioning distribution bay.** The gasper distribution system originates at the cold ports of both air-mixing valves and the conditioned-air distribution systems originate at the main distribution manifold. A drawing of the air-conditioning distribution bay is shown in Fig. 16·6.

Duct sections throughout both cabins are joined with clamps or tape. Means of equalizing the pressure in the ducts and headers and of balancing the flow from the outlets have been designed into each system. The distribution system ducts are protected against excessive pressure by a relief valve on the main distribution manifold.

The main distribution manifold is common to all the conditioned-air distribution systems. It is installed immediately downstream from the mixing chambers in the air-conditioning distribution bay. Protection against excessive pressure is afforded by means of a relief valve located as shown in Fig. 16·6. The relief valve is a spring-loaded flapper valve with a tension of 68.5 lb on each of two springs. The valve is designed to limit the distribution pressure to a maximum of 18 in. of water.

Approximately 10 percent of the conditioned air is directed to the airplane control cabin. This is accomplished by the **control-cabin flow-limiting venturi.**

A dual selector valve divides the total passenger-cabin conditioned-air flow between the overhead distribution system and the sidewall distribution system. The selector valve consists of two butterfly valves installed in the main distribution manifold. One controls air flow to the overhead duct riser and the other controls air flow to the passenger-cabin sidewall air distribution manifold. The valves are designed so that when one is fully closed the other is fully open and vice versa. The selector valve is controlled by a lever mounted in the control cabin. The lever can be operated by the third crewman from his seat.

Air is exhausted from the passenger cabin through air-exit grills and outflow holes in the sidewall just above the floor. It then flows around the cargo-compartment walls, where it assists in compartment temperature control. Some air then flows to the cargo-heat-distribution duct under the compartment floor and is discharged overboard through the cargo-heat outflow valves.

Part of the cabin air flows overboard through the two pressure-system outflow valves located in the rear of the aft cargo compartment. These valves regulate cabin air pressure.

Below each hole in the floor where air is exhausted from the passenger cabin to the cargo compartment is a **flotation check valve.** This valve consists of a plastic ball retained by a cage. If the cargo compartment should become flooded, the ball will float up in its cage and block the hole to prevent flooding of the passenger cabin from the cargo compartment.

Pressurization control system

The **pressurization control system** is a pneumatically operated system which meters the exhaust of cabin ventilating air to provide controlled pressurization of the control and passenger cabins, the electronic compartment, both cargo compartments, and the lower nose compartment. Safety features of the system override selected control settings to prevent a pressure condition harmful to passengers or airplane structure.

The pressurization control system maintains constant low-altitude cabin pressure during airplane flight

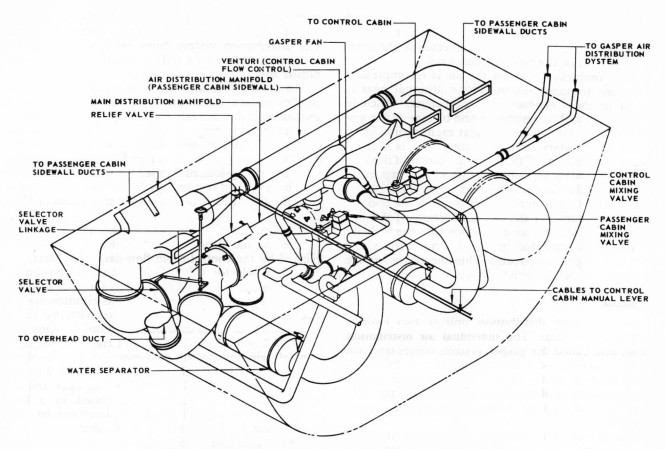

Figure 16·6 Air conditioning distribution bay. (Boeing Co.)

at high altitudes and controls the rate of pressure change in the cabin. Positive pressure relief at 9.42 ($\pm$0.15) psi pressure differential is provided to protect the airplane structure in the event of a pressure control system failure.

A negative pressure relief mechanism lets air into the cabin when outside pressure exceeds cabin pressure and limits the negative pressure differential to 10 in. of water. A barometric-correction selector helps select proper landing-field altitude so the pressure differential at landing may approach 0 psi.

A **cabin-altitude limit control** will maintain a maximum of 13,000 ($\pm$1500) ft cabin altitude if other control components fail and as long as the pneumatic system provides sufficient air for pressurization.

A **mode selector switch,** when placed in the GROUND VENTURI position, moves the outflow valves full open for ground operation of the air-conditioning system.

The pressurization control system consists of one automatic controller, one manual control, two outflow valves, one test valve, one mode selector switch, two cabin-to-ambient venturis, and one fan venturi. The schematic drawing of Fig. 16·7 shows the relative position of these units in the system.

The indicating system includes a rate-of-climb indicator to show rate of pressure change in the cabin, an altitude warning horn to indicate low cabin pressure, and a dual altimeter and differential-pressure indicator.

✳ During normal operation of the airplane, pressurized air is delivered from the pneumatic system, through the air-conditioning-and-distribution system to the pressurized compartments of the airplane. The desired cabin pressure and rate of pressure change are selected on either the automatic controller or the manual control. These controllers pneumatically signal the outflow valves so that the valve openings to the outside increase or decrease to vary air outflow in order to maintain the desired pressure. The automatic controller also regulates the rate of pressure change in the cabin and limits pressure differential between the interior of the cabin and the outside to 8.6 psi.

The pressurization control system components are shown in Fig. 16·7. The device at the lower left of the illustration is the cabin-pressure automatic controller, that at the upper right is the rate controller, and the unit at the lower right is the manual controller.

The **cabin-altitude selector** controls isobaric (constant-pressure) operation and can be set for cabin altitudes from 1000 ft below sea level to 10,000 ft altitude. The selector dial also shows maximum airplane altitude (isobaric operation) for the selected cabin altitude and barometric correction. The selector setting affects the outflow valves through the controller components and the control lines to the outflow-valve pneumatic relays. The control line from the automatic controller connects to the manual controller, and

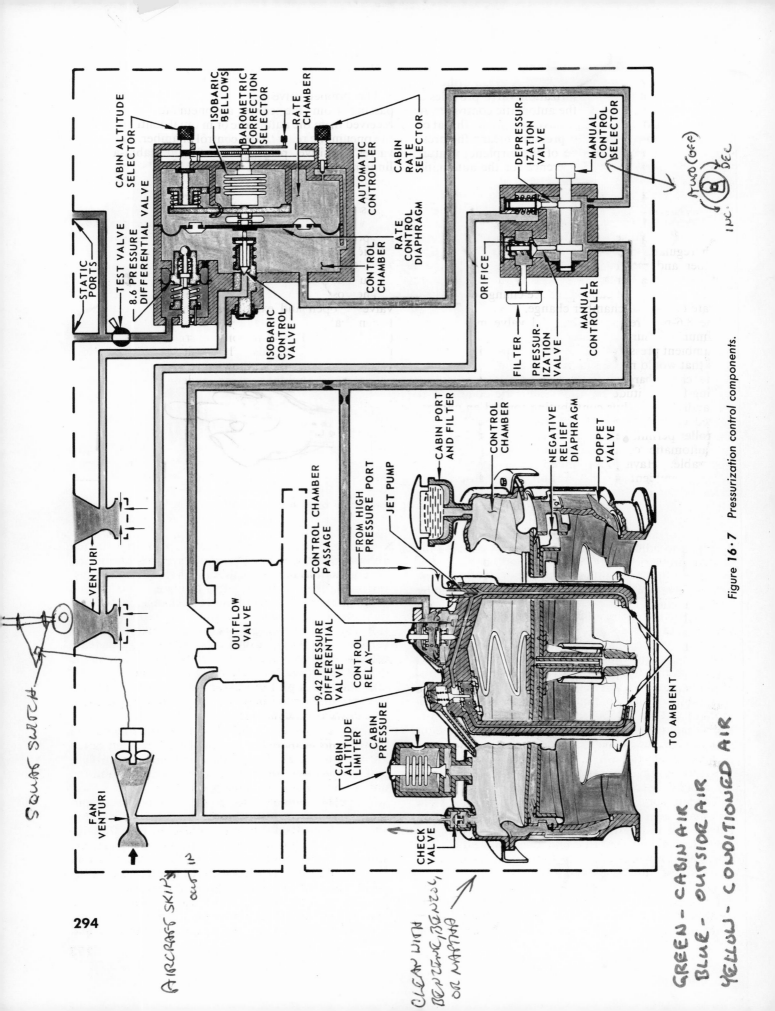

Figure 16·7 Pressurization control components.

SQUAT SWITCH

AIRCRAFT SKIN

CLEAN WITH
BENZINE, BENZOL,
OR NAPTHA

GREEN - CABIN AIR
BLUE - OUTSIDE AIR
YELLOW - CONDITIONED AIR

another line from the manual controller connects to the outflow-valve pneumatic relays. A small orifice in the manual controller pressurization valve provides a high-pressure reference for the automatic controller. A line from the isobaric control valve port to the throat of a cabin-to-ambient (**ambient pressure** means the pressure surrounding the outside of the airplane) venturi provides the low-pressure reference for the automatic controller.

The cabin **rate-of-change selector** controls the rate of change of cabin pressure and can be set for rates from 50 to 2000 ($\pm$500) ft per min, though it is not calibrated. The rate-selector setting affects an orifice which regulates the rate of airflow between control chamber and rate chamber. Cabin pressure follows control-chamber pressure via the outflow valves; therefore, the rate of cabin-pressure change will follow the rate of control-chamber change.

The 8.6-psi pressure-differential valve maintains a maximum pressure differential of 8.6 psi between cabin and ambient pressures, overriding cabin-altitude selections that would require more than 8.6 psi differential.

The cabin **barometric correction selector** corrects landing-field altitude for the barometric condition at the landing field, thus contributing toward an unpressurized cabin at landing. The **cabin-pressure manual controller** permits regulation of cabin pressure in case the automatic controller malfunctions or becomes inoperable. Having an independent low-pressure (cabin-to-ambient pressure venturi) and high-pressure (cabin-pressure) source, the manual controller will override any pneumatic signal from the automatic controller to the outflow valves. By adjusting the manual control, pressure in the outflow valve relays may be regulated to adjust outflow valve exhaust opening for desired pressurization. The controller consists of a chamber with a pressurization valve and a depressurization valve adjusted by a camshaft which is moved by a manual control selector. The manual controller is on the third crewman's panel.

The cabin-pressure manual control selector consists of a dial, an indicator, and a control knob. The knob moves a camshaft which adjusts the pressurization and depressurization valves so that when the knob indicator points to the right, pressure increases; when the indicator points to the left, the pressure decreases. Either operation overrides the automatic controller. When the knob indicator points to "AUTO," the valves in the manual controller are closed, and only the automatic controller remains effective.

Two cabin-pressure outflow valves, mentioned previously, provide cabin-pressure regulation, cabin-altitude limiting, vacuum relief, and positive pressure relief. These valves are located to the right and left of the bottom center line of the airplane, to the rear of the aft bulkhead of the aft cargo compartment. Each valve assembly includes a pneumatically balanced poppet valve with a vacuum relief diaphragm, a control chamber, a cabin air port and filter, a positive pressure relief valve, a pneumatic relay, a jet pump, an atmosphere port, a cabin-altitude limit control, and a ground venturi port.

The poppet valve assembly moves to regulate air passing from the cabin as pneumatic signals are received from the automatic or manual control through the pneumatic relay to the control chamber. The safety valves' positive pressure relief and cabin-altitude limiter also move the poppet valve by changing control-chamber pressure. Thus, the poppet valve either maintains a selected pressure or effects a change at a selected rate.

A vacuum-relief diaphragm lifts to contact and raise the poppet valve assembly to admit ambient air when ambient air pressure becomes higher than cabin pressure. The vacuum-relief system overrides automatic or manual control signals.

The positive pressure relief valve causes the outflow valve to open and exhaust air when differential between cabin and ambient pressure exceeds 9.42 ($\pm$0.15) psi. This function overrides automatic or manual control signals. The positive pressure relief valve is built into the outflow valve and consists of two chambers divided by a spring-loaded diaphragm.

Summary of air conditioning

In the foregoing section we have given a brief description of the principal functions and components of a typical air-conditioning system for a jet airliner. Numerous details have been omitted because space does not permit their description. The technician is reminded that he should consult the manufacturer's maintenance manual for service instructions and for information on the finer details.

Air conditioning includes heating, ventilating, cooling, and pressurization. The methods used for each of these functions have been explained, and the principal units have been described. The illustrations will assist in providing understanding of the systems and components.

Heating for an aircraft is accomplished by drawing air across a heated exhaust manifold, drawing air through a combustion heater, or utilizing the heated air from the compressor of a jet engine.

Ventilation is accomplished as air is caused to flow into and out of the cabin.

Cooling is provided by refrigeration-type coolers in which a refrigerant, such as Freon, is compressed, cooled, and evaporated to produce low temperatures and by air-expansion coolers where the expansion of compressed air produces low temperatures.

Pressurization of the airplane cabin is accomplished by directing compressed air into the cabin from engine compressors or engine-driven compressors. The pressure in the cabin is controlled at the desired level through the use of outflow valves which are regulated by means of automatic pressure controllers. Suitable instruments such as altimeters and rate-of-climb indicators are used to show the cabin pressure and rate of pressure change.

The pressurized compartments of the airplane are sealed at the seams to eliminate undesired leakage of air. The structure is designed to withstand the internal applied pressure.

OXYGEN SYSTEMS

Oxygen systems are required on airplanes which fly for extended periods at altitudes substantially above 10,000 ft. Although the normal human body can survive without a special supply of oxygen at altitudes of over 15,000 ft, the mental and physical capacities of the human being are reduced when the usual supply of oxygen is not available in the air. It is particularly important that the pilot and crew of an airplane have an adequate supply of oxygen when operating an unpressurized airplane at altitudes in excess of 10,000 ft.

A lack of oxygen causes a person to experience a condition called **anoxia.** This condition results in "light-headedness," headaches, dizziness, nausea, unconsciousness, or death, depending upon the time and degree of anoxia.

Oxygen systems for light aircraft

Light aircraft which are capable of flying at very high altitudes are often equipped with portable oxygen systems when the airplane is to be flown at altitudes where oxygen is needed. Such a system includes a high-pressure oxygen tank, a pressure regulator, pressure gage, manifold, and various types of oxygen outlets to which tubing connected to masks can be attached. The system can be equipped with either **demand regulators** or **constant-flow valves** at the low-pressure outlet. A demand regulator is designed to permit oxygen flow only when the wearer of the mask is drawing a breath. The regulator is equipped with a flow indicator to show when oxygen is flowing and to warn the user when his supply is exhausted or failing to supply oxygen for any other reason.

Permanently installed oxygen systems are often installed in light aircraft which regularly operate at high altitudes. Figure 16·8 is a schematic diagram of the system employed for some models of the Cessna 310, twin-engine airplane. This system is designed to supply oxygen for a pilot, copilot, and three passengers. The system consists of an oxygen cylinder, filler valve, plumbing, an oxygen pressure gage, pressure regulator, outlet couplings, and five disposable-type oxygen masks complete with rubber hoses and flow indicators.

In the system shown, oxygen is routed from the high-pressure cylinder to the pressure gage and through a regulator which reduces the high cylinder pressure to a low, usable pressure. From the regulator, low-pressure oxygen is routed to five outlet couplings which supply a continuous flow of oxygen to the masks whenever the mask hoses are plugged into the couplings. Each coupling contains a spring-loaded valve which restricts the flow of oxygen until the mask hose is plugged into the coupling. Each mask hose contains a flow indicator for visual proof of oxygen flow. The

masks, rubber hoses, and flow indicators are stored in the oxygen-mask case on the baggage shelf when not in use.

The high-pressure tubing used to carry the oxygen from the oxygen cylinder to the pressure regulator is made of copper. Aluminum tubing is used on the low-pressure side of the regulator to carry the oxygen to the oxygen manifold. Copper tubing is also used between the filler valve and the cylinder. The high-pressure cylinder is charged to 1800 psi; hence the plumbing, fittings, and installation must be of suitable quality to avoid any possibility of rupture or leakage. The accidental release of high-pressure oxygen can cause serious injury or death.

In servicing and maintaining the oxygen system, the technician must make certain that no grease or oil comes in contact with any of the parts. Fitting threads should be lightly lubricated with MIL-T-5542 thread compound applied to male fittings only. No compound should be placed on the first two threads. Fitting and valves should be tested for leakage by applying type CG-1 solution in accordance with specification MIL-L-25567A, or equivalent. Formation of bubbles indicates leakage. After testing, all solution should be removed from the fittings and valves. When the system is fully pressurized, the leakage rate should not exceed 1 percent in a period of 24 hr.

Oxygen system for the DC-9 jet airliner

Oxygen systems for large jet airliners are primarily installed for emergency use in case of cabin pressurization failure or cabin decompression. The oxygen supply is sufficient to take care of all passengers and crew until the airplane is at a low altitude where oxygen is no longer necessary.

On the Douglas DC-9, two independent gaseous systems are installed, one in the flight compartment for the crew and one in the passenger compartment for the passengers and cabin attendants. Thus, failure in one system will not affect the operation of the other system. In addition, a portable oxygen cylinder is located in the flight compartment to assure an emergency supply of oxygen for the flight crew. The portable cylinder is mounted on a bracket and secured by a quick-disconnect clamp.

A portable oxygen cylinder is also installed at each cabin attendant's station to enable the attendant to be mobile in the event of cabin decompression. The cylinder with a mask attached is mounted on a bracket and secured by quick-disconnect clamps.

Both the passenger and crew oxygen systems have thermal-expansion safety discharge features and use a common discharge-indicator. Discharge will occur if cylinder pressure exceeds about 2650 psig. This indicator is mounted in the fuselage skin below the first officer's side window and contains a green plastic disk. Absence of this disk requires an inspection of both the passenger and crew oxygen cylinders.

A drawing showing the layout of the oxygen system for the Douglas DC-9 airplane is shown in Fig. 16·9. Note that the passenger oxygen manifolds extend the

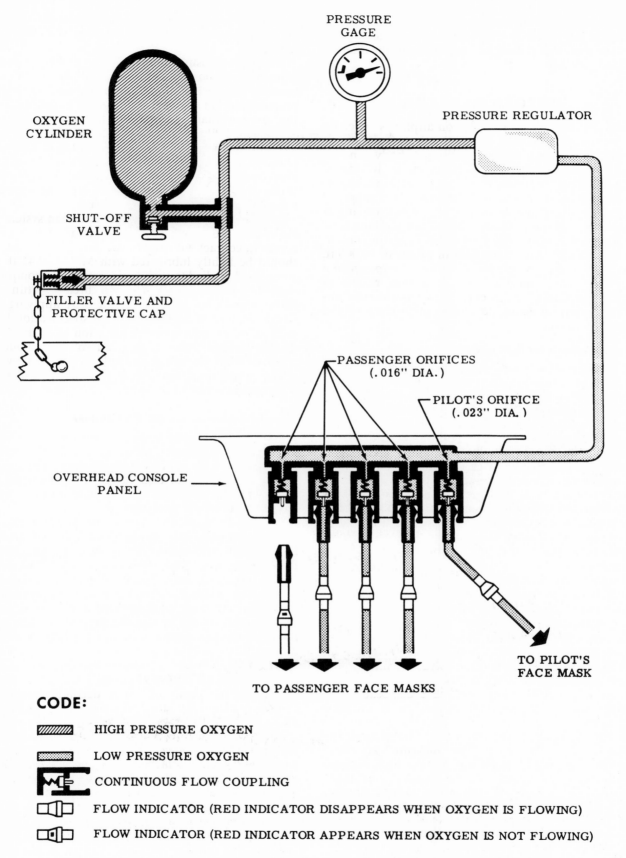

PRESSURE
GAGE

OXYGEN
CYLINDER

PRESSURE REGULATOR

SHUT-OFF
VALVE

FILLER VALVE AND
PROTECTIVE CAP

PASSENGER ORIFICES
(.016" DIA.)

PILOT'S ORIFICE
(.023" DIA.)

OVERHEAD CONSOLE
PANEL

TO PILOT'S
FACE MASK

TO PASSENGER FACE MASKS

CODE:

HIGH PRESSURE OXYGEN

LOW PRESSURE OXYGEN

CONTINUOUS FLOW COUPLING

FLOW INDICATOR (RED INDICATOR DISAPPEARS WHEN OXYGEN IS FLOWING)

FLOW INDICATOR (RED INDICATOR APPEARS WHEN OXYGEN IS NOT FLOWING)

Figure 16·8   An oxygen system used for the Cessna 310 airplane. (Cessna Aircraft Co.)

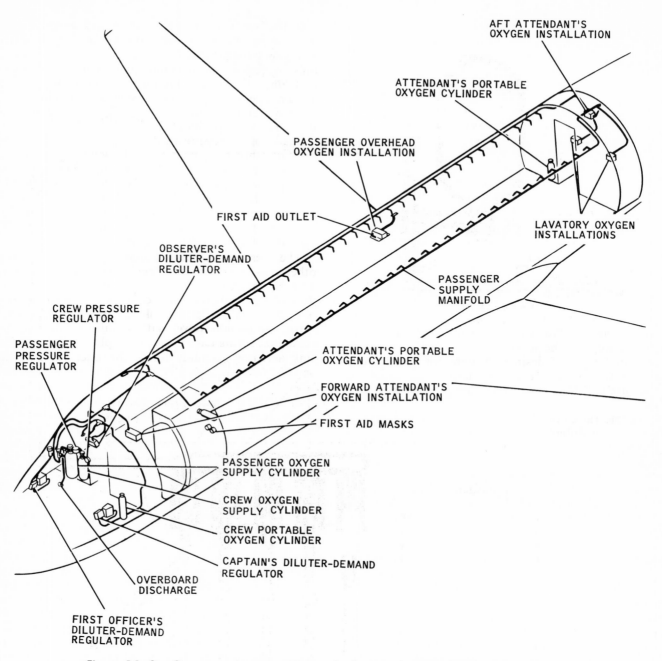

AFT ATTENDANT'S OXYGEN INSTALLATION

ATTENDANT'S PORTABLE OXYGEN CYLINDER

PASSENGER OVERHEAD OXYGEN INSTALLATION

FIRST AID OUTLET

LAVATORY OXYGEN INSTALLATIONS

OBSERVER'S DILUTER-DEMAND REGULATOR

PASSENGER SUPPLY MANIFOLD

CREW PRESSURE REGULATOR

PASSENGER PRESSURE REGULATOR

ATTENDANT'S PORTABLE OXYGEN CYLINDER

FORWARD ATTENDANT'S OXYGEN INSTALLATION

FIRST AID MASKS

PASSENGER OXYGEN SUPPLY CYLINDER

CREW OXYGEN SUPPLY CYLINDER

CREW PORTABLE OXYGEN CYLINDER

CAPTAIN'S DILUTER-DEMAND REGULATOR

OVERBOARD DISCHARGE

FIRST OFFICER'S DILUTER-DEMAND REGULATOR

Figure 16·9 Oxygen system arrangement in the Douglas DC-9 airliner. (Douglas Aircraft Co., Inc.)

full length of the cabin on each side. Only one passenger overhead oxygen installation is shown; however, such an installation is provided for each passenger.

The **crew oxygen system** shown in the schematic diagram of Fig. 16·10 consists of a high-pressure **supply cylinder,** a **shutoff valve** with a **cylinder pressure gage,** a **pressure regulator, automatic pressure breathing-demand regulators, oronasal masks,** and a quick-disconnect test fitting. The term **oronasal** means that the mask fits over both the mouth and the nose.

The capacity of the crew oxygen supply cylinder is 48 cu ft of oxygen at standard atmosphere and pres-

sure. The pressure gage, installed in the body of the shutoff valve, indicates cylinder pressure with the valve in either the open or closed position. The **pressure reducing regulator,** attached by means of a union fitting to the cylinder shutoff valve, reduces the high cylinder pressure of 1850 (0, −20) psig to a constant supply pressure of approximately 65 psig.

The **diluter-demand pressure breathing regulator** installed at each flight-crew station automatically controls the mixture ratio of air to oxygen, the ratio varying with cabin pressure. As explained previously, this type of regulator supplies the mixture of oxygen

298

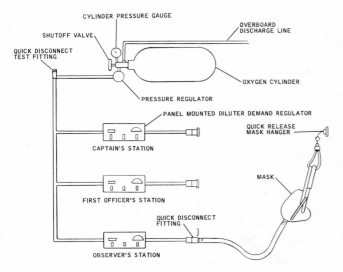

CYLINDER PRESSURE GAUGE

SHUTOFF VALVE

QUICK DISCONNECT
TEST FITTING

OVERBOARD
DISCHARGE LINE

OXYGEN CYLINDER

PRESSURE REGULATOR

PANEL MOUNTED DILUTER DEMAND REGULATOR

QUICK RELEASE
MASK HANGER

CAPTAIN'S STATION

MASK

FIRST OFFICER'S STATION

QUICK DISCONNECT
FITTING

OBSERVER'S STATION

Figure 16·10   Crew oxygen system for the DC-9.

and air as it is "demanded" by the breathing of the person wearing the mask. It is possible to select 100 percent oxygen if desired. A light for panel illumination is installed in the regulator. The supply-line pressure is indicated by a pressure gage on each regulator.

Toggle valves on the demand regulators permit the selection of different methods of supplying oxygen to the masks. The supply toggle on the right side of the regulator panel can be safetied to the ON position if desired. When this toggle is in the OFF position, the regulator will not supply oxygen to the mask. The center toggle is placarded NORMAL OXYGEN and 100% OXYGEN. When this toggle is in the 100% OXYGEN position, only pure oxygen is supplied to the mask. In the NORMAL OXYGEN position, ambient air is mixed with oxygen according to cabin altitude (internal cabin pressure). The emergency toggle on the left side of the regulator panel is placarded EMERGENCY, NORMAL, and TEST MASK. In the TEST MASK position, oxygen is supplied to the mask for test purposes. The toggle is spring-loaded from the TEST MASK position to the NORMAL, or center, position. In the EMERGENCY position, positive pressure is sent to the mask.

For normal operation of the system, the supply toggle must be in the ON position with the center and emergency toggles in the NORMAL position. This supplies oxygen to the mask upon demand. A dilution of oxygen with air is controlled by an aneroid within the regulator. In the event of cabin decompression at altitudes above 28,000 ft, aneroids within the regulator automatically sense the change in cabin pressure and supply pure oxygen at a positive pressure to the masks by closing the air valve and overriding the demand valve. For protective breathing purposes, when the cabin air is contaminated with smoke or other noxious gases, the center toggle must be in the 100% OXYGEN position. This closes the air valve in the regulator, thus permitting only pure oxygen to reach the mask.

In the event of regulator failure, the center toggle must be placed in the 100% OXYGEN position and the emergency toggle must be in the EMERGENCY position, thus overriding the demand diaphragm in the regulator unit. This feeds only pure oxygen to the masks. The emergency toggle is guarded by a safety pin, which must be removed before the toggle can be placed in the EMERGENCY position.

The **supply pressure regulator** for the crew oxygen system is shown in the cutaway drawing of Fig. 16·11. As explained previously, this regulator reduces the high pressure from the oxygen cylinder to a usable range in the supply lines. This range is from 50 to 75 psig. A relief valve in the regulator automatically opens to relieve line pressure at approximately 100 psig and closes at 100 ($\pm$ 10) psig.

The pressure regulator is similar in design to many other gas- or air-pressure regulators in that it utilizes a diaphragm balanced against a spring to control the flow of gas. This regulator consists of a **housing, diaphragm, regulator spring, link actuator assembly, relief valve,** and an **inlet valve.** With no inlet pressure on the regulator, spring tension on the diaphragm through the link actuator assembly forces the inlet valve to the normal open position. When oxygen is flowing, high pressure in the lower diaphragm chamber compresses the regulator spring, thus causing the diaphragm to move upward. The link actuator assembly then mechanically causes the regulator valve to move toward the closed position, thus reducing the flow of oxygen. When the pressure in the lower chamber of the diaphragm is equal to the regulator spring force, the diaphragm ceases to move and positions the inlet valve to maintain the proper oxygen flow.

A cutaway drawing to illustrate the **operation of the diluter-demand regulator** is shown in Fig. 16·12. Oxygen at supply pressure (50 to 75 psig) enters the regulator inlet port and passes through the filter to the inlet valve. This valve serves as a combined shutoff and pressure reducing valve. When the **supply toggle** is placed in the ON position, the **pressure reducer spring** acts on the piston to open the valve. Pressure in the reducer outlet chamber builds up on the piston, overcomes the spring and closes the valve. The piston and valve then regulate the reduced pressure according to demand. When the supply toggle is in the OFF position, the reducer spring is unloaded and the inlet valve is closed by the spring-plus-inlet pressure.

With the **diluter toggle** in the NORMAL OXYGEN position, the regulator will deliver a mixture of air and oxygen in the quantity demanded by inhalation. When pressure at the outlet is reduced by inhalation, the **breathing diaphragm** moves the **counterweight** and **demand valve levers** to open the **demand valve.** Oxygen is delivered to the outlet through the **injector** which serves to create a low-pressure, high-velocity stream, drawing in air for dilution in normal operation. The air-to-oxygen ratio varies with cabin pressure altitude, automatically controlled by an aneroid bellows assembly. As cabin altitude increases, the quantity of air mixed with oxygen increases. At 28,000 to 30,000 ft

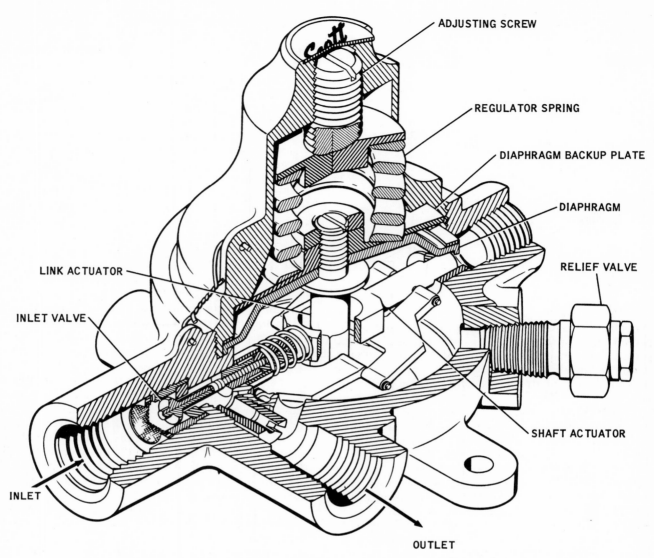

ADJUSTING SCREW

REGULATOR SPRING

DIAPHRAGM BACKUP PLATE

DIAPHRAGM

RELIEF VALVE

LINK ACTUATOR

INLET VALVE

SHAFT ACTUATOR

INLET

OUTLET

Figure 16·11   Crew oxygen-supply pressure regulator for the Douglas DC-9 airliner.

cabin pressure altitude, only 100 percent oxygen is delivered to the masks. With the diluter toggle in the 100% OXYGEN position, 100 percent oxygen is delivered in the quantity determined by inhalation.

With the **emergency toggle** placed in the EMERGENCY position, a positive pressure is delivered to the mask. The safety pin must be removed before the toggle can be placed in the EMERGENCY position. The emergency toggle, when placed in the TEST MASK position, is spring-loaded and must be held down to become effective. When released, the toggle will return to the NORMAL position.

An **oxygen mask** is provided for each crew member as well as for each passenger. As explained previously, the **crew oxygen masks** are of the oronasal type and fit over the mouth and nose. The mask housing is plastic with a rubber seal between the housing and the user's face.

A breathing tube extends from the mask housing. The tube is equipped with a quick-disconnect fitting which connects into the crew oxygen supply connector or the portable cylinder.

A microphone and oxygen valve are inside the mask housing. A cable and jack extends from the microphone and is plugged into the radio system jack located adjacent to the oxygen connector. The oxygen valve opens and closes as the wearer inhales and exhales. The mask is ready for immediate use when removed from stowage and placed on the user's face.

A portion of the **passenger oxygen system** is illustrated schematically in Fig. 16·13. This drawing shows the high-pressure oxygen cylinder, pressure regulator, shutoff valve, manifolding, passenger outlets, and associated parts. The cylinder has a capacity of 64 cu ft, weighs approximately 28 lb, and is charged to a pressure of 1850 (0, −20) psig under normal atmospheric conditions. The cylinder is secured with strap clamps in an upright position in the aft right-hand corner of the flight compartment.

A direct-reading **pressure gage** is installed in the

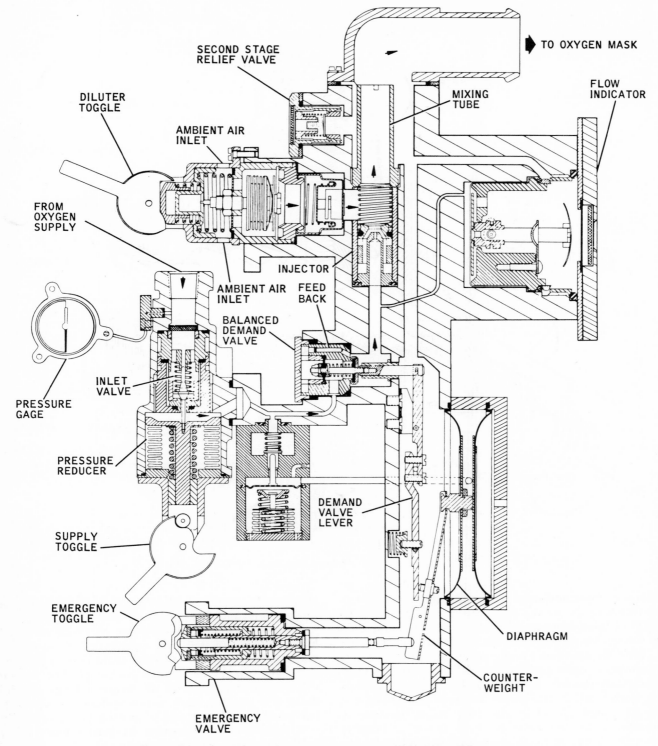

Figure 16·12   Diluter demand regulator. (Douglas Aircraft Co., Inc.)

shutoff valve body between the valve and the cylinder. The pressure gage indicates cylinder pressure with the valve in either the OPEN or CLOSED position. An adapter containing a frangible ("burstible")-type blowout disk is connected to the shutoff valve body. The blowout disk will rupture and allow oxygen to escape overboard in the event that cylinder pressure should exceed approximately 2650 psig.

The **pressure regulator,** illustrated in Fig. 16·14, is attached to the cylinder hand shutoff valve. It is a continuous-flow altitude-compensating type which varies supply-line pressure with altitude. The regulator

301

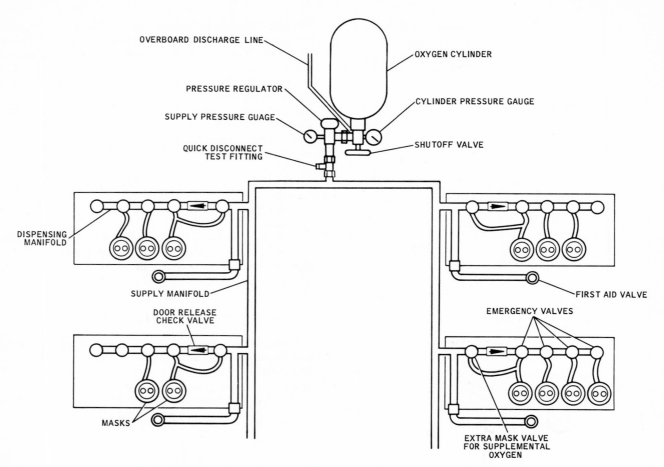

Figure **16·13** *Schematic diagram of a portion of the passenger oxygen system for the Douglas DC-9.*

is actuated automatically by sensing a rise in cabin-pressure altitude, or manually by controls located on the body of the regulator. A relief valve in the regulator will open to prevent outlet pressure from exceeding approximately 150 psig.

At 10,500- to 12,000-ft cabin-pressure altitude, the **automatic-opening aneroid** expands, thus causing the valve to open and supply pressure to the **pressure surge unit.** Increased pressure through the surge unit actuates the **door-release check valve,** unlatches the mask container doors, and pressurizes the dispensing manifolds. On descent, at a cabin pressure altitude of 6000 to 10,000 ft, the automatic-opening aneroid will contract, causing the valve to close and shutting off the oxygen supply. It is then necessary to place the manual control to the ON position to supply supplemental oxygen to passengers as necessary. If the automatic-opening valve should fail to function properly, the system is pressurized by placing the regulator manual control in the ON position and turning the manual oxygen-door release knob to the full-rotated position.

Oxygen entering the regulator passes through the **pressure reducer** and the **automatic-opening valve** and then enters the **altitude-compensating aneroid chamber.** As the aneroid expands and contracts due to the changes in cabin pressure altitude, the outlet flow and

pressure varies. When the cylinder is fully charged to approximately 1850 psig, the maximum outlet flow at the regulator is 430 liters per min, and the maximum pressure is approximately 80 psig, at 35,000 ft.

First-aid oxygen can be made available during normal operation of the pressurized airplane if necessary. This is accomplished by a crew member placing the regulator manual control in the ON position.

The **passenger oxygen masks** are of the oronasal type and are made of a plastic-type rubber which forms around the mouth and nose area. The mask consists of a facepiece, three valves, a rebreathing bag, a length of plastic tubing, a pull cord, and a head strap to secure the mask to the wearer's head. The masks are connected to outlet valves by a plastic tube. The mask is connected to an outlet-valve pull pin by a pull cord.

The passenger masks are stowed in oxygen stowage boxes above each seat row in the overhead stowage-rack utility panel, in each lavatory washstand, and at each attendant's station. All masks, except those installed at the attendant's forward station, are held in position on the stowage box door by a plastic holder and must be manually removed. The attendant's forward-station masks will fall free when the door is opened.

During operation of the passenger mask, when the

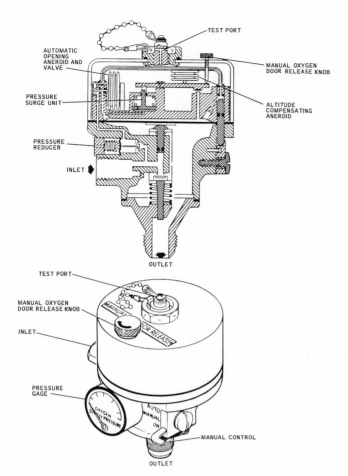

Figure 16·14   *Passenger oxygen pressure regulator.*

wearer inhales, oxygen is withdrawn from the re-breathing bag through the inhalation valve. Air from the atmosphere then automatically dilutes the oxygen as necessary through the safety and dilution valve. This valve also permits the wearer to breathe if the oxygen supply becomes restricted. The wearer exhales to the atmosphere through the exhalation valve. During exhalation, the bag is refilled with oxygen from the supply manifold.

Oxygen system summary

The foregoing descriptions are examples of what may be installed in modern aircraft. The requirements for oxygen vary; however, oxygen systems must be provided on all aircraft which are to operate at high altitudes where the lack of oxygen in the air can cause disability of either crew or passengers.

On nonpressurized aircraft, oxygen is essential for crew and passengers when high altitudes are reached. For pressurized aircraft, the oxygen system is an emergency provision to protect passengers and crew in case of cabin depressurization.

The technician handling oxygen equipment and servicing oxygen systems must be alert to the dangers involved. It has been emphasized that pure oxygen in contact with grease or oil is likely to cause an explosion.

For this reason, everything that comes in contact with oxygen must be free of oil or grease. Even the thin film of grease that may be on the technician's hands can cause trouble.

The high-pressure portions of an oxygen system usually employ stainless-steel tubing and fittings. The low-pressure sections have aluminum tubing and flexible hose for carrying the oxygen. Fittings are lubricated with special nongreasy lubricants (MIL-T-5542) or equivalent.

Oxygen cylinders on large aircraft can be recharged from outside the airplane through special recharging fittings. Recharging must be done according to the instructions provided by the manufacturer of the airplane.

Pure oxygen must not be allowed to come into contact with objects or materials which are heated to a glowing level. The oxygen will usually cause the material to burst into an extremely hot flame.

FIRE-PROTECTION SYSTEMS

Fire-protection systems on aircraft usually consist of two separate operating systems. One system is for **detection,** and the other is for **extinguishing.** In some cases the systems can be interconnected so extinguishing takes place automatically when a fire is detected.

Fire-detection systems

A **fire-detection system** consists of electric circuitry connected with fire-sensing elements and indicating devices. The **fire-sensing elements** employed on large aircraft consist of Inconel tubing filled with a ceramic material impregnated with an inorganic salt and a single nickel wire passing through the center. The Inconel tubing forms the ground circuit, and the nickel wire is the ungrounded or "hot" part of the circuit.

When the sensing element is exposed to the temperature established as the warning temperature, the ceramic and salt mixture changes in resistance quickly and actuates the control circuit. This circuit, or unit, turns on warning lights, sounds a horn, or rings a bell. On a large airliner the sensing elements are placed in each engine nacelle, at the auxiliary power unit, in the cargo compartments, in the nosewheel compartment, in electronic equipment compartments, and in other areas where the danger of fire is possible.

The warning lights and aural signaling devices are placed where they are immediately apparent to the crew so that action can be taken at once to eliminate the fire.

Fire-extinguishing systems

A fire-extinguishing system consists of an extinguishing agent stored in pressurized bottles, tubing to carry the agent to fire areas, control valves, indicators, and associated components.

A schematic diagram of the engine fire-extinguishing system for a Boeing 727 airliner is shown in Fig. 16·15. The system consists of two spherical steel bottles charged with Freon and nitrogen gas to a pressure of

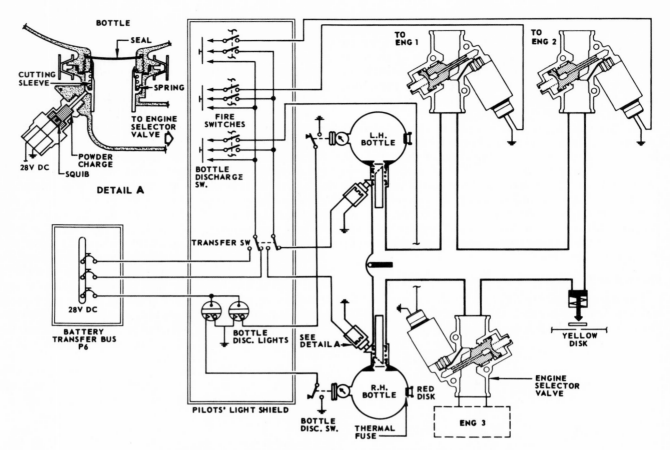

Figure 16·15 Engine fire-extinguishing system. (Boeing Co.)

600 psi, connecting tubing to the engine valves, and control circuitry. By operating a fire switch, a crew member can cause the extinguishing agent to be discharged into the area selected.

When a fire-extinguishing switch is closed, an explosive charge at the neck of the storage bottle is detonated and a cutter is driven through the seal in the neck of the bottle. This releases the extinguishing agent from the bottle instantaneously and permits it to flow to the engine valves. The pilot or other crewman will have selected the appropriate engine by operating a switch on the fire control panel and the valve for this engine will be open. The engine nacelle will then be flooded with extinguishing agent, and the fire will be extinguished. Usually the fuel to this engine will have been turned off automatically when the engine fire-extinguishing switch is operated.

Fire-extinguishing systems for other areas in the airplane operate in the same manner as that described above. Systems similar to this are employed in almost all large aircraft.

ICE- AND RAIN-PROTECTION SYSTEMS

All aircraft which operate in weather conditions where ice is likely to form must be provided with ice protection. This protection may be in the form of anti-

icing systems or deicing systems. An **anti-icing system** prevents the formation of ice on the airplane, and a **deicing system** removes ice which has already formed.

Among the parts of the airplane where ice prevention or removal is essential are the windshield, wing leading edges, tail airfoil leading edges, propellers, engine air inlets, pitot tubes, water drains, and any other part where the formation of ice can interfere with the operation of the airplane or its systems.

On piston-engine airplanes, especially those equipped with float-type carburetors, carburetor anti-icing is necessary, even in clear weather when the temperature and humidity are conducive to the formation of ice in the throat of the carburetor.

Mechanical deicing systems

For many years, various airplanes have utilized mechanical deicing systems consisting of inflatable rubber "boots" formed to the leading edge of wings and stabilizers. The deicing boots are attached to the leading edge of the airfoils by means of cement and fasteners such as rivnuts, also called "bootnuts."

The inflatable boots are usually constructed with several separate air passages or chambers such that some can be inflated while alternate chambers are deflated. The inflation of the boot is accomplished by utilizing the output pressure from a vacuum pump for inflation and the inlet side of the pump for deflation.

The control of the pressure and suction and pressure is accomplished by means of a distributor valve which rotates and periodically changes the flow of air to or from the different section of the boots. This results in alternate raising and lowering of sections of the boots, and this action cracks off any ice which has formed on the boots.

Another mechanical system used for smaller aircraft utilizes a boot with a pressure bottle for the air supply. When ice forms on the leading edge of the wing, the pilot or copilot operates a valve to allow air pressure to enter the boot. This inflates the boot and cracks off the ice. This is not a continuously operating system and is used as sparingly as necessary to remove ice. The air-supply bottle contains sufficient air to operate the boots through several cycles, thus giving the pilot time to fly out of the icing area.

Thermal anti-icing

The most commonly employed anti-icing system for modern airliners is called thermal anti-icing (TAI) because it utilizes the heated compressed air from the jet engines to heat the areas of the airplane where ice can form. Figure 16·16 is a drawing of the layout of the thermal anti-icing system on the Douglas DC-9 together with enlarged drawings of control components.

The airfoil ice-protection system provides for the control of engine bleed air distributed to the leading edges of the wings and horizontal stabilizer. The ice-protection-system air temperature is maintained between 450 and 490°F by controls placed in the pneumatic system. When either or both airfoil ice-protection switches are placed in the ON position, the ice-protection pressure-regulator and shutoff valve will open and allow engine bleed air to flow into the system. The same switches will cause the right, left, or both pneumatic system-augmentation valves to open and admit the amount of thirteenth-stage engine bleed air necessary to raise the temperature of the air to 450°F or above. The ice-protection pressure regulator and shutoff valve regulates the pressure of the air passing into the ice-protection system at 18.5 psig. With the airfoil ice-protection switches in the ON position, the

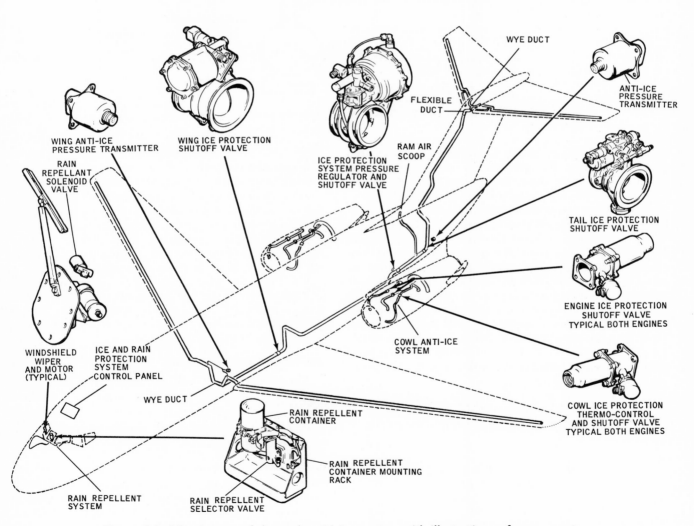

Figure **16·16** *Layout of thermal anti-icing system with illustrations of components. (Douglas Aircraft Co., Inc.)*

flow of engine bleed air is normally directed to the wing leading edge and the ram air scoop. However, by pushing the switch marked TAIL, the **wing ice-protection shutoff valve** will close, the **tail ice-protection shutoff valve** will open, and air will flow to the horizontal stabilizer for a period of 2 to 2½ min. After this interval the air is automatically redirected to the wing until the tail switch is pushed again. Thus, it can be seen that the tail ice protection is deicing while the wing ice protection is anti-icing.

The ice-protection air is supplied to the wing- and horizontal-stabilizer leading edges through drilled ducting within the leading-edge "D" duct. Chem-milled skins form the chordwise double-skin passages in the leading edges.

The wing ice-protection valve on the Douglas DC-9 is installed on the inboard side of the left-hand wheel well in the wing ice-protection supply duct. It is an electrically controlled, pneumatically actuated, butterfly-type valve. The valve is normally open when the solenoid valve is deenergized. The valve consists of a solenoid and selector valve assembly, actuator assembly, and butterfly housing. The valve has a V-band-type clamp-mounting flange at each end. A mechanically operated indicator located on the actuator housing indicates the butterfly position.

The wing ice-protection shutoff valve works in conjunction with the tail ice-protection shutoff valve. When the ice-protection system is turned on, the wing shutoff valve is spring-loaded open. The shutoff will remain open until the tail deicing timer relay is actuated. At this time the solenoid on the wing shutoff valve is energized to open a valve and permit air to close the shutoff valve butterfly. At the same time, the tail ice-protection shutoff valve opens and now air is diverted to deice the horizontal stabilizer. Approximately 2½ min later the timer relay automatically releases and shuts off the current to both valves. This causes the wing shutoff valve to open and the tail shutoff valve to close. A light on the annunciator panel comes on when the airfoil ice-protection switches are turned on, indicating that the wing leading edge is being anti-iced. When the tail deicing timer relay is pressed, the wing deice light goes out and the tail deice light comes on, indicating that the horizontal stabilizer leading edge is being deiced. A drawing of the tail ice-protection shutoff valve is illustrated in Fig. 16·17.

Electrically heated anti-icing devices

Ice formation on such units as pitot tubes, static ports, and stall warning units is prevented by means of electric heating elements. These elements consist of fine resistance wire sealed in each assembly. The heaters are controlled by switches and may be supplied with either a-c or d-c, depending upon the design of the system.

Windshields are also anti-iced by means of electrical heating; however, the heating elements are conductive coatings of transparent material bonded to the inner side of the outer layer of glass. Heating of the windshield panels anti-ices and defogs the windshield and

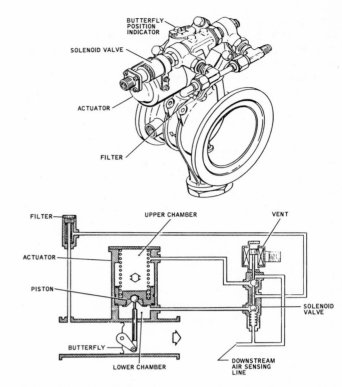

Figure 16·17   Tail ice-protection shutoff valve. (Douglas Aircraft Co., Inc.)

also increases the elasticity of the windshield. This makes the windshield more resistant to the impact of objects, such as birds.

Rain-repellant systems

To help maintain the clarity of vision through the windshield during rain conditions, a rain-repellant system is provided for the windshields of modern airliners. This system consists of pressurized fluid containers, a selector valve, solenoid-actuated valves, spray nozzles, pushbutton switches, a control switch, a time-delay relay, and necessary plumbing. The rain-repellant system and windshield wipers for the Douglas DC-9 airplane are shown in Fig. 16·18.

During rain conditions, the windshield wipers are turned on, and the repellant is sprayed on the windshield. The repellant is spread evenly by the wiper blades. The rain repellant should not be sprayed on the windshield unless the windshield is wet and the wipers are operated; neither should the windshield wipers be operated on a dry windshield.

The effect of the rain repellant is to cause the water to form small globules which are quickly blown away by the rush of air over the windshield in flight.

Windshield-wiper systems

A typical **windshield-wiper system** is illustrated in Fig. 16·19. This drawing shows the components of the wipers installed on the Boeing 727 airplane. Each wiper on the airplane is operated by a separate system to ensure that clear vision through one of the windows will be maintained in the event of a system failure. The wiper blades clear a path 15 in. wide through an arc of 40°.

Both wiper systems are electrically operated and controlled by a common gang switch located on the pilot's overhead panel. The switch provides a selection of four wiper-action speeds ranging from 190 to 275 strokes per minute and controls the stowing of the wiper blades in a PARK position when the system is not in use.

Each windshield-wiper system consists of a drive motor, a control switch, a resistor box, a flexible drive shaft, a torque converter, and a windshield-wiper assembly.

Speed control for the windshield wipers is accomplished by changing the voltage applied to the windshield-wiper motor by means of resistances arranged in the resistor box. The required resistance is connected into the motor circuit by turning the windshield-wiper switch to a selected speed. The rotary motion of the windshield-wiper motor is transmitted by the flexible

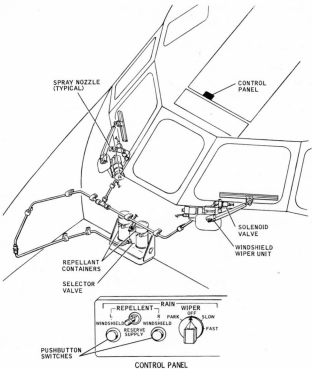

Figure 16·18   Rain-repellant system. (Douglas Aircraft Co., Inc.)

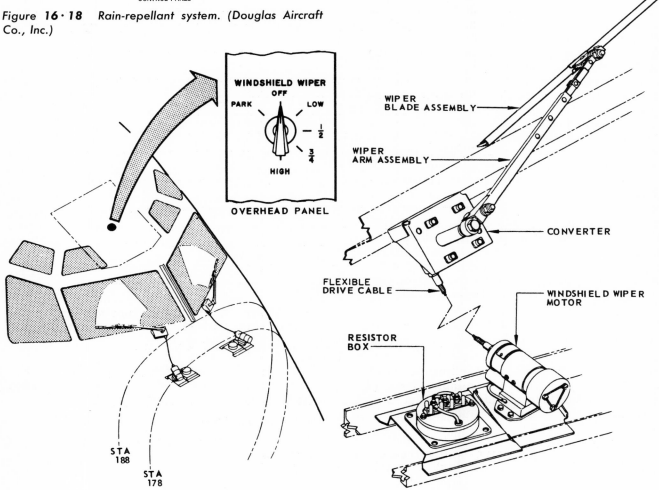

Figure 16·19   Windshield-wiper system. (Douglas Aircraft Co., Inc.)

shaft to the converter. The converter reduces the shaft speed and changes the rotary motion to an oscillating motion of the windshield-wiper arm. The electrical circuit for the windshield wipers is shown schematically in Fig. 16 · 20.

WATER AND WASTE SYSTEMS

All modern airliners are required to incorporate water systems to supply the needs and comforts of the passengers and crew. Such systems include potable (drinkable) water for the galley and drinking fountains, water for the lavatories, and water for the toilet systems. Systems may include one or more tanks of water with connections to the various units which require a water supply. The passenger water system for the Boeing 727 airplane is illustrated in Fig. 16 · 21.

Potable water supply

The water for drinking fountains or faucets is usually drawn from main pressurized water tanks, passed through filters to remove any impurities and solids, cooled by Dry Ice or other means of cooling, and delivered to the faucets and/or drinking fountains. Disposable drinking cups are supplied at each location in the forward and rear parts of the passenger cabin.

Lavatory water

Water for the lavatories is also drawn from the main water tanks and passed directly through suitable plumbing and valves to the lavatories. Hot water for

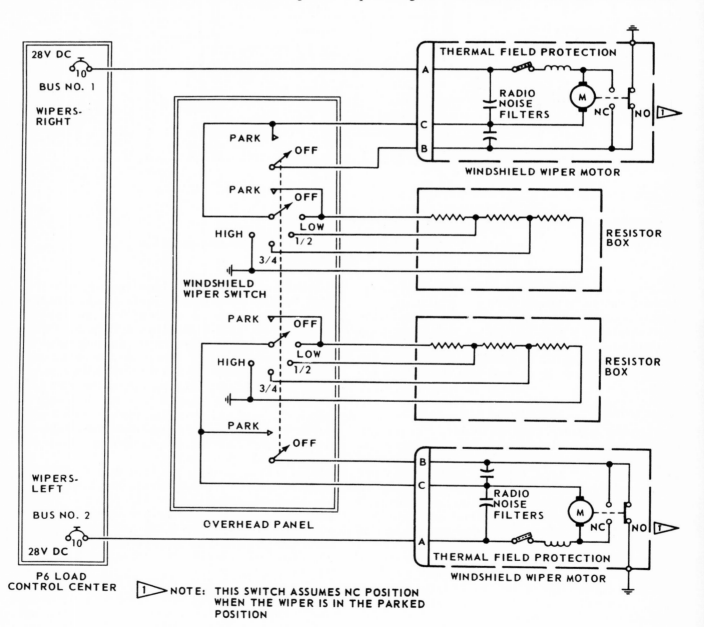

Figure 16 · 20 Electrical system for windshield wipers. (Boeing Co.)

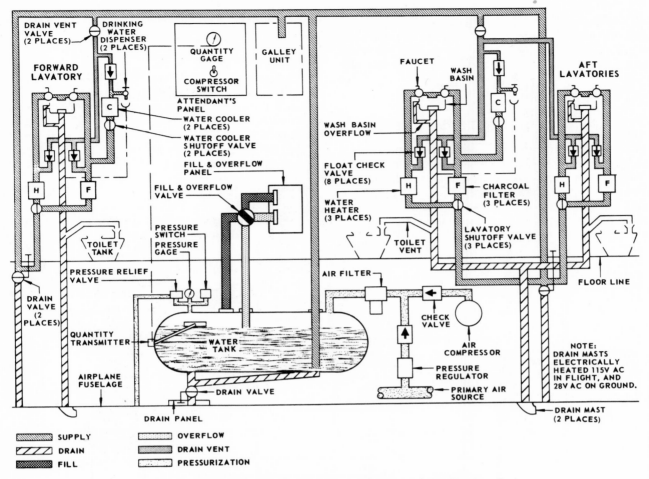

Figure 16·21 Passenger water system for jet airliner. (Boeing Co.)

washing is provided by means of electric water heaters located beneath the lavatory bowls. A typical hot-water supply is contained in a 2-qt tank which includes the thermostatically controlled heating unit to maintain the water at a temperature of 110 to 120°F. Drain water from the lavatories can be drained overboard through drain masts or can be drained into the toilet waste tanks.

Toilet system

The **toilet system** is designed so there is no possible contamination of the passenger water supply from the system. In the Boeing 727 airplane, separate, independent toilet systems are provided in the forward and aft passenger cabin. Toilets in each lavatory compartment are electrically powered flushing units which collect the waste material in a waste tank and combine it with the flushing agent by chemical and mechanical treatment. The units are primed initially with 3 gal of a concentrated solution of disinfectant, deodorant, and dye. The toilet units are installed in each lavatory compartment entirely above the lavatory compartment floor. Each unit consists of a toilet shroud assembly, flushing components, and a waste tank. The components of a toilet system are shown in Fig. 16·22.

Toilet flushing action is initiated by turning the toilet flush handle. This begins a cycle in which flushing liquid is drawn into a rotating filter and pumped through the toilet-bowl flush ring into the bowl with a swirling action. Waste material and flushing liquid flow out the bottom of the bowl into the waste tank. Servicing components in the forward and aft systems allow ground draining and cleansing of the toilet units.

The toilet shroud assembly consists of a standard commercial seat and cover attached to a shroud which covers the flushing components mounted on the tank top. The shroud is attached to the upper and lower ends of the shroud support angles.

The flushing components include a flush handle, timer, motor-and-pump assembly, filter assembly, and the required tubing. All the components, with the exception of the flush handle and timer, are mounted on the tank top. The flush handle and timer are located on the cabinet aft of the toilet unit. The stainless-steel toilet bowl with a flexible restrictor in the bottom is also mounted in the tank top.

The toilet waste tank assembly includes a glass-fiber tank of 17 gal capacity fitted with a bulb-type spring-loaded drain valve and a tank top. The drain valve is operated by a cable from the toilet service

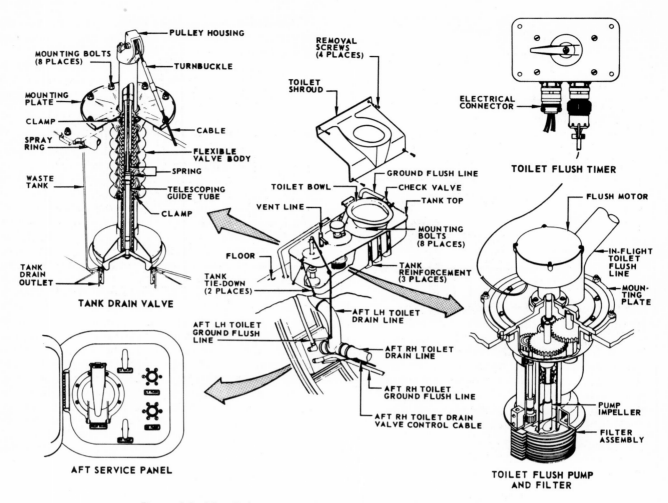

Figure 16·22   Toilet system components for an airliner. (Boeing Co.)

panel. A rubber gasket is placed along the top edge of the tank to form a watertight seal when the tank top is installed. Access into the tank for maintenance purposes is obtained by removing the toilet bowl and base plate.

The drain valve, when fully open, permits unrestricted passage of waste from the tank to a service cart. In the closed position, it forms a positive seal. The valve is spring-loaded and self-closing and does not require lubrication. It is opened by pulling a handle on its related exterior service panel. When the handle is in the extended position, it can be rotated to latch it. A safety valve which is operated by a control on the service attachment is installed in the drain tube.

FUEL-SYSTEM REQUIREMENTS

Even though the airplane fuel system cannot be called an *auxiliary system* (because it is an essential system for the operation of the airplane), it is installed in the airframe and therefore should be discussed in connection with airframe inspection, maintenance, and repair. Additional information on fuel systems and components is provided in the text *Powerplants for*

Aerospace Vehicles. The requirements for aircraft fuel systems are set forth in Federal Aviation Regulations, Parts 23 and 25.

Types of fuel systems

As can be readily understood, fuel systems vary in design from the very simple types used in small, single-engine airplanes to the very complex systems installed in large jet airliners. The former types consist of one or more fuel tanks, usually installed in the wing of the airplane; fuel-quantity indicators; selector valves; fuel strainers; and one or more fuel pumps for systems which do not employ gravity feed. A fuel system for a single-engine airplane is illustrated in Fig. 16·23.

A more intricate fuel system for a light airplane is shown in Fig. 16·24. This system is installed in some models of the Piper Cherokee airplane. The fuel tanks consist of two aluminum tanks contained in the in-board leading-edge sections of the wings. Each fuel cell holds a maximum of 25 gal of fuel. A strainer is installed in the fuel outlet of each tank, and from the tank outlet a fuel line is routed through the wings to the fuel selector valve located on the left side of the cabin in front of the pilot's seat. From the fuel selector valve,

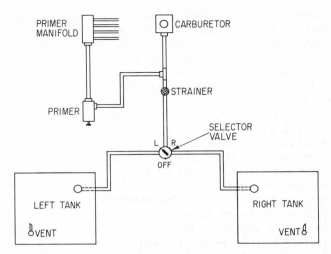

Figure 16·23 *Fuel system for a light airplane.*

a line leads to the fuel **gascolator** mounted on the left forward face of the firewall. The sediment bowl must have a capacity of 1 oz for every 20 gal of fuel. A fuel line is routed from the gascolator to the electric fuel pump, engine-driven fuel pump, and to the carburetor fuel inlet port. A **gascolator** is a fuel strainer, sediment bowl, and drain valve assembly which removes dirt and water from the fuel. The dirt and water settle to the bottom of the bowl and can be drained from the bowl through the drain valve. Periodically the bowl is removed for cleaning and inspecting of the screen.

Two electric fuel-quantity gages are mounted on the instrument panel in the cockpit. Each gage is connected to a transmitter unit installed in the fuel tanks.

Other models of the Piper PA-28 Cherokee airplane have additional glass-fiber tanks, one located in each wing tip. When these are installed, fuel-quantity gages are required for each of the tanks.

Fuel systems for large aircraft

As mentioned previously, the fuel system for a large jet airplane is quite complex. The requirements for such systems are set forth in Federal Aviation Regulations (FAR), Part 25. In addition to the normal purposes of storing fuel and delivering fuel to the engines, the system is equipped for rapid pressure fueling and defueling, fuel deicing, and for dumping fuel in flight. The tanks, lines, fittings, and operating components must be compatible with all fuels meeting the engine manufacturer's specification.

Each fuel tank for a transport-type aircraft must be vented from the top part of the expansion space so that venting is effective under any normal flight condition. In addition, each vent must be arranged to avoid stoppage by dirt or ice formation. The vent arrangement must prevent siphoning of fuel during normal operation. The venting capacity and vent pressure levels must maintain acceptable differences of pressure between the interior and exterior of the tank during normal flight operation, maximum rate of ascent and descent, and during refueling and defueling.

Airspaces of tanks with interconnected outlets must

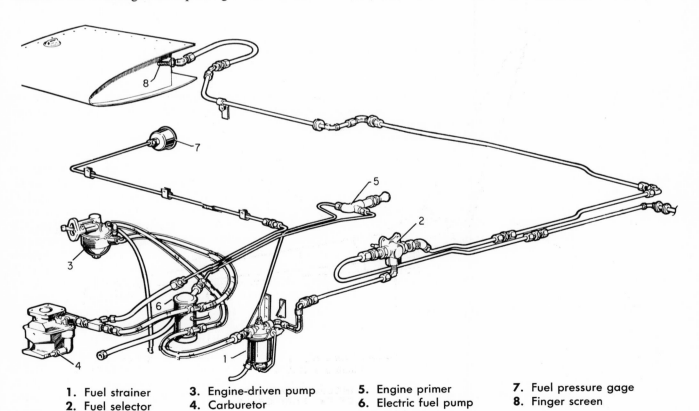

1. Fuel strainer	**5.** Engine primer
2. Fuel selector	**6.** Electric fuel pump
3. Engine-driven pump	**7.** Fuel pressure gage
4. Carburetor	**8.** Finger screen

Figure 16·24 *Fuel system for Piper Cherokee airplane. (Piper Aircraft Corp.)*

be interconnected, and there must be no point in any vent line where moisture can accumulate with the airplane in the ground attitude or the level flight position unless drainage is provided.

No vent or drainage provision may end at any point where the discharge of fuel from the vent outlet would constitute a fire hazard or from which fumes could enter personnel compartments.

On the Boeing 727 airliner, all fuel is stored within vented areas of the wing and wing center section. These fuel storage areas are divided into three main tanks as shown in Fig. 16·25. The tank sections in the wings are integral tanks, utilizing the sealed structure of the wings to retain the fuel. This is called a "wet-wing" fuel-tank system. Removable, bladder-type fuel cells are used in a ventilated wing-center-section area as a part of tank No. 2. Fuel can be pumped into the tanks from a ground source through an underwing, pressure fueling station. The pressure fueling system provides rapid loading of all tanks simultaneously or each tank separately for partial or total filling. Rapid defueling of the tanks can be accomplished through the pressure

fueling receptacles. Only tanks No. 1 and 3 are provided with overwing fueling ports. An electronic, capacitance-type, fuel-quantity indicating system is provided to indicate the amount of fuel contained in the tanks. A manual method of mechanical gaging through the use of **drip sticks** is provided for use on the ground.

Fuel is delivered from the tanks to the engines through a fuel feed system which permits fuel to be supplied from any tank to any or all engines. The fuel is pumped from the tanks by individually controlled, electric-motor-driven boost pumps. Fuel from the pumps is normally delivered directly to the engine feed lines or through a **crossfeed manifold.** Fuel from the pumps can also be delivered through fuel-dump valves or a defueling valve into the fueling and fuel-dump manifold. This interconnection allows the tank fuel boost pumps to pump the fuel from the tanks for fuel dumping and defueling operations as well as for normal engine feed. Electrically operated valves provide for the control of shutoff and crossfeed in the system. All pump and valve controls, along with the instru-

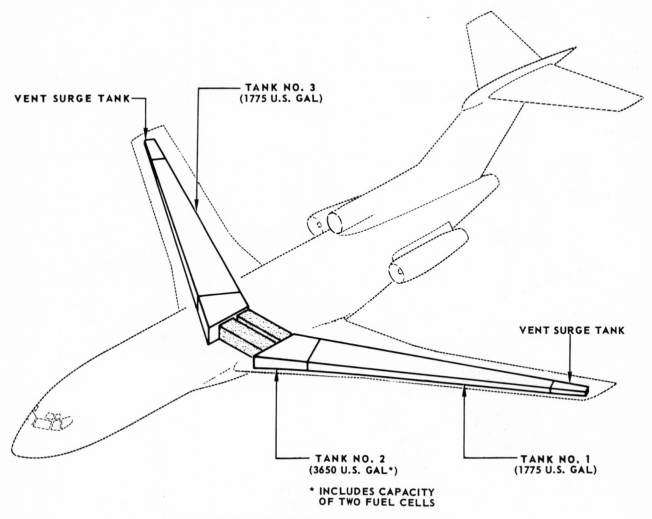

VENT SURGE TANK

TANK NO. 3
(1775 U.S. GAL)

VENT SURGE TANK

TANK NO. 2
(3650 U.S. GAL*)

TANK NO. 1
(1775 U.S. GAL)

* INCLUDES CAPACITY
OF TWO FUEL CELLS

Figure 16·25   Fuel-tank location for Boeing airplane.

ments and indicating lights for monitoring the system are arranged on a system control panel at the third crewman's station.

A schematic diagram of the fuel system for the Boeing 727 airplane fuel system is shown in Fig. 16·26. This diagram shows how the various components are interconnected with respect to one another.

The arrangement of the fuel system lines and components in the airplane is shown in Fig. 16·27. This drawing illustrates the complex nature of the system and emphasizes the need for thorough knowledge of the system by those who operate and service it.

The wing fuel tanks actually consist of many cells with the wing ribs serving as walls between the cells. Openings through the ribs permit fuel to flow from one cell to another, but the fuel cannot surge back and forth through the wing to cause instability and unbalance of the aircraft. Access openings are provided for necessary service to the inside of the cells. The details of access openings are given in the manufacturer's overhaul manual.

In servicing and maintaining the "wet-wing" type of fuel system, a primary consideration is the proper **sealing** of the wing seams and the components attached to the tanks. During manufacture, an approved sealing compound consisting of a liquid or semiliquid synthetic-rubber compound is used in all seams, around rivets and bolts, and in any area where a leak could develop. After fabrication, the tank areas are "slushed" with a liquid compound which, in effect, forms a bladder or continuous coating inside the area to form a positive seal. Details of some of the sealing construction are shown in Fig. 16·28. When a repair is made, the seal must be restored to the same effectiveness as the original.

Components of the fuel system which are removable from the tanks are provided with special types of sealed fasteners as shown in Fig. 16·29. Each fastener is provided with an O ring or other type of synthetic-rubber sealing unit to assure that no fuel can pass the fastener.

Typical of the **fuel valves** used for jet-aircraft systems is the one illustrated in the drawing of Fig. 16·30. These valves have large-diameter openings to permit rapid flow of large quantities of fuel. The valve consists of a slide moved across the opening by an electric motor. The motor is reversible and is provided with limit switches to prevent overtravel. Each valve has an override to permit operation in case of motor failure. The override handle also serves as a valve position indicator.

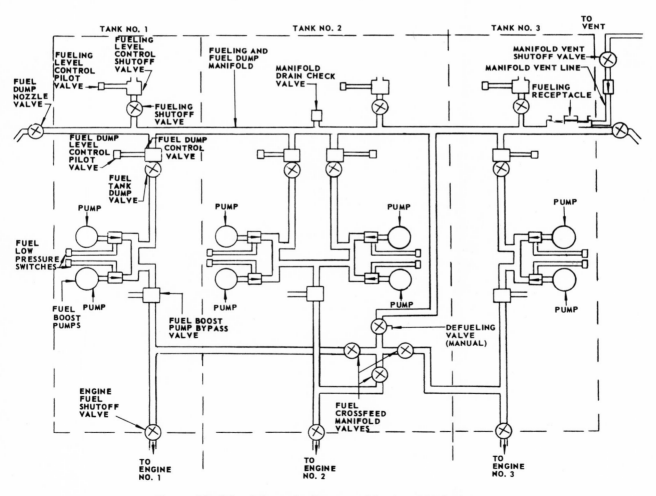

Figure 16·26   Schematic diagram of Boeing 727 fuel system.

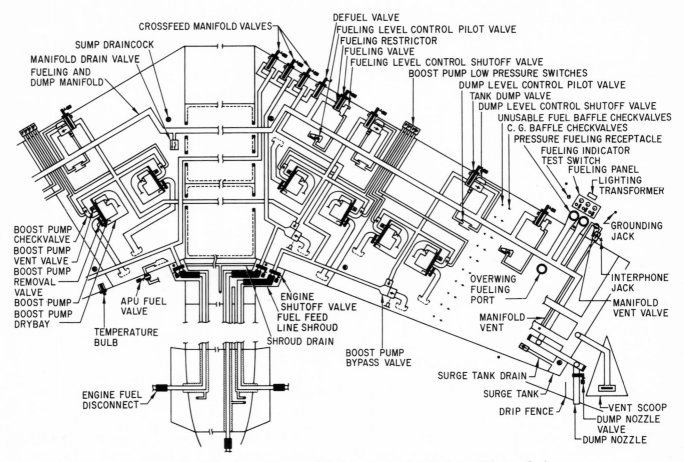

Figure **16·27** *Arrangement of fuel system in the airplane. (Boeing Co.)*

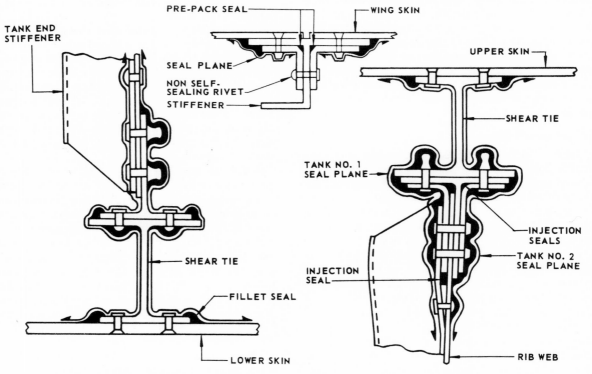

Figure **16·28** *Methods for sealing joints and seams in an integral fuel-tank system.*
(Boeing Co.)

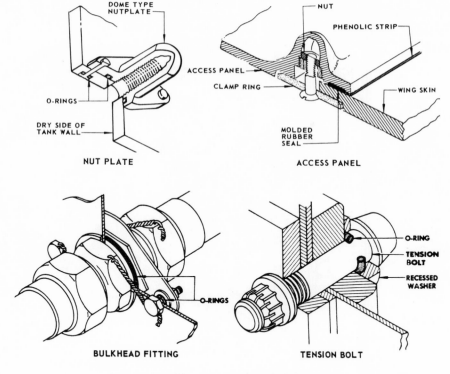

Figure 16·29 Types of sealed fasteners.

The valve motors are operated by 28-volt d-c power and are controlled by individual switches in the crew compartment.

In addition to the components and details mentioned in this section, large aircraft fuel systems include electrically operated boost pumps, fueling control valves to prevent overfilling of the tanks, dump valves, defueling valves, venting systems, and numerous other parts. Information details for all such parts and components should be obtained from the manufacturer's manual before the technician performs service or repair operations.

Fuel-system specifications

The aircraft fuel system must be capable of storing sufficient fuel for normal flight requirements plus additional fuel for alternate landing fields and emergencies. The range of an airplane is determined by the amount of fuel which can be carried in the fuel tanks, allowing for alternate landing fields, emergency fuel, and unusable fuel.

The plumbing for an aircraft fuel system should be capable of carrying twice the amount of fuel normally required for the operation of the engine or engines during takeoff. These requirements establish the size of fuel tubing and fuel pumps, either those that are engine-driven or electrically driven.

During takeoff and landing of an airplane, the auxiliary (electrically driven) fuel pump should be turned on to supply fuel in case of engine fuel-pump failure. This does not apply to small aircraft equipped with gravity-feed fuel systems.

All fuel tanks must be equipped with a fuel indicating system, either a direct-reading gage or an electrically operated remote indicating system. Fuel-quantity indicators must be located so they are clearly visible to the pilot.

Fuel lines must be installed so there are no low points which will collect water and sediment and thus interfere with the normal flow of fuel to the engine. Water collected in fuel lines will freeze in low-temperature conditions and shut off the fuel flow to the engine. Low points in the fuel tanks and at the fuel strainer (gascolator) must be provided with drains so the operator can drain any water or sediment before flying the airplane. This drainage of fuel should be a part of every preflight inspection.

Fuel lines must not be installed where they are near any exhaust manifold or heater where the temperature of the fuel can rise to a vaporization temperature. Fuel vapor in the lines, pumps, and valves is likely to cause vapor lock and cause failure of the engine.

If vapor lock should occur, operation of a tank-installed electrical booster pump will usually clear the lock. Since all airplanes do not have tank-installed booster pumps, it is important to see that the likelihood of vapor lock is eliminated as completely as possible.

Fuel-system maintenance

The maintenance of fuel systems is usually described in the aircraft manufacturer's manual. However, there are some general standards for fuel-system maintenance which may be applied to the majority of systems.

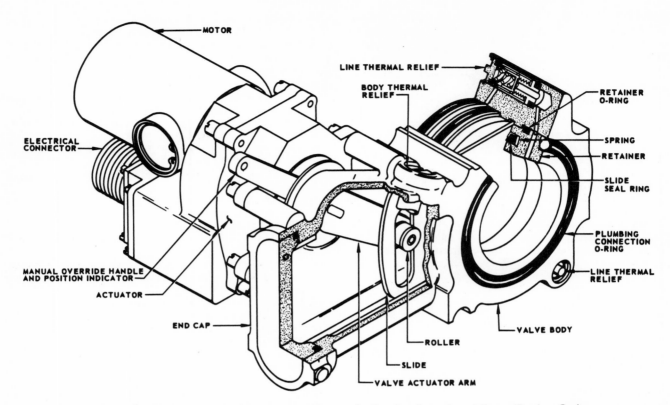

MOTOR

LINE THERMAL RELIEF

BODY THERMAL RELIEF

RETAINER O-RING

ELECTRICAL CONNECTOR

SPRING

RETAINER

SLIDE SEAL RING

PLUMBING CONNECTION O-RING

MANUAL OVERRIDE HANDLE AND POSITION INDICATOR

ACTUATOR

LINE THERMAL RELIEF

END CAP

VALVE BODY

ROLLER

SLIDE

VALVE ACTUATOR ARM

Figure 16·30   *An electrically driven fuel shutoff valve for a jet airliner. (Boeing Co.)*

In all cases, the technician should follow the standards set forth by Federal Aviation Regulations.

The plumbing of fuel systems is the same as that of other fluid systems in an aircraft. The plumbing consists of seamless aluminum tubing, standard fittings, special fittings, and flexible hose which is fuel-resistant. Torque values which have been established as satisfactory for fittings and attachments must be used during assembly.

The repair of fuel tanks or cells depends upon the type of tank and the nature of the leak or damage. Fuel tanks for light aircraft made of welded aluminum (alloys 1100, 3003, or 5052) can be repaired by welding with the appropriate rod and flux. Before welding such a tank, however, the tank must be completely free of gasoline fumes. This is best accomplished by flowing steam or hot water through the tank for approximately 3-5 HRS, 1 hr to vaporize all residual fuel and remove it from the tank. Even though a tank may appear to be dry and free of fuel, some fuel remains in the pores of the metal and in the seams. When heat is applied by the welding torch, a sufficient amount of vaporized fuel may be produced to cause a disastrous explosion.

After repairing a fuel tank by welding, it is particularly important to remove all flux from the metal. This is accomplished by washing both the inside and outside of the tank with liberal quantities of hot water. The tank should then be immersed in a 5 percent solution of nitric or sulfuric acid or the tank should be filled with this solution and the outside of the tank washed with the same solution. After approximately 1 hr the tanks should be rinsed with clean hot water. The rinsing water can be tested for effectiveness of the cleaning job by adding some acidified 5 percent silver nitrate solution to a small amount of the rinsing water. If a white precipitate forms, the rinsing operation is not satisfactory and should be repeated.

Aluminum-alloy tanks constructed by riveting or tanks which are an integral part of the wing must be resealed from inside the tank. Tanks for small aircraft can be removed from the airplane and sealed by sloshing the inside with a suitable sealer such as 3M EC776SR compound. After the tank is sealed, it should be tested by applying 3.5 psi air pressure and using a soap solution to check for leaks.

If leaks are found in integral fuel tanks for large aircraft, repairs should be accomplished according to the manufacturer's directions. This may require that a technician go inside the wing to apply the sealing compound. In such cases, the area in which the technician is working should be thoroughly ventilated by means of a high-rate airflow from a ventilating blower. The breathing of concentrated fuel fumes can cause nausea, dizziness, unconsciousness, or even death; hence every precaution must be observed to see that the repairman is protected.

Synthetic-rubber fuel cells can be removed from the airplane compartment in which they are installed and repaired outside the aircraft. The directions for removal, repair, and reinstallation are given in the manufacturer's maintenance manual.

Fuel tank accessory fittings such as caps, vents, etc.,

should be inspected for fit, security, and effectiveness. Markings for fuel-tank caps should show quantity and grade of fuel, either on the cap or adjacent to the cap. Vents should be checked to determine that they are clear. A plugged vent line can cause engine failure because of reduced fuel flow.

REVIEW QUESTIONS

1. Name the principal auxiliary systems installed in a large airliner.
2. What functions are included in an air-conditioning system for a large, high-altitude airplane?
3. Describe the heating system for a small airplane.
4. What danger exists in the operation of a system which takes heat from the engine exhaust manifold?
5. Describe the operation of a fuel combustion heater.
6. From what source is heat obtained for a large jet airliner?
7. What is the function of an *outflow valve*?
8. How is temperature controlled in a large airliner?
9. Describe the operation of a *cooling pack*.
10. Why is a *water separator* required in the duct from the cooling pack?
11. Describe an air-cycle machine.
12. Explain the function of the two separate air distribution systems in the Boeing 727 airliner.
13. What is the function of the *flotation check valves* under the passenger-cabin floor?
14. Explain how the air pressure in the cabin is controlled.
15. How can a crew member tell the level of cabin pressure?
16. What is the purpose of the *cabin-altitude limit control*?
17. What differential pressure is permitted between cabin pressure and ambient pressure in the Boeing 727 airliner?
18. How is the differential pressure limit controlled?
19. Discuss the importance of the oxygen system in a high-altitude airplane.
20. Describe an oxygen system suitable for a light airplane.
21. Describe the operation of an oxygen pressure regulator.
22. To what pressure is an oxygen bottle usually charged?
23. What are the two oxygen systems installed in the Douglas DC-9 airliner?
24. What is the function of the *thermal-expansion safety valve*?
25. How can a crew member determine that a safety valve has discharged the oxygen from a cylinder?

26. Describe a crew oxygen system.
27. What is a *diluter-demand breathing regulator*?
28. What can be done to obtain oxygen if a regulator fails?
29. How many oxygen outlets are available to the passengers in an airliner?
30. What is the purpose of the portable oxygen units?
31. At what cabin-pressure altitude range does the automatic oxygen system begin to supply oxygen for passengers?
32. If the automatic system fails, how can oxygen be supplied?
33. Describe a passenger oxygen mask.
34. What precautions must be observed in handling oxygen and servicing oxygen equipment?
35. What lubricant can be used with the fittings in an oxygen system?
36. Describe a fire-sensing device.
37. How is the crew warned that a fire exists?
38. Describe a fire-extinguishing system.
39. What parts of an airplane are subject to the collection of ice during icing conditions?
40. Describe the operation of a mechanical deicing system.
41. How are deicing *boots* attached to the leading edge of wings and other airfoils?
42. How are deicing boots inflated and deflated?
43. Describe the process of thermal anti-icing.
44. What units are electrically anti-iced?
45. Describe a rain-repellant system.
46. How are windshield wipers employed on an airplane?
47. Describe the water system for a modern airliner.
48. By what method is water for the lavatory heated?
49. How is drinking water cooled?
50. Describe the operation of the toilet system.
51. Give some of the basic requirements of an aircraft fuel system.
52. Discuss the venting of fuel tanks.
53. Describe the wet-wing fuel-tank system.
54. What is the function of a *crossfeed system*?
55. What prevents the surging of fuel in a wet-wing fuel tank?
56. Discuss the sealing of fuel tanks in an integral fuel-tank-and-wing system.
57. Describe a fuel valve for a high-capacity, jet-aircraft fuel system.
58. What is the purpose of fuel drainage during a preflight inspection for a small aircraft?
59. Describe three different types of fuel tanks.
60. What must be done after an aluminum tank is repaired by welding?

CHAPTER 17

Assembly and Rigging

The **assembly** of an aircraft refers to the joining of parts or subassemblies by various means until the entire aircraft is in condition for operation. **Rigging** is the alignment of aircraft parts or sections for flight. A certain amount of rigging is necessary during the assembly of an airplane, but even after final assembly, certain rigging adjustments must be made. Thus there is some overlap between the assembly operation and rigging operation.

Throughout the other chapters of this text and the related texts, there are many detailed explanations of the installation, adjustment, inspection, and operation of aircraft units, subassemblies, assemblies, etc. All these explanations pertain to aircraft assembly, at least to some degree in each case. The purpose of this discussion of assembly is to tie together what the student has already learned in previous chapters and to provide examples of rigging instructions.

Airplane assembly

Major assemblies, such as the fuselage, wings, engine nacelles, and landing gear, are normally constructed as complete subunits. These subunits are inspected for workmanship and for conformance to applicable specifications. During the manufacture of an airplane, the inspected and approved subunits are brought into the final assembly line at certain stations where they can be joined to the main structure most effectively.

The actual assembly of the airplane obviously varies greatly according to the type, make, and model, but a few general principles apply. In a factory all operations can be planned for the greatest efficiency but in a repair shop where the jobs vary to a great extent, this type of planning cannot be done so easily.

The tools required for assembly work vary with every job but they usually include an assortment of mallets, hammers, wrenches, screwdrivers, drift punches, drills,

drill motors, rivet guns, bucking bars, files, and various other items. To handle the large parts of the aircraft, jigs, cradles, wooden horses, ladders, slings, block and tackle, jacks, and similar items are necessary. The larger the aircraft, the greater will be the size and variety of equipment needed for assembly operations.

In a repair shop, all the tools and equipment are placed where they can be reached easily at any time during the work. After the airplane is disassembled and cleaned, it is inspected for wear and damage. Bolts, nuts, washers, clevis bolts, clevis pins, and similar parts are reinserted in their respective fittings if they are found to be airworthy after inspection. This reduces the time required for sorting and locating small parts. Defective parts or those which are not approved for the airplane are replaced.

An assortment of tapered drifts is useful for lining up bolt holes. If a drift of the correct size is not available, an undersized bolt can be used for this purpose. During assembly operations, the technician must not distort or overstress any part in order to make the bolt holes line up. If parts will not fit together properly, the cause of the misfit must be determined and corrected.

The disassembly and assembly of complex parts and subunits of an airplane are usually clearly described in the manufacturer's maintenance manual. In every case where manufacturer's instructions are available, the technician should follow them in detail.

The final assembly of an airplane usually starts with the fuselage subassembly and progresses through various subassemblies until the entire airplane is ready for test. In some cases the fuselage is assembled in sections. For example, the center portion of the fuselage will be placed on a fixture or jig for support, while the other subassemblies are attached to it. Then, depending upon the particular design and type of airplane, the nose section, tail section, wings, landing gear, and other parts are joined to the main assembly.

A fuselage is provided with fittings or attachments for the purpose of hoisting or jacking. These fittings may be a permanent part of the airplane or they may be separate attachments which can be installed when it is necessary to lift the airplane. When it is necessary to hoist or jack the airplane, the technician must make sure that he uses the correct procedure and that the proper fittings are available. The manufacturer's manual gives detailed instructions for handling the airplane.

In some cases, the airplane fuselage may be hoisted by means of a sling. The sling may attach to fittings on the upper portion of the fuselage or it may be constructed of webbing which passes under the fuselage at specified points and is connected to the hoisting fittings at the top. It is often necessary that a

spreader bar be used to prevent the cable or chain of the sling from rubbing against the fuselage and causing damage. The use of a spreader bar is shown in Fig. 17·1.

The **landing gear** of an airplane includes floats or pontoons, skis, skids, and wheels, together with their shock absorbers and devices necessary for the attachment of the gear to the wings or fuselage. To assemble the main landing gear to a fuselage, the fuselage is raised high enough so that the gear can be attached. The best way to do this for a particular airplane is given in the manufacturer's instructions. In some cases a hoist will be used; in others the fuselage will be jacked up or placed in a suitable jig or cradle. If a chain hoist is used, the hoist should be placed above the forward portion of the fuselage. The hoist will be suspended from rafters or crossbeams of the shop, but these must be strong enough to hold the hoist and the airplane without failure, and without damaging the building. A weak rafter may break and drop the airplane on the floor, thus causing great damage. If there is any doubt about the security of the support, the rafters or crossbeams should be reinforced with temporary staging or props. The hoist is attached with a strong chain or cable. If the chain has no hooks, a clevis is fastened through the two end links.

In an emergency, if a chain or cable is not available, a light airplane can be hoisted with a strong rope. The rope should be well padded around all corners so that it will not chafe the airplane. In tying the rope, nonslip knots, such as the bowline, should be used.

After attaching the hoist to the chain or rope, the hook should be "moused." This is accomplished by closing the open throat of the hook by wrapping soft wire or twine around the tip and shank of the hook.

Before starting an assembly, the fuselage should be securely braced and padded with suitable supports both fore and aft. In some cases, such as emergency field assemblies, the supports may be nothing more than wooden horses or wooden-block staging. In a good shop, especially designed steel supports and dollies are built for the purpose.

If lifting points are not built into a fuselage, or if they cannot be used, the exterior supports used for lifting must be well padded to prevent chafing. In every case, the technician must make sure that the airplane structure is well supported in a manner which will prevent damage.

At the beginning of a major assembly job, the work crew should be properly organized so each member will know his responsibilities and from whom he should take directions. One man should be in charge of the operation, but other men can be assigned to be in charge of subdivisions of the job.

In fastening a "bridle" or lifting sling to a fuselage, the attachments must be correctly located. The "sta-

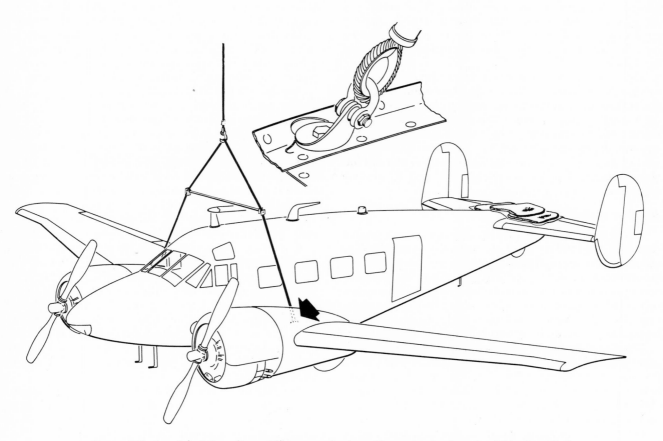

Figure 17·1   A hoisting sling with a spreader bar. The spreader bar should be installed to obtain a minimum clearance of 2 in. between hoist cables and cabin top.

319

tion points" on either the fuselage or the engine mount are often used as lifting points; however, the lifting points designed by the manufacturer should be used when available.

When the hoisting gear is in place and securely attached, the fuselage is ready for lifting. The hoist should be operated slowly and smoothly until the fuselage clears the forward support. Members of the assembly crew should be alert to detect any rocking or swinging of the fuselage which could cause the fuselage to strike any object and cause damage. The fuselage should be raised just enough to permit installation of the gear shock-strut assemblies, and a support structure should be kept under the fuselage to keep it from falling on crew members in case of hoisting-gear failure. After the landing-gear struts are properly attached to the aircraft, all fittings are tightened and safetied. If bonding connections are necessary, these are secured. Hydraulic lines for the brakes and electrical wiring for safety switches are connected and secured. Other attachments are installed as required. When the gear is completely installed with wheels in place and tires properly inflated, the airplane weight can be supported on the gear.

Following assembly of the landing gear to the airplane, the subsequent assembly operations can vary considerably. The manufacturer's manual may specify the sequence of assembly events or the choice may be up to the technician. In some cases it may be preferable to install the empennage before installing the wings; for other aircraft, the reverse may be better.

AIRCRAFT FASTENERS AND FITTINGS

Before discussing the details of assembly and rigging of aircraft, it is advisable to describe some of the more common types of fastening devices and other small hardware items used for joining and adjusting the many parts of aircraft and aircraft assemblies. Among the fasteners and devices to be described are bolts, nuts, screws, washers, pins, turnbuckles, pulleys, and clevises.

Bolts

The most common type of bolt employed in general aircraft assembly work is the standard **AN hex-head bolt.** This is an all-purpose bolt made of nickel steel (SAE 2330), corrosion-resistant steel, or 2024-T3 aluminum alloy. The nickel-steel bolt is marked with an X or a cross on the top of the head, the corrosion-resistant steel bolt is marked with a dash, and the aluminum-alloy bolt is marked with a double dash, one dash on each side of the head. These are illustrated in Fig. 17·2.

Figure 17·2   Markings to identify bolts.

Standard AN hex-head bolts carry the basic numbers AN3 to AN20. The number indicates the number of sixteenths of an inch of the bolt shank diameter. For example, the AN3 bolt is 3/16 in. in diameter, the AN4 bolt is 1/4 in. in diameter, the AN8 is 1/2 in. in diameter, and the AN20 bolt is 1 1/4 in. in diameter.

The first dash number of the AN bolt indicates the overall length of the shank in eighths of an inch up to the length of 7/8 in. For example, an AN6-7 bolt is 7/8 in. long. The dash number then changes to −10 which indicates a bolt with a 1-in. shank. The dash numbers again increase in increments of 1/8 in. until dash number 17 is reached. It then jumps to −20 to indicate a bolt with a 2-in. shank. This sequence of numbering continues up to a dash number of 80 which indicates a bolt shank length of 8 in.

The material from which an AN bolt is made is indicated by a letter code. The letter C indicates a bolt made from corrosion-resistant steel, and the letters DD indicate a bolt made from aluminum alloy. A nickel-steel bolt is indicated when no letter is shown before the dash number. An aluminum-alloy bolt 5/16 in. in diameter and 3/4 in. long would be coded AN5DD6.

AN bolts are manufactured with drilled shanks to accommodate a cotter pin for safetying. If the shank is not drilled, the letter A is placed in the coding after the dash number. For example, the code number AN6C11A designates a bolt made from corrosion-resistant steel, 3/8 in. in diameter, 1 1/8 in. in shank length, and without a drilled shank.

AN bolts are manufactured with drilled heads for the application of safety wire. Where a drilled head is to be indicated, the letter H is placed between the material code letter and the dash number. AN6CH11 indicates a bolt, with the same dimensions shown above, having a drilled head and a drilled shank.

Clevis bolts are coded with AN numbers from 21 to 36. The diameters of these bolts are shown in Table 17·1. The dash number indicating overall length of the shank (grip and threaded portion) is in increments

Table 17·1   Diameters of clevis bolts

AN part number	Thread	Diameter of shank, +.000, −.002
AN21	No. 6–40	0.136
AN22	No. 8–36	0.162
AN23	No. 10–32	0.186
AN24	1/4–28	0.248
AN25	5/16–24	0.311
AN26	3/8–24	0.373
AN27	7/16–20	0.436
AN28	1/2–20	0.497
AN29	9/16–18	0.560
AN30	5/8–18	0.622
AN31	3/4–16	0.747
AN34	7/8–14	0.871
AN36	1–14	0.996

of 1/16 in. For example, an AN26-14 clevis bolt is 3/8 in. in diameter and 7/8 in. in length.

Clevis bolts have a short thread and are not designed to be used in tension. For this reason a **shear nut** is employed rather than the thicker nut used with the standard hex-head bolt.

Eye bolts are designated by the AN numbers from AN42 to AN49. The eye bolt is designed for the attachment of a clevis or other fitting.

Figure 17·3 shows a hex-head bolt, a clevis bolt, and an eye bolt.

Drilled head bolts in which the head is drilled with three passages are indicated by AN numbers from AN73 to AN81. There is no hole in the threaded shank as is the case with the AN hex-head bolt described previously. The diameters and lengths of these bolts can be determined by the AN numbers and dash numbers.

Bolts designed for use in structural parts where there may be severe vibration or load reversals are called **close-tolerance bolts.** These are placed in carefully reamed holes such that the clearance between the bolt and the hole is from 0.000 to 0.002 in. The tolerance will be specified in the assembly drawing. Close-tolerance bolts in the AN designation are numbered AN173 through AN186. Close-tolerance bolts are identified by means of a cross or X inside a triangle on the bolt head.

Internal-wrenching bolts, designated by numbers NAS144 through NAS158 and MS20004 through MS20024, are high-strength bolts used wherever exceptional strength is required either in tension or shear. As shown in Fig. 17·4, the bolt is manufactured with a radius between the base of the head and the shank. This radius distributes the tension load more effectively and provides greater resistance to vibration and fatigue because the radius reduces the stress concentration. Because of the radius, the hole in which the bolt is installed must be countersunk, or a countersunk washer (NAS143C or MS20002 countersunk washer) must be installed under the head of the bolt.

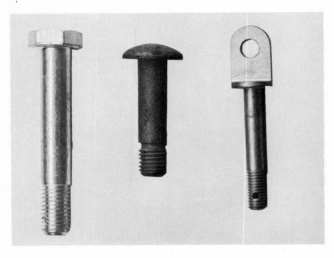

Figure 17·3   AN bolts.

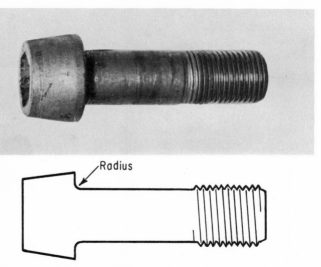

Figure 17·4   An internal-wrenching bolt.

A special heat-treated plain washer (NAS143 or MS20002) is used under the nut. The technician is cautioned that, under the head of an internal wrenching bolt, the use of any washer other than the countersunk washer designed for the purpose is likely to cause failure. Furthermore, the countersunk side of the washer must be placed next to the head of the bolt to accommodate the bolt radius.

For any type of bolt, the **grip length** is the length of the unthreaded portion of the shank. As nearly as possible, the grip length should equal the thickness of the parts bolted together. If the grip length is any greater than the thickness of the materials, the difference must be made up by installing washers under the nut or under the bolt head.

The **fit** of bolts should be taken into consideration during any assembly operation. As mentioned previously, close-tolerance and high-strength bolts require extremely close fits, often with zero tolerance or even a press fit where the hole is actually slightly smaller than the bolt. In these cases, the fit is expressed as **tight** by a few ten-thousandths of an inch. The close-tolerance bolts and high-strength bolts are usually employed on high-performance aircraft in critical structural joints or junctions. For other structural assemblies where standard hex-head bolts are used, the hole tolerance allowed varies to some extent, but it is usually permissable to use a hole size drilled by a letter drill one size larger then the nominal bolt diameter. For example, an F drill size can be used for a 1/4-in. bolt because the F drill has a diameter of 0.2570 in. This gives a bolt clearance of 0.007 in. or more when used with a 1/4-in bolt.

During the overhaul of an airplane, if a bolt hole is found to be elongated or otherwise worn in a primary structural member, an FAA safety agent or manufacturer's agent should be consulted to determine whether it would be permissible to ream the hole to the next larger size. If the method of repair is described in the manufacturer's manual, this method should be followed. NOTE

Nuts

A variety of **nuts** are available for bolts; however, in the assembly of aircraft it is important that the correct type of nut be used in each installation. **Plain, castle (castellated), shear, check,** and **wing nuts** are common types. The most commonly used nuts for general purposes are the castle nut (AN310) and the **self-locking nut** (AN365).

The plain nut is designated AN315, the check nut is AN316, and the shear nut is AN320. Another plain hex nut is designated AN335, and the wing nut is AN350. For details of size and thread, the AN specification sheet should be examined. Typical AN nuts are shown in Fig. 17·5.

Self-locking nuts are used extensively; however, their use is limited to certain conditions. These nuts are either all-metal or with a fiber or nylon insert to provide the locking action. Self-locking nuts for high-temperature applications are of all-metal construction and are so designed that the threads provide a binding action when the nut is tightened on the bolt. This effect is obtained by making the threads in a locking insert out of phase with the other threads, by making the nut slightly "out-of-round," or by a saw cut with a pinched-in thread in the locking section.

Fiber lock nuts with the fiber or nylon insert, illustrated in Fig. 17·6, provide a locking action as the threads are ~~cut~~ *PRESSED* into the insert when the nut is turned onto the bolt. Since the insert is elastic, it presses tightly into the bolt threads and holds the nut in place. If the nut is used more than once, the locking action should be checked. When the nut can be turned by hand it will no longer hold on the bolt and should be discarded.

A fiber lock nut is usually installed on a bolt without a cotter-pin hole. If used on a drilled bolt, the edges of the hole tend to cut out the fiber and destroy the locking friction. Bolts 5/16 in. in diameter and larger with cotter-pin holes can be used with fiber lock nuts, provided the holes are free from sharp edges or burrs which will cut the fiber. The nuts should never be installed on bolts with rough ends or damaged threads. The threads of the nut should not be cleaned out with a tap because this will destroy the binding friction of the fiber.

For certain types of assemblies, fiber lock nuts with mounting lugs are attached in channels or on flanges to provide a permanent installation. A two-lug anchor nut of the self-locking type is shown in Fig. 17·7. This nut carries the designation AN366.

Self-locking nuts are limited according to the type of installation. In general they can be used where there is no relative movement between the parts which they join and where temperature is not excessive (less than 250°F). Special high-temperature, self-locking nuts are approved for use within given temperature ranges. AN363 high-temperature self-locking nuts can be used where temperatures reach 550°F. These nuts are marked with an H on the side.

Self-locking nuts cannot be used as hinge bolts or in any installation where there is relative movement between the nut and the surface against which it bears. If a bushing is installed in a hinge and the nut binds against the bushing in such a manner that there is no relative movement between the nut and the bushing, a self-locking nut can be used. Such a nut can also be used in a pulley installation where the pulley is designed with an antifriction bearing and the nut binds tightly against the inner race of the bearing.

When a self-locking nut is installed on a bolt or screw with a chamfered or rounded end, the chamfered or rounded portion of the bolt must extend entirely through the nut. A flat-ended bolt, stud, or screw must be extended at least 1/32 in. through the nut.

Nuts for internal-wrenching bolts must be designed to carry the extreme loads which may be applied to such bolts. Two types of nuts for such bolts are made

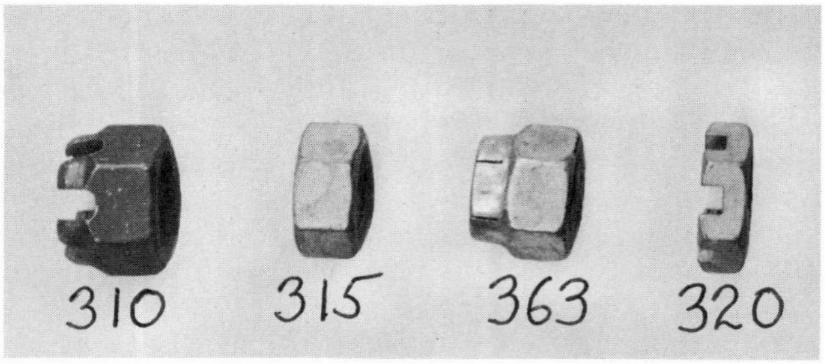

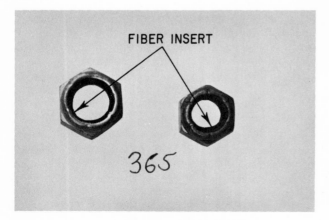

Figure 17·5   Typical AN nuts.

Figure 17·7   A two-lug anchor nut.

FIBER INSERT

Figure 17·6   Fiber lock nuts.

by the Elastic Stop Nut Corporation and the Standard Pressed Steel Company. An external wrenching nut for such bolts is called the **ESNA EB nut.** Any nut which meets the same specifications is suitable for use with internal-wrenching bolts. The nuts mentioned above have nylon locking inserts to provide the locking friction when the nut is installed.

Threads for nuts and bolts are either **fine** (NF) or **coarse** (NC). The technician must be particularly careful during assembly operations to make sure that he uses fine-thread nuts for fine-thread bolts and coarse-thread nuts for coarse-thread bolts. The number of threads per inch for a fine or coarse configuration depends upon the diameter of the bolt or screw. For example, a ¼-in. bolt with coarse threads has 20 threads per inch and a ¼-in. bolt with fine threads has 28 threads per inch. A ⅜-in. bolt has 24 threads per inch for the NF type and 16 threads for the NC type.

Washers

Washers of various types are used with nuts, bolts, and screws for various purposes. Common types of washers are shown in Fig. 17·8.

The AN960 **flat washer** is used under heads of bolts and under nuts, both for spacing and for protection of the metal surfaces under the heads or nuts. They are also used under lock nuts to prevent damage to the surface.

The **common lock washer** is designated AN935. This washer is used in many applications to keep nuts from coming loose. Another type of lock washer is called the **shakeproof washer** and is designated AN936, types A, B, C, and D. A and B types are shown in Fig. 17·8.

Screws

Screws may be considered as small bolts; however, there are some differences in design and construction. In general, a screw head is slotted or recessed to accommodate a screwdriver. Common types of screws are shown in Fig. 17·9.

The AN515-520 screw is a common **roundheaded machine screw** used in many nonstructural applications. This type of screw is made of carbon steel and is not as strong as an AN bolt of the same size. **Fillister-head screws** are designated AN500-501 for the undrilled types and AN502-503 for the types with a drilled head.

Screws which must be flush with a surface are called

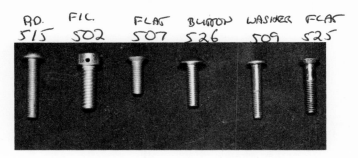

RO. FIC. FLAT BUTTON WASHER FLAT
515 502 507 526 509 525

Figure 17·9   Screws used for aircraft assembly.

flathead screws and are designated AN507 for the 100° countersunk hole and AN505 for the 82° countersunk hole.

A **buttonhead screw,** designated AN526, is shown in Fig. 17·9. This type of screw is used where a minimum of head thickness is required.

Some screws are designed for structural use. These are made of heat-treated nickel steel and have unthreaded shanks. This design makes them capable of withstanding shear loads equal to that of an AN bolt. A **washer-head structural screw,** AN509, and a **flathead structural screw,** AN525, are shown in Fig. 17·9. — 2330

A **recessed-head screw** is designed for use with a Phillips screwdriver or another type of special screwdriver. Screws designed for use with a Phillips screwdriver are shown in Fig. 17·10.

Screw diameters under ¼ in. are indicated by the numbers 2 through 10. Table 17·2 gives the approximate diameters of machine screws in these sizes.

The threads for machine screws are either fine or coarse, depending upon the number of threads per inch and the diameter of the screw. A No. 6 screw with 32 threads per in. is a coarse-thread screw and is called a 632 screw. A No. 10 screw with 32 threads per inch is called a 1032 screw and is classed as a fine-thread

Figure 17·10   Recessed-head screws.

Table 17·2

No.	Screw diameter, in.
2	0.08
3	0.10
4	0.11
5	0.130
6	0.140
8	0.165
10	0.186

AN960   AN935   AN936A   AN936B

Figure 17·8   Common types of washers.

screw. A fine-thread for a No. 2 screw is 64 per in. and a coarse thread for the same screw is 56 per in.

A typical AN part number for a machine screw is AN515-836-8. This is a roundheaded, carbon-steel screw, No. 8 size, fine thread, ½ in. in length. The final dash number indicates the length in sixteenths of an inch.

Self-tapping screws

Self-tapping screws are made of hard steel to cut their own threads in softer metal or to be used with sheet-metal nuts designed for the purpose. Figure 17·11 illustrates several types of such screws. One of the principal makes of self-tapping screws is the Parker-Kalon (PK) type. Head and shank styles vary to accommodate different requirements. The shank styles are designated type A for the tapered shank, type Z for the nearly straight shank, and type U for the straight-shank drive screw. The type-Z self-tapping screws correspond to the AN530 and AN531 screws. The AN530 is a roundheaded, type-Z screw; the AN531 is a flathead screw of the same shank style. The first dash number indicates the shank diameter and the second dash number indicates the length. For example, AN530-8-12 indicates a self-tapping screw with a round head, No. 8 size, and ¾ in. in length.

The type-U self-tapping screw is a multiple-thread drive screw used primarily for installing identification plates and for similar permanent installations. A hole is drilled slightly smaller than the diameter of the screw and then the screw is driven with a hammer into the hole. The threads cut corresponding threads in the material into which the screw is driven and the screw is held tightly in place.

Self-tapping screws are not approved for use in structural assemblies. They can be used for temporary assembly operations and for attaching nonstructural parts.

Pins

Various types of pins are used in the assembly and safetying of parts. Among these are **clevis pins** (AN392 through AN406), **cotter pins** (AN380 and AN381), **taper pins** (AN385 and AN386), and ESNA **roll pins**. These pins are illustrated in Fig. 17·12.

Clevis pins are generally used with washers and cotter pins to connect tie rods, serve as hinge pins, and act as pulley guards. They are installed with the head up, if possible, to prevent their falling out in case of cotter-pin failure.

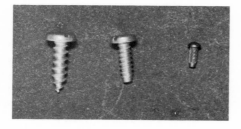

Figure 17·11   Self-tapping screws.

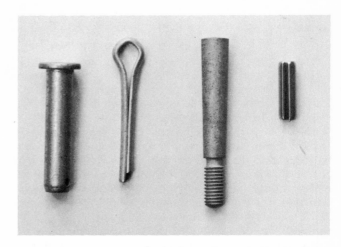

Figure 17·12   Types of metal pins for aircraft assemblies.

The AN380 **cotter pin** is a low-carbon steel, cadmium-plated pin used for safetying castle nuts, for securing washers on clevis pins, and for other similar purposes. When a cotter pin is installed to safety a castle nut, the pin is placed through the grooves in the castellated portion of the nut and through the drilled hole in the shank of the bolt. One-half the pin shank is bent down alongside the nut, and the other end is bent up and over the end of the bolt. The excess length of the pin is cut off with diagonal-cutting pliers (dikes). Where it is impossible to bend the ends of the pin in this manner, it is permissible to bend the ends sideways around the nut.

The AN381 cotter pin is made of corrosion-resistant steel and is used for the same purposes as those described above. The corrosion-resistant pin should always be used inside engines or in any location where corrosion is likely to occur.

The dash numbers for AN381 cotter pins indicate size. The first dash number indicates diameter in thirty-seconds of an inch, and the second dash number indicates length in sixteenths of an inch. For example, an AN381-3-14 cotter pin is corrosion-resistant, 3/32 in. in diameter, and ⅞ in. in length.

Taper pins are either plain or threaded on the end; they are used in joints which carry shear loads and in which there must be no movement. By pulling a taper pin tight with a shear nut, all play is taken up and the joint becomes rigid.

Taper pins of the threaded type are usually installed with a washer, shear nut, and cotter pin or lock washer. Such pins should be used only where their installation is specifically required.

Roll pins such as the **ESNA roll pin** are tubular with a slot running the full length of the pin. They are chamfered on the end to facilitate installation and must be pressed into place. After the pin is installed, it exerts a steady pressure against the sides of the hole and will not come out until deliberately driven or pressed out. These pins are used for a variety of purposes such as attaching fittings to the ends of rods or tubes, joining sections of tubes, anchoring small gears on shafts, and similar purposes. Care must be taken to assure that the hole in which the pin is pressed is of the correct size to produce a tight press fit.

Safety wire

We have discussed safety wire previously; however, certain principles must be emphasized, and these are discussed here.

Safety wire is made of soft iron, brass, copper, corrosion-resistant steel (annealed), Monel metal, and aluminum. The type to be used should comply with manufacturer's instructions or with MS33540, *General Instructions for the Selection and Application of Safety Wire.*

For use with cadmium-plated nuts, bolts, and fittings, soft iron or corrosion-resistant steel safety wire is usually most satisfactory. Wherever the atmosphere is likely to be corrosive, corrosion-resistant or Monel metal wire should be used. Inconel wire is also satisfactory for these installations.

For general-purpose safety wiring, the diameter of the wire should be 0.032 in. In situations where the hole for the safety wire is too small to accommodate 0.032 wire, a smaller size of wire can be used. Smaller wire can be used as a seal for valves, switches, and covers in nonstructural items to indicate whether the item has been opened or otherwise disturbed.

The double-twist method of safetying should normally be used. This is illustrated in Fig. 17·13 which also shows various applications of safety wire. The wire may be twisted or applied with a safety-wiring tool. If pliers are used to twist safety wire, the jaws should be taped to prevent scratching or cutting the wire.

It will be noted in Fig. 17·13 that the safety wire is always installed in such a manner that the tension on the wire will be increased if the nut, bolt, or screw starts to loosen. Thus, the safety wire should be applied so it will tend to tighten the item safetied.

The twisted ends ("pigtail") of safety wire should be cut off with three to six twists remaining and the end bent down or back so it will not be easily snagged. Care must be taken to see that the pigtail has not been twisted to the extent that it is overstressed and is likely to break off.

Torque values

During the installation of bolts, nuts, and screws, the torque applied is most important. In some cases it must be within very close limits because of the tension range which the bolt must sustain.

Torque values are measured in either inch-pounds or in foot-pounds. This means that the force applied to the turning of a nut or bolt is equal to the length of the twisting arm (wrench handle) multiplied by the force exerted at right angles to the twisting arm. For example, if a technician applies a force of 20 lb to a wrench handle at a point 8 in. from the center of the nut or bolt which he is turning, the torque will be 20×8 or 160 in.-lb. This would be in the torque range for a standard AN365 nut, 3/8 in., with a 24 (fine) thread.

Recommended torque values for cadmium-plated

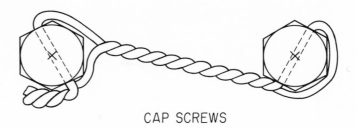

CAP SCREWS

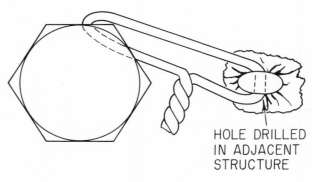

HOLE DRILLED IN ADJACENT STRUCTURE

PLUG

SINGLE WIRE SAFETYING FOR DRILLED HEAD SCREWS CLOSELY SPACED

Figure 17·13   Applications of safety wire.

nuts with oilfree threads are given in Table 17·3. Note particularly that the torques recommended are for *tap size* and not for nut size. The tap size is 3/16 in. when the nut size is 3/8 in., 1/4 in. when the nut size is 7/16 in., and 5/16 in. when the nut size is 1/2 in. The technician must therefore be sure he is reading the correct information when he studies the chart to obtain torque values.

To measure the torque applied to a nut or bolt, a **torque wrench** is used. The torque wrench may be

Table 17·3   Recommended torque values

Tap size	Torque range for tension-type nuts AN-365 and AN-310, in.-lb	Torque range for shear-type nuts AN-364 and AN-320, in.-lb
	Fine-thread bolts	
8–36	12–15	7–9
10–32	20–25	12–15
¼–28	50–70	30–40
⁵⁄₁₆–24	100–140	60–85
⅜–24	160–190	95–110
⁷⁄₁₆–20	450–500	270–300
½–20	480–690	290–410
⁹⁄₁₆–18	800–1000	480–600
⅝–18	1100–1300	600–780
¾–16	2300–2500	1300–1500
⅞–14	2500–3000	1500–1800
1–14	3700–5500	2200–3300[1]
1⅛–12	5000–7000	3000–4200[1]
1¼–12	9000–11000	5400–6600[1]
	Coarse-thread bolts	
8–32	12–15	7–9
10–24	20–25	12–15
¼–20	40–50	25–30
⁵⁄₁₆–18	80–90	48–55
⅜–16	160–185	95–100
⁷⁄₁₆–14	235–255	140–155
½–13	400–480	240–290
⁹⁄₁₆–12	500–700	300–420
⅝–11	700–900	420–540
¾–10	1150–1600	700–950
⅞–9	2200–3000	1300–1800

[1] Estimated corresponding values.

equipped with a dial gage to read the torque value, or it may have a pointer which shows the torque value as a function of the deflection of the spring-steel torque wrench handle when force is applied. A torque wrench is shown in Fig. 17·14.

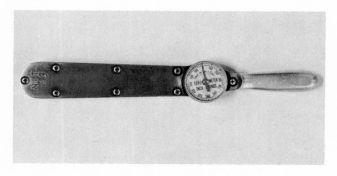

Figure 17·14   A torque wrench.

AIRCRAFT CABLE WORK

Types of cables

Steel cables of several types and sizes are used for the operation of control systems on aircraft. **Corrosion-resistant steel cable** is considered most satisfactory for the majority of applications. **Flexible carbon-steel cable** for aircraft use is covered by specification MIL-C-1511, and **flexible corrosion-resistant cable** is covered by specification MIL-C-5424.

Extra-flexible cable consists of six outer strands composed of 19 wires each and one inner strand composed of 19 wires. Thus there are 7 strands of 19 wires each in the cable which is normally designated as 7 × 19. Flexible cable is designated 7 × 7 and has 7 strands of 7 wires each. For the main control cables in aircraft, the 7 × 19 type cable is used.

Preformed cable is cable whose individual strands are formed to the spiral, or helical, position they occupy in the finished cable. The purpose of preforming is (1) to secure more flexibility, (2) to relieve the bending and twisting of the strands as they are woven into the cable, and (3) to prevent them from spreading out when the cable is cut. Preformed cable should be used for aircraft applications.

Prestretching is stretching of a cable before it is put into use in order to eliminate or reduce **constructional stretch.** This is the permanent stretching or elongation of a cable which occurs as the individual wires and strands are tightened against each other when the load or stretching force is first applied. To prestretch a cable, after the end fittings are attached and the splices made, one end of the cable is attached to a stationary stud, or bolt, and the other end is attached to a hydraulic jack or similar force-producing device. A load of about 60 percent of the breaking strength of the cable is applied for a specified period of time. Cable is stretched in a trough with a screen cover to prevent injury to personnel in case the cable should break.

The **proof load** for a cable is the tension applied to test a cable and its terminals. The load is applied gradually and continuously until the full proof load is reached, after which the load is maintained for a period of not less than 3 min. Proof load is usually expressed in pounds and is about 60 percent of the breaking strength of the cable.

Use of cables in aircraft

Several types of cables may be used in a single airplane, depending upon the types of mechanisms to be operated. For primary control systems, ⅛-in. diameter, 7 × 19 cable or larger should be used. The cable is measured across the greatest diameter as shown in Fig. 17·15. Cable ³⁄₃₂ in. in diameter is often used in secondary control systems, such as operating the trim tabs. For light-aircraft trim-tab systems, ¹⁄₁₆-in. cable is often used.

Cables are used to operate ailerons, elevators, and rudders directly on small aircraft. On large aircraft, cables operate hydraulic control valves which, in turn,

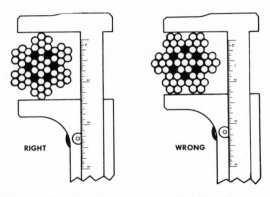

Figure 17·15   Measurement of cable diameter.

cause the operation of the control hydraulically. Trim-tab systems are operated directly on many aircraft through a cable and drum system; however, on very large aircraft the trim tabs and control tabs are often operated by means of electrical actuators.

Swaged cable fittings

The most common method for attaching fittings to the end of control cables is **swaging.** This is a process in which the metal of the fitting is pressed into the cable with great force, and the resulting strength is approximately 100 percent of the cable strength.

Standard swaged fittings are designated AN666 through AN669. AN667 is a forked-end terminal, and AN668 is an eye-end terminal. The appropriate specification should be studied to determine what type of swaged terminal should be used in a particular application. Swage-type terminals are shown in Fig. 17·16.

The swaged terminal consists of a steel sleeve with the desired fitting at one end. To attach the fitting or terminal to a cable, the end of the cable is inserted into the sleeve as far as it will go; the fitting and cable are then placed in the swaging machine, and the swaging operation performed.

Before a particular cable is made up with terminals attached to the ends, the technician must obtain the dimensions required for the cable section. When he cuts the cable to the final length, he must make sure

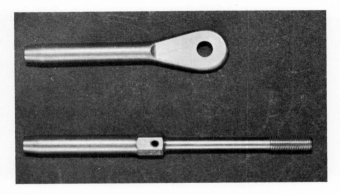

Figure 17·16   Swaged cable terminals.

that he has allowed for the length of the terminal and the stretch which will occur when the terminal is swaged. The cable is then cut with a cable cutter or a pair of heavy-duty diagonal-cutting pliers. The cable must not be cut with a torch because this will draw the temper from the end of the cable. If the cable is not preformed, the ends of the cable should be wrapped tightly with a few turns of annealed wire at each side of the cut. This will prevent the strands of the cable from separating and fraying.

When the cable has been cut to the desired length, the end of the cable is inserted into the sleeve of the proper terminal. It is recommended that the cable be inserted one-half the depth of the sleeve and then be bent sideways about 45°. This puts a slight bend in the cable which will help to hold it in place during the swaging operation. The cable is then pushed all the way to the bottom of the hole in the sleeve. Before installing the sleeve, it is good practice to mark the depth of the sleeve on the cable with masking tape. When the cable is inserted in the sleeve, the taped mark will show that the cable end is at the bottom of the hole.

After the terminal is swaged onto the cable, a spot of red paint should be placed at the point where the cable enters the sleeve. At a later inspection, this will serve to show whether there has been any slippage. The diameter of the sleeve is checked with a go–no-go gage to assure that the swaging meets specifications. For example, when a fitting is swaged onto a ⅛-in. cable, the sleeve diameter should be 0.219 (0.000, −0.005) in. in diameter.

When preparing to swage a terminal to a cable end, the technician must select the correct size dies for the swaging tool. The hand-swaging tool has a set of properly marked dies in a kit to provide for several sizes of cable.

Nicopress swaged sleeve

The **Nicopress oval sleeve** is designed to provide a strong splice; however, it should not be used where the load will be more than 75 percent of the breaking strength of the cable. The Nicopress sleeve is manufactured by the National Telephone and Supply Company. This sleeve is used commercially as well as for aircraft cable work.

The Nicopress sleeve is made of copper (either plated or unplated); when swaged to the cable, the copper flows around and between the strands. This forms a strong attachment which is easily and quickly installed.

When making a **thimble eye splice** using the AN100 thimble, the sleeve of the proper size is slid onto the end of the cable a sufficient distance so the cable extending through the sleeve will be long enough to go around the thimble and back through the sleeve. The thimble is placed in the cable loop, and the sleeve is drawn up to the points of the thimble. When the sleeve is compressed, the points of the thimble should touch the end of the sleeve. When the thimble is firmly secured in the cable loop and the sleeve is against the points of the thimble, the sleeve can be compressed.

The Nicopress compressing tool is shown in Fig. 17·17. One handle of the tool can be placed in a vise if desired, or the tool can be operated using both hands. When the sleeve is correctly located on the cable the tool is placed over the sleeve. When making a three-compression splice, the center compression should be made first. The compression next to the thimble is made next, and the one farthest from the thimble is made last. There should be a space of approximately ¹⁄₁₆ in. between compressions.

For a Nicopress splice on ⅛-in. cable, the 18-3-M sleeve is used and tool number 51-M-850 is used for the compression. The sleeve length before compressing is ⁹⁄₁₆ in.; after compressing it is ¾ in. The diameter of the compressed or swaged sections is checked with a go–no-go gage as shown in Fig. 17·18. The completed splice appears as shown in Fig. 17·19.

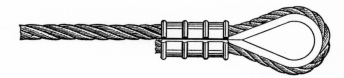

Figure 17·19   The completed Nicopress splice.

Five-tuck woven cable splice

The five-tuck woven cable splice is not often used; however, a knowledge of its application is considered important for the technician who works with general aviation aircraft, especially in remote areas where swaging equipment may not be available. This splice may be used on 7 × 7 flexible cable and 7 × 19 extra flexible cable of ³⁄₃₂ in. or larger. When this type of splice is used to attach a terminal (either a thimble or a bushing), 75 percent of the cable strength is developed. The splice should not be used unless it is known that the maximum load on the cable will not exceed 75 percent of the cable breaking strength.

The method for starting and finishing the five-tuck splice is shown in Fig. 17·20.

The strands for the cable are numbered on the free end of the cable and lettered on the standing length of the cable. The cable is clamped with a fitting, such as the AN111 bushing shown in the drawing of Fig. 17·20 or an AN100 thimble, in a splicing clamp mounted in a vise. The No. 1 strand is nearest the fitting and is inserted with the help of a marlin spike behind strands

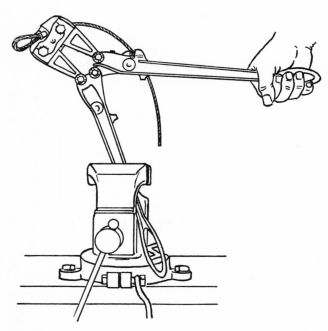

Figure 17·17   Nicopress swaging tool. (National Telephone and Supply Co.)

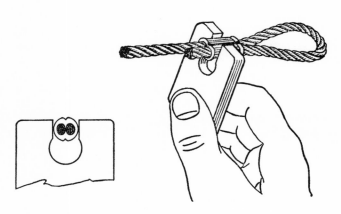

Figure 17·18   Checking the diameter of a compression.

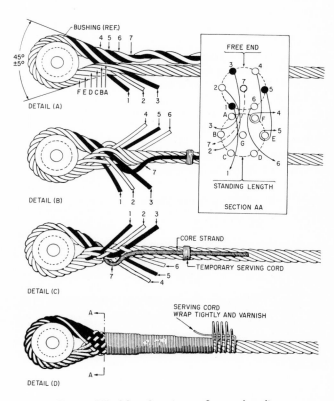

Figure 17·20   Starting a five-tuck splice.

A, B, and C of the standing length. The core strand, No. 7, is pulled out from the center of the free end and is brought between strands B and C. The No. 2 strand is inserted behind strands A and B, and the No. 3 strand is inserted behind strand A as shown. The other strands of the free end are woven into the standing length as shown in the diagram. At the completion of this operation, one strand comes out between each pair of strands of the standing length. All strands are now pulled tight and back toward the terminal fitting to make the cable snug around the fitting.

The free strands are then woven around the standing length of the cable in a counterclockwise direction, going over one strand and under the next. When all strands have been woven in a second time, they are again pulled tight. Another tuck is then made, and the strands are pulled tight the third time. At the completion of the third tuck, the strands are reduced in size by cutting away one-half the fine wires in each. The fourth tuck is made, and the strands are reduced by one-half again. The fifth and final tuck is then made, and the splice is pounded with a soft mallet on a piece of hardwood while rotating the splice. This shapes and tightens the splice.

The remaining strands of wire are cut off and the splice is served with waxed linen cord as shown. It is common practice to shellac the serving cord after insulation to protect it from moisture and to make it more resistant to wear.

Turnbuckles

Turnbuckles have been mentioned before in this text and also in the text, *Basic Science for Aerospace Vehicles.* However, a brief discussion is in order at this point because of the wide use of turnbuckles in rigging aircraft cables.

A standard AN turnbuckle assembly is shown in Fig. 17 · 21. This turnbuckle consists of an AN155 barrel, an AN170 cable eye, and an AN161 fork. With this same barrel, several other types of end fittings can be used. Among these are the AN165 pin eye and an AN669 swaging terminal.

Turnbuckle barrels are threaded with a right-hand thread in one end and a left-hand thread in the other end. The end with the left-hand thread is grooved to show which has the left-hand thread. The different types of turnbuckle ends are made with both left-hand and right-hand threads to provide versatility in their application.

When a turnbuckle is installed, not more than three threads must be showing on the end fitting outside the barrel. The turnbuckle must be safetied with safety wire as shown in the drawings of Fig. 17 · 22. These methods are set forth in FAA Advisory Circular 43-13-1 and apply to all civil aircraft. Note that after the safety wire is installed, at least four turns of wire are wrapped around the shank of the end fitting.

Pulleys

Pulleys are used in cable systems to permit a change in the cable direction. They are designated by numbers AN210, AN219, AN220, and AN221.

Aircraft pulleys are made of metal and compressed phenolic sheet, Teflon, and other plastic materials. The pulley bearings are usually of the sealed type and require no lubrication. The pulley is bonded to the bearing in such a manner that the bearing cannot be removed. Figure 17 · 23 illustrates typical control pulleys. In the replacement of a pulley, the technician must make sure that he is installing the correct type. This can be determined from the manufacturer's instructions or by the number on the pulley.

AIRCRAFT RIGGING

Aircraft rigging involves two principal types of operations. First, the aircraft structure must be rigged for correct alignment of all fixed components. The fuselage is aligned at the time of manufacture in the assembly jigs. All parts are correctly positioned in the assembly jig and then they are riveted, bolted, or welded into a complete assembly. Some types of fuselages require realignment at major overhaul periods or after damage.

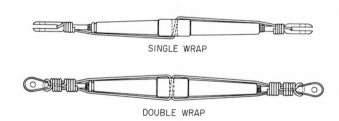

SINGLE WRAP

DOUBLE WRAP

Figure 17 · 22   Properly safetied turnbuckles.

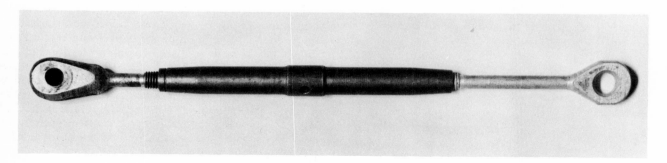

Figure 17 · 21   A standard AN turnbuckle.

Figure 17·23 Typical aircraft control pulleys.

Wings and other large structures are aligned and assembled in jigs and fixtures to assure correct shape and positioning of attachment fittings.

The second type of rigging is the alignment of control surfaces and the controls which move the surfaces. These operations require the adjustment of cable length, cable tension, push-pull rods, bell cranks, cable drums, and various other parts. Angular deflection of control surfaces must be measured with protractors or other measuring devices to assure that the movements comply with the appropriate specifications.

Rigging and assembly of a biplane

Although the biplane is considered by many to be an obsolete type of aircraft, there are hundreds of these airplanes still in operation for pleasure, sport, and agricultural work. It is therefore deemed important that the well-qualified maintenance technician be familiar with the procedures required for this operation. A typical biplane is shown in Fig. 17·24.

Before starting the rigging and assembly of an aircraft, the technician must be sure he has the correct specifications for the type of aircraft on which he is working and that he has all the tools, supporting fixtures, and other equipment which he will need for the job. He should also have one or more qualified helpers to assist in handling parts.

The information the technician must have for rigging the biplane includes **stagger, angle of incidence, dihedral angle,** and **decalage.**

Figure 17·24 A typical biplane.

Stagger is the longitudinal difference in the positions of the leading edges of the wings of a biplane. If the leading edge of the upper wing is ahead of the leading edge of the lower wing, the stagger is **positive.**

The **angle of incidence** is the angle which the chord of a wing makes with the longitudinal axis of the fuselage. When the angle of incidence is positive, the leading edge of the wing chord is higher than the trailing edge when considered in reference to the longitudinal axis of the fuselage.

The **dihedral angle** is the angle between one wing of the airplane and the transverse axis of the airplane. The transverse axis is the same as the lateral axis and is an imaginary straight line from one wing tip to the other. It is the axis about which the aircraft rotates when the elevator is moved to cause the airplane to go up or down.

Decalage is the difference between the angles of incidence of the upper and lower wings. If the upper wing has a greater angle of incidence than the lower wing, the decalage is said to be positive.

The first step in rigging a biplane is to level the fuselage, both laterally and longitudinally, in a location free from wind. The front of the fuselage should be supported in a cradle or by means of jacks. If the fuselage is supported by means of the landing gear the flexibility of the shock struts and tires will permit movement which is not desirable. The tail of the airplane should be on an adjustable stand to premit raising or lowering to obtain a perfectly level condition longitudinally.

Level positions are determined by placing a level on the leveling lugs provided on the fuselage or on the members designated as **leveling means** in the aircraft specifications. Leveling means are provided for both lateral and longitudinal leveling.

The second step (or first step in actual rigging procedure) in rigging the biplane is to install the **center section** of the wing on the fuselage. The center section is lifted into position above the fuselage, either by means of a suitable hoist or by hand. Depending upon the size of the center section, either two or four men will be required to lift the center section into position safely. While the center section is being held in position, the **cabane struts** and **stagger struts** are attached, either with temporary bolts or the regular assembly bolts. The **cross-brace** wires should also be installed at this time in order to support the center section laterally.

The next step is to adjust and secure the center section. It must be adjusted for lateral position, stagger, and angle of incidence. These adjustments must be made in an orderly sequence, and secondary adjustments may have to be made because of the effect of one adjustment upon another. The first operation is to adjust the cross-brace wires until the center section is aligned with the center line of the fuselage. The symmetry of the center section with the fuselage is checked with a plumb line, a straightedge, a spirit level, and a steel measuring tape or scale. When the spirit level is placed laterally across the top of the center section, a level reading should be obtained. Plumb bobs dropped from identical points on each end of the center section should indicate that the center section is centered laterally. Measuring from the plumb line to reference points on the fuselage will show whether the center section is centered.

The stagger of the center section may or may not be adjustable. If fixed-length stagger struts are used on the airplane, no adjustment can be made. On the other hand, if the stagger struts are adjustable or if the airplane has **stagger and drift wires** between the cabane struts, adjustment must be made. Adjustment of the stagger struts or wires will move the center section forward or aft. The position is checked by dropping a plumb line from the leading edge of the center section on each side of the fuselage and measuring the distance from the plumb line to a fixed reference point such as the front fitting for the lower wing.

The final check on the rigging of the center section is to see that all wires have the correct tension, all lock nuts are properly tightened, and the correct bolts are installed in all fittings. Safetying of nuts and bolts must be checked.

The next step in the rigging of the biplane is the attachment of the lower wings. A padded support is placed where it can support the outer end of the lower wing, and then the wing is lifted into place and attached at the fuselage fittings. The wing attachment bolts are inserted with the heads forward as a standard practice.

The **interplane struts** are attached to fittings on the top of each lower wing near the outer end. The struts must be held in an almost vertical position until the upper-wing panels are attached to the fittings on the ends of the center section. The upper ends of the struts are then attached to the fittings on the lower side of each upper wing. When this is done, both the upper and lower wings are supported by the stand or other support under the lower wing. The upper wing is supported through the interplane struts.

After the wing panels are in place, the **landing wires,** sometimes called **ground wires,** are installed between the fittings at the tops of the cabane struts and the fittings at the lower ends of the interplane struts. These wires are tightened to support the weight of both wing panels on each side of the fuselage. After the landing wires are tightened, the supports can be removed from under the lower wing.

The **flying wires,** which carry the wing load in flight, are installed between the fittings at the butt end of the lower wing and the fittings at the upper ends of the interplane struts. These wires are tightened just enough to take up the slack at this time.

The dihedral angle of the wings is established by adjusting the landing wires. A bubble protractor or a dihedral board with the correct angle is used for checking the dihedral angle. When the dihedral angle is correct, the flying wires are tightened. The wires are of the streamline design and are manufactured with right-hand threads at one end and left-hand threads at the other end. Thus, by turning the wire in one direction, it is tightened and by turning it in the opposite

direction it is loosened. Tightening the landing wires increases the dihedral angle. After the wires are all tightened to the correct tension, the dihedral angle should be rechecked to see that it is correct.

The stagger at the outer ends of the wings should be checked to determine that it is correct. Some biplanes use a fixed N-strut arrangement such that no adjustment of stagger is required. If the airplane has incidence wires between the interplane struts, it is necessary to adjust these wires by means of turnbuckles or other means to set the correct stagger at these points.

After the wings and empennage are adjusted and set according to specifications, the airplane must be flown to determine whether the rigging is exactly as it should be. It is necessary to **wash in** and **wash out** the wings to compensate for propeller torque. Since the propeller of a conventional biplane turns to the right, the airplane will tend to rotate to the left about the longitudinal axis. For this reason it is necessary to rig the wings so the left wings will have more lift than the right. To increase the lift, the left-wing angle of incidence is increased slightly and the right-wing angle is decreased slightly. Decreasing the angle of incidence at the tip of a wing is called **washing out,** and increasing the angle of incidence is called **washing in.** From experience it is known approximately how much washout and washin is required for a particular airplane at cruising speed and this amount is rigged in at first. The airplane is then test flown and if a tendency to roll is found during the flight, the pilot makes his report and the rigging is corrected. The washin and washout is adjusted by shortening or lengthening the rear landing wires and adjusting the other wires to provide a reasonable balance in tension. If the airplane uses incidence wires between the interplane struts, these are also adjusted.

The washin of the left wing will increase the drag of that wing because of the greater lift. This will cause the airplane to yaw to the left; however, the tendency to yaw can be corrected by the use of an adjustable **trim tab** on the rudder. The tab is adjusted to deflect the rudder slightly to the right, thus providing a balancing force to overcome the yaw.

To make the adjustments as small as possible for the correction of engine and propeller torque, it is common practice to divide the amount of correction equally between the right and left wings. Thus, if the left wing is given 1° of washin, the right wing is given 1° of washout.

Basic principles of control rigging

Although the actual rigging of controls for any particular airplane should be accomplished according to the instructions of the manufacturer, there are certain operations common to almost all systems and by which rigging of the majority of small airplanes can be accomplished. The control systems for very large aircraft are so complex that adjustment and rigging can only be accomplished in the operator's overhaul shops or similar large shops, and according to manufacturer's directions.

Among the objectives to be accomplished during the rigging procedure are (1) correct cable tensions, (2) balance or synchronization between dual controls, (3) synchronization of the cockpit control with the control surfaces to which it is linked, and (4) setting the range of control-surface movement.

Cable tensions must be set at the same time the control units are positioned because any change in control cable tension will likely produce a change in control-surface position. Cable tension is measured by means of a **tensiometer** or cable-tension indicator as shown in Fig. 17·25. The correct riser for the cable size is installed on the indicator, and then the indicator is hooked over the cable. The control lever is moved up against the case, and the reading on the dial is noted. This reading is located on the conversion chart supplied with the instrument, and the cable tension is shown opposite the indicator reading in the column for the size of cable being checked.

The objective in rigging a control system is to have the cockpit control in neutral at the same time that the control surface involved is in neutral. Usually the cockpit control (stick or control column and wheels) is locked in the neutral position by means of the control lock in the airplane or by an installed locking arrangement such as a bar, block, or rod with clamps which will hold the control in neutral. The control cables are then adjusted and tensioned so the control surface affected is in neutral. All adjusting elements, such as turnbuckles, and rod ends, must be checked after rigging to see that they are within limits. Rod ends must be screwed into or onto the rod a distance sufficient to prevent the insertion of safety wire through the inspection hole. Turnbuckles must not have more than three threads showing outside the barrel.

Another point to remember in the final inspection of a control rigging job is to see that no cable splice or fitting can come within 2 in. of a fairlead, pulley, guide, cable guard, or other unit which could cause the control to jam. The control should be moved to its extreme position both ways in making this inspection.

The range of control-surface movement is given in the manufacturer's instructions or in the aircraft specifications. The control surface may have fixed or adjustable stops; this should be determined by inspection. If the stops are fixed and the control surface moves beyond its proper range, a repair must be made to set the stop correctly. This may involve welding a new stop in place or repairing the part of the surface which strikes the stop. The nature of the correction will be determined by examination. Adjustable stops are merely adjusted to bring the control surface into the correct range.

Control system components

We have already discussed some of the control system components such as cables, pulleys, and turnbuckles; however, there are other units involved which require description. Among these are **push-pull rods, bell cranks, quadrants, torque tubes, cable guards,** and **fairleads.**

The **push-pull rod** is used between bell cranks and from bell cranks to **torque arms** ("horns") to transmit the force and motion from one to the other. A push-pull rod connected to a bell crank is shown in Fig. 17·26. Push-pull rods are also called **control rods** because they are often used in control systems.

A **bell crank** is used to transmit force and permit a change in the direction of the force. In the illustration of 17·26 the effect of the bell crank operation can be seen.

A **quadrant** serves the same purpose as a wheel; however, the quadrant moves through a relatively small arc; perhaps as much as 100°. A quadrant, shown in Fig. 17·27, is often employed at the base of a control column or control stick to impart force and motion to a cable system.

A **torque tube** is a hollow shaft by which the linear motion of a cable or push-pull tube is changed to rotary motion. A torque arm or "horn" is attached to the tube by welding or bolting and imparts a twisting

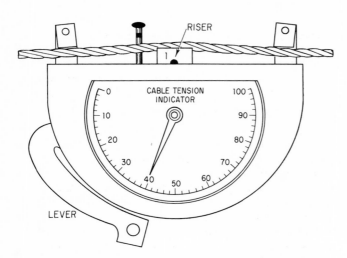

Figure 17·25   Use of a tensiometer.

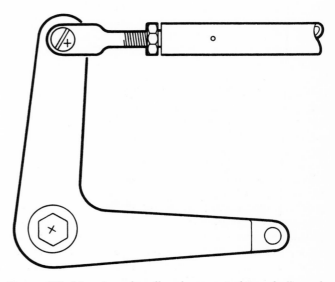

Figure 17·26   A push-pull rod connected to a bell crank.

332

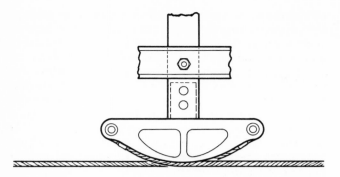

Figure **17·27**   *A quadrant used for operation of control cables.*

motion to the tube as the arm is moved back and forth. This is illustrated in Fig. 17·28.

Cable guards or **guard pins** are installed in the flanges of pulley brackets to prevent the cable from jumping out of the pulley, as shown in Fig. 17·29. The guard must be located so it does not interfere with the rotation of the pulley. A guard pin can be either a bolt or a clevis pin.

A **fairlead** serves as a guide to prevent wear and vibration of a cable. The fairlead is made of phenolic material, plastic, or soft aluminum and is either split or slotted to permit the installation of the cable. These

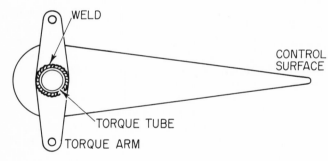

Figure **17·28**   *A torque arm, or "horn."*

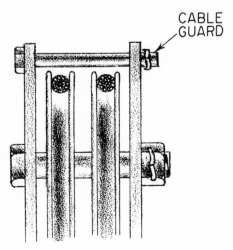

Figure **17·29**   *A cable guard pin.*

units must be installed in such a manner that there is no contact between the cable and the aircraft structure. The principal functions of fairleads are to dampen vibration, maintain cable alignment, and to seal openings in bulkheads. In no case should the fairlead be permitted to deflect a cable more than 3°, and it is good practice to install fairleads so cable deflection is as small as possible. Since cables are tightened to the extent that from 25 to more than 160 lb (on large transport-type aircraft) is exerted on the cable, an appreciable deflection at a fairlead will cause excessive wear of the cable and the fairlead. A fairlead is shown in Fig. 17·30.

In a pressurized jet airplane, cables leading from a pressurized section of the airplane to a nonpressurized section must have **air-pressure seals** installed where the cable passes through the bulkhead. A seal of this type is shown in Fig. 17·31. The air-pressure seals are

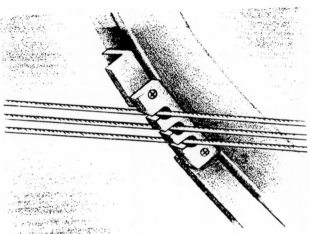

Figure **17·30**   *A fairlead.*

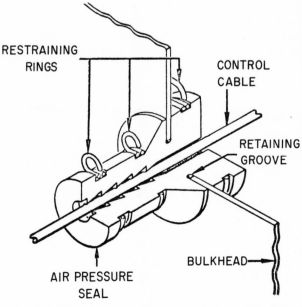

Figure **17·31**   *An air pressure seal for cable installations. (Boeing Co.)*

made of ozone-resistant rubber and are installed according to the manufacturer's instructions. Typical instructions are as follows:

Fill the seal with graphite grease MIL-G-7187.

Lubricate the cable with graphite grease for the length of travel within the seal.

Bend the seal open and place it on the cable on the unpressurized side of the bulkhead, with the small end of the seal toward the bulkhead.

Insert the seal in the bulkhead so that the bulkhead web is entirely within the retainer groove of the seal and the small end of the seal is in the pressurized section.

Install two restraining rings on the seal on the pressurized side and one restraining ring on the unpressurized side of the bulkhead.

Controls and control systems

The three primary controls for an airplane are the ailerons, elevators, and rudder or rudders. On small aircraft these are operated manually through cockpit controls.

The ailerons are mounted on the rear portions (trailing edges) of the wings, usually near the outer end of each wing, and are operated by moving the control stick sideways or by rotating the control wheel. The movement of the control to the right causes a right rolling effect and vice versa.

In early aircraft the operation of ailerons would often cause the aircraft to yaw against the direction of the control movement; that is, a movement of the control for a left roll would cause the airplane to yaw to the right. This is because the aileron which moves downward creates lift and drag, whereas the aileron which moves upward reduces lift and causes much less drag. The drag causes the condition which is called **adverse yaw.** To overcome adverse yaw a number of modifications were made in the design and operation of the ailerons.

One method of combating adverse yaw was to design the aileron so that a substantial section extends forward of the hinge line. This forward section moves down into the airstream when the aileron is moved up and creates drag to balance the increased drag of the down aileron. The top portion of the forward section of the aileron is rounded-off so it will not extend upward on the down aileron. This type of aileron is called a Friese aileron.

Another, more common, method for controlling adverse yaw through the operation of the ailerons is to design the control system so there is differential movement between the ailerons. The aileron moving upward moves approximately twice as far as the aileron moving downward. In this way the drag on the up aileron tends to balance the drag on the down aileron. The difference in the amount of aileron travel between the upward and downward movement is caused by a **differential control.** This can be accomplished by several methods, one being the placement of the control-rod connections on the drive wheels. An example of differential control movement is illustrated in Fig. 17·32. In this illustration, it can be seen that the movement of the control stick in one direction will cause an aileron to move up a greater distance than the other aileron moves down. When the stick is moved in the opposite direction, the opposite effect occurs.

Typical control system

A typical aileron control system for a light airplane is shown in Fig. 17·33. This system consists of control wheels mounted on a yoke with sprocket chains inter-

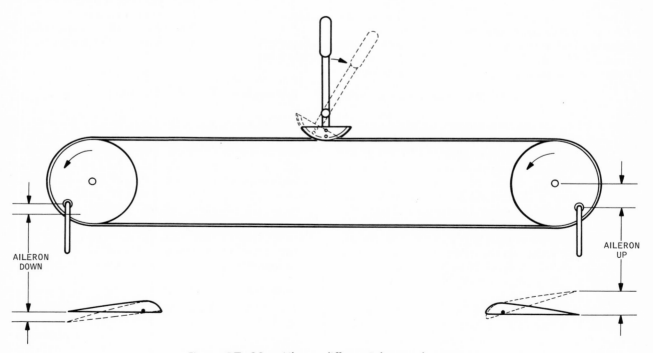

Figure 17·32 Aileron differential control system.

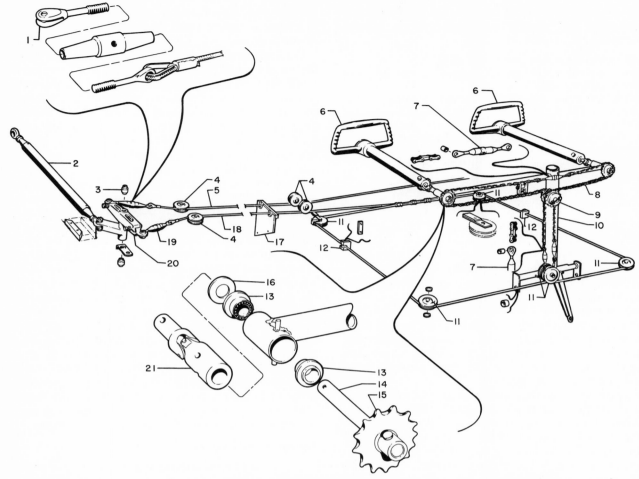

1. Turnbuckle fork
2. Aileron control tube assembly
3. Bearing
4. Pulley
5. Aileron balance cable assembly
6. Control wheel assembly
7. Turnbuckle barrel
8. Roller chain assembly
9. Control-column sprocket assembly
10. Control-column assembly
11. Pulley
12. Aileron cable rub block
13. Bearing
14. Control-column pulley shaft
15. Control-column pulley shaft sprocket
16. Shim washer
17. Aileron cable rub block
18. Aileron control cable assembly
19. Turnbuckle barrel
20. Aileron bellcrank assembly
21. Universal joint assembly

Figure 17·33   Aileron control system for a light airplane. (Piper Aircraft Corp.)

connected between the two wheels to a cable drive pulley. Rotation of the control wheels is changed to angular movement of the ailerons through the cables, bell cranks, and aileron control tube assembly.

To rig and adjust the aileron system, the control wheels are placed in the neutral position laterally with the lower surfaces of the wheels horizontal. The cables are rigged by means of the turnbuckles so that the aileron bell-crank assemblies [(20) in Fig. 17·33] are in the neutral position and the cable tension is between 28 and 42 lb on a tensiometer. A fabricated special tool is inserted to determine aileron bell-crank neutral position.

The aileron control tubes [(2) in Fig. 17·33] are adjusted so that the ailerons are in neutral position. The aileron travel is set by adjusting the aileron stop bolts in the bell-cranks. The travel is measured by means of a bubble protractor.

An elevator control system which utilizes push-pull control rods (control tubes) is illustrated in Fig. 17·34. When the control wheels are moved forward and rearward, the control arm at the lower end of the control column assembly is moved. This motion is transmitted through the push-pull rods to the bell crank at the rear of the airplane which, in turn, transmits the motion to the rear elevator control tube assembly, thus moving the elevator up and down. Adjustments of the elevator movement and travel is made by means of adjustable rod ends on the control tubes.

Inspection of control systems

The following inspections are typical of those which should be made for control systems; however, the inspections for a particular type of airplane should follow the instructions given in the manufacturer's service or maintenance manual.

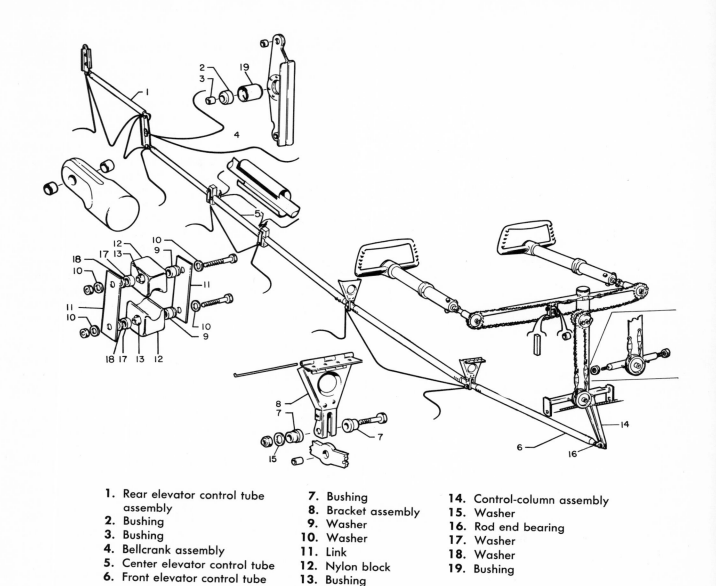

1. Rear elevator control tube assembly
2. Bushing
3. Bushing
4. Bellcrank assembly
5. Center elevator control tube
6. Front elevator control tube
7. Bushing
8. Bracket assembly
9. Washer
10. Washer
11. Link
12. Nylon block
13. Bushing
14. Control-column assembly
15. Washer
16. Rod end bearing
17. Washer
18. Washer
19. Bushing

Figure 17·34   Elevator control system utilizing push-pull rods. (Piper Aircraft Corp.)

1. Examine all cables for wear or corrosion. Wear will be most apparent at or near pulleys, the ends of cable fittings, fairleads, and other points where the cable may come into contact with another part of the system. Broken strands of cable can be detected by wrapping a rag around the cable and moving the rag back and forth. Cables which are badly worn, have broken strands, or are appreciably corroded should be replaced.
2. Examine all pulleys for wear, cracks, and alignment. If a pulley is worn or cracked to an appreciable extent, it should be replaced. The pulleys should turn freely when the control cables are moved. If a pulley is out of line, it will cause wear to both the pulley and the cable. The mountings for such pulleys should be corrected and the cable carefully examined for wear.
3. Where cables pass through fairleads or guides, the deflection of the cable should be noted. If it is more than 3°, a correction must be made. The wear of the cable and the fairlead should be checked.
4. Wear of pulley bearings, bearing bolts, bushings, clevis pins,

and all other moving parts should be checked. Replacement must be made of all parts worn beyond specified limits.
5. Cable tension should be checked by means of a tensiometer; however, an experienced technician can often determine whether the tension on a small airplane system is correct by "feel." The cable tension is adjusted by means of turnbuckles.
6. The system should be checked to see that no cable fitting comes within 2 in. of a pulley, fairlead, or guide when the control is moved to its limits.
7. Control-surface travel should be checked by means of a bubble protractor or a template. Travel can be adjusted by means of the stop bolts and/or rod ends. The control-surface stops should be set to make contact before the cockpit control has reached the end of its travel. The cockpit-control stops should be adjusted so they will make contact if the control-surface stop does not stop the movement of the control at the limit of its prescribed travel.
8. After all adjustments are made, all safetying of turnbuckles, clevis pins, nuts, etc., must be examined for correct appli-

cation and effectiveness. Defective safetying must be corrected.

9. Upon completion of inspection, adjustment, and service, the control system should be given an operational check. The controls should move smoothly and easily through their full range of travel and should not exhibit any looseness or play. The systems must be checked for direction of control movement because it is often possible to cross cables and cause reverse movement. This is particularly true of aileron systems. When the right rudder pedal is pressed, the rudder should move to the right; when the control is pulled back, the elevator should move upward; and when the stick or wheel is moved to the right, the left aileron should move down and the right aileron should move up.

Unconventional systems

Some aircraft are equipped with special types of controls which involve interconnections between aileron and rudder systems so the airplane can be turned by means of the control wheel only. This is usually a spring-type interconnection, such that the controls can be operated independently without difficulty. Adjustment of these systems must be exact and in accordance with specifications.

A **two-control airplane** does not have rudder controls. A rudder which has a very small range of travel is interconnected with the aileron system through the control wheel such that reasonably well-coordinated turns can be made by means of the wheel only.

The Beechcraft Bonanza airplane is equipped with tail control surfaces arranged in a V configuration. These surfaces provide both rudder and elevator action. When the control wheel is pulled back, both surfaces raise. When the right rudder pedal is pressed, the left surface moves upward and to the right and the right surface moves downward and to the right. This action is accomplished by means of an ingenious mechanism which combines the action of the rudder pedals and the elevator control.

Tabs and tab systems

Various types of **tab systems** are employed on aircraft control surfaces to "trim" the aircraft so the pilot can fly straight and level without having to exert continuous pressure on the controls.

A **fixed trim tab** is one that can be adjusted on the ground but cannot be adjusted in flight. This type of tab is usually a sheet-metal plate attached to the rear of the control surface and extending to the rear of the trailing edge. If the pilot reports that the airplane will not fly straight and level at cruising speed, the appropriate tab is adjusted on the ground by bending a rudder tab to the right or left, and bending the aileron and elevator tabs up or down, depending upon the correction required.

When a rudder tab is moved or bent to the right, it causes deflection of the rudder to the left, thus causing the airplane to turn to the left. If an elevator tab is bent or moved upward, the elevator will be deflected downward and the nose of the aircraft will tend to move downward.

Modern aircraft employ adjustable trim tabs such that the pilot can make adjustments in flight. The tabs are operated through cable systems, utilizing cable smaller than that required for the primary controls. The mechanisms employed for the operation of the aileron trim control on a Cessna 310 airplane are shown in Fig. 17 · 35. It will be noted that the trim is adjusted by a control wheel located in the cockpit. The wheel is turned to the right to lower the right wing and vice versa. The control wheel turns a sprocket and drives a sprocket chain. The chain turns another sprocket wheel connected through a shaft to a miter gear. Through the pair of gears, the axis of rotation is changed 90° and the motion is delivered to another sprocket. This sprocket wheel drives a chain which is connected to cable fittings. The cable is connected by means of conventional turnbuckles and routed through pulleys to the chain which drives the aileron trim-tab actuator.

The foregoing description provides a sample of a typical trim-tab system, although many systems on large aircraft are driven by means of electrical actuators.

Control tabs are similar in effect to trim tabs; however, they are used on large aircraft to produce primary control forces. An example of the action of a control tab is shown in Fig. 17 · 36 for the elevator on the Boeing 720 airliner.

The control tab provides aerodynamic actuation of the control surface. On the Boeing 720 airplane, the elevator control tab is a thin, tapered, lightweight clad-aluminum-alloy surface with aluminum honeycomb core. It is statically balanced about the tab-hinge center line by means of nose weights which extend forward into cavities in the trailing edge of the elevator. The control tab is balanced into the elevator by means of an adjust weight attached to the lower surface of the No. 2 balance panel. The tab is attached to the rear spar of the elevator with six low-friction hinges. The outboard hinge takes thrust loads. The lower inboard end contains a horn fitting to which the control pushrod is attached.

The control tab for the elevator produces a force to raise or lower the elevator in response to the operation of the control column. When the tab is caused to move down, the elevator receives an *up* force. The effect of the tab is assisted by the static balance weight and by the air pressure on the elevator balance panel shown in Fig. 17 · 36.

In addition to the control tab, the stabilizer of the Boeing 720 airplane is equipped with a stabilizer-actuated elevator tab. This tab helps streamline the elevator with the horizontal stabilizer when the stabilizer is raised or lowered. It also provides an approximately constant force gradient in the elevator control system.

A **balance tab** is similar in function to the control tab in that it is designed to assist the pilot in moving the control surface. The action of a balance tab is illustrated in Fig. 17 · 37. As the control surface begins to move in a certain direction, the balance tab moves in the opposite direction. This produces an aerodynamic force to help move the control surface. In some designs,

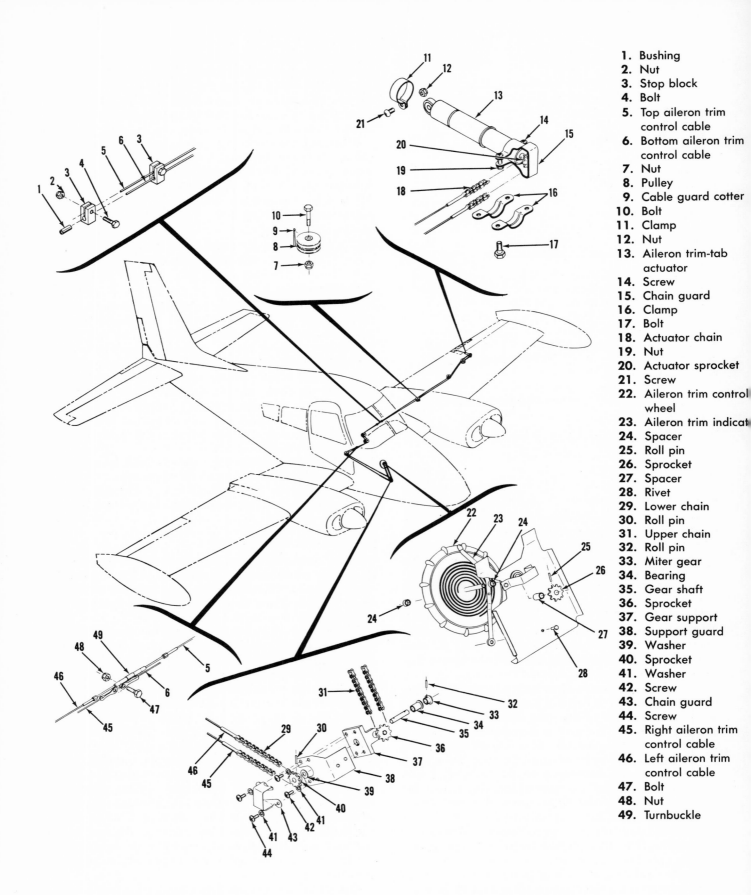

1. Bushing
2. Nut
3. Stop block
4. Bolt
5. Top aileron trim control cable
6. Bottom aileron trim control cable
7. Nut
8. Pulley
9. Cable guard cotter
10. Bolt
11. Clamp
12. Nut
13. Aileron trim-tab actuator
14. Screw
15. Chain guard
16. Clamp
17. Bolt
18. Actuator chain
19. Nut
20. Actuator sprocket
21. Screw
22. Aileron trim control wheel
23. Aileron trim indicat
24. Spacer
25. Roll pin
26. Sprocket
27. Spacer
28. Rivet
29. Lower chain
30. Roll pin
31. Upper chain
32. Roll pin
33. Miter gear
34. Bearing
35. Gear shaft
36. Sprocket
37. Gear support
38. Support guard
39. Washer
40. Sprocket
41. Washer
42. Screw
43. Chain guard
44. Screw
45. Right aileron trim control cable
46. Left aileron trim control cable
47. Bolt
48. Nut
49. Turnbuckle

Figure **17·35**   *Aileron trim-tab control system for the Cessna 310 airplane. (Cessna Aircraft Co.)*

338

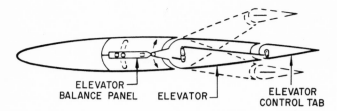

Figure 17·36 Elevator control tab for the Boeing 720 airplane. (Boeing Co.)

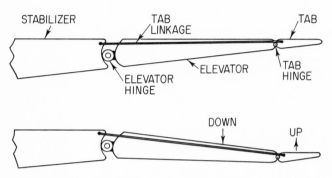

Figure 17·37 Action of a balance tab.

the balance tab is combined in function so that it can be actuated in flight. In these cases it also serves as a controllable trim tab.

Auxiliary control surfaces

In addition to the primary control surfaces mentioned, modern airplanes are often equipped with other surfaces which help to provide safe operation of the airplane. These surfaces are usually found on larger aircraft and those which fly at high speeds.

Among the most necessary types of auxiliary control surfaces are the **flaps.** An extended flap often adds to the lifting area of the wing and provides additional drag which assists in slowing the speed of the airplane. Flaps are made in various designs including the **plain flap,** the **split flap,** the **Fowler flap,** and the **slotted flap.**

The plain flap acts as a part of the trailing edge of the wing and merely turns downward to increase the drag of the wing. The split flap is a section of the lower side of the trailing edge of the wing and turns downward into the airstream. The Fowler flap moves rearward on tracks as it turns downward. This flap increases effective wing area and also increases the drag of the wing.

The slotted flap moves rearward on a track and forms a slot at the trailing edge of the wing to increase the effectiveness of the airflow over this part of the wing. It makes the flap more effective and enables the airplane to fly at a lower airspeed than would otherwise be possible. Thus it is most effective in reducing the landing speed of the airplane.

Another aid designed to enable the airplane to fly at low airspeeds is the **slat** on the leading edge of the wing. The slat is an airfoil which works automatically and its purpose is to reduce stalling speed. It is not spring-

loaded but rather operates as a result of changing air pressures as the aircraft reduces speed. As the airplane approaches stalling speed, the slat moves forward and creates an opening between itself and the wing. The rush of air through the narrow opening and over the wing restores the lift of the wing.

Modern jet aircraft employ devices called **spoilers** to reduce the lift of the wing. A spoiler is merely a surface which is raised into the airstream to destroy the lift in a certain section of the wing's length. The reduction of lift enables the airplane to descend rapidly without increasing speed or stalling.

INSTALLATION OF PLASTIC PARTS AND ASSEMBLIES

Types of plastics

A large number of transparent plastics have been invented to provide flexible and vibration-resistant windows and windshields for aircraft. The two most commonly employed types of plastic materials for aircraft are **acrylic** (also referred to as methacrylate base) and cellulose acetate plastic sheet. These materials are used for windows and windshields. They are called **thermoplastic** because they can be softened by the application of heat. This is advantageous because it makes the forming and fabrication of the sheets a comparatively simple process.

Thermosetting plastics are those which take a permanent and hard set upon the application of heat. These are usually the synthetic resin compounds such as epoxy, polyester, phenolic urea, and formaldehyde resins.

Cleaning and handling plastics

Great care must be used in the cleaning and handling of plastic windshields and windows. This is because the polished surfaces of these materials are soft and easily scratched and they are also subject to attack by certain types of solvents.

When sheets of plastic are stored, they should be laid flat, one sheet stacked upon another, with clean, smooth paper between each pair of sheets. New plastic sheet often has a layer of paper bonded to the surface by means of a soft adhesive so that it is easily removed when the plastic is put in service.

The best cleaning agent for plastic windshields and windows is gritfree soap and water. Dirty wash water should not be used because of the small particles of dirt or sand which may be suspended in the solution.

Solvents such as lacquer thinner, benzine, carbon tetrachloride, acetone, and other similar materials should never be used on plastic sheet because they will penetrate the surface and cause **crazing.** Crazing is the formation of a network of fine cracks in the surface of the material. The effect of crazing is to destroy the clarity of vision through the material and to weaken the structural strength.

One of the most commonly employed acrylic plastic materials employed in the aircraft industry is manufactured by the Rohm and Haas Company and is trade-named Plexiglas. This is a high-quality material and is available in almost any aircraft supply store.

Cutting and drilling plastics

Plastics, such as Plexiglas, may be cut with saws, hand shears, and foot-operated shears. The best means of cutting is determined by the thickness of the material and the temperature. If a hand shear is to be used, it is often advisable to soften the line of the cut by means of a strip heater or similar device. Thick sheet should be cut by means of a fine-tooth bandsaw.

The drilling of plastic sheet can be done with an ordinary metal drill; however, the rake angle of the cutting edge should be ground straight to produce a scraping action rather than a shaving action. The angle of the drill point can be ground according to the desires of the operator. Some prefer a flattened point (140° or more), and others prefer a point as sharp as 60°.

Cementing plastics

Plastic materials, particularly acrylics, can be cemented easily through the use of the proper cements or solvents. For acrylic plastics, ethylene dichloride (EDC) or methylene dichloride (MDC) are suitable. The solvent dissolves the surface of the plastic and makes it possible to make a homogenous, solid joint between two parts. Some operators dissolve small chips of the acrylic plastic in the solvent to make a **syrup** cement for bonding parts togther.

In patching holes in acrylic plastic, a syrup cement or one of the solvents mentioned can be used. The hole is cut out smoothly as shown in Fig. 17·38, and a patch of the same material (but greater in thickness) is prepared to fit the hole. The bonding surfaces are softened with the solvent or cement, and the patch is then pressed into place and held with a weight or other means of pressure. When the material has hardened the patch is ground- or sanded-off so the surface of the patch is even with the surface of the base material. The surface must then be further smoothed with fine wet-or-dry sandpaper, and finally it must be polished with a rubbing compound and washed clean with soap and water.

Installation of acrylic sheet

When replacing windshields or windows with acrylic sheet, the original installation should be followed as closely as possible. Since plastic sheet expands and shrinks with changes in temperature about three times as much as aluminum, it is necessary that clearances be allowed to prevent strain and cracking.

When plastic sheet is installed with bolts and nuts, which pass through the sheet, the nut should be tightened to a firm fit and then backed off one turn. Rivets

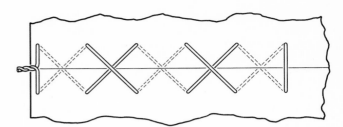

Figure 17·39   Repair of cracks in acrylic plastic.

should not be used through acrylic sheet unless suitable bushings are installed to prevent binding on the sheet.

When drilling holes for bolts or similar fasteners in plastic materials, the hole should be ⅛ in. larger in diameter than the bolt which will be installed in the hole. The bolt should be centered in the hole so it will not bind or create undue pressure as the plastic sheet shrinks or expands. Slotted holes are recommended as a means of permitting movement without stress.

The edges of acrylic sheet should be mounted in channels lined with cork, synthetic rubber, or a similar compound. A clearance of ⅛ in. should be allowed around the edges of small sheets and greater clearances around larger sheets. The basic principle to be remembered is that the acrylic sheet must be free to move as it expands or contracts and yet must be installed so it cannot come out.

Repair of cracks

Small cracks in the edges of acrylic sheet can be repaired easily, at least for temporary purposes. The cemented repair method required the drilling of a stop hole at the end of the crack to eliminate the stress concentration. The hole and crack are then filled with a syrup-type cement as explained previously. The cement should be of a consistency such that it will flow easily into the crack and completely close the crack.

Another method involves the drilling of a stop hole at the end of the crack and then lacing the crack with safety wire as shown in Fig. 17·39.

REVIEW QUESTIONS

1. Define the process of airplane assembly.
2. Define rigging of an airplane.
3. Discuss the use of jigs and supports in the assembly of an airplane.
4. What precautions must be taken in the hoisting of an airplane?
5. What is the function of a spreader bar in a hoist?
6. What materials are used in the manufacture of AN bolts?
7. What is the diameter of an AN6 bolt?
8. What is an internal wrenching bolt?
9. Discuss the installation of a high-strength bolt.
10. What precautions must be taken in the installation of a washer under the head of a high-strength bolt?
11. What limitations must be observed in the installation of self-locking nuts?
12. What are the common designations for threads of aircraft nuts and bolts?
13. Why are common screws not approved for use in place of AN bolts of the same size?

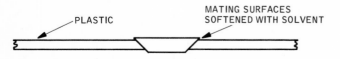

Figure 17·38   Installation of a patch in a plastic sheet.

14. Describe a *recessed-head screw.*
15. Describe self-tapping screws and their installation.
16. For what purpose is a taper pin used?
17. Explain the installation of cotter pins.
18. Why is a shear nut often used with a clevis bolt?
19. Describe the principal requirements of safety-wire installation.
20. How does the technician measure the torque he is applying to a nut during installation?
21. Under what conditions are torque values measured?
22. What is the MIL specification for corrosion-resistant-aircraft flexible cable?
23. What is meant by *proof load* of a cable assembly?
24. Describe the installation of swaged cable fittings.
25. How is a swaged cable terminal inspected to determine that it meets specifications?
26. What markings are employed to assure that a swaged cable terminal has not slipped?
27. By what methods can aircraft cable be cut?
28. Why is it not permissible to cut a cable with a torch?
29. Describe the installation of *Nicopress oval sleeves.*
30. Briefly describe a five-tuck cable splice.
31. What are the strength limitations for the five-tuck splice and the Nicopress splice?
32. Describe the safetying of a turnbuckle in a control system.
33. Give a brief description of the rigging of a biplane when installing wings and tail surfaces.
34. Define *stagger, angle of incidence, dihedral angle,* and *decalage.*
35. How is the level position of an airplane determined?
36. What is the effect of shortening the landing wires on a biplane?
37. How are *washin* and *washout* accomplished for a biplane?
38. Give the basic requirements of control-system rigging.
39. How are cable tensions measured?
40. How is the travel of a control surface measured?
41. List the mechanical devices found in an aircraft control system.
42. Describe the use and installation of a control cable guard.
43. What precaution must be observed in the installation of a cable-guard pin.
44. Describe a *fairlead,* and give the limit of cable deflection permitted at a fairlead.
45. What is the function of an air-pressure seal around a cable where it passes through a bulkhead?
46. What is meant by *adverse yaw* and how is it overcome?
47. Explain the importance of control-surface stops.
48. How are control-surface stops checked for adjustment?
49. Describe the inspection of pulleys in a control system.
50. How close may a cable fitting or splice approach a pulley fairlead or guide in a control system?
51. What is the final inspection required for control systems?
52. What precaution must be taken in connecting cables in control systems and how is correct connection determined?
53. What would be the effect of crossed control cables in an aileron system?
54. What is meant by a *two-control* airplane?
55. Discuss the use of fixed trim tabs.
56. What is an adjustable trim tab and how is it used?
57. How does an adjustable trim tab differ from a control tab?
58. If the trim tab on the rudder is moved to the right, what effect does it have on the flight of the airplane?
59. Explain the operation of a balance tab.
60. What are the advantages of flaps on an airplane?
61. Describe a slat.
62. What is the purpose of a spoiler?
63. Name the two principal types of plastics used for aircraft windows and windshields.
64. Discuss the cleaning and handling of plastic sheet.
65. What clearances should be provided in the installation of acrylic-sheet windows or windshields?
66. Describe the tightening of a bolt and nut through acrylic sheet.
67. Why are slotted bolt or screw holes recommended in the installation of acrylic plastic sheet?
68. What materials are used to cement acrylic plastic sheet?
69. Briefly describe the repair of a crack in an acrylic sheet.
70. What is the purpose of a drilled stop hole?

CHAPTER 18

Repair-station Requirements and Practices

The aviation **repair station** is to the aviation industry what the garage or automobile repair service is to the automotive industry. However, the aviation repair station, because of the need for airworthiness in all aircraft, parts, and accessories, must be under strict direction and control in order to meet the standards required for safe aircraft operation.

The function of the repair station is to make repairs on aircraft and engines and to provide routine maintenance and inspection services. The certificated repair station must perform these functions in accordance with the rules, regulations, and specifications set forth in its application for certification and its **inspection-procedures manual.** In addition, the repair station is obligated to abide by the regulations set forth in Federal Aviation Regulations, Part 145.

The Federal Aviation Administration has the responsibility for establishing standards of aircraft and powerplant repair and provides for the maintenance of these standards by certificating repair stations and repair-station personnel, inspecting repair facilities and equipment, and examining the methods and procedures employed by certificated repair stations.

ORGANIZATION OF A REPAIR STATION

Depending upon the type and size of a repair station, it may be organized in many ways. To be certificated by the Federal Aviation Administration, a repair station must meet rigid standards and adhere to certain principles. One of the most important of these principles is complete separation of the inspection function from other operating divisions of the station. The purpose of this is to make it possible for the inspection personnel to be independent in their judgments regarding the airworthiness of any repaired item. Inspection divisions should therefore be responsible to the administration only.

A suggested organization for a reasonably large repair station is shown by Fig. 18·1. This could be varied in many ways; however, it provides a guide to the principal operating divisions and subdivisions. It will be noted that the repair station is organized in three major divisions and that the inspection division is separate from the others.

Production division

The production division of a repair station must operate efficiently and effectively in order to make the business a success. This division receives aircraft, engines, accessories and components for repair or maintenance. At the time the unit is received, a **work order** is prepared. The work order includes a complete description of the item with serial numbers, model number, make, type, etc. The owner's name and address and the date the unit is received are recorded. The owner provides information regarding the repair and maintenance to be performed and offers all possible assistance in determining the cause of any discrepancies or malfunctions. The **service manager** records all

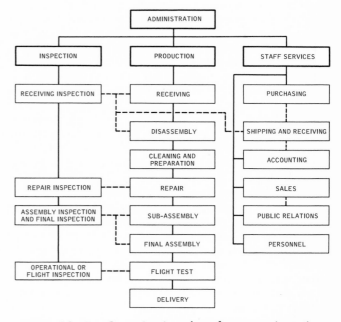

Figure 18·1   Organization chart for a repair station.

required repair items on the work order; if additional repair or maintenance are found necessary after the initial **receiving inspection,** he makes provision for these. The owner is given an estimate of the costs involved and informed that any additional work found necessary will involve additional cost. To avoid misunderstandings, the owner must be given complete information on all known and potential costs for the job. During the receiving inspection, a member of the inspection department should be present to note the existing conditions and prepare a checklist for future reference. This list will be used in the inspections as the aircraft or component continues through the repair processes to final assembly. Receiving inspection is performed, primarily, to record all conditions existing and to list any discrepancies noted in components, accessories, etc. If a particular instrument or other component is missing, the owner should be notified so there will be no future misunderstanding regarding the airplane and its parts.

The next step, or steps, in the processing of an aircraft repair is the required disassembly. This is often done by components or units, especially in cases where an airplane is not to be overhauled completely. For example, one wheel and brake assembly can be disassembled, inspected, repaired, reassembled, and inspected for airworthiness before continuing to another section or component of the airplane. The sequence of events is governed by type and size of aircraft, nature of repair operation required, personnel and facilities available, and the schedule most likely to return the aircraft to service in the shortest possible time.

The function of the inspection department should be carefully noted. Figure 18 · 1 shows connecting lines from the inspection functions to the repair functions to indicate points at which the inspections are made. **Receiving inspection** is twofold. First, the inspection division examines the aircraft and components at the time they are received for repair. Second, the inspection division examines new parts and materials when they are received from vendors. This is to assure that all materials received meet airworthiness requirements. It is not necessary to inspect standard manufactured parts which are received from a dealer or distributor in properly identified, sealed packages. Care must be taken, however, to make sure that a part scheduled for a particular work order bears the correct part number.

After a part or subassembly has been repaired, the inspection division should examine the repair for quality of workmanship and conformance with approved practice and specifications. This inspection is usually performed prior to final assembly.

Assembly inspection and final assembly inspection may be separate or identical, depending upon the unit inspected. The guiding principle is that every repair or assembly operation must be checked by an official inspector of the repair station. Units which cannot be inspected after final assembly must be inspected before.

Completed units or aircraft must be given an operational test where an overhaul or repair procedure could affect the operation of the aircraft or component.

An aircraft may be given a flight test, and a component may be operated either on the aircraft or on a test stand.

The staff services division provides necessary supporting operations for the entire company. In Fig. 18 · 1, sections are shown which supply services as indicated. The organization of these sections can and does vary considerably; however, all the services listed must be performed in one way or another.

The sales division of a company is often separate from other divisions and is responsible directly to the administration. If the organization sells both products and services, the sales division is likely to be separate from, but will work closely with, the public relations division.

CERTIFICATION REQUIREMENTS

As mentioned previously, the requirements or regulations governing a certificated repair station are set forth in FAR, Part 145. These regulations cover both **domestic** and **foreign repair stations** and state that no person may set up and operate as a certificated repair station without, or in violation of, a repair-station certificate. Furthermore, an applicant for a certificate cannot advertise as a certificated repair station until the certificate is issued.

The regulation (145.11) covering the application for and issue of a repair-station certificate is as follows:

An application for a repair station certificate and rating, or for an additional rating, is made on a form and in a manner prescribed by the Administrator (of the FAA) and submitted with duplicate copies of

1. Employment summaries for the chief inspector and other personnel having technical responsibility for final airworthiness determinations before releasing an article for service; where the privilege of final airworthiness determination is retained by the management officials of the station, an employment summary for each of those officials.
2. Its inspection procedures manual.
3. A list of the maintenance functions to be performed for it, under contract, by another agency (as approved).
4. In the case of an applicant for a propeller rating (class 2) or any accessory rating (class 1, 2, or 3), a list, by type or make, as applicable, of the propeller or accessory for which he seeks approval.

An applicant who meets the requirements of this Part is entitled to a repair station certificate with appropriate ratings prescribing such operations, specifications, and limitations as are necessary in the interests of safety.

All the documents submitted to the Federal Aviation Administration in support of the application for a repair-station certificate are examined and evaluated by representatives of the FAA. Facilities and equipment of the repair station are inspected to assure compliance with the documents submitted and ascertain that the repair station is adequately equipped to perform the services for which it is being certificated. The employment and experience records of key personnel are checked to see that those responsible for the repair and final approval of aircraft and components for return to service are qualified for their responsibilities. This includes verification of the FAA certification of individual employees of the organization.

Continuation of certificate

To retain approval as a certificated repair station, an organization must comply with further requirements set forth in FAR, Part 145. These regulations include application for approval whenever certain changes are made or contemplated, proper display of the repair-station certificate, submission to periodic inspections of the station by FAA representatives, and conformance with rules regarding the use of the station certificate number in advertising.

The certificate of a domestic repair station remains in effect until it is surrendered, suspended, or revoked. Suspension or revocation of a certificate will occur only when the repair station violates the terms of its certification or otherwise fails to meet its obligations and responsibilities.

Repair-station ratings

A repair station may be certificated for one or more of the following ratings: (1) airframe, (2) powerplant, (3) propeller, (4) radio, (5) instrument, (6) accessory, and (7) limited.

Airframe ratings are classified in four categories. Class 1 is approved for small aircraft of composite construction, and class 2 is for large aircraft of composite construction. **Composite construction** usually includes all aircraft other than those in which the airplane structure is entirely of metal.

The class 3 airframe rating is for small aircraft of all-metal construction and class 4 is for large aircraft of all-metal construction.

A **large aircraft** is one which has an approved maximum takeoff weight of more than 12,500 lb.

Powerplant ratings for a repair station are classified in three categories. A repair station having a class 1 rating is approved for the overhaul of reciprocating engines rated at 400 hp or less. Class 2 is for reciprocating engines having more than 400 hp, and class 3 is for gas-turbine engines. The term "gas-turbine" includes turbojet, turboprop, and turboshaft engines.

Propeller ratings are classified in two categories: class 1 for all fixed-pitch and ground-adjustable propellers of wood, metal, or composite construction and class 2 for all other propellers, by make.

Radio ratings are issued for three categories of equipment. Briefly, these are as follows: class 1 for general communications radio; class 2 for navigational radio equipment, except that which operates on the radar, or pulsed-radiofrequency, principle; and class 3 for radar and all other equipment operating on the pulsed-radiofrequency principle.

Instrument ratings are issued in four categories. Class 1 is for mechanically operated instruments, class 2 for electrical instruments, class 3 for gyroscopic instruments, and class 4 for electronic instruments.

Accessory ratings cover three classes of equipment. Class 1 is for mechanical accessories, class 2 for electrical accessories, and class 3 for electronic or electronically controlled accessories.

Limited ratings are issued to repair stations which limit their repair functions to particular makes and models of aircraft, engines, propellers, instruments, radio equipment, landing gear, or other components.

FEDERAL AVIATION REGULATIONS FOR REPAIR-STATION PERSONNEL

Federal Aviation Regulations (FAR) represent a recodification of the Civil Air Regulations and are established by the Federal Aviation Administration (FAA) to assure safe, convenient, and effective operation of commercial and private aircraft. FARs affect aircraft design, operation, maintenance, repair, and personnel involved in any of these areas.

In this section we shall discuss those regulations of particular importance to aircraft-repair stations and the personnel owning, operating, or employed by such repair stations.

Federal Aviation Regulations of particular interest to maintenance personnel

The following numbered parts of the Federal Aviation Regulations should be familiar to aviation maintenance technicians, repair-station operators, and others involved in the maintenance of aircraft or engines:

Part 1	Definitions and Abbreviations
Part 21	Certification Procedures for Products and Parts
Part 23	Airworthiness Standards: Normal, Utility, and Acrobatic Category Airplanes
Part 25	Airworthiness Standards: Transport Category Airplanes
Part 27	Airworthiness Standards: Normal Category Rotorcraft
Part 33	Airworthiness Standards: Aircraft Engines
Part 39	Airworthiness Directives
Part 43	Maintenance, Preventive Maintenance, Rebuilding, and Alterations
Part 45	Identification and Registration Marking
Part 47	Aircraft Registration
Part 49	Recording of Aircraft Titles and Security Documents
Part 65	Certification: Airmen Other Than Flight Crew Members
Part 91	General Operating and Flight Rules
Part 145	Repair Stations

Note: Federal Aviation Regulations may be obtained by ordering from the Superintendent of Documents, Government Printing Office, Washington, D.C. 20402.

The above-listed FARs all apply in some degree to the functions of the repair station and repair-station personnel; however, Parts 1, 39, 43, 45, 65, 91, and 145 should be very thoroughly understood by persons involved in the maintenance, repair, and alteration of aircraft and engines. Part 43 and the advisory circulars associated with this part set forth approved methods of repair and alteration which are approved by the FAA administrator and provide the guides by which the maintenance technician determines the nature of various repairs. If a repair is not described or approved in **Advisory Circular** 43.13-1, it must be described in the manufacturer's manual or be given special approval by a representative of the Federal Aviation Administration.

Part 39 of the Federal Aviation Regulations establishes the requirements for **airworthiness directives** (ADs) issued by the Federal Aviation Administration. Airworthiness directives are issued when operational experience for a particular aircraft, engine, accessory, or appliance indicates that a special inspection, modification, alteration, or repair is required in order to ensure safety in the operation of the item for which the AD is issued. FAR, part 39, states that *no person may operate a product (aircraft, engine, propeller, or appliance) to which an airworthiness directive applies, except in accordance with the requirements of that airworthiness directive.*

Every repair station must maintain a file of the ADs which apply to any product which is, or may be, inspected, maintained, altered, or repaired by that repair station. When any product is brought in for service, the records of the product (log book or other maintenance record) should be examined to make sure that the provisions of all ADs have been followed.

TYPES OF MAINTENANCE, REPAIR, AND ALTERATIONS

Preventive maintenance

Preventive maintenance is defined as simple or minor preservation operations and the replacement of small standard parts not involving complex assembly operations. Operations classed as preventive maintenance are as follows:

Removal, installation, and repair of landing gear tires

Replacing elastic shock-absorber cords on landing gear

Servicing landing-gear shock struts by adding oil, air, or both

Servicing landing-gear wheel bearings, such as cleaning and greasing

Replacing defective safety wiring or cotter keys

Lubrication not requiring disassembly other than removal of nonstructural items such as cover plates, cowlings, and fairings

Making simple fabric patches not requiring rib stitching or the removal of structural parts or control surfaces

Replenishing hydraulic fluid in the hydraulic reservoir

Refinishing decorative coating of fuselage, wings, tail group surfaces (excluding balanced control surfaces), fairings, cowling, landing gear, cabin, or cockpit interior when removal or disassembly of any primary structure or operating system is not required

Applying preservative or protective material to components where no disassembly of any primary structure or operating system is involved and where such coating is not prohibited or is not contrary to good practices

Repairing upholstery and decorative furnishings or the cabin or cockpit interior when the repairing does not require disassembly of any primary structure or operating system or affect the primary structure of the aircraft

Making small simple repairs to fairings, nonstructural cover plates, cowlings, and small patches and reinforcements not changing the contour so as to interfere with the proper airflow

Replacing side windows where that work does not interfere with the structure of any operating system such as controls, electrical equipment, etc.

Replacing safety belts

Replacing seats or seat parts with replacement parts approved for the aircraft, not involving disassembly of any primary structure or operating system

Troubleshooting and repairing broken circuits in landing light wiring circuits

Replacing bulbs, reflectors, and lenses of position and landing lights

Replacing wheels and skis where no weight and balance computation is involved

Replacing any cowling not requiring removal of the propeller or disconnecting of flight controls

Replacing or cleaning spark plugs and setting of spark plug gap clearance

Replacing any nose connections except hydraulic connections

Replacing prefabricated fuel lines

Cleaning fuel and oil strainers

Replacing batteries and checking fluid level and specific gravity

Removing and installing glider wings and tail surfaces that are specifically designed for quick removal and installation and when such removal and installation can be accomplished by the pilot

The holder of a pilot certificate issued under FAR, Part 61, may perform preventive maintenance on any aircraft owned or operated by him that is not used in air carrier service. Preventive maintenance may also be performed by certificated mechanics, repair stations, repairmen, air carriers, and others authorized by the FAA. A person who plans to perform preventive maintenance must ascertain that the operation falls within this category and that he is authorized to perform the work.

Classification of alterations

A **major alteration** is an alteration not listed in the aircraft, aircraft engine, or propeller specifications (1) that might appreciably affect weight, balance, structural strength, performance, powerplant operation, flight characteristics, or other factors of airworthiness or (2) that is not done according to accepted practices or cannot be done by elementary operations.

Alterations of the following parts and alterations of

the following types, when not listed in the aircraft specifications issued by the FAA, are **airframe major alterations:**

Wings
Tail surfaces
Fuselage
Engine mounts
Control system
Landing gear
Hull or floats
Elements of an airframe, including spars, ribs, fittings, shock absorbers, bracing, cowlings, fairings, and balance weights
Hydraulic and electrical actuating systems or components
Rotor blades
Changes to the empty weight or empty balance which result in an increase in the maximum certificated weight or center-of-gravity limits of the aircraft
Changes in the basic design of the fuel, oil, cooling, cabin pressurization, electrical, hydraulic, deicing, or exhaust systems
Changes to the wing or to fixed or movable control surfaces which affect flutter and vibration characteristics

The following alterations of a powerplant, when not listed in the engine specifications issued by the FAA, are **powerplant major alterations.**

Conversion of an aircraft engine from one approved model to another, involving any changes in compression ratio, propeller reduction gear, impeller gear ratios, or the substitution of major engine parts which requires extensive rework and testing of the engine
Changes to the engine by replacing aircraft engine structural parts with parts not supplied by the original manufacturer or parts not specifically approved by the FAA administrator
Installation of an accessory which is not approved for the engine
Removal of accessories that are listed as required equipment on the aircraft or engine specification
Installation of structural parts other than the type of parts approved for the installation
Conversions of any sort for the purpose of using fuel of a rating or grade other than that listed in the engine specifications

Minor alterations of either an airframe or a powerplant are alterations other than major alterations.

Classifications of repairs (TEST)

Repairs of airframes and powerplants are classified as either **major** or **minor** depending upon the type and effect of the repair. A major repair is one which, if improperly done, might appreciably affect the weight, balance, structural strength, performance, powerplant operation, flight characteristics, or other qualities affecting airworthiness; or one which is not done

according to accepted practices or cannot be done by elementary operations.

Repairs to the following parts of an airframe and repairs of the following types, involving the strengthening, reinforcing, splicing, and manufacturing of primary structural members, or their replacement (when replacement is by fabrication such as riveting or welding), are **airframe major repairs:**

Box beams
Monocoque or semimonocoque wings or control surfaces
Wing stringers or chord members
Spars
Spar flanges
Members of truss-type beams
Thin sheet webs of beams
Keel and chine members or boat hulls or floats
Corrugated-sheet compression members which act as flange material of wings or tail surfaces
Wing main ribs and compression members
Wing- or tail-surface brace struts
Engine mounts
Fuselage longerons
Members of the side truss, horizontal truss, or bulk heads
Main seat support braces and brackets
Landing-gear brace struts
Axles
Wheels
Skis and ski pedestals
Parts of the control system such as control columns, pedals, shafts, brackets, or horns
Repairs involving the substitution of material
The repair of damaged areas in metal or plywood stressed covering exceeding 6 in. in any direction
The repair of portions of skin sheets by making additional seams
The splicing of skin sheets
The repair of three or more adjacent wing- or control-surface ribs or the leading edge of wings and control surfaces between such adjacent ribs
Repair of fabric covering involving an area greater than that required to repair two adjacent ribs
Replacement of fabric on fabric covered parts such as wings, fuselages, stabilizers, and control surfaces
Repairing of removable or integral fuel tanks and oil tanks, including rebottoming the tanks

Repairs of the following parts of an engine and repairs of the following types are **powerplant major repairs:**

Separation or disassembly of a crankcase or crankshaft of a reciprocating engine equipped with an integral supercharger
Separation or disassembly of a crankcase or crankshaft of a reciprocating engine equipped with other than spur-type propeller reduction gearing
Special repairs to structural engine parts by welding, plating, metalizing, or other methods

346

INSPECTIONS

As previously explained in this chapter, an inspection department must be maintained in every certificated repair station. The inspector or inspectors must make the inspections previously described to ascertain that repairs are made to all damaged or worn items or that such items are replaced with others which are in airworthy condition.

Annual and 100-hr inspections

According to the provisions of FAR, Part 91, no person may operate an aircraft unless, within the preceding 12 calendar months, it has had an **annual inspection** and has been approved for return to service by an authorized person. An inspection for the issuance of an Airworthiness Certificate will serve as a substitute for the annual inspection.

A **100-hr inspection** is similar to the annual inspection; however, it may not be substituted for the annual inspection unless it is performed by a person certificated or otherwise authorized to make annual inspections and is entered as an annual inspection in the aircraft maintenance records (log book).

A 100-hr inspection is required on every aircraft used for carrying persons for hire other than the crew or for giving flight instruction. This means the aircraft must undergo a complete inspection, as set forth in FAR, Part 43, within every 100 hrs of operating time. After the 100-hr inspection the aircraft must be authorized for return to service by a properly certificated person. The 100-hr limitation may be exceeded by not more than 10 hr if necessary to reach a place at which the inspection can be made. The excess time, however, is included in computing the next 100 hr of time in service.

Progressive inspection

A **progressive inspection** requires the setting up of a schedule, specifying the intervals in hours or days when routine and detailed inspections will be performed, including instructions for exceeding an inspection interval by not more than 10 hr while enroute, and for changing an inspection interval because of service experience. The instructions and schedule for a progressive inspection must be approved by a representative of the Flight Standards District Office of the FAA having jurisdiction over the area in which the applicant for the progressive inspection is located.

Progressive inspections are usually established by air carriers in order to provide for better utilization of aircraft. Approval for such an inspection system requires that a properly authorized person or agency supervise the inspection procedures and that an inspection-procedures manual be available and readily understandable to pilot and maintenance personnel. Aircraft subject to an approved progressive inspection system need not undergo the 100-hr inspection otherwise required.

Typical inspection requirements

In the performance of 100-hr or annual inspections, the inspector must use a suitable checklist to assure that all items will be inspected. The inspection list can be arranged in groupings according to the configuration of the aircraft being inspected. In many cases, the manufacturer's maintenance manual will provide an inspection checklist designed for the aircraft.

Prior to making a 100-hr or annual inspection, the inspector must remove all inspection plates, cowlings, fairings, and access doors so every part of the aircraft to be inspected is easily accessible. The inspector should also have all necessary tools, inspection lights, and mirrors needed to perform the inspection.

FAR, Part 43, lists a typical inspection checklist which covers the majority of items to be inspected on a conventional aircraft. The items listed are as follows:

Fuselage and hull group

Fabric and skin: for deterioration, distortion, other evidence of failure, and defective or insecure attachment of fittings

Systems and components: for improper installation, apparent defects, and unsatisfactory operation

Envelope, gas bags, ballast tanks, and related parts: for poor condition

Cabin and cockpit group

Generally: for uncleanliness and loose equipment that might foul the controls

Seats and safety belts: for poor condition and apparent defects

Windows and windshields: for deterioration and breakage

Instruments: for poor condition, mounting, marking, and for improper operation

Flight and engine controls: for improper installation and improper operation

Batteries: for improper installation, improper charge and corrosion in the battery compartment

All systems: for improper installation, poor general condition, apparent and obvious defects, and insecurity of attachments

Engine and nacelle group

Engine section: for visual evidence of excessive oil, fuel, or hydraulic leaks, and sources of such leaks. The condition of fittings, hoses, tubing, and electrical wiring should be examined carefully

Studs and nuts: for improper torquing, safetying, and obvious defects

Internal engine: for cylinder compression and for metal particles or foreign matter on screens and sump drain plugs

If there is weak cylinder compression: for poor internal condition, and improper internal clearances or tolerances

Engine mount: for cracks, looseness of mounting, and looseness of engine to mount

Flexible vibration dampeners: for poor condition and deterioration

Engine controls: for defects, improper travel, and improper or lack of safetying

Lines, hoses, clamps, and fittings: for leaks, poor condition, and looseness

Exhaust stacks: for cracks, defects, and improper attachment

Accessories: for apparent defects and insecure mounting

All systems: for improper installation, poor general condition, defects, and insecure attachment

Cowling: for cracks and other defects

Landing-gear group

All units: for poor condition and insecure attachment
Shock-absorbing devices: for improper oleo fluid level and for amount of strut inflation
Linkage, trusses, and members: for undue or excessive wear, fatigue, and distortion
Retracting and locking mechanisms: for improper operation
Hydraulic lines and fittings: for leakage and damage
Electrical system: for chafing of wiring and improper operation of switches
Wheels: for cracks, defects, and condition of bearings
Tires: for wear and cuts or other damage
Brakes: for improper adjustment and operation
Floats and skis: for insecure attachment and obvious or apparent damage or other defects

Wing group

All components: for damage and deterioration
Fabric cover: for deterioration, condition of finish, damage, and strength of covering
Metal skin: for damage, loose rivets, signs of buckling, and corrosion
Struts and brace wires: for damage, wear, insecure attachment, and corrosion
Ailerons and flaps: for loose hinge fittings, insecure attachments, and improper operation of control system

Empennage group

Stabilizers: for condition of covering, insecure attachment, and alignment
Rudder and elevators: for insecure attachment, condition of covering, looseness of hinge fittings, insecure control fittings, and alignment

Propeller group

Propeller assembly: for cracks, nicks, binds, and oil leakage
Bolts: for improper torquing, lack of safetying, and corrosion
Anti-icing devices: for improper operation and obvious defects
Control mechanisms: for improper operation, insecure mounting, and restricted travel

Radio and electronic equipment group

Radio and electronic equipment: for improper installation, insecure mounting, and condition of units
Wiring and conduits: for improper routing, insecure mounting, and obvious defects
Bonding and shielding: for improper installation and poor condition
Antenna, including trailing antenna: for poor condition, insecure mounting, and improper operation

The foregoing listing is provided merely as a guide, and it will be readily noted that many additional items and conditions will come to the inspector's attention. It is the inspector's responsibility to see that the aircraft is in airworthy condition and that it will remain in that condition for at least an additional 100 hr. All defects noted must be reported to the owner or operator, and it is his responsibility to see that they are corrected before the airplane is operated.

Upon completion of an annual inspection, the person making the inspection shall execute FAA Form 2350, Aircraft Use and Inspection Report (Fig. 18 · 2) and send the form to the local FAA district office within 48 hr after the aircraft is approved for return to service. If the aircraft is not approved for return to service, the form and the list of discrepancies is sent to the local FAA district office within 48 hr after completing the inspection.

A certificated airframe and powerplant mechanic holding an **inspection authorization rating** may authorize the return to service of an airplane after having performed an annual inspection. Upon completion of the inspection and authorization for return of the aircraft to service, the inspector affixes an Inspection Reminder, FAA Form 2912, to the aircraft. Figure 18 · 3 illustrates an example of such a form.

The return of an aircraft to service after an annual inspection, a major repair, a major alteration, a progressive inspection, or a continual maintenance program may be authorized by personnel and agencies in accordance with FAR, Parts 43, 65, 121, 127, or 145, depending upon which agency performs the work or makes the inspection.

FEDERAL AVIATION AGENCY
AIRCRAFT USE AND INSPECTION REPORT

PRINT OR TYPE ALL ENTRIES EXCEPT SIGNATURES.
SHADED BOXES ARE FOR FAA USE

SECTION I—IDENTIFICATION

1. AIRCRAFT REGISTRATION MARK N— | AIRCRAFT MFR. SERIAL NO.
2. AIRCRAFT MAKE | AIRCRAFT MODEL
3. NAME OF OWNER *(As shown on Certificate of Registration)*
4. ADDRESS OF OWNER *(As shown on Certificate of Registration)*
NUMBER AND STREET:
CITY: STATE:
5. AIRCRAFT IS BASED AT: COUNTY:
AIRPORT:
CITY: STATE OF:

SECTION II—ACTIVITY DATA

6. DATE OF PREVIOUS PERIODIC INSPECTION | AIRCRAFT TIME IN SERVICE PREVIOUS 12 MONTHS HRS.
7. PRIMARY USE OF AIRCRAFT *(Check one box only)*

1	EXECUTIVE TRANSPORTATION	6	AIR TAXI
2	BUSINESS TRANSPORTATION	7	INDUSTRIAL, SPECIAL
3	PERSONAL	8	OTHER *(Specify)*
4	AERIAL APPLICATION		
5	INSTRUCTION		

SECTION III—INSPECTION REPORT

8. NAME OF INSPECTING AGENCY
9. TYPE INSPECTING AGENCY: 3 ☐ INSPECTION AUTHORIZATION 5 ☐ MANUFACTURER 6 ☐ REPAIR STATION | CERTIFICATE NO. AND TYPE
10. TYPE OF INSPECTION: 1 ☐ PERIODIC 2 ☐ PROGRESSIVE | DATE OF INSPECTION | CONDITION OF AIRCRAFT: 1 ☐ AIRWORTHY 2 ☐ UNAIRWORTHY
11. SIGNATURE OF CONDUCTOR OF THIS INSPECTION

EA	SW	CE	WE	AL	PC	SO	EU	FAA DIST. OFF NO.
1	2	3	4	5	6	7	9	

FAA Form 2350 (1-65) OBSOLETE PREVIOUS EDITION 0052-071-2000 (8320)

Figure 18 · 2 Aircraft Use and Inspection Report form.

FEDERAL AVIATION AGENCY

INSPECTION REMINDER

The next periodic inspection of this aircraft required by Federal Aviation Regulations is due:

DATE

FAA Form 2912 (2 - 65)   (8320)
OBSOLETE PREVIOUS EDITION

Figure 18·3   Inspection Reminder form.

AIRCRAFT RECORDS

Every certificated aircraft must have a set of records pertinent to that aircraft and these records must be kept up-to-date. For any particular aircraft these required records include the Operator's Manual, supplied by the manufacturer and containing all information necessary for the safe and efficient operation of the aircraft; log books for both the aircraft and the engine; Airworthiness Certificate, issued by the FAA; Registration Certificate; Ownership Certificate; Weight and Balance Data; and reports of major repairs and major alterations.

Operator's Manual

The **Operator's (or Owner's) Manual** is supplied by the manufacturer to assure that the owner or operator of the aircraft has all needed information regarding the operation of the aircraft. The manual for a particular airplane may include all the necessary information in one booklet or some may be provided as separate records. Much of the information contained in the Operator's Manual will be applicable to all aircraft of a particular model while other information will apply only to one specific airplane. For example, weight and balance data for a particular airplane will not usually apply to another airplane of the same make and model. No two airplanes are likely to have the same basic weight or center-of-gravity (CG) location. The weights may vary from a fraction of an ounce to several pounds and the empty-weight CG location may differ in position by more than 1 in., depending upon equipment, finish, etc.

The airplane specifications must also be available and may be included in the Operator's Manual. The specifications provide a technical description of the airplane including type, number of persons which can be carried, maximum allowable weight, baggage capacity, fuel capacity, oil capacity of the engine oil system, hydraulic fluid capacity, CG range, leveling means, engine requirements, and a variety of other information. Much of the same information is included in the Type Certificate Data Sheet issued by the FAA for airplanes by make and model.

The airplane record file should contain the **equipment list** for the airplane together with weight and balance data; thus any change in equipment can be recorded and a new CG location determined as necessary. When a new airplane is purchased from a dealer, all the equipment information must be supplied to the buyer.

Weight and balance data

Since the safe operation of an airplane depends upon the CG location being in a position which will not cause the airplane to be either excessively nose-heavy or tail-heavy, accurate information on CG location must be maintained. The airplane records must show that the empty-weight center of gravity (EWCG) is within the limits prescribed and **loading information** must be such that the operator can easily determine that the loaded condition of the airplane maintains the CG within the safe operating range. Loading information is often provided in the form of charts and graphs so the operator can determine quickly the effect of any particular type of loading. For some airplanes it is necessary that limitations be placed on fuel, baggage, or number of passengers for certain loading configurations. In these cases the airplane must be placarded to indicate the limitations.

As explained previously, weight and balance data must include a list of the permanently installed equipment carried in the airplane. When any equipment change is made, the effect on the CG location must be considered. If the change causes the CG to move out of the approved range, corrections must be made by the installation or removal of fixed ballast or by the establishment of necessary loading restrictions.

If accurate and current weight and balance information for an airplane is not available, the empty-weight center-of-gravity (EWCG) location can be determined by weighing the aircraft in the empty-weight condition and recomputing the CG location. Information regarding the procedures for computing CG location is provided in the text *Basic Science for Aerospace Vehicles* and in *FAA Advisory Circular* 43.13-1.

Repair and alteration records (TEST)

Upon completion of a major alteration or major repair by an individual or by a repair station, records must be prepared for the owner and for submission to the FAA district office having jurisdiction of the area. The standard form for this report is FAA Form 337, illustrated in Fig. 18·4. This form must be executed at least in duplicate and preferably in triplicate. One copy is given to the owner, one copy is sent to the FAA dis-

ORIGINAL

DUPLICATE COPY REQUIRES
ORIGINAL SIGNATURES.

349

FEDERAL AVIATION AGENCY
MAJOR REPAIR AND ALTERATION
(Airframe, Powerplant, Propeller, or Appliance)

Form Approved
Budget Bureau No. 04-R060.1

FOR FAA USE ONLY
OFFICE IDENTIFICATION

INSTRUCTIONS: Print or type all entries. See FAR 43.9, FAR 43 Appendix B, and AC 43.9-1 (or subsequent revision thereof) for instructions and disposition of this form.

1. AIRCRAFT	MAKE	MODEL
	SERIAL NO.	NATIONALITY AND REGISTRATION MARK
2. OWNER	NAME (As shown on registration certificate)	ADDRESS (As shown on registration certificate)

3. FOR FAA USE ONLY

4. UNIT IDENTIFICATION — **5. TYPE**

UNIT	MAKE	MODEL	SERIAL NO.	REPAIR	ALTER-ATION
AIRFRAME	◆◆◆◆◆◆◆◆◆◆◆◆◆◆ (As described in item 1 above) ◆◆◆◆◆◆◆◆◆◆◆◆				
POWERPLANT					
PROPELLER					
APPLIANCE	TYPE				
	MANUFACTURER				

6. CONFORMITY STATEMENT

A. AGENCY'S NAME AND ADDRESS	B. KIND OF AGENCY	C. CERTIFICATE NO.
	U.S. CERTIFICATED MECHANIC	
	FOREIGN CERTIFICATED MECHANIC	
	CERTIFICATED REPAIR STATION	
	MANUFACTURER	

D. I certify that the repair and/or alteration made to the unit(s) identified in item 4 above and described on the reverse or attachments hereto have been made in accordance with the requirements of Part 43 of the U.S. Federal Aviation Regulations and that the information furnished herein is true and correct to the best of my knowledge.

| DATE | SIGNATURE OF AUTHORIZED INDIVIDUAL |

7. APPROVAL FOR RETURN TO SERVICE

Pursuant to the authority given persons specified below, the unit identified in item 4 was inspected in the manner prescribed by the Administrator of the Federal Aviation Agency and is ☐ APPROVED ☐ REJECTED

BY	FAA FLT. STANDARDS INSPECTOR	MANUFACTURER	INSPECTION AUTHORIZATION	OTHER (Specify)
	FAA DESIGNEE	REPAIR STATION	CANADIAN DEPARTMENT OF TRANSPORT INSPECTOR OF AIRCRAFT	
DATE OF APPROVAL OR REJECTION	CERTIFICATE OR DESIGNATION NO.	SIGNATURE OF AUTHORIZED INDIVIDUAL	

FAA Form 337 (1-65) OBSOLETE PREVIOUS EDITION   0052-025-8000 (8320)

Figure 18·4 Major Repair and Alteration form.

trict office within 48 hr after the airplane is returned to service, and a third form should be kept by the repair agency. Form 337 applies to aircraft, powerplants, propellers, and appliances.

In addition to the preparation of the Form 337 for a major alteration or repair, a record must be made in the aircraft log book. The record must be signed and dated by the person who performed the alteration or repair or by an official inspector of the repair station.

If a certificated repair station performs a major alteration or repair on an aircraft, aircraft engine, propeller, or appliance in accordance with a manual or specifications approved by the FAA Administrator, the repair station can use the customer's work order in place of the FAA Form 337 for reporting the alteration or repair. When this is done, the aircraft owner must be given a signed copy of the work order, and a copy must be kept in the repair-station files for at least two years from the date of approval for return to service of the item involved. The aircraft owner must also be given a **maintenance release** which includes the following information:

Identity of the aircraft, airframe, engine, propeller, or appliance

If an aircraft, the make, model, serial number, nationality and registration marks, and location of the repaired area

If an airframe, aircraft engine, propeller, or appliance, the manufacturer's name, name of the part, model, and serial number (if any)

In addition to the information listed above, the maintenance release should contain a statement worded as follows or in a similar manner:

The aircraft, airframe, aircraft engine, propeller, or appliance identified above was repaired in accordance with current regulations of the Federal Aviation Administration and is approved for return to service.

Pertinent details of the repair are on file at this repair station under Order No. _____ Date _____

Signed _____ for
    (Signature of authorized representative)

_____   _____
(Repair station name)   (Certificate number)

_____
(Address)

SUMMARY OF REPAIR-STATION REQUIREMENTS

The operation of a certificated repair station must be carried out in accordance with the provisions or the operation and inspection methods approved for the repair station by the FAA. The tools, equipment, and test apparatus must be adequate to complete the repair work in accordance with accepted industry practices. If special equipment is required by the manufacturer of an item, the repair station should use this equipment or the equivalent.

The repair work performed should be accomplished in a manner which will restore the item being repaired to a condition at least equal to its original condition with respect to airworthiness and function.

The repair station must have an adequate inspection system to assure that all items are inspected independently. The final inspectors must be persons other than those who made the repair.

During the process of overhaul, annual inspection, major repair, or major alteration, the repair station must make certain that all pertinent manufacturer's bulletins, FAA airworthiness directives, and discrepancy reports are given consideration and complied with as indicated. The Aircraft Specifications, Type Certificate Data Sheet, and equipment lists should also be examined to ascertain that the aircraft or other item has been kept up as required.

The repair station must prepare the required records and log-book entries to show the work performed, and must maintain records as required by Federal Aviation Regulations.

REVIEW QUESTIONS

1. What is a certificated repair station?
2. Why should the inspection department of a repair station be separate from the repair department?

3. Explain the function of a *work order*.
4. What are the purposes of *receiving inspections?*
5. Discuss *assembly inspections* and *final inspections*.
6. Describe the responsibility of the Federal Aviation Administration in approving a repair station for certification.
7. What are repair-station *ratings?*
8. What Parts of the Federal Aviation Regulations govern the certification of repair personnel and repair stations?
9. What is an airworthiness directive?
10. What is meant by *preventive maintenance?*
11. Define a *major alteration; a major repair*.
12. If the tip of a metal wing is damaged to the extent that repairs of the last four wing ribs are necessary, is the repair minor or major?
13. What is the difference between a *100-hr inspection* and an *annual inspection?*

14. Explain the requirements of a *progressive inspection*.
15. Why is a check list required when making a 100-hr or annual inspection?
16. What FAA form is prepared after making an annual inspection?
17. What provision is made to warn the owner of an airplane that an annual inspection is due?
18. From what source does an airplane owner obtain his operator's manual?
19. List the items which should be included in the airplane record file.
20. Why is weight and balance data important?
21. What is the purpose of the equipment list?
22. What records and forms must be prepared after an airplane or other item has undergone a major repair?

Index